The Illustrated Encyclopedia

of

American Birds

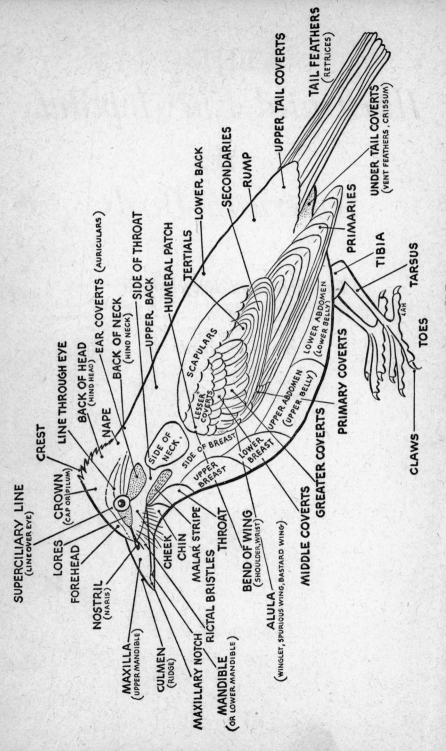

TOPOGRAPHY OF A BIRD

SUPERCILIARY LINE
(LINE OVER EYE)

CREST

LORES

CROWN
(CAP OR PILUM)

FOREHEAD

LINE THROUGH EYE

BACK OF HEAD
(HIND HEAD)

EAR COVERTS (AURICULARS)

BACK OF NECK
(HIND NECK)

SIDE OF THROAT

UPPER BACK

HUMERAL PATCH

TERTIALS

LOWER BACK

SECONDARIES

RUMP

UPPER TAIL COVERTS

TAIL FEATHERS
(RETRICES)

UNDER TAIL COVERTS
(VENT FEATHERS, CRISSUM)

PRIMARIES

TIBIA

TARSUS

TOES

CLAWS

NOSTRIL
(NARIS)

MAXILLA
(UPPER MANDIBLE)

CULMEN
(RIDGE)

MAXILLARY NOTCH

MANDIBLE
(OR LOWER MANDIBLE)

RICTAL BRISTLES

MALAR STRIPE

CHIN

CHEEK

THROAT

BEND OF WING
(SHOULDER, WRIST)

ALULA
(WINGLET, SPURIOUS WING, BASTARD WING)

MIDDLE COVERTS

GREATER COVERTS

PRIMARY COVERTS

SIDE OF NECK

NAPE

SIDE OF NECK

SIDE OF BREAST

UPPER BREAST

LOWER BREAST

SCAPULARS

LESSER COVERTS

UPPER ABDOMEN
(UPPER BELLY)

LOWER ABDOMEN
(LOWER BELLY)

THE
Illustrated Encyclopedia
OF
American Birds

BY

LEON AUGUSTUS HAUSMAN, PH.D.

*Professor of Zoology, New Jersey College for Women, Consulting Ornithologist,
New Jersey State Agricultural Experiment Station, and Lecturer in Ornithology,
New Jersey State College of Agriculture, Rutgers University*

Illustrated by

JACOB BATES ABBOTT

Halcyon House
NEW YORK

To My
FATHER *and* MOTHER

Introduction

AT THE PRESENT TIME there are between 13,000 and 14,000 species of living birds, and including subspecies or "kinds" there are about 23,000 altogether. Of these, 1,422 are found in North America, allocated to seventy-five families. Each of these 1,422 birds, and each of the seventy-five families is treated in this Encyclopedia. The authority for the names and the individual numbers of the birds is the "Check List of North American Birds," of the American Ornithologists' Union, referred to as the "A. O. U. Check List." The number assigned to each bird is known as the "A. O. U. Number."

In addition to the 23,000 kinds of living or existing birds, there must have been many others which in former ages existed over the earth, and which have since become extinct, and have left no trace. Some, however, have left us their remains in the form of fossils in the sedimentary rocks, or in the form of bones in various earthy deposits. There are several hundred of these fossil birds now known, of which more than one hundred have been found in North America. Of fossil birds this Encyclopedia takes no account, except in the single instance of the famous *Archaeopteryx*, or Lizard Tailed Bird, which, being at the present time the oldest known bird, is a matter of first interest to all devotees of ornithology.

The birds (CLASS AVES) are distinguished from all other animal forms by the single characteristic of the possession of feathers, structures which are outgrowths of the epidermis, or outer layer of the skin. In their origin, therefore, feathers are fundamentally similar to the hairs of mammals, and to their hollow horns, their hoofs, claws, and nails of the fingers and toes; and are also similar to the scales of reptiles and of fishes. No bird possesses true hair; the long, filamentous, hair-like structures sometimes found arising from the skin of certain birds, are not hairs, but only highly modified and simplified feathers.

The CLASS AVES is divided into numerous smaller divisions called

ORDERS. These divisions are made on the basis of anatomical similarities. Thus we have, e.g. the ORDER ANSERIFORMES (duck-like birds), including such forms as the ducks, geese, mergansers, and swans; the ORDER CHARADRIIFORMES (shore birds), including among others the gulls, auks, sandpipers, snipe, plovers, curlews, and terns; the ORDER PICIFORMES, including the woodpeckers; and the great ORDER PASSERIFORMES (perching birds) inclusive of the smaller, and generally better-known birds, such as the swallows, flycatchers, thrushes, sparrows and finches, warblers, and the like. In North America there are represented no less than twenty orders of birds.

The ORDERS of birds are further subdivided into FAMILIES. A knowledge of the families of our native birds is of first importance to all those who would learn to know our American birds in the field and forest. Suppose for example, that you have seen a rather small, dull-colored bird, and wish to find out its name. If you know the characteristics of the families of birds, you would know that the bird you have seen is a member of the family of finches, or of warblers, or of flycatchers, even if you cannot name the particular kind of finch, or warbler, or flycatcher that it is. Let us further suppose that the bird you have seen was olive-grayish or olive-brownish above, and light-colored or white, below, and that it sat upright and almost motionless on an exposed perch, and occasionally sailed out into the air, turned, and came back to the same perch, and repeated this performance again and again. If you knew the characteristics of the families you would say at once, "This is a member of the family of flycatchers (*Tyrannidae*)." Turning to FLYCATCHER in this book, you read the accounts, and examine the illustrations, of the members of this family, for your part of the country, and soon find the particular bird of which you are in search. Anyone not acquainted with bird families would pore over hundreds of pages, and over hundreds of different accounts and pictures, in a sort of hit-or-miss attempt to locate the problematical bird—often without success.

Make yourself familiar with the characteristics of six or eight of the commonest families, as a beginning, and see how your interest in our native birds will grow. Begin, for example, with such families as the sparrows and finches (Family *Fringillidae*), the warblers (Family *Compsothlypidae*), the blackbirds and their kin (Family *Icteridae*), the thrushes (Family *Turdidae*), the wrens (Family *Troglodytidae*), and the woodpeckers (Family *Picidae*). Leave the families of the water birds, and the shore birds until later, as they are more difficult, at least for a beginner. After you know several families of land birds, then turn your attention to the water and shore birds, taking up such families as the gulls and terns (Family *Laridae*), the herons and bitterns (Family *Ardeidae*), the ducks, geese, swans, and mergansers (Family *Anatidae*), and the snipe, sandpipers, curlews, woodcock, etc. (Family *Scolopacidae*).

While there are seventy-five families of birds in North America, containing 1,422 different kinds of birds, yet many of these are uncommon, or extremely rare—some birds are known only from one or two specimens taken many years ago—and hence will not be encountered by any except professional ornithologists. In any one given section of the country—in the particular region where you happen to be living at present—there will not be more than approximately two or three hundred birds or so to be learned. In this connection, the numbers of birds that have been listed in some of our states is interesting. We have, for example, in New Hampshire, 283; Vermont, 255; Massachusetts, 369; Rhode Island, 293; Connecticut, 334; New York, 412; New Jersey, 358; Colorado, 403; Nebraska, 418; Illinois, 390; California, 541; Arizona, 371; New Mexico, 314; Alabama, 275; and Florida, 362.

Instead of saying different "kinds" of birds, scientists say "species and subspecies." What does this mean? You will notice, underneath the common or vernacular name of each bird, its scientific, or technical name. This technical name is made up of two (sometimes three) parts. The first part is the *generic* part, that is, the name of the *genus* or group to which the bird belongs. (Each family is divided into groups, or *genera*, usually on the basis of color or pattern differences.) The second part of the name is the *specific* (or *species*) name. If the bird has a third part to its name, this third part is the *subspecific* (or *subspecies*) name—*variety-of-the-species* name, we might call it.

Let us consider for a moment what we mean when we say *species* of a bird (or of any animal, for that matter). *A species is a great group of individuals, so closely similar that they all might have been derived from the same pair of parents.* (*Species* is a Latin word meaning likeness, image, or kind, and its plural and singular forms are the same. Thus we may not speak of a "specie" in this connection, for the word "specie" means coined money.) This definition of a species that we have given, is a rough and ready one, but quite usable for general purposes, quite accurate enough, and plainly understandable.

A song sparrow, for example, is a species. Scientists have called it *Melospiza melodia,* which translated means, "the melodious song finch." But if you were to examine a song sparrow from New England, and one from Alaska, and one from our southwestern deserts, you would see at once that although each one was undoubtedly a song sparrow, yet each one was appreciably different from the others. And so, you might say, "Let us call these all song sparrows (*Melospiza melodia*). But let us call the very dark brown Alaskan bird the *Sooty* Song Sparrow (*Melospiza melodia rufina*), which, translated means the "very dark brown song sparrow." (The Latin word, *rufus,* means, literally reddish brown.) And let us call the song sparrow from the desert—which is a very pale colored song sparrow, pale like the desert sands—the Desert Song Sparrow (*Melospiza melodia saltonis*). This, translated means "the song sparrow from the region of Salton"—the bird having been discovered in the region of the Salton Lake, in California.

But this leaves our Eastern Song Sparrow with only its double name, *Melospiza melodia.* To leave it thus, with but two names, would mean that this bird is the *species,* from which these others have been derived. This may not be the case; we do not know the original species, from which all our many song sparrow kinds have come, so we put the Eastern Song Sparrow on the same plane as the others—that is, we make it also a subspecies by repeating its species name, thus, *Melospiza melodia melodia.*

Thus birds (and all other animals as well) have either two or three parts to their scientific names. The first part, the generic name is capitalized; the second and third parts, the specific name and the subspecific name begin always with a small letter, even though they may be proper adjectives, thus: Southern Parula Warbler (*Compsothlypis americana americana*), or Lucy's Warbler (*Vermivora luciae*). The names are derived from the Latin or the Greek, or sometimes from other languages, and given the proper terminations. Latin and Greek are used because these are the languages of scholars the world over, and are understood by any scientist, whether he be Chinese, Turkish, French, English, German, Italian—though it must be said that English is rapidly becoming the language of science everywhere. When translated, it will be seen that the names describe the bird's color, or anatomical structure, or form, or pattern, or some bodily characteristic, or tell of the bird's voice, or food, or distinguishing habit, or place where it was first discovered, or where it habitually lives in greatest numbers, or there may be affixed to the name, the name of some person or place which it is desired to memorialize in this way. Furthermore, for North American birds, each bird has been given an identification number by the American Ornithologists' Union, a number known as the A. O. U. Number. This number appears in this Encyclopedia after the technical name of each species. In technical works, also, after the scientific name of each bird (or other animal), is given the name of the person responsible for the name, as, for example, in the case of the Gray Sage Sparrow, *Amphispiza belli cinerea* Townsend. If a parenthesis encloses the name of the describer, it indicates that whereas he described (i.e. first placed on record) the species, he did not place it in the genus where it now is lodged, as, for example in the Eastern Wood Pewee, *Myiochanes virens* (Linnaeus).

At the end of the book there is given the complete classification and record of all North American birds, with their standard vernacular and scientific names, A. O. U. numbers, and the names of their describers. This compact classification, or, as we might term it, the "Directory of Who's Who Among North American Birds" is interesting to study. For example, the birds are listed in the order of their general evolutionary status, or perhaps rather in the order of their complexity. Thus the more primitive birds come first—the loons, grebes, etc.—and the more highly organized and more complex families last—the warblers, blackbirds, finches, and sparrows. Note also the relative sizes of the families. Some families contain but one genus and one species (e.g. the Family *Anhingidae,* water turkeys); some contain but one genus, with one species represented by only a few subspecies (e.g. the Family *Certhiidae,* creepers); whereas the great Family *Fringillidae* contains a host of genera, including nearly 240 species and subspecies! Again note how many apparently diverse birds may be contained in one family—diverse only superficially however—as, e.g. in the Family *Icteridae,* blackbirds, which embraces the true blackbirds, as well as the meadowlarks, bobolinks, grackles, orioles, and cowbirds. Many instructive minutes may be spent over such a classified list, a list which might appear at first glance to be only an arid catalogue.

In the body of this book, the descriptions of the birds aim to set forth only the essential or most important colors and patterns of the plumage, and sometimes the characters of bill, wings, feet and tail generally, and not the smaller details concerned with such matters, in order that the reader may have presented to his view, a simple, easily visualized image of the bird, and not be confused with a mass of intricate and particularized description. In all cases these accounts of the appearance are of adult individuals in full breeding plumage (that is, in the plumage in which they occur after the second season, since some birds breed in their immature dress). Where no mention of sex is made, the male is to be understood.

The *length* of each bird is the length of its entire body, as though stretched out flat upon its back upon a flat surface with its bill and tail so pressed down as to form one continuous straight line from the tip of the bill to the tip of the tail. The length of this line is measured and the result expressed in inches and hundredths. This dimension in each case is for the male bird. However one never sees birds in the field in this attitude, since in life a bird's head is invariably bent at more or less of an angle to the body, and the tail often so. Wherever in the treatment of a species, no length is given, it is to be understood that this dimension is the same, or closely the same, as that of the species to which it is similar.

With respect to the *distribution* data, it should be pointed out that the inflexible necessity of compressing the textual matter within specified limits has precluded any detailed discussion of the ranges and local variations in the migrational movements or occupational status of the various species, though in many species the region of the wintering grounds has been indicated.

Rigid exigency of space has also dictated that only the "chief," or "most important" species be accorded lengthy treatments. While not every reader need agree with the author in his definition of these principal species (or subspecies), yet it is hoped that in the main, the selections will meet with general approval.

The central purpose which has been kept steadily and uncloudedly in view in the preparation of this book, has been the answering of such questions as the writer's experience in many years of teaching beginning college students in ornithology, he has found are invariably asked, i.e. What does the bird look like? Is the female different from the male, and if so, what is this difference? How large is the bird? Where in North

America does it live? What kind of countryside does it usually inhabit? What is the sound of its call? What are some of its characteristic or distinctive habits? For each bird information covering substantially these points has been included.

GRATEFUL ACKNOWLEDGMENT is here made of the aid given to the writer by the librarians of the American Museum of Natural History in New York, the National Audubon Society in New York, Yale University, Rutgers University, Cornell University, Princeton University, The Library of Congress, The Surgeon General's Library, and the Library of the United States Department of Agriculture.

Especially helpful has been the critical reading of the manuscript by my wife, Ethel Hinckley Hausman, herself a long-time teacher of biology and nature study.

L. A. H.

How To Use This Encyclopedia

EACH SPECIES and subspecies ("kind") of bird found in North America is listed in this book in its proper alphabetical order, the last word in its common or vernacular name placed first, thus: FLYCATCHER, OLIVE SIDED; WREN-TIT, RUDDY. Also in proper alphabetical order come the names of the seventy-five families of North American birds, thus: THRUSHES (Family *Turdidae*). Notice that the name of every family ends in *idae*.

If you do not find a bird listed under the name by which it is known to you, turn to the alphabetical list of OTHER NAMES at the end of the book. For example, the name *chewink* does not appear in the body of the book. But in the list of OTHER NAMES you will find that under *chewink* you are referred to *towhee*. Look under *towhee*, therefore, in the body of the book. This arrangement of names is made necessary because birds are known under such a variety of names in different parts of our country. Thus the little Ruddy Duck (*Erismatura jamaicensis rubida*), No. 167, is known by over sixty different names!

At the end of the book you will find a CLASSIFIED LIST OF NORTH AMERICAN BIRDS. This shows you the birds in their structural, or "family" relationships to one another. From this list you will see that some birds do not show in their names to what family they belong. For example the name *robin* does not tell you that the robin is a thrush (of the Family *Turdidae*), nor does the name *oriole* tell you that this bird is a member of the great family of icterids (Family *Icteridae*), a family which includes such birds as the meadowlarks, cowbirds, grackles, blackbirds, and bobolinks. A study of the classified list, therefore, will teach you much about the fundamental relationships of the different birds.

In the body of the book under each family of birds, you will find an account of the anatomical characteristics of the family, and in each case immediately following you will note that there is a description of the kinds of nests and eggs characteristic of that family. This information concerning anatomical characteristics, nests and eggs has been

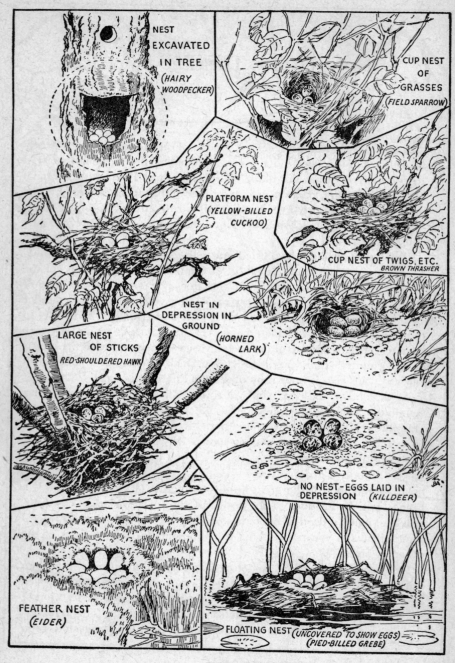

NEST EXCAVATED IN TREE (HAIRY WOODPECKER)

CUP NEST OF GRASSES (FIELD SPARROW)

PLATFORM NEST (YELLOW-BILLED CUCKOO)

CUP NEST OF TWIGS, ETC. BROWN THRASHER

NEST IN DEPRESSION IN GROUND (HORNED LARK)

LARGE NEST OF STICKS RED-SHOULDERED HAWK

NO NEST-EGGS LAID IN DEPRESSION (KILLDEER)

FEATHER NEST (EIDER)

FLOATING NEST (UNCOVERED TO SHOW EGGS) (PIED-BILLED GREBE)

THE PRINCIPAL TYPES OF NESTS

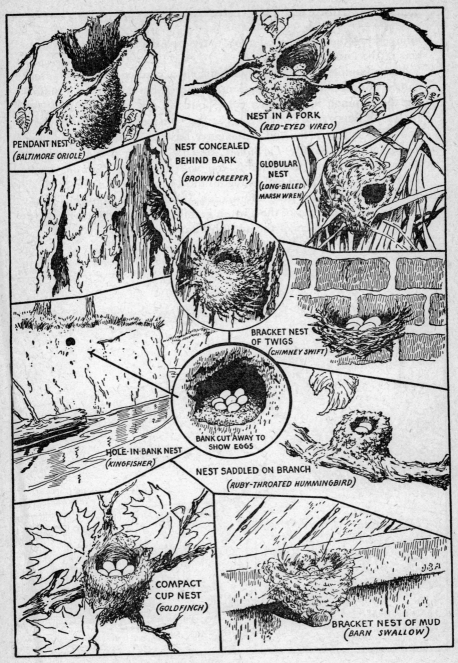

PENDANT NEST
(BALTIMORE ORIOLE)

NEST IN A FORK
(RED-EYED VIREO)

NEST CONCEALED
BEHIND BARK
(BROWN CREEPER)

GLOBULAR
NEST
(LONG-BILLED
MARSH WREN)

BRACKET NEST
OF TWIGS
(CHIMNEY SWIFT)

HOLE-IN-BANK NEST
(KINGFISHER)

BANK CUT AWAY TO
SHOW EGGS

NEST SADDLED ON BRANCH
(RUBY-THROATED HUMMINGBIRD)

COMPACT
CUP NEST
(GOLDFINCH)

BRACKET NEST OF MUD
(BARN SWALLOW)

OF NORTH AMERICAN BIRDS

grouped together under the Family entry, because it applies to *all* members of the family.

These families are placed alphabetically according to their common names, not according to their scientific names. For convenience in finding the common name which corresponds to any scientific name, see INDEX OF SCIENTIFIC NAMES OF FAMILIES on page 534. For instance, under BLUEBIRD, at the end of the entry Eastern Bluebird you will find in parenthesis (Family *Turdidae*), and by turning to the INDEX OF SCIENTIFIC NAMES OF FAMILIES you will note that *Turdidae* is the THRUSH FAMILY. Then by looking up the THRUSH FAMILY in the body of the book you will find information about the anatomical characteristics, nests and eggs of the Thrush Family, which applies to Bluebirds and all other members of the Thrush Family.

Contents

The Illustrated Encyclopedia of American Birds

ACCENTOR FAMILY
Prunellidae

The Accentors are small dark-colored birds, with short weak wings; short, sharply pointed bills; and nearly

square, or but slightly forked tails. They are found mainly in Europe and northern Asia. The familiar Hedge Sparrow of Europe and the British Isles is a member of this family. Of the twenty or so forms known, only one, the Mountain Accentor (*Prunella montanella*), has been reported for North America.

NESTING. Accentors build cup shaped nests of grasses, fine weed stems, and weed bark, sometimes admixed with mosses and fine soft lichens, and lined with fine grasses, coarse hair, and sometimes wool. They are located in clefts and cavities among rocks (the mountain-dwelling species), or in dense hedges or low bushes near the ground. The four or five eggs are blue.

ACCENTOR

Mountain Accentor
Prunella montanella [749.1]

ADULT MALE AND FEMALE—Upper parts dark reddish brown; rump and tail olive brown. Crown and face black. Line over the eye, throat, and under parts dark grayish buff, with blackish and purplish-brown streaks on the flanks. The side of the neck bears a gray spot. Legs and feet flesh color.

LENGTH—7.00 inches.

DISTRIBUTION—This Siberian and oriental species occurs as an accidental straggler on Nunivak Island, Alaska.

The Accentor, as its name implies, is a bird of the mountains, and of bleak and barren regions generally, where in rather warbler-like fashion it busies

itself among the low shrubbery, flitting here and there in its quest for insects, other small invertebrates, and small seeds. (Family *Prunellidae*)

ALBATROSS FAMILY
Diomedeidae

Albatrosses are among the largest of flying birds, with a wingspread (in the case of the great Wandering Albatross) of from ten to twelve feet. It is this giant bird which Coleridge writes of in *The Rime of the Ancient Mariner*. In spite of its enormous wing-length, the width of its wings is

no greater than about nine inches.
In the air, Albatrosses resemble giant
gulls, as they ride the air currents
hour after hour, with almost no perceptible motion of their great pinions.
Their food consists of jellyfish, squids
(or "cuttlefish"), fish, elasmobranchs
(sharks and their kin), floating carrion and offal thrown from vessels.
Ships are often followed for days or
even weeks by these extremely graceful birds. Most Albatrosses are found
only in the oceans of the Southern
Hemisphere, where they nest in great
colonies on islands. Their bills are
about as long as their heads, and are
flattened laterally. The upper mandible is hooked over the lower, and the
nostrils come to the exterior through
two long tubes. The wings are extremely long and narrow. The body
is relatively short, and the feet are

webbed for swimming. Of the seven-
teen-odd species, four have been reported from the coasts of North
America. These are contained in the
two genera *Diomedea* and *Thalassogeron*.

NESTING. Albatrosses breed usually
on isolated oceanic islands, the nest
being on the bare ground, a mere
depression, sometimes surrounded by
seaweed, or in the basin of a slightly
elevated mound. In any event, the
birds make little or no attempt at
nest construction. Sometimes the egg
is laid in a burrow in the soil. So far
as is known, the female lays but a
single egg. When the young are

hatched they do not run about at
once but are quite helpless. They are
covered with a sooty brownish, soft
down, and grow but slowly.

ALBATROSS
Black-footed Albatross
Diomedea nigripes [81]

ADULT MALE AND FEMALE—Upper
parts blackish fading to a soiled white

on the upper tail coverts and base of
the tail. Face and chin whitish. Under
parts blackish gray. Bill dusky. Feet
and legs black.

LENGTH—32.50 inches.

DISTRIBUTION—From Alaska to
southern California, in the North
Pacific. (Family *Diomedeidae*)

Laysan Albatross
Diomedea immutabilis [82.1]

ADULT MALE AND FEMALE—Upper
parts, wings, and the end of the tail,

dark sooty brown; a paler area between the shoulders. Head, neck,

rump, and upper tail coverts white. Lores, black. Under parts pure white. Bill yellow.

LENGTH—32.00 inches.

DISTRIBUTION—Occurs as a straggler off the coast of Lower California. (Family *Diomedeidae*)

Short-tailed Albatross
Diomedea albatrus [82]

ADULT MALE AND FEMALE—Plumage mostly white, but with the wings

and tail washed with dusky gray, and the head and neck with yellowish. The primaries show yellow shafts. Bill and feet dusky yellow.

LENGTH—35.00 inches.

DISTRIBUTION—From Alaska to southern California in the North Pacific; more common in the northern part of its range. (Family *Diomedeidae*)

Yellow-nosed Albatross
Thalassogeron chlororhynchos [83]

ADULT MALE AND FEMALE—Back, wings, and tail, blackish, fading to gray on the shoulders, neck, and head. Bill with its sides black, its upper and under edges yellow. Under parts pure white.

LENGTH—36.00 inches.

DISTRIBUTION—Over the oceans of the Southern Hemisphere, straggling northward occasionally to the Gulf of St. Lawrence, and the Oregon coast. (Family *Diomedeidae*)

ANI
Groove-billed Ani
Crotophaga sulcirostris sulcirostris [384]

ADULT MALE AND FEMALE—Black or blackish, the feathers showing dull metallic sheens of bronze, purplish, and greenish edgings; wings and tail with iridescent washes of the same. The bill is large and thick, with a convex culmen, and the upper mandible bears several longitudinal grooves.

LENGTH—13.25 inches.

DISTRIBUTION—From Lower California and southeastern Texas (though not commonly) through Mexico into northwestern South America. Occasionally some individuals are observed in Arizona, Louisiana, and Florida.

The peculiar Anis somewhat resemble our common Cowbirds in their habits of associating with cattle, not only for the purpose of feeding on

their parasites, but also to seize the insects which their hoofs stir up from the grass. They are found chiefly in meadows and low lands, and are not forest nor mountain lovers. They do not resent the presence of man's dwellings, but are fearless, and come close to farms, and roost tamely about amid the rural stir. (Family *Cuculidae*)

San Lucas Ani

Crotophaga sulcirostris pallidula [384a]

Similar to the Groove-billed Ani, but much paler; the feathers exhibiting a purplish iridescence, and the head and neck suffused with a grayish bronze.

DISTRIBUTION—Restricted to the Cape district of Lower California. (Family *Cuculidae*)

Smooth-billed Ani

Crotophaga ani [383]

Similar to the Groove-billed Ani, but the bill smooth and without grooves.

DISTRIBUTION—From southern Florida (rarely), south to the West Indies and eastern South America. Bahama Islands.

"Its long tail, short wings, singularly shaped bill, and long-drawn, whining whistled call, are distinctive." (Taylor) (Family *Cuculidae*)

AUK FAMILY
Auks, Murres and Puffins
Alcidae

These birds are, without exception, ocean species, spending most of their

time in the open seas, but coming into bays and harbors occasionally at certain seasons of the year. They are essentially birds of the arctic regions of the globe, and are found most abundantly on the coasts of

Alaska and Siberia. Puffins somewhat resemble little parrots. They run about actively, but the Auks and Murres stand on the whole foot and the tail, and move about with no grace whatever. These birds use their wings instead of their feet when swimming under water, in which mode of progression they are most expert. Twenty-three species comprise the family. Twenty-five species and subspecies contained in fourteen genera, are found in North America.

NESTING. Puffins nest in colonies on sea islands, placing the nest, or rather depositing the eggs under a rock, in a crevice, or more frequently in a burrow in the soil. One or two eggs are laid, of a dull whitish chalky exterior, sometimes marked with faint spots or scrawls of purple, or clouded and dully splashed with pale yellowish brown, or faint chocolate.

Guillemots also nest in colonies on cliffs along a shore, the eggs being laid on the bare rock, on a shelf, or on the bare ground. One egg is the normal clutch (rarely two), bluish and unmarked, or whitish, creamy, light green, or light brownish, washed, clouded, spotted, speckled, or splotched with various shades of browns, lilacs, olives, etc., and very variable in ground color and markings.

Auks and Murres, likewise nesting in colonies, make no nest, but deposit the eggs on a rocky shelf in a cliff, or on the bare ground. The single egg (very rarely two) for each pair of birds is similar in general to those of the Guillemots.

AUK
Great Auk
Plautus impennis [33]

ADULT MALE AND FEMALE—Upper parts dark brownish black, the secondaries of the wing tipped with white. A large white spot in front of the eye, and a seal-brown color extending down the sides of the throat and neck. Under parts silvery white.

LENGTH—29.00 inches.

DISTRIBUTION—Extinct. Formerly known from "Funk Island, Newfoundland, the Faroes, Orkneys, islands off the southwest coast of Iceland, and probably on the coast of Norway. In winter south to Maine and Massachusetts, casually to South Carolina and Florida." (A.O.U. Check List)

Early voyagers and fishermen found that the bird fell an easy prey to clubs, and slaughtered them without either mercy or judgment for their feathers, flesh, and oil. No living Auk has been taken since 1844. The bird was flightless, diving and pursuing its fishy food

under water. About seventy specimens exist in collections of museums, universities, etc. (Family *Alcidae*)

Razor-billed Auk
Alca torda [32]

ADULT MALE AND FEMALE—Upper parts sooty black. Secondaries tipped with white. Foreneck sooty brown. Line from eye to the upper base of the upper mandible, white. Under parts white. Bill black, laterally compressed, and encircled by a narrow white band.

LENGTH—16.50 inches.

DISTRIBUTION—From southern Greenland to Newfoundland and New

Brunswick, formerly spreading southward to Maine. In winter it occurs from southern Labrador to Long Island, New York, and casually down the coast as far as North Carolina.

Like the other members of its race, the Razor-billed Auk is an excellent swimmer and diver, propelling itself under water by both feet and wings with the speed of lightning, capturing fish and other aquatic creatures in its sharp powerful beak. Its habits are much like those of other Auks, and its notes are also low and guttural. When incubating, the bird utters a series of hoarse grunts or groaning notes. (Family *Alcidae*)

AUKLET
Cassin's Auklet
Ptychoramphus aleuticus [16]

ADULT MALE AND FEMALE—Upper parts slaty black. Sides of head, neck, and throat leaden gray. Lower eyelid with a white spot. Under parts white. Bill at the base broader than deep. Culmen almost straight.

LENGTH—8.75 inches.

DISTRIBUTION—From the Aleutian Islands southward along the Pacific coast to Lower California.

The Cassin's Auklet is also known as the Sea Quail because of its size and its plump little body. The birds burrow in the soil to nest, after the manner of Petrels and Puffins, and in their nesting habits are mainly nocturnal. Dawson says that a chorus of Auklets

in their burrows reminded him of a frog pond in full cry. (Family *Alcidae*)

Crested Auklet
Aethia cristatella [18]

ADULT MALE AND FEMALE—Upper parts brownish black; under parts brownish gray, and lighter in tone. From the hinder portion of the forehead a crest of slender black plumes arises, curving forward over the base of the bill. From behind each eye springs a series of filamentous white plumes, curving backwards and downwards. Bill short, bearing a basal knob, red.

LENGTH—9.50 inches.

DISTRIBUTION—In the extreme North Pacific and islands of the Bering Sea, southwards to Kodiak Island, and Japan.

Crested Auklets appear by the thousands in Yukon Harbor, Alaska, where they nest mainly in the crevices of cliffs. Their flight is rapid, and they wheel and turn together like a well-drilled regiment. They are also expert swimmers and divers. A goodly portion of their food is composed of small crustaceans, "beach fleas," which they find underneath the tidal ridges of

seaweed. Their notes are described as low and chirping. (Family *Alcidae*)

Least Auklet
Aethia pusilla [20]

ADULT MALE AND FEMALE—Upper parts blackish, speckled and marked with white on the scapulars. Before and behind the eyes are crests of slender white feathers. Under parts white, irregularly blotched with dusky. Up-

per breast sometimes bearing a dusky band. Bill very short, and knobbed at its base.

LENGTH—6.35 inches.

DISTRIBUTION—From Bering Strait, on the coasts and islands of the North Pacific southwards to Washington, and to Japan. Has been recorded from Puget Sound. (Family *Alcidae*)

Paroquet Auklet
Cyclorrhynchus psittacula [17]

ADULT MALE AND FEMALE—Upper parts sooty black. From the lower eyelid, reaching back over the region of the ear, a white line terminates in a thin white crest. Throat black; rest of under parts white. Bill high and thin, its sickle-shaped lower mandible curved upward; dark red.

LENGTH—9.70 inches.

DISTRIBUTION—From the extreme northern part of the North Pacific south to the coasts and islands, Kurile Islands, Sitka, and San Francisco Bay. Of this bird in the Bering Sea, Bailey says that the water "became covered with thousands of the strange little Auklets." The Paroquet Auklets breed in large numbers on the Fur Seal Islands. (Family *Alcidae*)

Rhinoceros Auklet
Cerorhinca monocerata [15]

ADULT MALE AND FEMALE—Upper parts dusky; sides of head, throat,

and under parts leaden gray; abdomen white. Sides of head ornamented with two series of white pointed feathers. Bill compressed, and at its base an upright horn.

LENGTH—14.75 inches.

DISTRIBUTION—From the coasts and islands of the North Pacific

Ocean southwards, to Lower California.

A small, chunky little Auk, which is said to resemble (when seen at a distance) a block of wood floating on the water. On being disturbed the birds dive rather than take wing. (Family *Alcidae*)

Whiskered Auklet
Aethia pygmaea [19]

ADULT MALE AND FEMALE—Upper parts dark slaty gray. From the sides of the base of the bill arise elongated, filamentous white feathers. Similar groups arise from above and below the eye. From the forehead springs a crest of several long, slender, backwardly curved feathers. Throat dark slate gray; breast lighter, fading to white on the lower abdomen.

LENGTH—7.50 inches.

DISTRIBUTION—"Commander Islands to Kamchatka and Japan; rare in the Aleutian Islands, east to Unalaska; largely resident." (A.O.U. Check List) (Family *Alcidae*)

AVOCET FAMILY
Avocets and Stilts
Recurvirostridae

These peculiar but graceful birds are characterized by the possession of long necks, long legs, webbed feet, and long very slender bills, which in some species are curved upward at the tip, hence the name of the family *Recurvirostridae*. They are birds of the beaches and flats, and wade about in shallow water, usually in flocks. The webbed feet of some species enable them to swim very well. About twelve species make up this family. They are found in the subtropical parts of the globe, usually, though two: the Black Necked Stilt (*Himantopus mexicanus*) and the Avocet (*Recurvirostra americana*) occur in middle or northern North America.

NESTING. These curious birds construct rather slovenly nests of rushes,

weed stems, grasses and the like, which are placed on the ground in swampy situations. The eggs, usually numbering three or four, are olive brown, lighter or darker, or buffy, and are profusely spotted with dark brown.

AVOCET

Avocet

Recurvirostra americana [225]

ADULT MALE AND FEMALE—Entire anterior end of the bird as far down as the upper breast and shoulders, light pinkish brown, or light cinnamon. Region around the base of the bill white, or whitish. Primaries, half of the scapulars, and base of the wing, black; the rest of the wing, pure white. Rump and under parts, pure white. Feet and legs, bluish gray; bill black, long, and slightly upturned near the tip.

LENGTH—18.00 inches.

DISTRIBUTION—From Saskatchewan to Texas, east into Washington and California, and west only to the Rockies. Used to occur occasionally as far east as New Jersey. In winter it passes to Guatemala and the West Indies.

In the west the Avocet is the most striking and conspicuous of any of the wading birds. It is found along the shores of shallow lakes and ponds,

where small flocks of birds may be seen wading about picking up insects from the surface of the water, or delving into the film of mud on the bottom for small crustaceans, or any small animal form that they can capture. The birds swim as well as wade, but never venture out very far from a footing on the bottom. Sometimes they are found feeding in wet meadows and marshes. Their loud cry, *peeeeelk* or *weeeek*, is arresting. Avocets may be identified as far as they can be seen by their long thin legs,

and striking black and white pattern, the pinkish-cinnamon head and neck not being conspicuous at great distances. (Family *Recurvirostridae*)

BALDPATE

Baldpate

Mareca americana [137]

ADULT MALE—Back brown; wing with a broad patch; its speculum metallic green bordered with black. Forehead and top of head, white. Sides of head blackish. Rest of head and neck light brown, black-speckled. Upper breast and sides, chestnut brown; rest of the under parts white. Bill and feet, slate-colored.

ADULT FEMALE—Grayish mottled above, whitish below; speculum bluish, breast and sides brownish. Bill and feet brownish or yellowish brown.

LENGTH—19.00 inches.

DISTRIBUTION—Alaska to British

Columbia and Minnesota; wintering from British Columbia, Virginia, to

South America. To Labrador on migrations. (Family *Anatidae*)

BARN OWL FAMILY
Tytonidae
(See Owl Family)

The Barn Owl differs somewhat from the Typical Owls in possessing a conspicuous heart-shaped face, a prominent facial ruff, no ear-tufts, an

elongated bill, relatively small eyes (for an owl), long legs, and an inner toe as long as the middle one. The wings are very long; the tail relatively short, and the plumage tone generally light (white, yellowish, tawny, buffy, etc.). About twenty-five species and subspecies are found distributed throughout the temperate and tropical portions of the globe. Only one, the common Barn Owl (*Tyto alba pratincola*) occurs in North America.

NESTING. Our only representative of the *Tytonidae* family, the common Barn Owl breeds in many diverse situations, such as a hole in a tree, a cavity in a tall stump, a hole in a bank, a cavity in more or less level ground, in old outbuildings, in church towers, or in ruined walls; sometimes in the deserted nests of woodpeckers, or less often in such large deserted open nests as those of Crows or Hawks. The nest is clumsily thrown together—a mass of sticks, straws, leaves, miscellaneous plant materials, bones, sometimes with the addition of string, paper, rags, and refuse of various kinds. The eggs number from three to eleven (but usually from five to seven), and are a dull, unmarked white.

BECARD
Xantus's Becard
Platypsaris aglaiae albiventris [441.1]

ADULT MALE—Upper parts slaty gray; top of head black; forehead and back of neck grayish. Under parts gray, fading to white on the lower abdomen. Throat rosy pink. The tip of the bill is slightly hooked, and the nostrils are covered by bristles.

ADULT FEMALE—Upper parts brownish gray; top of head dark slate gray. Under parts dark brown shading to whitish on the abdomen.

LENGTH—6.75 inches.

DISTRIBUTION—Chiefly in western Mexico, but reported from the Huhchuca Mountains of Arizona.

The Xantus's Becard is the only member of the family *Cotingidae* found in

the United States. These birds are structurally most nearly like the Larks and the Flycatchers. (Family *Cotingidae*)

BITTERN
American Bittern
Botaurus lentiginosus [190]

ADULT MALE AND FEMALE—Upper parts dark brown, streaked with lighter brown; wings yellowish brown, deeply tipped with black. Sides of neck black; top of head rich chestnut brown. Under parts light yellowish brown, streaked with dark brown. Bill yellow.

LENGTH—28.00 inches.

DISTRIBUTION—From Labrador and British Columbia southwards through the United States to about latitude 35 degrees (southern South Carolina). In winter it is found below this latitude.

The Bittern is a bird of the marshes and low wet meadowlands where bushes abound, and is also found along the estuaries of tidal streams in the salt marsh regions of the coast. Although it is fairly common, it is seldom seen, for upon the approach of an observer it thrusts its head and bill straight up, and this attitude, together with its brown-streaked plumage causes it so closely to resemble the reeds in which it is standing as to escape detection. In flight, which is

heavy and labored, it utters a hoarse croak, *quaarrk*. The bird is often called the Stake Driver or Pumper from its call notes, which are among the most curious notes uttered by any native bird. They sound like the syllables *punk-a-dunk,* as though the bird were driving a stout stake into a resonant mud bank. Some listeners liken them to the sounds made by a musically gurgling pump. It has been averred that while uttering these notes the bird's bill is driven deep into the mud. This, however, is not the case, the bird's bill being thrust forward into the air with each utterance. (Family *Ardeidae*)

Eastern Least Bittern
Ixobrychus exilis exilis [191]

ADULT MALE—Top of head, a line along the back of the neck, back, and

tail, jet black. Sides of neck yellowish brown; back of neck rich chestnut brown. Wing with a broad yellowish, brown-edged patch. Under parts white, washed with light yellowish brown. Patch on side of breast, blackish.

ADULT FEMALE—Similar to the male, but brown where the male is black. Under parts brown, streaked with dusky brown.

LENGTH—13.00 inches.

DISTRIBUTION—From New Brunswick and Manitoba southwards to the Gulf States, and on the Pacific coast not farther north than northern California. In winter it is found in the Gulf States and southwards through Mexico.

A very attractive little species, only about three inches longer than the common Robin. It is an inhabitant of cat-tail swamps, and the borders of swampy streams and ponds. Its colors are very obliterative and protective. Its commonest notes are a sort of *coo coo*, like those of the Mourning Dove. (Family *Ardeidae*)

Western Least Bittern
Ixobrychus exilis hesperis [191a]

Similar to the Eastern Least Bittern, but larger, and with longer and heavier legs and feet.

DISTRIBUTION—Ranges from the southern part of Oregon southwards to central Lower California, and western Guatemala; spending the winter from Arizona and Southern California southwards. (Family *Ardeidae*)

BLACKBIRD FAMILY
Blackbirds, Orioles, Meadowlarks, Cowbirds, Bobolinks, Grackles
Icteridae

The Icteridae are birds only of the Americas. The bill is always stout, and sharp, sometimes short, sometimes long, but never longer than the head. The tail is not longer than the wing, and is usually rounded or squarish at its tip—never forked, and is composed of twelve feathers. In general, black or blackish is prominent in the plumage. The voice is usually either rich and full, or harsh and guttural. This family has the distinction of containing the only American parasitic species, the Cowbird. About two hundred and forty species and subspecies are now known, of which forty-two are reported from North America (contained in ten genera), the rest being confined to the tropics and subtropics.

NESTING. This varied family of birds includes those which nest in widely different situations, and construct nests of widely different forms and materials. Our Bobolink nests largely in clover and grass fields, or low damp grassy meadows, or along the grassy tracts of streams. The nest itself is placed on the ground among tall grasses, sometimes at the base of a prominent tuft, or near a small bush. It is composed of fine weed stems and dry grasses and rootlets, and is lined with similar but finer materials. The eggs are whitish, gray, or light grayish blue—sometimes very

pale brownish—and are spotted and splotched, sparsely but more often heavily, with various tones of brown, lavender, gray, purple, etc. The larger markings are often at the larger end of the egg, the smaller and lighter ones at the smaller end.

Like the Bobolink, our Meadowlark nests on the ground amid the deep grasses, making the nest of local materials with an over-arching roof and side entrance, to which a short runway in the grass often leads. The eggs are white, spotted sparsely or heavily with rich browns.

The various Red-winged Blackbirds, and the Yellow-headed Blackbird often nest in large companies in swamps and marshy bushy places—though sometimes on the uplands—placing their nests in rushes, small bushes, or trees. The nests are composed of rushes and similar plants, weed stems, grasses, and the like, and are lined with similar but finer materials. The eggs are light grayish, pale greenish, pale bluish, sometimes almost white, spotted, blotched, and scrawled with lines of reddish brown, gray, purplish brown and similar shades.

Grackles' nests are rather bulky affairs of small twigs, weed stalks, coarse grasses (seaweeds near the coast), often with a supporting layer of mud or clay, and lined with fine grasses, rootlets, feathers, and sometimes bits of string, paper, or cloth. They are placed in a variety of situations, sometimes in trees as high as fifty or sixty feet, sometimes in bushes, infrequently in hollow trees, on the tops of tall stumps, in old church steeples, and in barns and other outbuildings. Near the coast the nests are quite often to be found in the lower parts of Osprey's or Fish Hawk's nests, tucked in among the larger sticks and twigs. Both the Ospreys and the Grackles seem to enjoy this close neighborliness. The eggs vary from a greenish white to a light brownish, and are blotched, spotted, and scrawled, sparsely or heavily, with shades of dark brown and lavender, etc.

The familiar nest of the Baltimore Oriole is commonly suspended from the tip of a drooping branch (often of an elm) from ten or twelve to seventy or eighty feet or more from the ground, quite often over a roadway or pathway, and is a long purse or pouch, usually with a side opening near the top, and closely woven together of grasses, weed bark, and other long soft tough vegetable fibers, into which are often interlaced soft plant down, hair, string, wool, and strips of cloth. The whole fabric is soft, yet resistant, and outlasts the storms of many winters. The eggs are dull white, grayish white, or bluish white, with spots, blotches, streaks, and irregular lines and scrawls of dark gray, black, brown, lavender, etc., all the markings usually more thickly clustered at the larger end.

The eggs of the Orchard Oriole are similar to those of the Baltimore, and the nest is lodged often among the forks of a branch, sometimes closely suspended from a fork, and is a much shorter more compact structure. It is composed of grasses (or of "Spanish Moss" in the south) and lined with soft plant fibers.

The Cowbirds, our only parasitic birds, make no nest, the female depositing her eggs singly in the nests of smaller birds, such as Warblers and Sparrows. Towhees (chewinks) and the Yellow Warbler are often thus victimized, and forced to rear a fosterchild much larger than their own offspring. Cowbirds' eggs are bluish without markings, or whitish with heavy markings of brown. The eggs of *Icterid* birds vary from three to six or eight.

BLACKBIRD
Bicolored Red-winged Blackbird
Agelaius phoeniceus californicus [499]

Similar to the Eastern Red-winged Blackbird, but with the red epaulette

patches not showing edges of yellowish or buff. Female somewhat darker than the female of the eastern form.

LENGTH—8.20 inches.

DISTRIBUTION—From the western portion of Oregon and along the northern and middle coastal region of California. (Family *Icteridae*)

Brewer's Blackbird

Euphagus cyanocephalus [510]

ADULT MALE—Entire plumage a glossy, shining greenish black, changing to purplish black on the head and neck.

ADULT FEMALE—Upper parts dark brownish gray, the wings and tail darker, and with greenish glossy reflections. Head, neck, and under parts brownish gray, the head and neck with violet iridescence, and the under parts with greenish.

LENGTH—9.05 inches.

DISTRIBUTION—Over the western portion of North America from Saskatchewan and British Columbia southward to Texas and the northern part of Lower California, between the Great Plains and the Pacific coast. Straggles eastward sometimes into the valley of the Mississippi River.

A very domestic bird is the Brewer's Blackbird, commonly found about houses both in towns, cities, and the open country about farms. In the spring the birds consume enormous numbers of harmful grubs in the newly ploughed land, but offset this by devouring ripened grain in the fall. (Family *Icteridae*)

Eastern Red-winged Blackbird

Agelaius phoeniceus phoeniceus [498]

ADULT MALE—Entire bird jet black, with the shoulders, or bend of the wing bright scarlet, edged with yellow, fading to whitish. When the wing is tightly closed, only the yellowish edging is apparent.

ADULT FEMALE—Utterly different from the male; entire bird brown (throat and upper breast sometimes lighter), streaked with darker brown.

LENGTH—9.50 inches.

DISTRIBUTION—The whole of eastern North America from New Brunswick to Manitoba, and south to the Gulf of Mexico. In winter it is found south of the latitude of Virginia and southern Illinois.

Great flocks of "blackbirds" go over in the spring, streaming through the upper air like long waving columns of smoke. Often these flocks are composed largely of the Red-winged Blackbird. The males, arriving first, settle in marshes, particularly those

fringed with bushes, and there begin their loud song, *O-ka-léeee* or *o-rak-a-reéee*, the last portion of which is most prominent—often a long musical scream because of the vigor the birds put into this last phrase. Occasionally the *leeeee* note is more subdued, becoming a musical, though harsh, loud trill. Soon the females arrive—dull sparrowy birds—and are chased hither and yon over the meadows and lowlands by their ardent black and scarlet suitors, in that species of headlong-dash courtship, so dear to the hearts of many of our native birds. The call note of the Red-wing is a deep emphatic *chucckk,* and when many birds are flying together, their notes blend into a heavy throaty rattle. Many different forms of Redwings occur in North America, penetrating to almost every corner of the continent. (Family *Icteridae*)

European Blackbird
Turdus merula merula [761.1]

ADULT MALE—Entire bird glossy black; the rim of the eyes, and bill, orange yellow.

ADULT FEMALE—Upper parts olive brown. Under parts whitish with dark streaks, or brownish like the breast. Abdomen grayish brown.

LENGTH—10.00 inches.

DISTRIBUTION—An accidental straggler in Greenland.

The song of this celebrated British songster is much like that of our own American Catbird, but far sweeter. It sings mostly during the early hours of morning and the late hours of the afternoon, and is one of the commonest birds heard by the traveler in the British Isles. Note that this bird is a true Thrush, and *not* a member of the Blackbird (*Icteridae*) Family. (Family *Turdidae*)

Florida Red-winged Blackbird
Agelaius phoeniceus mearnsi [498c]

Similar to the Eastern Red-winged Blackbird, but smaller; the females with browner upper parts, and buffier, browner-streaked under parts.

DISTRIBUTION—From Texas, east along the Gulf Coast, and down into Florida, except the southern portion south of the Caloosahatchee River. (Family *Icteridae*)

Giant Red-winged Blackbird
Agelaius phoeniceus arctolegus [498i]

Somewhat similar to the Eastern Red-winged Blackbird, but larger; the bill heavier and longer.

DISTRIBUTION—From north of Saskatchewan and Manitoba south to Montana, North Dakota, Minnesota, and northern Michigan. Occurs as an accidental straggler in Connecticut. In winter it is found in Illinois, Arkansas, Texas, Louisiana, and Alabama. (Family *Icteridae*)

Gulf Coast Red-winged Blackbird
Agelaius phoeniceus littoralis [498h]

Similar to the Eastern Red-winged Blackbird, but the female much darker, and with the wings and tail somewhat shorter.

DISTRIBUTION—From about the region of Choctawhatchee Bay, Florida, west, about the region of Galveston, Texas, along the coast. (Family *Icteridae*)

Kern Red-winged Blackbird
Agelaius phoeniceus aciculatus [498l]

Similar to the San Diego Red-winged Blackbird, but larger, with a longer slenderer bill, and somewhat smaller feet.

DISTRIBUTION—In California, in the South Fork River, a tributary of the Kern River, Kern County. (Family *Icteridae*)

Maynard's Red-winged Blackbird
Agelaius phoeniceus floridanus [498b]

Similar to the Florida Red-winged Blackbird, but, in the female, the plumage paler and grayer, or with a whitish cast.

DISTRIBUTION—The southern tip of Florida, and the Keys. (Family *Icteridae*)

Nevada Red-winged Blackbird
Agelaius phoeniceus nevadensis [498j]

The male of this subspecies is closely similar (scarcely distinguishable) to the male Sonora Red-winged Blackbird. The female, however, is decidedly darker than the female Sonora, and the black markings of the upper and under parts are much broader and more pronounced.

DISTRIBUTION—From southeastern British Columbia and northern Idaho south through California and Nevada to eastern Mexico, New Mexico, and western Texas. (Family *Icteridae*)

Northwestern Red-winged Blackbird
Agelaius phoeniceus caurinus [498f]

Similar to the Eastern Red-winged Blackbird, but somewhat longer, with a longer bill, and darker buffy color in the "epaulettes." The female is much darker, with heavier streakings on the under parts.

DISTRIBUTION—From British Columbia southward along the coast to the northern portion of California, passing southwards in winter as far as southern California. (Family *Icteridae*)

Rio Grande Red-winged Blackbird
Agelaius phoeniceus megapotamus [498g]

The female of this subspecies possesses decidedly more grayish brown upper parts, and is less ochraceous below.

DISTRIBUTION—From the southern coast of Texas and the lower Rio Grande Valley, southwards through eastern Mexico and down to northern Vera Cruz. (Family *Icteridae*)

Rusty Blackbird
Euphagus carolinus [509]

ADULT MALE—Plumage glossy bluish black; in the fall with rusty edges to the feathers. Eye iris, pale yellow, or white.

ADULT FEMALE—Dark slate-gray, with edges of feathers rusty.

LENGTH—9.55 inches.

DISTRIBUTION—From New Brunswick and Labrador, through northern New England and New York, west to the Great Plains, and into Alaska. In winter it is found from Virginia,

southern Illinois, and Kansas, south to the Gulf.

In the New England States the Rusty Blackbird, while common, is virtually unknown by the casual observer of birds. Traveling in large flocks of other members of the Blackbird family in the spring, its similarity in the air to other members of

the flock renders it inconspicuous. Its note, however, is quite distinctive, and has been called a "split squeak." When on the ground, the Rusty Blackbird's gait is best described in the words of Griscom who says, "On the ground it walks with an absurd stagger much different from the stately tread of a Grackle, or the even glide of the Redwing." It resembles a small Grackle, and is frequently called the Small Grackle or the Rusty Grackle. In the spring, the plumage is uniform and glossy, without the rusty feather-edgings. (Family *Icteridae*)

San Diego Red-winged Blackbird
Agelaius phoeniceus neutralis [498e]

Similar to the Sonora Red-winged Blackbird of Arizona and California, but differing therefrom chiefly in being smaller; the female much darker.

LENGTH—8.90 inches.

DISTRIBUTION — Throughout the Great Basin region, and as far south as southern California, and the northern portion of Lower California. (Family *Icteridae*)

San Francisco Red-winged Blackbird

Agelaius phoeniceus mailliardorum [498k]

Quite similar to the Bi-colored Red-winged Blackbird, but with a smaller bill, less enlarged at its base. The exposed part of the middle wing coverts is usually solid black. The female is generally darker.

DISTRIBUTION—From the middle coastal region of California southwards to central Monterey County, and eastward including Suisun Bay and the valleys between the inner Coast Ranges. (Family *Icteridae*)

Sonora Red-winged Blackbird

Agelaius phoeniceus sonoriensis [498a]

Similar to the Eastern Red-winged Blackbird, but larger. The female is a paler brown, with darker streakings on the under parts.

DISTRIBUTION—From southern Arizona and California, southwards along the coast into northwestern Mexico. (Family *Icteridae*)

Thick-billed Red-winged Blackbird

Agelaius phoeniceus fortis [498d]

Similar to the Eastern Red-winged Blackbird, but larger, with a shorter, heavier bill. The female is a paler, yellower brown than the Eastern form. This is the largest member of the genus *Agelaius*.

DISTRIBUTION—From South Dakota, Wyoming, and Idaho, southwards into Colorado and northwestern Texas. In winter it spreads through the southern part of this range, and occurs irregularly in Arkansas and Louisiana. (Family *Icteridae*)

Tricolored Red-winged Blackbird

Agelaius tricolor [500]

Similar to the Eastern Red-winged Blackbird, but with the shoulder patches or epaulettes a deeper red, edged with white or whitish. The female shows little brownish, but is blackish above, the feathers edged with gray and whitish, and showing a bronzy greenish iridescence. The

under parts are a dark grayish black, with grayish white edges on the feathers. Throat and upper breast lighter, and streaked.

DISTRIBUTION—Between the Cascade and Sierra Nevada Mountains and the coast, in the valleys of Oregon, California, and Lower California. (Family *Icteridae*)

Yellow-headed Blackbird

Xanthocephalus xanthocephalus [497]

ADULT MALE—Jet black, except for head, throat, and upper breast, which are yellow or orange yellow. Bill short, sharply pointed. Wing with a large white patch.

ADULT FEMALE—Brownish, except for the throat and upper breast, which are dull yellowish. Lower breast mottled with white.

LENGTH—9.35 inches.

DISTRIBUTION—Over the western portion of North America, from the Hudson Bay region westward to British Columbia; east as far as Wisconsin, Indiana, and Texas; and southwards into northern Mexico, sometimes straggling into the eastern states.

The Yellow-head has much the same habits as our common Red-winged Blackbird, flocking and calling in voices harsher than the eastern bird. They are strikingly colored birds, the males with their bright heads, and

white patches in the wings, presenting a fine sight as they fly about over a marsh. They are sometimes seen in barnyards, corrals, and even in city streets. (Family *Icteridae*)

BLUEBIRD
Azure Bluebird
Sialia sialis fulva [766a]

Similar to the Eastern Bluebird, but with the upper parts a lighter, more ethereal blue, and with the under parts paler.

DISTRIBUTION—From southern Arizona southward into the mountains of eastern Mexico. (Family *Turdidae*)

Chestnut-backed Bluebird
Sialia mexicana bairdi [767a]

Similar to the Eastern Bluebird, but with the whole head and throat blue, and with the orange-brown of the

breast extending over the upper back. Forehead brown.

DISTRIBUTION—From Wyoming southwards following the mountains, into Mexico. (Family *Turdidae*)

Eastern Bluebird
Sialia sialis sialis [766]

ADULT MALE—Upper parts (when seen in strong light) bright vivid blue. Under parts bright orange-brown, except the middle of the lower abdomen and under tail coverts, which are white.

ADULT FEMALE—Upper parts grayish ashy, with a bluish tinge on the wings, upper tail coverts, and tail. Under parts as in the male, but much duller.

LENGTH—7.01 inches.

DISTRIBUTION—The whole of the eastern portion of the continent from Manitoba and Nova Scotia southward to the Gulf of Mexico. In winter it distributes itself from southern New England and southern Illinois southward, progressively increasing in numbers.

The Bluebird's cheerful *cher-weet, cher-weet* is one of the most heartening sounds of early spring. Its soft, sweetly-warbled, rather short song is less well-known, since it carries only to a short distance. The blue color of the male (being a refraction color and not a pigment color) is seen only when the bird is perched in favorable light. In our northern states from Connecticut southwards, many Bluebirds may be seen during all of the winter months, harboring in deep sheltered valleys or thick stands of

evergreens, and feeding on the berries of the red cedar, sumach, hackberry, barberry, bittersweet, and the like. They often come to window-sill feeding stations at such times. (Family *Turdidae*)

Mountain Bluebird
Sialia currucoides [768]

ADULT MALE—Upper parts light purplish or greenish blue; under parts pale greenish blue.

ADULT FEMALE—Upper parts brownish gray, the wings and tail alone being bright blue. Under parts fawn brown, washed with bluish.

LENGTH—7.20 inches.

DISTRIBUTION—From the Great Slave Lake country, Canada, southwards into New Mexico, and from the western border of the Great Plains westwards to the Pacific coast, largely

in the mountains. It is said that these hardy birds ascend in the mountains far above the timberline, up to about 13,000 feet. (Family *Turdidae*)

San Pedro Bluebird
Sialia mexicana anabelae [767b]

Somewhat similar to the Chestnut-backed Bluebird, but with the brown of the back much restricted, sometimes absent; and with a smaller area of brown on the breast. Throat blue, extending backward in a line that divides the brown of the breast.

DISTRIBUTION—Restricted to the mountains of Lower California. (Family *Turdidae*)

Western Bluebird
Sialia mexicana occidentalis [767]

ADULT MALE—Upper parts dark purplish blue, the upper back with

more or less chestnut brown. Throat purplish blue. Breast, dark brown; the rest of the under parts a mixture of purplish, gray, and brown.

ADULT FEMALE—Head, neck, and upper parts gray; the back washed with brownish. Rump and tail bright blue, the outer tail feathers edged with white.

LENGTH—6.80 inches.

DISTRIBUTION—From British Columbia to California, and eastward to western Nevada and Idaho. Straggles casually into New Mexico during migration. In winter it travels into southern Lower California.

The Western Bluebird is similar in habits, song, nesting, and food to its common eastern relative—so similar that differences between the two birds are difficult of detection. (Family *Turdidae*)

BLUETHROAT
Red-spotted Bluethroat
Cyanosylvia suecica [764]

ADULT MALE—Upper parts brown, the basal half of the wing chestnut brown. Upper breast blue, bearing a reddish-brown spot in its center. Beneath the blue is first a black band and then one of chestnut brown. Abdomen white; flanks grayish brown.

ADULT FEMALE—Similar to the male, but throat buffy with a dark stripe on each side and across the breast, and occasional traces of blue and brown.

LENGTH—5.75 inches.

DISTRIBUTION—This European species is a local and irregular straggler in western Alaska.

The beautiful Bluethroats, of which there should be more in our continent, are superb singers, somewhat

similar to our Brown Thrasher, but sweeter. They frequent low, swampy ground, or willows along streams. (Family *Turdidae*)

BOBOLINK
Bobolink
Dolichonyx oryzivorus [494]

ADULT MALE—Black, except for the nape which is buffy or yellowish white, and the shoulders and lower back which are white.

ADULT FEMALE—Utterly different from the male. Upper parts streaked brown; under parts unstreaked yellowish brown. Line over the eye and

through the crown, buffy or yellowish white.

LENGTH—7.25 inches.

DISTRIBUTION—The eastern portion of North America, from Nova Scotia, Manitoba and Montana; west to Utah, and southwards to central New Jersey, Illinois, and Kansas. In the fall it passes through our southern states, and the West Indies, and spends the winter in South America south of the Amazon.

The Bobolink of the north becomes the Reedbird or Ricebird of the south; for after the fall molt, the males and females are essentially alike. Trooping in great flocks through the rice-fields of the south, they consume large quantities of that grain. During the breeding season the Bobolink is the most joyous and vocal of birds. The males sail to and fro over wide grassy fields, pouring out as they go a bubbling, tinkling, irrepressible effusion, which is the delight of all hearers. "An hysterical music box in feathers" one observer calls the bird. No writer has better caught the spirit of the mating, nesting, singing, ebullient Bobolink than William Cullen Bryant in his peerless poem *Robert O'Lincoln*. The demure and concealing coloration of the female makes her a most inconspicuous object when on the ground amid a tangle of brownish grass stems. The male is equally well hidden when perched among the daisy and clover heads. (Family *Icteridae*)

BOB-WHITE
Eastern Bob-white
Colinus virginianus virginianus [289]

ADULT MALE—Back and wings chiefly reddish brown; tail gray. Line over the eye white, bordered above and below with jet black. Crown reddish brown, mixed with black. Back of neck reddish brown. Throat white. Upper breast bears a prominent band of black. Lower breast and abdomen white barred with black. Sides heavily washed over with rich reddish brown.

ADULT FEMALE—Similar to the male, but little or no black on the breast, and with the throat and the line over the eye buffy instead of white.

LENGTH—10.00 inches.

DISTRIBUTION—Over most of eastern North America, from the southern parts of Dakota, Minnesota, Ontario, Vermont, New Hampshire, and Maine southwards to Georgia and western Florida, and westward to Nebraska, Kansas, Oklahoma, and western Texas. It has been introduced and naturalized in parts of Colorado, New Mexico, Utah, Idaho, California, and Washington.

The familiar little Bob-white, or simply Quail as it is called in many places in the East, is generally better known by its voice than anything else. In country districts, its cheerful call of *Bob-White* or *Poor Bob-White* is a series of two or three clear whistles,

easily imitated, the last note rising abruptly (sol, re; or sol, sol, re). In New England these notes are believed to say *more wet* or *no more wet*, and are thought to be prognosticatory of the character of the approaching

weather. When the Quail is flushed it makes off with great speed, then turns slowly, and with its wings bent downward in a stiff curve scales along through the air with whistling velocity. The body of the Quail when plucked is small and its flesh is no better than that of a domestic fowl. It is of much more use as a songster and is a picturesque element in our rural scene. (Family *Perdicidae*)

Florida Bob-white
Colinus virginianus floridanus [289a]

Similar to the Eastern Bob-white, but smaller, and with the general plumage color darker throughout. The black of the upper parts is more extensive; the rump and the upper tail coverts are grayer; the black band on the throat is broader, and sometimes reaches down over the upper breast. The reddish brown on the sides of the body is more extensive; and the black bars on the breast and abdomen are much wider.

LENGTH—8.50 inches.

DISTRIBUTION—On the Keys and in the peninsula of Florida, except in the extreme northern part.

This subspecies is in general the extreme southern counterpart of the Eastern (and northern) Bob-white, common on the old plantations espe-cially. Chapman says it is more in-clined to take to the trees when flushed than is its northern congener. He says, "I have seen a whole covey fly up into the lofty pine trees, where, squatting close to the limbs, they be-come almost invisible." (Family *Per-dicidae*)

Key West Bob-white
Colinus virginianus insulanus [289c]

Similar to the Florida Bob-white, but with the crown a uniform dark brown, and with the forehead bearing a larger area of white. Smaller than the *floridanus*.

DISTRIBUTION—Formerly occurred on Key West, Florida, but now ex-tinct. (Family *Perdicidae*)

Masked Bob-white
Colinus ridgwayi [291]

ADULT MALE—Upper parts finely mottled with black, buff, and cinna-

mon brown. Face and throat with a black mask. Hind neck very finely streaked with white. Under parts red-dish brown.

ADULT FEMALE—Lacks the black markings. Upper parts a mixture of black, white, and brown. Throat patch tawny brown, as is also a line over the eye. A marked chest band, and heavy barrings on the abdomen.

LENGTH—About 10.00 inches.

DISTRIBUTION — In southwestern Arizona, and in the northwestern part of Sonora, Mexico.

The male Masked Bob-white is a strikingly handsome cavalier, with his deep reddish chestnut breast thrust proudly out as he stalks through the long grass of the mesas and valleys where these birds are chiefly found. The Bob-white call is loud and clear, and, like the call of the Eastern form is uttered from a post, rock, bush, or hummock. (Family *Perdicidae*)

Texas Bob-white
Colinus virginianus texanus [289b]

Similar to the Eastern Bob-white, but the plumage generally paler through-out. The upper back is prominently marked with black and creamy light brown; the rump is grayer. The ter-tials lack the definite black markings, and their edges are paler. The throat bears a much narrower black band.

DISTRIBUTION—Southeastern corner of New Mexico, to southern Texas, and southward through northeastern Coahuila and Nuevo Leon to central Tamaulipas. Introduced into various eastern states.

Thousands of the Texas Bob-whites have been introduced into various eastern states, where they interbreed with the forms already resident there. (Family *Perdicidae*)

BOOBY FAMILY
Boobies and Gannets
Sulidae

Boobies are strictly ocean birds, re-maining, however, near the coast, sailing and flapping on strong wings, and diving into the water after their fishy prey, in headlong plunges like those of the fish hawks. They are large heavy birds, with long strong bills and webbed feet, and are somewhat goose-like in appearance. About ten species are known, of which seven have been reported in American waters. They are contained in the genera *Sula* and *Moris*.

NESTING. The eggs of these large somewhat goose-like birds are laid on the bare sand or the bare rocks of some precipice overlooking the sea. Either no nest is built, or what might

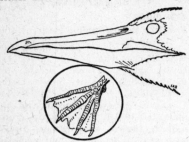

pass for one—a mere loose mass of dried seaweed. Sometimes the nest is placed on or in bushes on tropical keys. In this case it is a loose mass of sticks, weeds and similar materials. This contains the one or two eggs, in color a dull chalky white, or pale greenish, or bluish, flecked with whitish and grayish.

BOOBY
Atlantic Blue-faced Booby
Sula dactylatra dactylatra [114]

ADULT MALE AND FEMALE—Plumage white, the wing quills and tail

black. Face slaty bluish; feet light gray or yellowish gray.

LENGTH—27.00 inches.
DISTRIBUTION—An accidental straggler in southern Florida and Louisiana. (Family *Sulidae*)

Blue-footed Booby
Sula nebouxi [114.1]

ADULT MALE AND FEMALE—Upper parts brownish flecked with whitish. Head and neck white streaked with grayish. Under parts white. Legs and feet bright blue.
LENGTH—33.00 inches.
DISTRIBUTION—From Gulf of California southwards along the Pacific coast to the Galapagos Islands and Chile. (Family *Sulidae*)

Brewster's Booby
Sula brewsteri [115.1]

Similar to the White-bellied Booby, but with a paler head and neck, and with a bluish bill and greenish feet.
DISTRIBUTION—From the northern part of the Gulf of California southwards into the eastern South Pacific. (Family *Sulidae*)

Pacific Blue-faced Booby
Sula dactylatra californica [114a]

ADULT MALE AND FEMALE—Pure white, the wing quills and tail black. Bare area about the base of the bill bluish, or slate colored. Bill yellow, very large and thick. Legs and feet orange.
DISTRIBUTION—From about the region of the Los Alijos Rocks, Lower California, southwards along the western coast of Mexico.

Although these are entirely maritime birds, they are more common near coasts than in the open ocean, where they obtain their fishy food by plunging into the sea while sailing or flapping a short distance above the surface. Although the birds are heavy and, when sitting on the rocks, ungainly in appearance, yet their flight is strong, assured, and graceful. They make their way over the waves by alternately flapping and sailing. (Family *Sulidae*)

Red-footed Booby
Sula piscator [116]

ADULT MALE AND FEMALE—Plumage white, the head and nape washed with straw-yellowish; the primaries of the wing frosty grayish brown; tail white. Face, blue; feet, reddish.
LENGTH—29.00 inches.
DISTRIBUTION—The Pacific coast of America, and in the Atlantic, off the Bahamas; rarely to the southern coast of Florida. (Family *Sulidae*)

White-bellied Booby
Sula leucogaster leucogaster [115]

ADULT MALE AND FEMALE—Plumage a grayish brown, the lower breast

and abdomen white, sometimes flushed with pale grayish. Bill and feet yellowish.
LENGTH—30.00 inches.
DISTRIBUTION—From Georgia south along the Atlantic coasts of the tropical and subtropical Americas. An accidental straggler on Long Island. (Family *Sulidae*)

The Boobies and Gannets of the Family *Sulidae* (which see) are of similar habits. (Family *Sulidae*)

BRAMBLING
Brambling
Fringilla montifringilla [514.1]

ADULT MALE—Upper parts and face black. Rump and upper tail coverts white. Throat, breast, and shoulders bright orange-brown. Under parts white.
ADULT FEMALE—Similar to the male, but duller, and with the crown reddish brown, the feathers tipped with gray. The cheeks and neck are ashy gray, and there is a black streak over the eye.
LENGTH—6.25 inches.
DISTRIBUTION—An accidental visitor on St. Paul Island, in the Pribilof Group, Alaska.

The Brambling or Mountain Finch is found in the British Isles in winter, congregating in flocks commonly in beech woods. It breeds in the northernmost parts of Scandinavia, Russia, and northern Asia. (Family *Fringillidae*)

BRANT
American Brant
Branta bernicla hrota [173a]

ADULT MALE AND FEMALE—Back brownish gray, the feathers margined with light grayish brown. Head, neck, throat, and upper breast black. Sides of the neck finely speckled with white. Upper tail coverts like the back, but with the longer side feathers white. Lower breast grayish white, paling to white on the abdomen. Sides of the body a darker grayish.
LENGTH—26.00 inches.
DISTRIBUTION—In the arctic regions in general, descending into the United States in winter, and ranging from Massachusetts and Illinois south-

wards. It is rare in the interior of the country.

The American Brant has long been a favorite game-bird, an easy bird to shoot. It is the smallest of our wild geese, and may often be seen in flocks of many thousands feeding in shallow bays, where they cover great areas of water, thus resembling from a distance a low-lying island. Like the Canada Goose, the Brants are often called wild geese, and their migrations are noted with great interest, not only by the general lover of nature but by the sportsman. These hardy birds nest in the arctic regions, where conditions are tolerable enough in summer, but far less so as winter draws on. The flesh of brants is said

to be most toothsome, except when the birds have been feeding on material other than vegetable. Black breasts, absence of white on sides of head and throat, and smaller size, distinguish them from Canada Geese. (Family *Anatidae*)

Black Brant

Branta nigricans [174]

Similar to the American Brant, but with the black part of the neck extending down over the lower breast and under parts. Lower belly and vent region white.

DISTRIBUTION—From north Alaska eastward. In winter from British

Columbia along the coast to Lower California. Sometimes recorded along

the Atlantic coast in winter. (Family *Anatidae*)

BUFFLE-HEAD

Buffle-head

Charitonetta albeola [153]

ADULT MALE—Back and wings black, the latter with large white patches. Head somewhat crested, and puffed out at the sides; a shining purplish-greenish-violet black, with a large prominent patch of silvery white occupying more than half the head behind the eye. Neck pure white. Under parts pure white. Legs and feet flesh color.

ADULT FEMALE—Head, neck, and upper parts sooty brownish gray. Large white or whitish oblique spot back of the eye. Wings dark brown, revealing a large white patch in flight. Throat and upper neck like back; rest of under parts white.

LENGTH—14.75 inches.

DISTRIBUTION—In the extreme north of our continent southwards to Maine, Iowa, and British Columbia. In winter it is found from about southern Canada, Iowa, and northern New England southwards into Mexico and the West Indies.

The funny little Buffle-head is one of the smallest of our sea and ocean ducks, and even among the inland water ducks, only the little Green-winged Teal is smaller. It is somewhat grebe-like in its general habits and motions, and dives with the speed of a flash of light. Although ranked as a sea duck, it never goes far out from land, but prefers the neighbor-

hood of the friendly coast, and is therefore found about harbors, snug coves, and the mouths of broad rivers. The head feathers standing out from the skin give the head a bushy, rounded appearance (as though the bird had recently had its hair washed). The male Buffle-head is sometimes confused with the Hooded Merganser, but is smaller and much whiter. It is also confusingly similar to the rare Barrow's Golden-Eye, but in this latter species the white patch is in front of the eye, and is crescentic. (Family *Anatidae*)

BULLFINCH
Cassin's Bullfinch
Pyrrhula pyrrhula cassini [516]

Larger than the common European Bullfinch (*Pyrrhula vulgaris*). Upper parts ashy gray; upper wing, same. Side of head cinnamon gray. Rump and under tail coverts white. Wings, tail, upper tail coverts, top of head, region around the base of the bill, all shining violet-black. Greater wing coverts black with a broad band of whitish across their ends. The outer tail feathers bear a long patch of white in their terminal halves, but not extending to the tips of the feathers.
LENGTH—6.50 inches.
DISTRIBUTION—This Bullfinch occurs only as an accidental visitant in Alaska on Nulato and Nunivak Islands. (Family *Fringillidae*)

BUNTING
Beautiful Bunting
Passerina versicolor pulchra [600a]

Similar to the Varied Bunting, but with a more purplish-hued rump, with a less-red throat, and slightly smaller.
DISTRIBUTION—The Beautiful Bunting is restricted in its range to the southern part of Lower California. (Family *Fringillidae*)

Eastern Snow Bunting
Plectrophenax nivalis nivalis [534]

ADULT MALE (winter plumage)— Head and under parts white, washed with brownish on the crown, about the ears, and on the rump and sides of the breast. Outer ends of the primaries black. Inner tail feathers black, the outer ones white. Bill light reddish brown.
ADULT FEMALE (winter plumage) —Similar to the male, but with the entire upper parts streaked with blackish. Primaries a rusty brown; the secondaries tipped with brown.
LENGTH—6.88 inches.
DISTRIBUTION—Over the whole of the northern portion of the Northern Hemisphere, descending in winter southwards as far as the northern tier of states, and occasionally as far south as Georgia, Indiana, Kansas, Colorado, and eastern Oregon.

A hardy bird is the Snow Bunting or Snowflake, delighting in the icy blasts and swirling snows of winter. In the

United States in winter it is to be found chiefly along the seashore, on the flat muddy margins of shrunken ponds and streams, and in weed

patches in open fields and around the edges of farms. Snow Buntings travel in large flocks, uttering sweet, almost pensive calls, *tee* or *teeah* or *teeoo*. The alarm note is a *bzztt*. (Family *Fringillidae*)

Indigo Bunting
Passerina cyanea [598]

ADULT MALE—Deep indigo blue, darkest on the head and throat. Wings and tail blackish, with a brownish tinge in strong light, their feathers edged with blue.

ADULT FEMALE—Upper parts plain unstreaked light brown. Under parts light grayish. Sides of breast and abdomen light grayish washed with brown. Feathers of the wings and tail faintly margined with grayish blue.

LENGTH—5.60 inches.

DISTRIBUTION—Whole eastern portion of the United States westward as far as the Great Plains and northward as far as Manitoba and Nova Scotia. It passes the winters in Central America.

The Indigo Bunting is a bird of bushy pastures, coppices, roadside hedges, hillsides covered with scrub oaks, and situations of this sort. It is a far more common bird than many imagine, and its song, as it sits motionless in the very tip of some bush or small tree, is to be heard almost continually in some regions through the hot days of spring and summer. The song, jerkily uttered, and energetically repeated at short intervals, is a sweet, though somewhat sibilous refrain which can be very well represented by the syllables *Sweet, sweet, sweet; swit swit; sway-sway-sway-sway; sweet-sweet-sweet*—slightly accelerated at the end. The Bunting is a tireless singer, and its cheerful little lay is one of the characteristic sounds of a summer day in the country. Since the bird owes its color to light refraction and not

to pigment, it appears in all its blaze of startling indigo only when the full light at the back of the observer falls upon the plumage. Seen against the sky, or in a shadow, the bird is not blue, but may become anything from a dull gray to almost jet black. (Family *Fringillidae*)

Lark Bunting
Calamospiza melanocorys [605]

ADULT MALE—Entire plumage black or slaty-black, except for a broad white patch on the wings, and usually white markings on the outer tail feathers. Bill heavy and conical; tail rather short, with elongated upper tail coverts.

ADULT FEMALE—Upper parts grayish brown, streaked with blackish; the wing patch smaller than in the male, and washed with buffy. Tail, except the middle feathers, bearing white spots. Under parts white, streaked on the breast and sides with dark grayish brown.

LENGTH—6.67 inches.

DISTRIBUTION—Found in the western United States, mainly east of the Rocky Mountains, from western Minnesota and Manitoba to western Kansas and eastern Colorado. In passing to Mexico for the winter the birds sometimes reach Idaho and southern California.

In winter the Lark Buntings are dull gray, white, and brown. They are

rather shy birds, feeding on the ground among the grasses, where observation is difficult. When they fly, the white in the wings is conspicuous, and shows also in the males at rest. The common name for this bird is White-wing. They sing freely on their migrations. Their flight note is a characteristic soft, yet rather penetrating and somewhat melancholy *Thoo-eee*—the last syllable slurred upward. (Family *Fringillidae*)

Lazuli Bunting

Passerina amoena [599]

ADULT MALE—Entire head, neck, and upper parts, bright turquoise blue, with a slightly darker wash on the middle of the back and on the rump. A black patch appears between the eye and the bill. Wings duller than the back, with two white bars.

Breast chestnut brown; abdomen white.

ADULT FEMALE—Upper parts grayish brown, sometimes streaked with black. Rump washed with bluish. Breast pale buffy white, washed on its lower part with brownish. Abdomen white.

LENGTH—5.25 inches.

DISTRIBUTION—Western North America from Kansas westward to California, and in the north from British Columbia southward to Texas. It winters in Lower California and Mexico.

This charming little species is a common inhabitant of the chaparral country of the west, and ascends, in the shrubs and bushes on the higher mountains, to an altitude of nearly 8,000 feet. Its song, given with many variations according to locality, and perhaps also to desire, is bright and cheery, though without much volume, and may be represented by the words

Come! come! come! h-e-r-e, quick! quick! quick! quick! (Family *Fringillidae*)

McKay's Snow Bunting

Plectrophenax hyperboreus [535]

Similar to the Eastern Snow Bunting, but with greater areas of white.

DISTRIBUTION—In the Bering Sea on Hall and St. Matthews islands, spreading in winter to the western coast of Alaska. (Family *Fringillidae*)

Painted Bunting
Passerina ciris [601]

ADULT MALE—Entire head and back of neck, purplish blue. Back yellowish green; rump, upper tail coverts, and tail, dull red. Under parts bright red.

ADULT FEMALE—Upper parts and tail olive greenish. Under parts dull greenish yellow; abdomen yellow.

LENGTH—5.40 inches.

DISTRIBUTION—Southern United States, from North Carolina, southern Illinois, and Kansas, southward to the Gulf of Mexico, and westward to southern Arizona. It winters in Mexico and Central America.

The Painted Bunting, or Nonpareil as it is often called, is a common denizen of chaparral regions and cypress

swamps, where its cheerful, vigorous song—closely resembling that of its Indigo cousin of the East—is one of the characteristic sounds of hot summer days. The birds are shy, secretive creatures, and if flushed, dart out into the open, and then turn and plunge into the nearest cover. Even while singing, they seldom mount into the top of a bush, as does the eastern Indigo Bunting, but remaining concealed, jerk out their energetic song. (Family *Fringillidae*)

Pribilof Snow Bunting
Plectrophenax nivalis townsendi [534a]

Similar to the Eastern Snow Bunting, but larger, and with a longer bill.

DISTRIBUTION—On the Pribilof, Aleutian, Commander, and Shumagin islands. (Family *Fringillidae*)

Rustic Bunting
Emberiza rustica [535.1]

ADULT MALE—Upper parts chestnut brown marked with gray and black. Crown, face, and ear coverts, black. Sides and back of head each with a white patch. Under parts white, the upper breast crossed by a chestnut band. Flanks streaked with chestnut.

ADULT FEMALE—Similar to the male, but duller and browner, and with the chestnut band incomplete.

LENGTH—6.25 inches.

DISTRIBUTION—An accidental straggler on Kiska Island of the Aleutian Archipelago. (Family *Fringillidae*)

Varied Bunting
Passerina versicolor versicolor [600]

ADULT MALE—Back purplish red; forehead and rump purplish blue; back of neck bright red. Under parts purplish red, grading into a reddish purple on the abdomen.

ADULT FEMALE—Upper parts brownish washed with either olive or

bluish. Rump dull blue; wings and tail with grayish or bluish edgings. Under parts dull whitish and brown.

LENGTH—5.50 inches.

DISTRIBUTION—Southern North America, from southern Texas and southern Arizona southward into Mexico. It winters in Central America.

The Varied Bunting is a species closely allied in notes and in habits to the Painted Bunting. (Family *Fringillidae*)

BUSH-TIT
Black Tailed Bush-tit
Psaltriparus minimus melanurus [743c]

Similar to the Coast Bush-tit of southern California, but darker, and with a duller, more leaden hue. The wings and tail are much darker, being nearly black.

DISTRIBUTION—Restricted to about the northern third of Lower California. (Family *Paridae*)

California Bush-tit
Psaltriparus minimus californicus [743a]

Similar to the Coast Bush-tit, but with the brown of the crown brighter and paler, and the under parts paler.

DISTRIBUTION—California (except the high mountains), and the north coast region. (Family *Paridae*)

Coast Bush-tit
Psaltriparus minimus minimus [743]

ADULT MALE AND FEMALE—Upper parts, dark brownish-gray; top of head, darker brownish. Under parts, grayish or brownish-white, washed with brownish on the sides of the body.

LENGTH—4.25 inches.

DISTRIBUTION—Along the Pacific coastal region from Washington to northern California.

The Bush-tits are much like common Chickadees in their habits, moving about among the leaves and twigs in acrobatic fashion; and swinging their long, gray, hanging nests from the tips of the branches. Their notes are faint, high, and twittering. (Family *Paridae*)

Grinda's Bush-tit
Psaltriparus minimus grindae [743b]

Similar to the Coast Bush-tit, but the upper parts with a bluish-gray cast.

DISTRIBUTION—Restricted to the Cape Region of Lower California. (Family *Paridae*)

Lead-colored Bush-tit
Psaltriparus minimus plumbeus [744]

Similar to the Coast Bush-tit, but with the crown and upper parts, bluish-gray; sides of head, brownish; under parts, soiled white, and the abdomen washed with buff.

DISTRIBUTION—From Wyoming, Colorado, and eastern Texas, westward to eastern Oregon, and down into eastern California. (Family *Paridae*)

Lloyd's Bush-tit
Psaltriparus minimus lloydi [745]

ADULT MALE AND FEMALE—Upper parts, gray; with broad patches of black on the sides of the head and enclosing the eyes, and a partial collar of black about the neck. Under parts, grayish-white with a faint brownish tinge.

LENGTH—4.36 inches.

DISTRIBUTION—From the mountains of western Texas (between the

Rio Grande and the Pecos River), southward into northern Mexico. (Family *Paridae*)

CANVAS-BACK

Canvas-back

Nyroca valisineria [147]

ADULT MALE—Back and sides of the body light canvas-colored gray. Shoulders and upper breast black. Head and entire neck rich chestnut brown; the crown and face duskier. Tail and quills dark gray. Feathers about the base of the tail black. Lower breast and abdomen ashy or white. Bill about three times as long as broad.

ADULT FEMALE—Entire bird dull brown, the face and chin region whitish.

LENGTH—20.00 inches.

DISTRIBUTION—Over North America generally, but breeding in the interior, from Colorado, Nevada, Minnesota, northwards to Alaska, and eastward. In winter it is found from Maryland to British Columbia, and southward to southern California and Mexico, and eastward to the West Indies.

During the nesting season, the famous Canvas-back is a bird of the interior portions of North America, but during the winter it may be found chiefly in coves, bays, and the tidal estuaries of creeks and rivers along our southern coasts, where it feeds largely upon its favorite diet of wild celery or eel-grass (*Valisineria*). It is while on this succulent winter diet that the Canvas-back develops delicacy of flavor, and acquires deposits of toothsome fat which make the bird peerless as a table duck. The Canvas-back is an extremely swift flier, and unusually agile as a diver and swimmer. These capabilities, combined with its mental acumen and eternal vigilance, enable it to persist and multiply in spite of hunters. It is a

very hardy duck, and remains in the north in the fall until ice has begun to form and seal up its favorite foods. (Family *Anatidae*)

CARACARA

Audubon's Caracara

Polyborus cheriway auduboni [362]

ADULT MALE AND FEMALE—Back and wings rusty black; the latter with a large white patch at the base of the primaries, showing prominently when the bird is in flight. Tail white with numerous narrow black bars and a broad black tip. Upper tail coverts white. Face, bare of feathers, is bright red, orange, or orange-yellow. Crown black, with a slight crest. Nape buffy, barred with black. Throat and upper breast soiled whitish; lower breast barred with black; abdomen rusty black; under tail coverts white. Feet and legs yellow. Bill large and straw-colored.

LENGTH—23.00 inches.

DISTRIBUTION—From the northern part of Lower California, southeast through Arizona, Texas, Florida, Mexico, and as far south as Central America. An accidental straggler in Ontario.

Caracaras are large, ungainly birds on the ground, somewhat like the Falcons (to whose family they belong), but more like Vultures in their habits and food, being carrion-eaters. Its hoarse cries give the bird its name. It is often found in company with Turkey Vultures and Black Vultures, and prefers the open country over which it flaps and soars in its search for dead animals of all sorts, as well as for

small mammals, frogs, reptiles, fish, crayfish, and large insects. (Family *Falconidae*)

Guadalupe Caracara
Polyborus lutosus [363]

Similar to Audubon's Caracara, but paler and browner, with almost the entire plumage barred with darker.

DISTRIBUTION — Restricted to Guadalupe Island, off the coast of Lower California. Now probably extinct. (Family *Falconidae*)

CARDINAL
Arizona Cardinal
Richmondena cardinalis superba [593a]

Similar to the Eastern Cardinal, but paler and more rosy in color. The

breast of the female is brighter in color than that of the Eastern Cardinal.

LENGTH—9.50 inches.

DISTRIBUTION—From southern Arizona into Mexico.

This is the largest of all the six North American Cardinals. (Family *Fringillidae*)

Eastern Cardinal
Richmondena cardinalis cardinalis [593]

ADULT MALE—The throat and narrow region about the base of the bill, black; rest of plumage bright red, except the back, wings, and tail which are dull red washed with grayish. Head prominently crested. Bright red bill and unusually large and heavy.

ADULT FEMALE—Bill, crest on head, wings and tail, red. Narrow region about the base of the bill slate gray. Upper parts ashy brown. Under parts light buff, lighter on the abdomen, with a reddish wash on the breast.

LENGTH—8.25 inches.

DISTRIBUTION — Eastern United States, from the latitude of southern New York and Iowa, southwards to northern Florida and eastern Texas.

Low bushy coppices and tangles of vines along the margins of streams, and other low damp situations are the especial haunts of this, our most brilliantly colored bird. It also may be

found in city parks, along shady city streets, and in cleared woodlands among low, second growths. It frequently visits feeding stations in winter. The song most commonly uttered is a loud, clear, ringing series of whistles, easily imitated—*whoit, whoit, whoit; whait, whait, whait; white, white, white; whit, whit, whit.* The last notes are thinner and finer, and more rapidly brought to a close. (Family *Fringillidae*)

Florida Cardinal

Richmondena cardinalis floridana [593d]

Similar to the Eastern Cardinal, but smaller, and deeper and richer in color.

DISTRIBUTION—Southern half of Florida. (Family *Fringillidae*)

Gray-tailed Cardinal

Richmondena cardinalis canicauda [593c]

Similar to the Eastern Cardinal, but a brighter and richer red, and with less black on the forehead. The female is much grayer.

DISTRIBUTION—From most of Texas to northeastern Mexico. (Family *Fringillidae*)

Louisiana Cardinal

Richmondena cardinalis magnirostris [593e]

Similar to the Florida Cardinal, but with the head and the under parts not quite so dark, and with the bill appreciably larger and heavier.

DISTRIBUTION — From southern Louisiana into eastern Texas. (Family *Fringillidae*)

San Lucas Cardinal

Richmondena cardinalis ignea [593b]

Similar to the Eastern Cardinal but smaller and paler, with little or no black on the forehead.

DISTRIBUTION—Southern portion of Lower California. (Family *Fringillidae*)

CATBIRD

Catbird

Dumetella carolinensis [704]

ADULT MALE AND FEMALE—Entire body slate gray, except for a blackish crown, and a blackish shading on the crown and tail. Vent region rich chestnut brown, seen only occasionally.

LENGTH—8.94 inches.

DISTRIBUTION—Almost the whole of temperate North America, from New Brunswick westward through Saskatchewan to British Columbia, rarely as far as the Pacific Coast States, and southwards to the Gulf of Mexico.

In winter it is found in the Gulf States, and southwards.

The Catbird is a denizen of briar tangles (our common Catbriar might be termed "Catbirdbriar"), and of bushes bordering fields, roadsides, and

swamps, particularly dense ornamental shrub-growths in home gardens and public parks. Its call and alarm note is a harsh, nasal *aaoow,* somewhat similar to the long-drawn-out mew of a cat. This, it is surprising to find, is the only note by which this magnificent singer is known to some in whose gardens the bird has been nesting. The song is sometimes not much inferior to that of the Brown Thrasher and of the Mockingbird; in fact in some districts the bird is known under the name of the Gray Mockingbird. The song, while similar to the Thrasher's, is not quite so rich and florid, and contains some harsh mewing notes similar to the call note. Catbirds' nests are not difficult to find after the leaves have fallen. Every vine-tangle by the roadside may contain several nests (the accumulation of several years) placed in almost inaccessible situations among the thorns. Catbirds are inquisitive and pugnacious. Squeaking sounds

made in the vicinity of the nests in spring will usually draw forth a pair of very vocal and very belligerent birds which dash excitedly at one's head. From one to three broods are produced yearly. (Family *Mimidae*)

CHACHALACA

Chachalaca
Ortalis vetula vetula [311]

ADULT MALE AND FEMALE—Upper parts olive, with bronze-green reflections, the head and neck fading to dull slate-gray. Fan-shaped tail dull greenish-black, with bronzy sheen, and all except the middle feathers widely tipped with white. Skin of throat bare, and orange-red in color. Breast dull grayish green. Abdomen dull brownish, the under tail coverts much darker.

LENGTH—21.80 inches.

DISTRIBUTION—From the lower Rio Grande of Texas into northeastern Mexico (Vera Cruz).

The name by which this bird is known is one of its own choosing, *Chacha-*

lack, chachalack it calls from the dense mesquite and chaparral of the lower Rio Grande country, usually uttering this hard, loud note from an elevated perch, during the early morning and late afternoon. This is the only representative of the Guans in North America. (Family *Cracidae*)

CHAT
Long-tailed Chat
Icteria virens longicauda [683a]

Similar to the Yellow-breasted Chat, with a longer tail, and grayer or duller upper parts.

DISTRIBUTION — Western North America, from British Columbia to Mexico and west to the Great Plains. It winters in Mexico.

The Long-tailed Chat in coloration, habits, and song, is almost an exact counterpart of his eastern prankish relative, the Yellow-breasted Chat. (Family *Compsothlypidae*)

Yellow-breasted Chat
Icteria virens virens [683]

ADULT MALE AND FEMALE—Upper parts, brown with a slightly greenish cast in strong light; a short white line over the eye; lower half of eye-ring, white; line from base of bill downward to side of neck, white. Throat and breast, rich yellow; abdomen, white.

LENGTH—7.44 inches.

DISTRIBUTION — Eastern United States from South Dakota, southern Minnesota, and central New England, south and west to northeastern Mexico. It winters in Mexico and Central America.

The Yellow-breasted and the Long-tailed Chats are our largest warblers. The former is a bird of bushy pastures and hillsides covered with sproutlings —not at all a bird of forests or open meadows. Because of the dense and thickety nature of its haunts, it is able to live its life and rear its young in unobserved seclusion, and might be a species almost unknown to the average country-dweller, were it not for

the astonishing nature of its vocal performances. No bird, except the Mockingbird, possesses so great a medley of imitative calls. From near the

top of some tall bush, but usually almost concealed, the bird pours forth a farrago of the most unusual notes, varying in pitch, quality, and length, and often with long pauses between. The song may best be described as a loosely connected series of clucks, mews, chucks, toots, whistles, and "whits." Some of the tones are clear, loud, and carrying; others are low and almost purring; still others are harsh, hoarse, and throaty. The long pauses between some of the notes are a surprising characteristic of the song. Burroughs calls the bird a "rollicking polyglot." No other bird is the Chat's peer as a ventriloquist. Often the male will mount into the air, and thus elevated, with loosely dangling legs, will let loose a ribald cascade of tantalizing notes. Altogether the Chat is wild, eccentric, clownish, ventriloquial, erratic, eremetical, furtive, and problematical. It is well worth long and careful study as an individualist. (Family *Compsothlypidae*)

CHICKADEE
Acadian Chickadee
Penthestes hudsonicus littoralis [740a]

ADULT MALE AND FEMALE—Back, brownish-gray; cap, brown; sides of head, white. Throat, black; breast and middle of abdomen, white; sides of abdomen, light reddish-brown.

LENGTH—5.35 inches.

DISTRIBUTION — From Labrador and Newfoundland to central Quebec, Nova Scotia, southwards into the high mountains of New England and northern New York. In winter it spreads southwards. It is rarely found from New England to northern New Jersey.

In the higher mountains of northern New England one often hears a sweet, drawled *dee-dee-dee-dee* or *sheka sheka dee dee dee*, the notes of the

Acadian Chickadee. In other respects the bird is similar to the familiar "Black Cap." (Family *Paridae*)

Alaska Chickadee
Penthestes cinctus alascensis [739]

In general similar in pattern to the Black-capped Chickadee, but with the cap brown, the back lighter, the throat patch blackish, the sides of the body washed with buffy.

DISTRIBUTION—From eastern Siberia across into northern Alaska. (Family *Paridae*)

Bailey's Chickadee
Penthestes gambeli baileyae [738a]

This Chickadee, often called Bailey's Mountain Chickadee, is similar to the Mountain Chickadee, but with an appreciably larger bill, and with the

back and sides of the body a more leaden, less brownish, gray.

DISTRIBUTION—In southern California, in the higher mountains, from

the extreme southern part of the Sierra Nevada and Santa Lucia mountains to the Cuyamaca Mountains near San Diego. (Family *Paridae*)

Barlow's Chickadee
Penthestes rufescens barlowi [741b]

Similar to the Chestnut-backed Chickadee, but without brownish on the flanks or sides of the body.

DISTRIBUTION—Central California. (Family *Paridae*)

Black-capped Chickadee
Penthestes atricapillus atricapillus [735]

ADULT MALE AND FEMALE—Back, wings, and tail, gray; top of head and throat, jet black; sides of head and abdomen, white; the flanks washed with a light brownish-cream, especially in the winter plumage.

LENGTH—5.27 inches.

DISTRIBUTION—In eastern North America from Labrador southwards into southern Illinois and Pennsylvania, and along the Allegheny Mountains still farther south into North Carolina. In winter it spreads down a short way into the southern states, but in general is a permanent resident over its range.

The Chickadee is one of the best-loved birds in America. Present with us summer and winter, it is nevertheless much more frequently seen in the colder season, when it comes to the winter feeding stations on the window ledge. Its call and alarm notes, *chicka-dee-dee,* are as familiar in the winter woods as about the house, often lengthened into a long scolding *chicka chicka dee dee dee dee dee,* or sometimes only *dee-dee-dee-dee.* One of the sweetest and most inspiriting of spring bird calls is its clear, high, whistled *fee-bee,* the first note higher. The bird says *phoe-be* so plainly that many are astonished to learn that the call comes from the Chickadee, and not from a Phoebe. In the east, the call of the Phoebe is a husky, broken *fee a bee wit, fee bee*—even the last part of the phrase

being husky, almost whispered, in contrast to the bell-clear notes of the Chickadee. (Family *Paridae*)

Carolina Chickadee

Penthestes carolinensisca rolinensis [736]

Similar to the Black-capped Chickadee, but roughly about an inch shorter, and the wings grayer, the greater wing coverts not being margined with white.

DISTRIBUTION—From about the middle or southern part of New Jersey and southern Illinois southwards over the southeastern states. (Family *Paridae*)

Chestnut-backed Chickadee

Penthestes rufescens rufescens [741]

ADULT MALE AND FEMALE—Back, sides of body, and flanks, dark red-

dish-brown. Crown and nape, dull brown; line through eye, black. Throat, blackish brown, sides of head and under parts, white.

LENGTH—4.75 inches.

DISTRIBUTION — From southern Alaska down the Pacific coast into Oregon, and eastward to Idaho. (Family *Paridae*)

Columbian Chickadee

Penthestes hudsonicus columbianus [740b]

ADULT MALE AND FEMALE—Back, light brown; top of head, darker. Sides of head, white. Throat, black. Middle of under parts, whitish; the sides of the body, broadly reddish-brown.

DISTRIBUTION—In the Kenai Peninsula, Alaska, and along the Rocky

Mountains southward to Montana. (Family *Paridae*)

Florida Chickadee
Penthestes carolinensis impiger [736b]

Similar to the Carolina Chickadee, but smaller and with darker upper parts.
DISTRIBUTION—Restricted to Florida. (Family *Paridae*)

Grinnell's Chickadee
Penthestes gambeli grinnelli [738b]

Similar to the Mountain Chickadee, but smaller and darker. The region between the shoulders is of the same color as that of the Black-capped Chickadee.
DISTRIBUTION — From northern British Columbia to southeastern Oregon, eastern Washington, and northern Idaho. (Family *Paridae*)

Hudsonian Chickadee
Penthestes hudsonicus hudsonicus [740]

Similar to the Acadian Chickadee, but slightly larger, with the back slightly brighter brown, the crown somewhat lighter and more distinct from the back than in the Acadian species.
DISTRIBUTION—In Canada, from central Alaska eastward to Hudson Bay. (Family *Paridae*)

Inyo Chickadee
Penthestes gambeli inyoensis [738e]

Similar to the Bailey's Chickadee, but paler; the upper parts, sides, and flanks, pale buff or ashy. The palest of all the *gambeli* group.
DISTRIBUTION — In the higher mountains of Mono and Inyo counties, California. (Family *Paridae*)

Long-tailed Chickadee
Penthestes atricapillus septentrionalis [735a]

Similar to the Black-capped Chickadee, but with a longer tail.
DISTRIBUTION—From British Columbia southward through the Rocky Mountain region, and east to Manitoba and the Great Plains. (Family *Paridae*)

Mexican Chickadee
Penthestes sclateri eidos [737]

Similar to the Black-capped Chickadee, but with the black throat patch extending down over the upper breast; and the sides of the body with a broad gray zone, similar to the back. Middle zone of the under parts, clear white.
DISTRIBUTION—The higher mountainous portions of Mexico, and also in southern Arizona. (Family *Paridae*)

Mountain Chickadee
Penthestes gambeli gambeli [738]

Similar to the Black-capped Chickadee, but with a white line over the eye, through the black cap; the middle of the under parts, grayish; and the sides of the body, a dark grayish washed with light brown.
DISTRIBUTION—In the mountains of western United States, up into British Columbia, over the eastern slopes of the Rocky Mountains, and southward to Lower California. (Family *Paridae*)

Nicasio Chickadee
Penthestes rufescens neglectus [741a]

Similar to the Chestnut-backed Chickadee, but with the flanks tinged with light reddish-brown.
DISTRIBUTION—From central California northward along the Pacific coast. (Family *Paridae*)

Oregon Chickadee

Penthestes atricapillus occidentalis [735b]

Similar to the Black-capped Chickadee, but much darker, and with the

flanks washed with grayish, not brownish.

DISTRIBUTION—From the region of Sitka, Alaska, southward along the coast region to northern California. (Family *Paridae*)

Plumbeous Chickadee

Penthestes carolinensis agilis [736a]

Similar to the Black-capped Chickadee, but smaller, with the upper parts somewhat paler, and the under parts whiter.

DISTRIBUTION—Restricted to eastern and central Texas. (Family *Paridae*)

San Pedro Chickadee

Penthestes gambeli atratus [738d]

Similar to Bailey's Chickadee, but slightly darker; the white over the eye and on the frontal region, more restricted. Tail, slightly longer.

DISTRIBUTION—In northern Lower California among the mountains (Sierra San Pedro Martir, and Sierra Juarez). (Family *Paridae*)

Short-tailed Chickadee

Penthestes gambeli abbreviatus [738c]

Similar to the Mountain Chickadee, but with a shorter tail.

DISTRIBUTION—Found in northwestern California, and in the coniferous zones of the Sierra Nevada Mountains. Absent on the coast. (Family *Paridae*)

Yukon Chickadee

Penthestes atricapillus turneri [735c]

Similar to the Long-tailed Chickadee, but slightly smaller and differing chiefly in the possession of grayer upper parts and whiter under parts.

DISTRIBUTION—In Alaska to the north and west of Cook Inlet. (Family *Paridae*)

CHICKEN

Attwater's Prairie Chicken

Tympanuchus cupido attwateri [305a]

Similar to the Greater Prairie Chicken, but smaller and darker, and with the legs not fully feathered. The neck tufts are wider.

DISTRIBUTION—From eastern Texas to southwestern Louisiana. (Family *Tetraonidae*)

Greater Prairie Chicken

Tympanuchus cupido americanus [305]

ADULT MALE—Upper parts a mixture of light yellowish-brown, brown, and white, thickly crossed by black bars. Head, brown marked with blackish-brown stripes and blotches. Sides of neck with inflatable orange-colored air sacs, above which rise prominent tufts of feathers, about two and a half inches in length, and with broadly rounded tips. Under parts, white or whitish, barred with brown.

ADULT FEMALE—Similar to the male, but with very small neck tufts.

LENGTH—18.50 inches.

DISTRIBUTION — From Manitoba southwards to Texas and Louisiana, in the prairies of the Mississippi Valley, and westward into Colorado.

Prairie Chickens travel about in small flocks of a dozen birds more or less, except in winter, when they band together in great throngs of a hundred or more. First alighting in the treetops to scan the country for possible enemies, they later descend into the fields for scattered grains of various sorts. The courting antics of the male

consist of an inflation of the orange-colored neck sacs; a spreading of a yellowish fringe over the eyes; a spreading of the tail; a drooping of the wings; and a lowering of the head and neck. With a low booming sound the males strut and cavort before the apparently admiring females, "showing off" in true male fashion! The booming is ventriloquial in character, and coming from a near-by bird seems to be far away. Only a scattered remnant remains of the great flocks that formerly covered our interior prairies a generation or so ago. They are easy marks for sportsmen, since their flight is straight away, not the erratic zig-zag performed by some of our game birds. Moreover they are said to be one of the most deliciously-flavored of American game. (Family *Tetraonidae*)

Lesser Prairie Chicken
Tympanuchus pallidicinctus [307]

Similar to the Greater Prairie Chicken, but paler. The bars on the back are arranged in groups of three —a wide brown bar enclosed by two narrow black ones.

DISTRIBUTION — From Kansas southward into western Texas, on the eastern borders of the Great Plains. (Family *Tetraonidae*)

CHUCK-WILL'S-WIDOW
Chuck-will's-widow
Antrostomus carolinensis [416]

In general, similar in coloration to the Eastern Whip-poor-will, with a broken whitish band across the upper breast, the base of the bill beset with very long stiff bristles, which project forward, and form a sort of basket when the mouth is open. Mouth, wide and gaping; bill, short.

DISTRIBUTION—From Virginia and Illinois southward to the Gulf States, and westward as far as Kansas and central Texas. It spends its winters from the southern part of Florida southward.

Like the Whip-poor-will, the Chuck-will's-widow enunciates its name with tiresome iteration during the night, until one wonders that the bird's

power of speech and patience can endure. During the hours of dusk the bird feeds, swooping through the air with mouth agape, thus capturing not only large moths, and other nocturnal flying insects, but also humming-birds, and small birds, such as sparrows. However, small birds constitute only a minute fraction of its food. The mouth, when fully expanded, measures some two inches from side to side. (Family *Caprimulgidae*)

CONDOR
California Condor
Gymnogyps californianus [324]

ADULT MALE AND FEMALE—Plumage, sooty blackish. Bill, pale, yellowish-white; head and neck bare, yellow or orange in color. Outer webs of greater wing coverts, and secondaries, grayish. Wing coverts tipped with white; outer secondaries edged with white. Under wing coverts, white.

LENGTH—About 50 inches; wing spread, about 10 feet.

DISTRIBUTION—From the coast ranges of southern California (Monterey Bay region) south into Lower California, and eastward to Arizona.

The great California Condor, or Vulture, is the largest bird of prey in the

Western Hemisphere, and one of the largest in the world with respect to spread of wings, which may reach a dimension of eleven feet. It is exceedingly rare, and should be accorded complete protection to save it from extinction. (Family *Cathartidae*)

COOT
American Coot
Fulica americana americana [221]

ADULT MALE AND FEMALE—Back, wings, and tail, slate gray; the head and neck, blackish. The spread wing shows a patch of white. Under parts

similar to the back, but paler. Under tail coverts, white. Bill, whitish tipped with brown. Crown, pale brown. Legs and feet, greenish; the toes margined with scalloped flaps.

LENGTH—15.00 inches.

DISTRIBUTION—From New Brunswick westward to British Columbia, and southward to New England (rarely), New Jersey, Tennessee, Arkansas and southern Lower California. Occurs sporadically in Florida, southern Mexico, West Indies, and Guatemala. In winter it is found from central New England, Indiana, Illinois, and to southern British Columbia.

Shallow ponds, bogs, and morasses where reeds and rushes abound, are the habitats of the Coot. From their favorite haunts the birds derive the names of Mud Hen and Marsh Hen. Coots swim very well, and at a distance closely resemble ducks. They dive well also, and from the shallow depths pull up succulent aquatic plants for food. Coots are noisy birds. Their commonest call is a *coo-coo-coo-coo,* a constant note, which they utter day and night. They also give utterance to quacking notes, similar to those of ducks. When disturbed,

Coots spatter away over the surface with astonishing rapidity, using both wings and feet. (Family *Rallidae*)

European Coot
Fulica atra atra [220]

Similar to the American Coot, but without the white markings on the edge of the wing and on the feathers of the under tail coverts.

DISTRIBUTION—This Coot, an inhabitant of the northern portions of the Old World, occurs as an accidental visitant in Greenland, Labrador, and Newfoundland. (Family *Rallidae*)

CORMORANT FAMILY
Phalacrocoracidae

Cormorants are rather duck-like birds, with stout legs and large webbed feet,

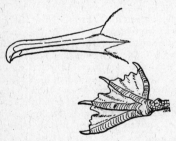

long slightly hooked bills, short tails, and thick compact plumage. They are large birds—averaging about thirty inches or so in length. Unlike Pelicans (to which they are nearly related), they do not plunge from a height into the water after their fishy prey, but pursue it under water, gliding along with the rapidity of fish, propelled either by their wings or large webbed feet, or by both together. Sometimes they dive into the water while resting on its surface, or slip into it from a low rock or spar. When perched, their large, flexible feet—appearing as though made of some soft yielding rubber or dark wax —clasp about and hug the object on which they are sitting. Cormorants number about fifty different forms, most of them being coastal birds, though they sometimes are found inland on fresh-water lakes. Of the fifty-odd Cormorants known, ten are reported from North America, all in the genus *Phalacrocorax*.

NESTING. Cormorants nest on the ground, on ledges of rock, on hummocks, sometimes on a prostrate and decaying log, and sometimes in low bushes. The nest itself is composed of some sticks, coarse and fine seaweed, often with a thin lining of grasses. From three to five eggs are laid; either greenish-white, greenish-gray, grayish, or greenish-blue in color, and often overlaid with a chalky incrustation, sometimes flaky in nature. The young birds feed by the unique procedure of thrusting their heads into the throats of their parents, where they find and gorge themselves upon a malodorous mass of partly digested fish. In spite of this unpromising diet, the flesh of young Cormorants has no very pronounced fishy flavor, and if parboiled in one or two waters, becomes a very palatable dish. The adult birds are only very infrequently eaten; their flesh not responding to this ameliorating treatment.

CORMORANT
Baird's Cormorant
Phalacrocorax pelagicus resplendens [123b]

Similar to the Pelagic Cormorant, but smaller, and with a slenderer bill.

DISTRIBUTION—Along the Pacific Coast from near Victoria, British Columbia, southward to Natividad Island and Mazatlan, Mexico.

"The Baird's Cormorant is usually less common than the Farallone or Brandt's

Cormorants, breeding apart from them in communities on the islands

or rocky points off shore." (Bailey). (Family *Phalacrocoracidae*)

Brandt's Cormorant
Phalacrocorax penicillatus [122]

ADULT MALE AND FEMALE—Patch at chin, light brownish, otherwise the

head and neck, glossy bluish-black. Bill, slender and nearly straight; no crest on the head. Shoulders and wing coverts, dull greenish-black. Under parts, glossy greenish-black.
LENGTH—35.00 inches.
DISTRIBUTION — From Vancouver

Island, British Columbia, to Magdalena Bay, Lower California, wintering from Puget Sound, southward to the tip of Lower California. (Family *Phalacrocoracidae*)

Double-crested Cormorant
Phalacrocorax auritus auritus [120]

ADULT MALE AND FEMALE—Plumage, a shining black; the upper back and shoulders, grayish-brown, the feathers margined with black. On each side of the head arises a tuft of black feathers. Chin patch, orange.
LENGTH—30.00 inches.
DISTRIBUTION—From the Bay of Fundy, Minnesota, and North Dakota northward; westward in Canada beyond Hudson Bay. In winter it is found southward from Virginia and southern Illinois.

Cormorants look black at a distance, and resemble large ducks or geese

with long necks. They frequently fly just over the surface of quiet water almost touching the surface at every wing stroke. When alighting on a buoy, spar, or bit of rock they stand upright, squatting on their broad feet, and arching their necks in a curve. Their feet clasp the perch in a "rubbery" and flexible fashion, and are webbed like a duck's. When flying high overhead in migration, Cormorants form v-shaped patterns in the sky, like migrating geese. They are frequently called Nigger Geese. The Double-crested Cormorant is the common one seen on the eastern Atlantic coast. (Family *Phalacrocoracidae*)

European Cormorant

Phalacrocorax carbo carbo [119]

Similar to the Double-crested Cormorant, but larger, with a white throat-patch, and before this a bright yellow larger chin patch flanked with a large white patch.

LENGTH—36.00 inches.

DISTRIBUTION—In the North Atlantic from Greenland to Nova Scotia, wintering as far south as South Carolina. These are the Cormorants most

common along the coast of New England in winter. (Family *Phalacrocoracidae*)

Farallon Cormorant

Phalacrocorax auritus albociliatus [120c]

Similar to the White-crested Cormorant, but smaller.

DISTRIBUTION—On the California coast, inland, and southward to Socorro Island. (Family *Phalacrocoracidae*)

Florida Cormorant

Phalacrocorax auritus floridanus [120a]

Similar to the Double-crested Cormorant, but smaller, and much darker.

DISTRIBUTION—From southern Illinois and North Carolina through the

South Atlantic and Gulf States. (Family *Phalacrocoracidae*)

Mexican Cormorant

Phalacrocorax olivaceus mexicanus [121]

Similar to the Florida Cormorant, but smaller, with the face and narrow border of the chin-pouch, white; and the neck with white plumes.

DISTRIBUTION—In summer found as far north, occasionally, as southern Illinois and Kansas. In breeding season from Mexico, Texas, and Louisiana to Central America and the West Indies. (Family *Phalacrocoracidae*)

Pelagic Cormorant

Phalacrocorax pelagicus pelagicus [123]

Similar to the Double-crested Cormorant, but with a tuft of prominent feathers on the forehead. Feathers of back uniform in color; flanks, broadly white; under parts, deep greenish. Feathery white plumes on neck; rump, white.

LENGTH—28.00 inches.

DISTRIBUTION—Among the Aleutian Islands. (Family *Phalacrocoracidae*)

Red-faced Cormorant

Phalacrocorax urile [124]

Similar to the Double-crested Cormorant, but with a red face. Forehead, black, also bearing a small crest. Flanks, white.

LENGTH—34.00 inches.

DISTRIBUTION—Pribilof and Aleutian Islands. (Family *Phalacrocoracidae*)

White-crested Cormorant

Phalacrocorax auritus cincinatus [120b]

Similar to the Double-crested Cormorant, but larger, and with the crests on the head in the breeding season, white.

DISTRIBUTION—Along the Pacific Coast from Alaska to California. (Family *Phalacrocoracidae*)

COTINGA FAMILY
Chatterers
Cotingidae

Cotingas are mostly brilliantly plumaged birds, with short tails, rather short wings, and broad bills; and are near relatives of the Flycatchers

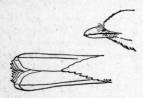

(Family *Tyrannidae*). They are most abundant in Brazil, the Amazon region, and Central America, being confined to the Western Hemisphere. About one hundred and fifty species are known, only one of which, the

Xantus's Becard (*Platypsaris aglaiae albiventris*) occurs in North America.

NESTING. The Chatterers nest in a wide variety of situations. Some weave elaborate pensile nests, which swing from the limbs of trees; others construct a rough platform of twigs; and still others deposit their eggs in holes in trees.

COWBIRD
Bronzed Cowbird

Tangavius aeneus aeneus [496a]

Similar to the Red-eyed Cowbird, but has plumage washed with bronzy.

DISTRIBUTION—From Arizona southward into Mexico.

Like its American cousins, the Bronzed Cowbird is a parasitic species, but no Cowbird should fall under human displeasure or censure for carrying out its nature and habits, developed during age-long operations of the machinery of evolution. (Family *Icteridae*)

California Cowbird

Molothrus ater californicus [495c]

Similar to the Dwarf Cowbird, but larger, and uniformly a darker slate color, especially on the under parts, with the streakings sharper and more conspicuous.

DISTRIBUTION—In California it occurs in the San Joaquin Valley from Merced County south into Kern County. Occasionally it straggles into Los Angeles, Ventura, and Santa Barbara counties, and also the Los Coronados Islands off the coast of Lower California. (Family *Icteridae*)

Dwarf Cowbird

Molothrus ater obscurus [495a]

Similar to the Eastern Cowbird, but slightly smaller.

DISTRIBUTION—From Lower California and Arizona, southeastward along the Mexican-American boundary to the Gulf Coast of Texas. (Family *Icteridae*)

Eastern Cowbird

Molothrus ater ater [495]

ADULT MALE—Plumage, iridescent black, except for the head and neck, which are a deep rich brown—as though the bird had been dipped head first into melted chocolate. The color is not apparent except in strong light.

ADULT FEMALE—Plain brownish gray. Body almost half an inch shorter than the male.

LENGTH—7.90 inches.

DISTRIBUTION—Practically over the whole of the United States, being rare west of the Rocky Mountains, but extending north to New Brunswick, and north of Alberta and Saskatchewan in Canada. In winter it is found from southern New Jersey across to northern Texas, and southeastern California, southwards.

The Cowbirds are our only parasitic birds in North America, laying their

eggs in the nests of smaller birds, such as Warblers and Sparrows, chiefly. They sit in the tops of trees in the early spring, in small groups, and there utter an absurd *split squeak*, en-

tirely characteristic. (Family *Icteridae*)

Nevada Cowbird

Molothrus ater artemisiae [495b]

Similar to the Eastern Cowbird, but somewhat larger, and with a longer, slenderer bill.

DISTRIBUTION — Western Canada southward to central California, southern Nevada, Utah, and Colorado; and from central Minnesota to southern South Dakota and western Nebraska. (Family *Icteridae*)

Red-eyed Cowbird

Tangavius aeneus involucratus [496]

ADULT MALE — Plumage, black, with a wash of bronzy-brown. An erectile ruff of soft feathers on the sides of the neck. Wings and tail showing greenish, bluish, and purplish iridescence. Iris of eye, bright garnet.

ADULT FEMALE—Black with faint bluish-green reflections. Neck ruffs inconspicuous.

LENGTH—7.65 inches.

DISTRIBUTION—From southern Texas southward into eastern Mexico. In winter it passes into Panama. (Family *Icteridae*)

CRAKE

Corn Crake

Crex crex [217]

ADULT MALE AND FEMALE—Upper parts, yellowish-brown, the feathers with darker centers. Wing coverts and wing quills, chestnut-brown. Ashy gray patches above the eyes and on the cheeks. Throat, white; breast, grayish-buff. Abdomen, white in the center, the sides and flanks broadly barred with brown and buff. Bill and feet, pale brown.

LENGTH—11.00 inches.

DISTRIBUTION—This common Rail of Europe and northern Asia occurs casually in Greenland, the Bermudas, and there are three records from Long Island.

The Corn Crake, or Land Rail, is one of the commonest birds of the British

Isles. It is most abundant in rich pasture lands, where its creaking or "craking" note is one of the familiar sounds of the English rural districts. In our continent it is only a casual straggler. (Family *Rallidae*)

Spotted Crake

Porzana porzana [213]

Similar to the Sora (Sora Rail), in general, the upper parts being olive-brown spotted with white; the crown, dark brown; the face and neck, leaden gray; and the breast, brownish spotted with white.

LENGTH—8.70 inches.

DISTRIBUTION — An Old World form, breeding rarely in various parts of Great Britain, and, like the Water Rail, occurring as an accidental visitant in Greenland. (Family *Rallidae*)

CRANE FAMILY

Gruidae

Cranes are large, long-billed, long-necked, long-legged birds, with dense, compact plumage. In general they resemble the members of the Heron and Bittern family (Family *Ardeidae*), except that in flight their necks are extended straight outward, not pulled back into an "S" as are those of herons. Marshes, wide wet meadows, and low plains are their haunts, where they feed upon snakes, frogs, field-mice, and the like, as well as upon grains and other vegetable substances. There are sixteen species of these birds in the Old World and two species in the New. In North America the two species are represented by four members, the Whooping, Little Brown, Sandhill, and Florida Cranes.

NESTING. The typical nest of gruid birds is a large well-fabricated structure from a foot and a half to two feet in diameter and about a foot and a half high, placed on the ground in a marshy spot. It is composed of reed stalks, rushes, and marsh grasses. Or it may be only a slight depression

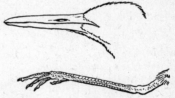

lined with weed stems and dry grasses in a knoll in some grassy field. The eggs are about two in number, with a ground color of olive or buffy brown, spotted and splotched with darker shades of browns and grays.

CRANE

Florida Crane

Grus canadensis pratensis [206a]

ADULT MALE AND FEMALE—Entire bird, a brownish-gray, with a silvery and light brownish cast. Head (as far as just below the eyes) covered with a reddish- or brownish-red, warty skin, from which arise short black, so-called hairs. Bill and legs, long; tail, short.

LENGTH—44.00 inches.

DISTRIBUTION—From South Carolina (rare), the Okefinokee Swamp of southern Georgia, into Florida. "Probably southern Alabama and Louisiana" (A.O.U. Check List).

A fairly common bird in the southern part of Florida, where it is found in the swampy, prairie country, especially in areas that have been burned over. Its notes are loud and trumpet-like. (Family *Gruidae*)

Little Brown Crane

Grus canadensis canadensis [205]

Similar to the Sandhill Crane; differing only in being smaller.

DISTRIBUTION—Arctic North America, from the region of Hudson Bay westward to Alaska. During its migration it passes south through the interior of Canada and the United States, and in winter is found from California, Texas, and northern Lower California, into Mexico. (Family *Gruidae*)

Sandhill Crane

Grus canadensis tabida [206]

Similar to the Florida Crane, but paler throughout.

DISTRIBUTION — Manitoba, British Columbia, and Oregon southward

through the Mississippi Valley to Texas, Florida, and Cuba. In winter it is found in California, the Gulf States, and southward. (Family *Gruidae*)

Whooping Crane

Grus americana [204]

ADULT MALE AND FEMALE—Entire bird, pure white; the primaries, black; and the head and sides of the throat,

reddish- or brownish-red, bare, and with a sparse growth of black, so-called hairs. Legs and neck, long; bill, moderate.

LENGTH—50.00 inches.

DISTRIBUTION—Restricted chiefly to northern Saskatchewan, and southern Mackenzie, passing to Texas in the winter.

This magnificent Crane was formerly common in America, but is now one of our rarest birds. Its range formerly extended from Mackenzie to Hudson Bay, Iowa, and Nebraska, and in migration all along the Atlantic coast from New England to Georgia, and was even found, occasionally, as far west as Colorado and Wyoming. It is a pity that this huge stately bird is so close to extinction. It is common only in very restricted areas in the far northern parts of its present range. (Family *Gruidae*)

CREEPER FAMILY
Certhiidae

(See also Honey Creeper Family)

The Tree Creepers, of the genus *Certhia*, are smallish birds, with slender bodies, slender, longish bills, decurved; and long pointed tails, the

feathers being stiffly spined, and acting as props as the birds climb up the trunks of trees. The plumage is dull-colored, flecked with grays, browns, black, and white. The under parts are white or light-colored. The best known species is the common *Certhia familiaris,* the Tree Creeper, represented in North America by five subspecies. Our common eastern form is the familiar Brown Creeper (*Certhia familiaris americana*), and is widely distributed.

NESTING. Our Creepers construct a loose nest—actually not much more than an irregular dish of fine twigs, some weed stems, strips of bark, soft plant down, and a few feathers. Sometimes there are added a little moss, a few wisps of hair, and some strands or threads of soft lichen (such as the Old Man's Beard, *Usnea*). Occasionally one finds in the nest some rabbit's fur and a few soft spider cocoons. This structure is lodged behind a loose flap of bark on the trunk of an old tree, or sometimes in the cleft of a broken trunk or large limb, or in a knot hole, or the cavity deserted by a Woodpecker. The tree chosen is often a fir balsam, a spruce, or hemlock; less frequently a deciduous tree. The nests are difficult to discover, partly because of the excellence of their concealment, and partly because

of the quiet goings and comings of the birds. They may be found in deep woods, often on the sides of mountains, and often also in cool wooded swamps. The eggs number from five or six to seven or eight, and are white or grayish white or creamy, sparsely sprinkled with fine specks of browns, purples, or lavenders, the markings sometimes being gathered into an irregular wreath about or near the larger end.

CREEPER
Bahama Honey Creeper
Coereba bahamensis [635]

ADULT MALE AND FEMALE—Upper parts, brownish-black, rump, yellow. Line over the eye, white. Throat, white; middle of under parts, yellow; abdomen, whitish.

DISTRIBUTION—Common in the Bahamas, and has been recorded from southeastern Florida.

Honey Creepers are very attractive little acrobatic birds, traveling in

flocks, and extracting the nectar of flowers, and feeding also on minute insects. The tail is shorter than the wings, and squarish which gives them a rather nuthatch-like appearance. The birds are sometimes called Guit-Guits. (Family *Coerebidae*)

Brown Creeper

Certhia familiaris americana [726]

ADULT MALE AND FEMALE—Bill, long, slender, and decurved. Upper parts, a mixed white, yellowish buff, and various shades of brown. Rump, pale yellowish-brown; tail, grayish-brown. Under parts, white. Tail feathers, stiffened and pointed. LENGTH—5.66 inches.

DISTRIBUTION — From Manitoba and Quebec to Maine and Minnesota, and along the higher mountains of New England. In winter it is found from about the latitude of central New England and Minnesota south to the Gulf States.

A singular interest attaches to the little Brown Creeper on account of

its eremetical habits, and the fact that the species (represented by five subspecies) is the only New World representative of the Old World family *Certhiidae,* which numbers more than two-score species and subspecies. It is a bird not often seen, except by the tireless observer of birds, because of its very unobtrusive habits, its obliterative coloration, and its almost complete silence. Like a bit of animated bark it hitches its way rapidly up a tree-trunk (usually taking a spiral course), peering into every crack and cranny as it goes, until,

suddenly dropping off, it flits to the base of the next tree to continue its tireless search. Occasionally it whispers into a crevice in the bark, some woodland secret couched in its faint sweet tones of *sreep, sreep,* or gives voice to a slightly louder utterance, like the syllables *zreeip, zreeip.* Both of these notes, however, are faint and dispersive, and do not carry far. In its northern breeding range, the bird utters a short song of pure tonal quality, "like the soft sigh of the wind among the pine boughs" (Brewster). (Family *Certhiidae*)

California Creeper

Certhia familiaris occidentalis [726c]

Similar to the Brown Creeper, but with the upper parts a yellowish-brown, and the under parts with a wash of the same.

DISTRIBUTION—From Alaska southward along the Pacific Coastal zone into the Santa Cruz Mountains of California. (Family *Certhiidae*)

Mexican Creeper

Certhia familiaris albescens [726a]

Similar to the Brown Creeper, but with a black back, a black crown streaked with white, a white band in the wing, and brown upper tail coverts.

DISTRIBUTION—From southern Arizona southward into the Mexican plateau country. (Family *Certhiidae*)

Rocky Mountain Creeper

Certhia familiaris montana [726b]

Similar to the Brown Creeper, but with a longer bill, and a white band in the wing.

DISTRIBUTION—From Alaska down along the Rocky Mountains to New Mexico and Arizona. (Family *Certhiidae*)

Sierra Creeper

Certhia familiaris zelotes [726d]

Similar to the Brown Creeper, but slightly darker.

DISTRIBUTION—"Southern Cascade Mountains of Oregon and the Sierra Nevada of California" (Osgood). (Family *Certhiidae*)

CROSSBILL

Bendire's Crossbill

Loxia curvirostra bendirei [521d]

Similar to the Red Crossbill, but decidedly larger. Similar also to the Mexican Crossbill, but much smaller.

DISTRIBUTION—Found in the mountainous district of western North America from northern British Columbia, Montana, Wyoming, and Colorado, westwards to the Cascade and Sierra Nevada mountains. In winter it ranges to Nebraska, Kansas, New Mexico, and the coast district of California. It occurs casually in Lower California and on Guadalupe Island. (Family *Fringillidae*)

Mexican Crossbill

Loxia curvirostra stricklandi [521a]

Similar to the Red Crossbill, but larger, with the under mandible heavier, and the colors, in general, brighter.

LENGTH—6.14 inches.

DISTRIBUTION—From Wyoming to Guatemala, and from Colorado west to the Sierra Nevada, restricted to the mountainous areas. (Family *Fringillidae*)

Newfoundland Crossbill

Loxia curvirostra percna [521b]

Similar to the Red Crossbill, but larger, with a larger bill, and appreciably darker than any of the other reddish American Crossbills. The red coloration is richer and more brilliant, and the greenish-yellow tones also deeper and brighter.

DISTRIBUTION — Found in Newfoundland and Nova Scotia. In winter it is found as far south as northern Virginia, along the Appalachian Mountains. (Family *Fringillidae*)

Red Crossbill

Loxia curvirostra pusilla [521]

ADULT MALE—Plumage, deep vermillion; lighter on the head, rump, and abdomen, and brownish on the back. Wings and tail, dark brown. Bill black, its sharp tips crossed over one another. Tail, deeply notched.

ADULT FEMALE—Grayish-olive above, with a yellowish wash on the rump. Wings and tail, a light slate-gray. Throat, ashy-white; the rest of the under parts, light gray washed with greenish-yellow. Bill and notched tail similar to those of the male.

LENGTH—6.19 inches.

DISTRIBUTION—From Alaska eastward to northern New England along the crests of the higher Allegheny Mountains into Georgia. In winter it spreads in irregular fashion southward into Nevada, Virginia, and infrequently as far as Louisiana and South Carolina.

Crossbills move about the country in an erratic fashion, their movements being governed by the local scarcity or abundance of their favorite food, the seeds of coniferous trees. Like their White-winged congeners, they feed by twisting apart or wrenching off the cone-scales with their curiously-shaped, well-adapted beaks, and whisking the seeds into their mouths with their flexible tongues. In this manipulation of their food, and in their habit of climbing about among the twigs—frequently even swinging by their beaks—they somewhat resemble small red parrots. The birds usually travel and feed in small flocks, and are fearless of man, allowing the near approach of an observer. While engaged in the operation of feeding, a flock of Crossbills often maintains a constant conversational chattering in a subdued tone, reminiscent of a group at a sewing society discussing

some parish secret! Their song, in the rendition given by Hoffman, is a soft whistled *too-tee, too-tee, too-tee; tee-teetee*. (Family *Fringillidae*)

Sitka Crossbill

Loxia curvirostra sitkensis [521c]

Similar to the Red Crossbill, but in general the plumage exhibiting an orange cast instead of pure red.

DISTRIBUTION—Occurs from the district about Sitka, Alaska, and thence southward along the coast as far as middle California. (Family *Fringillidae*)

White-winged Crossbill

Loxia leucoptera [522]

ADULT MALE—Head, back, and under parts, bright rosy-red. Back marked obscurely with black. Wings and tail, black, the former crossed by two broad bars or wedges of white. Bill, dark, its sharp tips crossed one over the other. Tail, deeply notched.

ADULT FEMALE—Grayish, marked with black; yellowish on the rump. Wings and tail, dark slate-gray, or blackish, the former with two white markings as in the male. Tail, deeply notched. Bill as in the male.

LENGTH—6.05 inches.

DISTRIBUTION—From northern New England and New York, and northern Michigan northward over the northern part of the continent. In winter spreading irregularly as far south as British Columbia, Nevada, Illinois, and Virginia.

The White-winged Crossbills are inhabitants of cool dark coniferous forests, sometimes found in summer on the higher Adirondacks, or on the high spruce-clad slopes of northern New England mountains. While feeding among evergreens, which they seldom leave, they utter rather plaintive, sweet notes, like the syllables *wheet, wheet,* either singly given or

repeated several times. In flight they give voice to a subdued chippering or chattering call. The song is quite unlike the call notes in quality of tone, and is reminiscent of the song of the Goldfinch, though louder and clearer —a combination of whistled, twittering notes, often *pianissimo,* and always pleasing. The female is slightly smaller than the male. The two very wide white wing bars will identify this bird, and distinguish it from the Red Crossbill, and from the Pine Grosbeak (which it somewhat resembles in color; the Grosbeak, however, being larger by nearly three inches). (Family *Fringillidae*)

CROW FAMILY
Crows, Jays, Ravens, Magpies, Rooks, Nutcrackers
Corvidae

This family comprises relatively large birds, with black plumage, or black extensively represented in the plumage. Feet and heavy bills are large. Their voices are loud and raucous. Over four hundred species and subspecies have been described, about one hundred of these inhabiting the

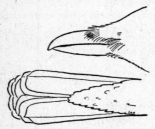

Western Hemisphere. Forty-one of these occur in North America, contained in eight genera.

NESTING. Our members of this family construct rather big, bulky, sometimes flattish nests of sticks, twigs, rootlets, pieces of vines, strips of bark, weed stems, grasses, leaves, mosses, wool, feathers, and (near the coast) some seaweeds. These are placed rather high in trees or on the shelf of a cliff (Northern Raven). The Magpie constructs a hollow bowl of grass and mud, arched over by a large bristling mass of sticks and twigs, and entered by a side opening. The whole structure may sometimes be the size of a barrel. This is located in bushes, or in trees from five or six to fifty or sixty feet from the ground. The Canada Jay's nest is a deep structure thickly and warmly lined with

plant down and feathers for the complete protection of the eggs, since these are laid in March or April when the thermometer sometimes falls as low as thirty degrees below zero. The eggs of our corvid birds number from three or five to six or nine, and are bluish white, pearl gray, bluish green, green, olive green, greenish buff, or robin's egg blue, either plain or spotted and blotched with varying tones of grays, browns, purples, lavenders, etc.

CROW.
Eastern Crow
Corvus brachyrhynchos brachyrhynchos [488]

ADULT MALE AND FEMALE—Jet black, the feathers of the upper parts showing a faint metallic bluish or purplish sheen; those of the under parts do not.

LENGTH—19.30 inches.

DISTRIBUTION — From southwest Mackenzie, northern Manitoba, across southern and central Quebec into Newfoundland, and southward into Maryland, and thence southwestward across the northern part of the Gulf States and into northern Texas. In winter it is found in extreme southern Canada and from there southward.

Undoubtedly the Crow is the best known bird in America. There are several subspecies, as may be seen in the accompanying articles, all difficult of separation in the field. The common note of the crow is the familiar deep throaty *caww*, but besides this note the bird gives vent to many others, expressive of all sorts of matters that are in the mind of this versatile bird. To list and describe these notes would take too much space. Go out into the fields on a spring morning, and the Crows will tell you all. Whether you can interpret their language is another matter! Crows are easily tamed, and make amusing, though irritating pets. Their powers of imitation make it possible for them to pronounce certain words in the human vocabulary. It is not necessary —in fact it hampers matters—to split a Crow's tongue to help him toward this accomplishment. Crows eat a great variety of foods. In their dietary are represented eggs and nestlings of smaller birds. Crows undoubtedly do

injury on farm lands; but they also consume enormous numbers of injurious insects. (Family *Corvidae*)

Fish Crow

Corvus ossifragus [490]

Similar to the Eastern Crow, and in the field indistinguishable from it by color, though examination in the hand shows that usually the Fish Crow may be known by the more uniform hue of the upper parts, and the brighter, more iridescent sheen on the under parts. It is readily identifiable in the field (when in company with the Common Crow) by its size, being about three inches shorter. Its voice, too, is different from that of the Common Crow, being a more highly-pitched, nasal, and less throaty *car* or *kaa*. These notes must be heard and compared in the field to be distinguished.

LENGTH—16.00 inches.

DISTRIBUTION—From southern Massachusetts, and from the lower portion of the Hudson River, south-

wards along the coastal zone to Florida, and westward along the Gulf Coast to eastern Texas.

The Fish Crow is chiefly a bird of the Atlantic coastal zone, never being

found very far inland. Its habits are similar to those of the Common or Eastern Crow. (Family *Corvidae*)

Florida Crow

Corvus brachyrhynchos pascuus [488a]

Similar to the Eastern Crow, but with slightly shorter wings and tail, and slightly larger bill and feet.

DISTRIBUTION—Restricted to Florida. (Family *Corvidae*)

Hooded Crow

Corvus cornix cornix [490.2]

ADULT MALE AND FEMALE—Back, shoulders, and under parts, ashy-gray; the rest of the plumage, black.

LENGTH—19.50 inches.

DISTRIBUTION — This Continental and British species occurs infrequently

in Iceland and the east coast of Greenland. (Family *Corvidae*)

Northwestern Crow
Corvus brachyryhnchos caurinus [489]
Similar to the Eastern Crow, but about three inches shorter.

DISTRIBUTION—From Alaska down the Pacific Coast to Oregon. (Family *Corvidae*)

Southern Crow
Corvus brachyrhynchos paulus [488c]
Similar to the Eastern Crow, but smaller; the bill, slenderer.

DISTRIBUTION—From the lower reaches of the Potomac and Ohio rivers southward into eastern Texas, and along the Gulf Coast, but not into Florida. (Family *Corvidae*)

Western Crow
Corvus brachyrhynchos hesperis [488b]
Similar to the Eastern Crow but smaller; the bill, smaller and slenderer.

DISTRIBUTION—From Puget Sound southward and eastward to the Rocky Mountains and into northern Mexico. (Family *Corvidae*)

CUCKOO FAMILY
Cuckoos, Anis and Road-runners
Cuculidae

This large family comprises some peculiar birds. The Anis and Road-runners are described under those heads. The Cuckoos, rather solitary birds, more often heard than seen, are long-tailed, short-winged, dull-plumaged birds, with slender bills, slightly decurved at the tip. When a nest is built it is of loose and apparently careless construction. Our Cuckoos construct their own nests and rear their young, but many other-world species are parasitic in their domestic relationships, laying their eggs in the nests of smaller birds, and depending thus upon foster-parent nurture for the rearing of their young. The young are naked when hatched, and unusually helpless. Cuckoos are distributed all over the world, except in the colder northern areas where insects are scarce, and are most abundant in the tropical zones. Over two hundred species and subspecies are known, more occurring in the Eastern than in the

Western Hemisphere. Ten species and subspecies (representing four genera) are found in North America.

NESTING. Our Black-billed and Yellow-billed Cuckoos construct crude, rather flimsy and shallow platforms of twigs, weed stems, grasses, strips of bark, leaves, catkins, etc., placing them in bushes of thickly branched trees about five or ten feet (rarely twenty or more) from the ground. The nest of the Black-billed species is somewhat more carefully made than that of the Yellow-billed, and is more often to be found in lower damper areas. The eggs of both number from two to six (rarely), or eight (very rarely); and in color are pale dull bluish green. The European Cuckoo is as truly parasitic as our Cowbirds; it makes no nest of its own but deposits its eggs in the nests of other smaller birds. Our American Cuckoos are quite different in habit, and are virtually as domestic as any, yet there are modifications. Forbush says of our species, "The Yellow-billed Cuckoo and the Black-billed species each occasionally deposits an egg (or eggs) in the nest of the other, and perhaps more rarely in that of the Robin or of some smaller bird, but this is unusual." The Road-runner of the West constructs a nest which is a larger, coarser, and more bulky affair than that of Cuckoos. It is composed of sticks, weed stalks, and strips of bark, and lined with bark, grasses, rootlets, feathers, and snake skins. Its usual location is thorny bushes, cacti, mesquite, or sage brush. The eggs are dull chalky white, creamy, or pale yellowish, and number from two to twelve (usually four to six).

CUCKOO
Baker's Cuckoo
Cuculus canorus bakeri [388.2]

ADULT MALE AND FEMALE—Upper parts, dark slaty-gray, slightly darker on the wings. Tail, black, spotted and tipped with white. Throat and breast, slaty-gray, slightly lighter than the back. Abdomen, white or whitish, thickly crossed by transverse, dusky, crinkled bars. Bill and feet, yellowish.
LENGTH—13.50 inches.
DISTRIBUTION—An accidental visitant in Alaska—St. Lawrence Bay on the Bering Sea.

The Baker's Cuckoo, reported only once in the locality given above in the summer of 1930, is closely similar to the famous Cuckoo of Europe. It is pleasant to think that so near a relative of this much-loved bird has been seen on our continent. Possibly it may be found again on some of the Aleutian Islands so that travelers there in the years to come may quote: "Summer is icumen in, Loud sing cuckoo." Baker's Cuckoo breeds in the mountains of Burma, and in northwestern Yunnan, western Szechewan, Kansu, and in eastern Thibet. If once established in our northwestern territory, there would seem to be no reason why it should not flourish there. The typical Cuckoos of the Family *Cuculidae* are, with very few exceptions, parasitic, depositing their eggs in the nests of other birds for incubation

and subsequent care, much after the manner of our American Cowbirds (Molothrus). Exceptions with us are our four American Cuckoos of the genus *Coccyzus*, which build their own nests and rear their own young. (Family *Cuculidae*)

Black-billed Cuckoo
Coccyzus erythrophthalmus [388]

ADULT MALE AND FEMALE—Upper parts, grayish-brown, with a greenish tinge when seen in strong light. Spread wings of the same color. Under parts, white. Circle of skin about the eye, bright red. Tail, long, its tip rounded, and all but its middle pair of feathers bearing small white tips which show from below. Bill, black.
LENGTH—11.83 inches.
DISTRIBUTION—From Labrador and Manitoba south over the entire eastern part of the United States and as far west as the Rocky Mountains. In winter it passes south of the United States and winters as far south as Brazil.

This species and the Yellow-billed Cuckoo are closely allied, and in gen-

eral habits, food, and notes much resemble each other. The Black-bill, however, is more a bird of damp lowlands, and is likely to be seen or heard oftener along swampy streams or wet meadow lands, where impenetrable thickets of catbrier and other tangles mingle with the alders and hawthorns. The Black-bill's song is somewhat similar to the Yellow-bill's. The *kuk* notes are softer, however, more liquid in tone, and without the retarded *kyow* syllables at the end of the song. They are given in groups, thus *kuk-kuk-kuk; kuk kuk kuk; kuk kuk kuk.* Frequently only two are given which are repeated over and over again. (Family *Cuculidae*)

California Cuckoo

Coccyzus americanus occidentalis [387a]

Similar to the Yellow-billed Cuckoo but larger, the bill longer, and the upper parts a grayer brown.

DISTRIBUTION—From southern British Columbia south over the western portion of the United States as far as eastern Texas. In winter it passes into Mexico. (Family *Cuculidae*)

Himalaya Cuckoo

Cuculus optatus [388.1]

ADULT MALE AND FEMALE—Upper parts, slate-gray; the wings barred with white. Tail feathers, a dark violet-brown, bearing a row of oblong white spots, and slightly tipped with white. Chin and breast, light gray; the rest of the under parts, buffy-white, crossed by bands of black. Eyes, bill, and feet, orange.

LENGTH—13.00 inches.

DISTRIBUTION — This Himalayan species is closely allied to the Common Cuckoo of Europe, and is found as an accidental straggler in the Pribilof Islands, Alaska. (Family *Cuculidae*)

Maynard's Cuckoo

Coccyzus minor maynardi [386a]

ADULT MALE AND FEMALE—Upper parts, brownish-gray, with an iridescent sheen in strong light. Crown, lighter gray; ear coverts, blackish. Tail feathers (except middle pair) broadly tipped with white. Under parts, white washed with light brownish. Upper mandible, black; lower mandible with yellow base and black tip.

LENGTH—12.50 inches.

DISTRIBUTION—From southern Florida to the Keys, Cuba, and the Bahama Islands. (Family *Cuculidae*)

Yellow-billed Cuckoo

Coccyzus americanus americanus [387]

ADULT MALE AND FEMALE—Upper parts, grayish-brown, sometimes showing a faint greenish tinge in strong light. Under parts, white. Tail, long and rounded at its tip. The three outer feathers are blackish, each one bearing a prominent white tip, which shows from below. The spread wing shows a broad area of rich reddish brown. Lower mandible, yellow, with a blackish tip.

LENGTH—12.20 inches.

DISTRIBUTION—From New Brunswick southwestward into Minnesota and south into Florida, passing in winter into Central and South America.

A long, flexible, graceful bird is this, our commonest Cuckoo which keeps itself well concealed among tangles of bushy shrubs and vines. As it flies across some open space on its way from one place of concealment to another, the observer sees a large, slender bird with a long narrow tail, and rather short rounded wings. After it dives like an arrow into a copse, and if the bird has not been unduly alarmed, its mysterious notes issue from the depths of its hiding place. The Yellow-bill gives voice to two sets of notes, one consisting of a series of low cooing notes, *coo, coo, coo, coo, coo;* the other, a louder, harsher, abruptly sounded strain, the peculiar notes sounding like the syllables *kuk, kuk, kuk, kuk, kuk, kuk—kyow, kyow, kyow.* The last three notes have a rounded "wooden-ball" sound, and

are progressively retarded, and rolled
out with a slurred intonation, making
them quite unlike the notes of any

other eastern bird. The nest of the
Yellow-bill is a loosely woven platform
of twigs, somewhat dished, and lined
with a few coarse bits of vine bark,
grass, leaves, and sometimes catkins.
From its close relative, the Black-
billed Cuckoo, the Yellow-bill may be
best recognized by the markings of the
tail. In the Black-billed species the
white tips of the tail feathers are very
small. (Family *Cuculidae*)

CURASSOW FAMILY
Curassows and Guans
Cracidae

These birds are large, striking, hen-
like birds, with rather long tails, and

crested heads, and large scratching
feet. There are about twelve genera
and about sixty species in all, confined
to Central and South America. The
peculiar Chachalaca (*Ortalis vetula
vetula*) is the only species that
reaches North America, in Mexico and
Texas.

NESTING. The Chachalaca's nest is
usually nothing more than a cavity
in a mesquite tree, lined thickly with
small twigs and leaves. The eggs are
white, with a very rough granular surface, and number usually three or
four.

CURLEW
Bristle-thighed Curlew
Phaeopus tahitiensis [268]

Similar in general to the Hudsonian
Curlew, but with the markings of the
back and wings a pale rusty-brown.

The tail is pale rusty-brown, barred
with black, and the thighs possess
long bristle-like feathers.

LENGTH—17.00 inches.

DISTRIBUTION—This rare bird is
found in Alaska and on the Pacific
islands in the vicinity. It has been
found in summer in western Alaska,
from the Kowak River to the Kenai
Peninsula, and also on Laysan and
Phoenix islands. In winter it is found
on the islands of the South Pacific,
from Hawaii to New Caledonia. (Family *Scolopacidae*)

Eskimo Curlew
Phaeopus borealis [266]

ADULT MALE AND FEMALE—Upper parts, black marked with buffy or whitish. Upper tail coverts barred with black and buff. Tail, grayish-brown, barred with black, and edged with buffy. Primaries of wing, brown. Under parts, buffy or whitish; the breast streaked with black. Sides of the body barred with black.

LENGTH—13.50 inches.

DISTRIBUTION—In eastern North America it breeds in the Arctic regions, migrates chiefly through the interior of the United States, and passes into South America. Almost, if not entirely, extinct.

The Eskimo Curlews, once so abundant, are following the Great Auk, the Passenger Pigeon, the Heath Hen, the Dodo, and others into the limbo of

extirpation. The bird resembles the Hudsonian Curlew, but is smaller. "Most of their habits closely resemble the Golden Plover. In migration they fly in much the same manner, with extended and . . . triangular lines and clusters similar to those of ducks, and geese. . . . They usually fly low before landing, sweeping slowly over the ground, apparently looking it over, generally standing motionless for quite a while after alighting, which, owing to their general color—approximating so closely the withered grass—renders it difficult at times to perceive them. The only note I ever heard them make is a kind of squeak, very much like one of the cries of the Common Tern. (Mackay)." Two of these rare Curlews were captured in Buenos Aires in 1924 and 1925. Eight birds were seen in Hastings, Nebraska in 1926. Peterson gives the notes of the bird as "a soft whistled *bee bee.*" (Family *Scolopacidae*)

European Curlew
Numenius arquatus arquatus [264.1]

ADULT MALE AND FEMALE—Upper parts, reddish-ashy brown, mottled with dusky spots. Rump and upper tail coverts, white. The tail barred with dark brown.

LENGTH—20.00 inches; female somewhat larger.

DISTRIBUTION—Occurs casually in Greenland, and on Long Island, New York.

This bird, very common in the British Isles, is an extremely noisy member of the companies of birds which gather on beaches. Its loud, clear, somewhat musical, and always cheerful note of *cur-lew, cur-lew* is one of the most pleasing, free, wild notes of nature. If only for its far-reaching and optimistic voice, the bird deserves protection. In Scotland, the bird's wild night-cries are heard with dread as prognosticators of coming disaster. Here the bird is sometimes known as the Whaup. (Family *Scolopacidae*)

Hudsonian Curlew
Phaeopus hudsonicus [265]

ADULT MALE AND FEMALE—Upper parts, grayish-brown, marked with buffy or whitish spots. Rump and tail barred with buffy and blackish. Primaries barred with buffy, or whitish, and black. Under parts, buffy or whitish. Neck and breast streaked with black. Sides of body barred with black.

LENGTH—17.00 inches.

DISTRIBUTION—Breeds in the Arctic region, and migrates south in winter to South America. Sometimes found in winter in Lower California.

On the coasts of our southern states the Hudsonian Curlew is a common

British Columbia in the interior. After the nesting season is over, it wanders to Ontario and Newfoundland, though not commonly. In winter it is found from southern California and the Gulf States southward.

The Long-billed Curlew was formerly more common on the Atlantic coast than now. It is an inhabitant of grassy meadows, plains, and muddy shores, where it searches for worms, large insects, crustaceans, and the like. When migrating at a considerable height, they fall into a triangular formation, and as they make their grace-

and abundant migrant. In New England the bird is a rather uncommon migrant along the coast in May, and again in August and September. It is found on mud flats and sandy beaches, along the water's edge, or in the shallows, where it gathers its food. Occasionally it may be seen in grassy sand dunes. Its alarm note is a shrill *pip-pip, pip-pip;* and its sweet, mournful cry repeats the syllables *kerlew, kerlew.* (Family *Scolopacidae*)

ful way through the air they utter a loud, prolonged whistle. (Family *Scolopacidae*)

Long-billed Curlew

Numenius americanus americanus [264]

ADULT MALE AND FEMALE—Back barred with buffy and black; head and neck streaked with black. Wings and tail, buffy to pale reddish-brown, barred or mottled with blackish. Under parts, buffy; breast more or less streaked with black. Sides of the body barred with black. Bill, about six inches long.

LENGTH—24.00 inches.

DISTRIBUTION—From North Carolina to Florida, and to Manitoba and

Northern Curlew

Numenius americanus occidentalis [264a]

Similar to the Long-billed Curlew, but smaller, and bearing a much shorter bill.

DISTRIBUTION — From Manitoba, Saskatchewan, and eastern British Columbia southwards to Oregon, Montana, Wyoming, and South Dakota. In winter it is found spreading through southern California and New Mexico into northern Mexico. (Family *Scolopacidae*)

DARTER FAMILY
Anhingidae

The *Anhingas* are variously called Water-turkeys, Darters, or Snake Birds. They are curious birds with long thin necks, thin heads, and long slender pointed bills, serrated on the sides to assist them in holding slippery fish which they pursue and capture under water. Often they sink down beneath the surface, leaving exposed only their long necks and bills, and looking at such times very much like snakes. Their feet are webbed

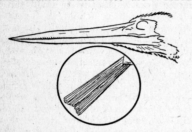

and their tails long. Darters are not birds of the seacoasts, but inhabit swamps, and densely overgrown shores of swampy lakes. Often they rise in the air and soar about after the manner of some hawks. Four species of these birds are known, only one of which, the so-called Water-turkey (*Anhinga anhinga*), inhabits North America.

NESTING. Our Water-turkey nests in bayous and in dense swamps, and on bushes or small trees which are inclined out over the water. The nest is a large, rather ill-constructed affair of sticks, twigs, roots, dry weed stems, dry grasses, with some mosses and leaves. On this rather flattish and insecure cradle, two to five eggs are laid. They are whitish, greenish-white, bluish-white, or grayish-green, encrusted with whitish chalky flakes, or a general crust of thin limy deposit. Many birds often congregate together in a rookery or nest, sometimes in the same neighborhood with Ibises and Herons. Pearson says that the long Spanish moss (Tillandsia) is used in the nest, and further observes, "All the nests I have ever examined also contained freshly plucked leaves, which appeared to have been placed as a finishing touch just before the eggs were laid."

DICKCISSEL

Dickcissel

Spiza americana [604]

ADULT MALE — Back, brownish, streaked with black, gray, and darker brown; rump, ashy brown. Head and side of neck, gray. Forehead, line over the eye, and another on the side of the throat, yellow. Throat patch, black; chin, white. Breast, yellow fading to white, or dull white on the abdomen. Shoulders (wrists), brown; wings and tail darker.

ADULT FEMALE—Similar to the male, but lacking the black throat patch. Breast, faint yellow, sometimes streaked with blackish. Head, grayish-brown, sometimes streaked with black.

LENGTH—6.00 inches.

DISTRIBUTION—Between the Allegheny and the Rocky mountains, from Minnesota to Alabama and Texas. It sometimes straggles into the Atlantic Coastal States, where it was formerly more common than now. It spends its winters in Central America, and in the northern portion of South America.

Old pastures, bushy meadows, and overgrown grassy fields are the favorite haunts of the vivacious and energetic little Dickcissel. In such situations, and from the top of a fence post, weed stalk, bush, or an elevated stone, the bird jerks out its bright, cheerful, vigorous little lay, a strain sounding somewhat like the repetition of its name. The performance somewhat resembles that of the Eastern Yellow Warbler, or the Eastern Redstart, but with a more decidedly buzzy and insectoid character. Throughout all its range this optimistic little sparrow is a favorite with those who know

it. It is of undoubted value to agriculture, since its food consists largely of the seeds of pestiferous weeds and grasses. It also feeds largely upon grasshoppers, particularly during the summer months. (Family *Fringillidae*)

DIPPER FAMILY
Cinclidae

Dippers (or Ouzels) are rather unobtrusive, brownish or grayish birds, without striking patterns, bars, spots, or streaks. Their bills are short and stout, their wings short, and their tails very short. The feet are large, and the

birds are sure and confident runners over wet and slippery rocks in mountain streams, and are, surprisingly for song birds, confident divers and swimmers under water, where they urge themselves forward with their wings, or walk on the bottom of a shallow rocky pool. In their general deportment they remind one of Wrens

(Family *Troglodytidae*). Dippers are widely distributed over the world, but are absent in the mountains of eastern North America. Upwards of thirty species and subspecies are now known. One of these, the Dipper or Water Ouzel (*Cinclus mexicanus unicolor*), is our only North American representative.

NESTING. The nest of our one representative of this family, the Dipper or Water Ouzel, is placed among the roots of a tree, or a crevice among the rocks, near running and splashing water from a cascade or small falls; often the nest is behind the curtain of water of the falls itself. It is a delicate beautiful globular structure of green mosses, about six or seven inches in diameter, often longer than wide, with a small circular entrance on one side, the whole fabric being supported by small twigs, weed stems, leaves, cemented together with mud. The situation of the nest insures that it shall be kept moist with the splashing spray and drifting mist, which keeps the mosses on the outside green, fresh and growing. The eggs number from three to five, and are a pure unmarked white.

DIPPER
Dipper
Cinclus mexicanus unicolor [701]

ADULT MALE AND FEMALE—Upper parts, uniform slate gray, the head and neck faintly washed with brown. Under parts, similar to the upper parts, but very slightly lighter. (In winter plumage, the feathers of the under parts and wings are narrowly tipped with white.)

LENGTH—7.75 inches.

DISTRIBUTION—From the Yukon Valley in Alaska southward through the mountains of central and western North America, to Guatemala, spreading over the Rocky Mountains to their eastern base.

The Dipper, commonly called the Ouzel or Water Ouzel, is one of our most remarkable birds. A denizen of rocky gorges, cascades, and swirling mountain stream country, it seems as wild and untamed as the rugged crags

and ravines themselves. Along the course of some mountain cascade it slips in and out of cold dank grottoes in the rocks, disappears behind the sheet of a waterfall, pirouettes on the cold streaming boulders amid-stream, bobbing up and down as though on springs, or vanishing beneath the surface of some rocky pool like the diver that he is. One observer even saw a bird making its way under the ice! The nest of this strange bird is placed on a tiny shelf of rock, or in a rocky niche, often so near a fall or cascade as to keep the moss in its structure green and fresh. The song is loud, clear, liquid, bubbling, sweet, and varied—like music of the water itself. (Family *Cinclidae*)

DOTTEREL

Dotterel

Eudromias morinellus [269.1]

ADULT MALE—Upper parts, ashy-brown; the inner secondary feathers with reddish-brown edges. Crown, dusky black bordered by a broad white stripe on the sides, extending backwards from above the eye to the nape and around it. Middle tail feathers

uniform, the outer ones broadly tipped with white. Throat, dull whitish. Upper breast, dark ashy-brown bordered below by a broad white band. Lower breast and flanks, bright chestnut-brown. Abdomen, black. Under tail coverts, white.

ADULT FEMALE—Larger than the male, and with the colors somewhat brighter.

LENGTH—9.00 inches.

DISTRIBUTION—This European species, breeding in the Alps, Scandinavia, Siberia, and Great Britain, is an accidental visitor in Alaska (King Island, and Cape Prince of Wales).

The beautiful little Dotterel—one of the most harmoniously colored of birds, if not the most brilliant—is a celebrated British bird, celebrated both by epicures and by the old writers of prose and poetry. Drayton spoke of it as "a very daintie dish." Because of this daintiness the bird has decreased steadily in numbers in the British Isles and in Europe in general. Once very common in the Lake District of north England it is now rare there. Its supposed foolishness is proverbial; the term Dotterel still being applied to weak-minded or dull persons. Hudson says of it, "It was believed that when the fowler, on approaching a bird, stretched forth an arm, the Dotterel responded by stretching out a wing; that when a leg was put forth, this action was immediately copied; and that the bird, being intent on watching and imitating the motions of the man, neglected its own safety, and was taken in the net." (Family *Charadriidae*)

DOVE

Bahama Ground Dove

Columbigallina passerina bahamensis [320b]

Similar to the Eastern Ground Dove, but with the upper parts grayer, and the under parts paler. The bill is usually black.

LENGTH—6.70 inches.

DISTRIBUTION — The Bahama Islands, and Bermuda. (Family *Columbidae*)

Chinese Spotted Dove

Spilopelia chinensis chinensis [315.1]

Somewhat similar to our common Eastern Mourning Dove, but with the upper parts darker, and with a browner tinge, the iridescence less pronounced. Back of the neck very dark, sprinkled over with numerous well-defined white spots, the feathers being forked at their ends.

LENGTH—12.50 inches.

DISTRIBUTION—This Chinese and Formosan Dove has been introduced into North America in the region about Los Angeles, California, where it has become naturalized. It may be distinguished from the Western Mourning Dove by its slightly greater size, and the white spottings on the dark hind neck. (Family *Columbidae*)

Eastern Ground Dove

Columbigallina passerina passerina [320]

ADULT MALE—Upper parts, brownish-gray; tail, blackish, its outer feathers narrowly tipped with white. Crown

and nape region, bluish slate-gray. Forehead and under parts, delicate light pinkish-brown; the breast flecked

with dark gray. The wing, when spread in flight shows brownish. Base of bill, coral red; its tip, jet black.

ADULT FEMALE—Similar to the male but with the forehead and under parts a pale brownish-gray.

LENGTH—6.75 inches.

DISTRIBUTION—From the northern part of North Carolina through the Atlantic and Gulf States, west to eastern Texas. Less common in the interior than along the coast. (Family *Columbidae*)

Eastern Mourning Dove

Zenaidura macroura carolinensis [316]

ADULT MALE—Back, wings, and tail (when closed), brown. Back of head, bluish-gray. Rest of head and neck, pinkish-brown, the sides with metallic iridescence. Below the ear, a small blackish spot. Spread wings and tail, bluish-gray. Outer tail much shorter than the others, banded with black and tipped with white. Breast, pinkish-brown; abdomen, buffy.

ADULT FEMALE—Similar to the male, but duller, with very little if any bluish about the head, and with the iridescence of the feathers at sides of neck slightly if ever seen.

LENGTH—11.85 inches.

DISTRIBUTION—From Quebec, Ontario, Manitoba, and British Columbia southwards to Mexico and the West Indies. In winter it is found from southern New York (sometimes southern Connecticut), southern Illinois, Kansas, and southern California, southwards.

The pretty and attractive little Mourning Dove (which some persons wish to make a game bird) is common, and familiar to all lovers of the rural districts. It may be found most frequently in sandy plains, wide stretches of cultivated lands separated by hedgerows, pine groves, and orchards; and in fall and winter in old stubble fields, or near the farm buildings where it searches for waste grains. In the spring the birds may be seen flying about the country in twos. Their low, sweet, pleasingly melancholy notes— *coo-ah, coo, coo, coo*—may be heard

from afar, and fall on the ear, mellowed by the distance, like the soft subdued strokes of a distant bell (to paraphrase a happy characterization of Hoffman's). Its flight is direct and swift, and as it goes, its rather short, but pointed wings, and long tail, and (in spring) its habit of flying by pairs are excellent field marks. (Family *Columbidae*)

Eastern White-winged Dove
Melopelia asiatica asiatica [319]

ADULT MALE—Upper parts, brownish, grading to bluish gray on the lower back. Sides of head with bluish black spot next to a bronzy iridescent patch. Top of head and neck, dull pinkish. The wing coverts bear a large white, prominent spot, conspicuous in contrast to the black quills. Under parts soft fawn brown, fading to grayish white on the abdomen.

ADULT FEMALE—Similar in general to the male, but somewhat smaller, and decidedly duller in color.

LENGTH—11.75 inches.

DISTRIBUTION—Along the southern boundary of the United States, from Arizona to Texas, and southwards into Lower California and Central America. Also to Jamaica and Cuba. Reported as casual on Key West, Florida.

The Eastern White-winged Dove is most at home in the parching mesquite and cactus valleys and bottoms of the lower parts of the Gila, Colorado, and Rio Grande rivers. Its note—an amplified cooing sound—is described as being more like the hollow hooting of an owl than the languid cooing of a Dove. (Family *Columbidae*)

Inca Dove
Scardafella inca inca [321]

ADULT MALE AND FEMALE—Entire plumage, because of color of feather edgings, apparently scaled. Upper parts, brownish, the inner webs of the wing quills, reddish-brown. Tail, brown and black, its two outer feathers chiefly white. Breast, pale grayish-pink, shading to buffy on the abdomen. The tail is peculiar in form, being doubly rounded. Its central and outer feathers are shorter than those between, and all are narrow and tapering. Legs, very short.

LENGTH—8.00 inches.

DISTRIBUTION—From southern Arizona and Rio Grande Valley of Texas, southward through Lower California and through Mexico to Nicaragua.

These little Doves are to be found very commonly in orchards, barnyards, country and village roads and streets —never very far removed from man's habitations and cultivations. They often mingle with the barn- and dooryard flocks of poultry. Their motions are quick, and they run rapidly about with bobbing heads, pouring forth a continual cascade of little accented cooing notes, as though they were talking to themselves about everything they are doing. This cooing sound is kept up throughout the day—an incessant, interminable chatter. Inca Doves are especially common in and about Tucson, Arizona, where they are accounted either exceptionally tame and confiding, or exceptionally stupid, for they seldom take flight until almost trodden upon. These Doves are the world's most persistent and indefatigable lovers. Hour after hour a pair of birds will sit on a branch or telephone wire, and coo tenderly to each other. (Family *Columbidae*)

Mexican Ground Dove
Columbigallina passerina pallescens [320a]

Similar to the Eastern Ground Dove, but with grayer upper parts, and much paler under parts and forehead.

DISTRIBUTION—From southern California eastward to Texas, and southwards through Mexico to Central America. (Family *Columbidae*)

Ringed Turtle Dove
Streptopelia risoria [315.2]

ADULT MALE AND FEMALE—Upper parts, ashy vinaceous, marked with darker; neck with a complete black collar. Under parts lighter than back.

LENGTH—about 11.00 inches.

DISTRIBUTION—The country of origin of this species is unknown, but the bird has been domesticated very nearly throughout the world, and in North America has become naturalized about Los Angeles, California, and also in Cuba, Haiti, and adjacent regions.

About fourteen forms of the genus *Streptopelia* are known, dispersed over southeastern Europe, Africa, central Asia, and the Orient. (Family *Columbidae*)

Rock Dove
Columba livia livia [313.1]

ADULT MALE AND FEMALE—Back and wings pale slate color; the head, neck, and breast darker. Neck and breast show purplish and greenish iridescent metallic colors. Tail similar to the back, with darker metallic sheen, and showing a broad black terminal band. Two black bands across the wing. Abdomen slaty gray. Rump white.

LENGTH—13.00 inches.

DISTRIBUTION—Introduced in North America. In the Old World it ranges from Europe, through the Mediterranean countries to central Asia, and to China.

The Rock Dove, now naturalized in our continent, and represented by numerous fancy cross-bred varieties,

has become, in its nearly-original form, wild in some places, and like the English Sparrow, the Ring-necked Pheasant, and the European Starling, is to be considered one of our own wild birds. In the British Isles it is found along the rocky coasts of Scotland, Ireland, and the south and east coasts of England, and is rare inland. It nests in caves, and on ledges of rock, where these are convenient, but also in old trees, and on shelves erected by farmers. Its cooing notes are a familiar sound to all dwellers of the country, and often of certain cities and towns. (Family *Columbidae*)

Western Mourning Dove
Zenaidura macroura marginella [316a]

Similar to the Eastern Mourning Dove, but much smaller.

DISTRIBUTION — From Manitoba, Saskatchewan, and British Columbia, Canada; Minnesota, western Arkansas and Oklahoma, west to the Pacific coast, and southward through Mexico; wintering as far south as western Panama. (Family *Columbidae*)

Western White-winged Dove
Melopelia asiatica mearnsi [319a]

Similar to the Eastern White-winged Dove, but decidedly larger, paler, and grayer.

DISTRIBUTION—From southwestern New Mexico, southeastern California,

southern Arizona, and northern Lower California; southward through Mexico to Puebla and Guerrero. It is reported accidental in British Columbia, Washington, and Colorado. (Family *Columbidae*)

White-fronted Dove
Leptotila fulviventris angelica [318]

ADULT MALE—Upper parts, dark brown; the back of the head, and upper portion of the back with a metallic sheen. Tail, dark sooty-brown or blackish, tipped with white. Forehead and throat, white or whitish. Breast, pale pinkish; the rest of the under parts, white or whitish. Tail, much shorter than the wings.

ADULT FEMALE—Similar to the male, but duller throughout, and with less of the iridescent sheen to the feathers.

LENGTH—12.00 inches.

DISTRIBUTION—From the Valley of the Lower Rio Grande in Texas southward to Mexico, and Guatemala. A bird of wooded country, frequenting the larger timber. (Family *Columbidae*)

Zenaida Dove
Zenaida zenaida zenaida [317]

Similar to the Eastern Mourning Dove, but the under parts are a deep, rich vinaceous color, with iridescent reflections, and the tail is square, and tipped with ashy white.

LENGTH—10.00 inches.

DISTRIBUTION — Found on the Greater and Lesser Antilles, the Bahama Islands, and the Florida Keys.

This Dove is more frequently seen on the ground than even the common Eastern Mourning Dove. Its notes are said to be louder than those of the Mourning Dove, and are richer,

deeper, more penetrating, with a somewhat more solemn character. (Family *Columbidae*)

DOVEKIE
Dovekie
Alle alle [34]

ADULT MALE AND FEMALE—Upper parts, sooty black; the secondaries tipped; and the scapulars streaked with white. Neck, sides, and upper breast, dark sooty-brown. Lower breast and abdomen, white. Bill, short.

LENGTH—8.00 inches.

DISTRIBUTION—On the islands near and on the north coasts of Greenland,

Iceland, Spitzbergen, and Nova Zemlya. In winter it occurs from southern Greenland to Long Island, New York; casually to Delaware Bay, and rarely to South Carolina. Found in small flocks in the open sea, where they feed by diving. (Family *Alcidae*)

DOWITCHER
Eastern Dowitcher
Limnodromus griseus griseus [231]

ADULT MALE AND FEMALE—Upper parts a mixture of buffy and black. Rump and tail pure white, spotted

with black. Sides of the head and the under parts, a delicate pinkish-brown, finely spotted with black.

LENGTH—10.50 inches.

DISTRIBUTION—Chiefly north and northwest of Hudson Bay, migrating largely through the eastern portion of North America and southward, spending the winter from Florida to northern South America.

The Dowitcher is a very unsuspicious bird, allowing a fairly close approach. It is a denizen of sand bars and mud flats, and usually is found occurring in small, compact flocks. Its note is a clear, rather musical *tew tew tew,* or *kew kew kew,* somewhat like that of the Yellow Legs. (Family *Scolopacidae*)

Long-billed Dowitcher
Limnodromus griseus scolopaceus [232]

Similar to the Eastern Dowitcher, but with the breeding plumage more barred on the under parts, the bill longer, and the whole bird larger.

DISTRIBUTION—From the Arctic coast to Alaska; migrating in winter through the Mississippi Valley and western United States to Mexico. It is a rather uncommon migrant along our Atlantic Coast. (Family *Scolopacidae*)

DUCK FAMILY
Ducks, Geese, and Swans
Anatidae

The shovel- or spoon-shaped bills of Ducks, their thick, soft, water-repelling plumage, and their webbed feet, are too well known to require detailed description; as are also their deep, resonant, quacking voices. In common with some other diving birds, the members of this family are peculiar in that, at the fall molt, they lose all their long wing-feathers at once, and hence, at this time, are unable to fly. This lack, however, is perhaps more than compensated for by their extraordinary diving and natatorial powers. The fall or postnuptial molt is followed by a plumage less brilliant than the nuptial one, and is known as the eclipse plumage. The bird is now less conspicuous than before, a provision of nature for the further protection of the bird at a time when flight is impossible. The wings of these birds are strong, even if short and seemingly ineffective, and their

remarkable migrational flights have long been a matter of wonderment and admiration. In former years they were present on our continent in un-countable millions; now, because of excessive shooting, they are sadly deci-mated. The draining of wide marshes, and the general clearing and filling in of wet lands has further diminished their dwindling hosts. Swift, strong, and effective measures of wise control are necessary, unless we wish to see many members of this once great, as well as economically and aesthetically important family tread the path of extinction, following the Great Auk and the Passenger Pigeon. Of the ap-proximately two hundred species of *Anatidae* found scattered throughout the world, roughly fifty species repre-senting seventy-seven kinds occur in North America.

NESTING. The nests of *Anatid* birds are placed usually near or on the ground, often in some depression, either among reeds, rushes, willows, grasses, or among rocks; sometimes in a hollow stump (e.g. Buffle-head), or in a hole in a tree (e.g. Wood Duck). Nests in the open are com-posed of reeds, grasses, mosses, leaves,

and similar materials, and are lined with small feathers and down from the breasts of the parent birds. Those in holes in trees are similarly lined. The Eider Ducks use a very large quantity of down for the nest lining. The common Canada Goose sometimes carries on its breeding in an aban-doned Eagle's or Fish Hawk's nest. Swans build up a large elevated nest (often itself on a slight elevation) of weeds, rushes, coarse grasses, moss, and other suitable herbage. The eggs of the members of this family number from six to twelve (in some species as many as fifteen or eighteen), and in general are whitish, creamy, pale green, olive green, greenish drab, bluish, dull olive, buffy, pale salmon, or gray.

DUCK
Common Black Duck
Anas rubripes tristis [133]

ADULT MALE AND FEMALE—Plum-age very dark brown; apparently black except in good light. Top of head blackish; sides of head, neck, and throat buffy-brown. Speculum, glossy shining iridescent purple or greenish-purple, edges with velvety black. In flight, the under sides of the wings glistening dull silvery. Bill broad and fairly long, and a yellowish-green or olive hue. Feet, dark brown.

LENGTH—22.00 inches.

DISTRIBUTION—Along the Atlantic Coast region from Maine southward as far as Delaware, and sparingly to North Carolina. Westward it ranges to northern Indiana, Wisconsin, and southern Ontario. In winter it is found from New England to Georgia and Louisiana.

The Black Duck rides the waves like a boat, but never dives. As night ap-proaches it flies back inland, where in ponds and marshes, in tidal creeks and estuaries or small streams it searches for its food of seeds and small aquatic animals. Its note is a loud resonant *quack,* closely resembling that of the Mallard. Black Ducks are extremely shy and wild, and phenomenally rugged; being able to withstand very low temperatures, and refusing

to leave the spot of their choice unless forced to do so by the formation of ice. The food of the Black Duck is surprisingly various. Its dietary includes grass roots from low meadows, aquatic plants, wild rice, seeds of all kinds, small nuts, and berries; as well as small fish, small shell-fish, and all sorts of small invertebrates such as worms, leeches, crayfish, toads, frogs, salamanders, tadpoles, and the like. When the bird has been feeding on seeds and vegetable food, it makes a very acceptable dish for the table. (Family *Anatidae*)

Eastern Harlequin Duck

Histrionicus histrionicus histrionicus [155]

ADULT MALE—Back and breast, bluish slate; abdomen, brown; sides, reddish-brown. Center of crown, black margined on the sides by white and reddish-brown. Front of sides of head, an ear-spot, a stripe back of this, a collar about the neck, a band in front of the wing, the inner scapulars, and a spot on the sides of the tail, all white. Bill and feet, bluish-gray.

ADULT FEMALE—Upper parts dull brown. Front of head, whitish, or two white spots in the region. A white ear-spot. Throat, breast, and sides of the body light grayish brown. Abdomen lighter, margined with ashy white.

LENGTH—17.00 inches.

DISTRIBUTION—From Iceland and southern Greenland across to northern Labrador. In winter it descends along the Atlantic coast of North America, south as far as the coast of Maine, and rarely to the shores of Long Island. It is reported as casual in South Carolina and Florida, and on Lake Ontario.

The Harlequin Duck is well named, but in spite of its apparently striking and conspicuous appearance, its camouflage coloration is highly successful as an obliterative pattern among the irregular rocks and seaweed covered ledges where it is found. It is frequently found in flocks of Golden Eyes, from which it can be easily separated by its dark and, at a dis-

tance, almost blackish appearance. In the water it seems to ride higher and more buoyantly than its comrades among the waves. From the female Old Squaw, the female Harlequin may be distinguished by the color of the abdomen, which is dusky or grayish rather than pure white. (Family *Anatidae*)

Florida Duck

Anas fulvigula fulvigula [134]

Similar to the Common Black Duck but with the throat unstreaked.

DISTRIBUTION—Florida, along the coast to Louisiana. (Family *Anatidae*)

Greater Scaup Duck

Nyroca marila [148]

ADULT MALE—Upper back, head, neck, and breast, black. The head shows a greenish iridescence in strong light. Middle of back, white covered with narrow wavy fine black lines. Speculum, white. When spread, the wing shows a long white stripe. Abdomen and sides, pure white. Under tail coverts, black. Bill, bluish gray; legs and feet, leaden gray.

ADULT FEMALE—Similar to the male in pattern, but with its black replaced by brown. Region about the base of the bill, white. Wings, dull brown. The speculum and stripe in the spread wing, white. Under parts, ashy white. Bill and feet resemble the male's.

LENGTH—18.50 inches; female slightly smaller.

DISTRIBUTION—Over the northern portions of the Northern Hemisphere generally. In America from the northern boreal regions southward, in the interior, to Minnesota (rarely) and North Dakota. In winter it is found from Long Island Sound, New York, southward to northern South America.

The Blue-bill, as it is often called, is found in winter abundantly along the Atlantic coast, and while a true sea duck, also occurs in great flocks on large inland rivers, and on bodies of fresh water not far from the ocean. Countless thousands of them may often be seen, appearing from a distance like a low dark island. When traveling, they fly in a distinctive wavy line, and plainly show the white stripe along the wing. It is more of a salt-water species than is its close congener, the Lesser Scaup. From this bird the male may be recognized in strong light by the greenish, instead of purplish, sheen of the head. Scaups

of both kinds are higher fliers than other sea ducks, except the Golden Eye. Their quacking notes are low, hoarse, or guttural, sounding more like the syllable *scaup* than *quack*. When the birds are feeding upon fresh-water vegetation, their flesh is considered very palatable. (Family *Anatidae*)

Labrador Duck

Camptorhynchus labradorius [156]

ADULT MALE AND FEMALE—Head, throat, and upper neck, white. Center of crown, black; center of upper back, black joined with a black band around the neck. Wings, white; primaries grayish brown. Front and sides of the upper breast, white; the lower breast and abdomen, black.

ADULT FEMALE—Similar to the male, but with the throat and the ends of the greater wing-covered feathers, white.

LENGTH—20.00 inches.

DISTRIBUTION—Now extinct, but formerly found on the south coast of Quebec, wintering on the Atlantic coast from Nova Scotia to New Jersey, and probably in decreasing numbers as far south as Chesapeake Bay. Reported at Elmira, New York, and on the St. Lawrence River above Montreal.

The extinct Labrador Duck is now known only from the forty-four existing specimens. The cause of its extinction is unknown. Of this bird, Chapman writes that William Dutcher in 1891 quoted George N. Lawrence as follows: "I recollect that about forty or more years ago [which would

be about 1850] it was not unusual to see them in Fulton Market [New York] and without doubt killed on Long Island. At one time I remember seeing six fine males, which hung in the market until spoiled for want of a purchaser; they were not considered desirable for the table." (Family *Anatidae*)

Lesser Scaup Duck

Nyroca affinis [149]

Similar to the Greater Scaup Duck, but with the head showing purplish

reflections, and the sides of the body bearing distinct fine black bars. Slightly smaller than the Greater Scaup.

DISTRIBUTION—From northern Canada southward to Iowa, North Dakota, and British Columbia. In winter it is found from British Columbia and Virginia southward into Guatemala and the West Indies. (Family *Anatidae*)

Masked Duck

Nomonyx dominicus [168]

ADULT MALE—Upper parts, reddish brown; wings, dark; speculum, white. Whole face, throat, and side of head, black. Under parts like back, but lighter.

ADULT FEMALE—Back, blackish barred with light brown. Above and

below the eye, light brown streaks; through the eye, a darker brown streak. Under parts, reddish brown. LENGTH—14.00 inches.

DISTRIBUTION — From the Rio Grande, Texas, southward; accidentally straggling northward to Massachusetts, Lake Champlain, and Wisconsin. (Family *Anatidae*)

Mottled Duck

Anas fulvigula maculosa [134a]

Similar to the Florida Duck, but with the under parts mottled with rounder black markings.

DISTRIBUTION—From Kansas southward into Texas as far as Corpus Christi. In winter it is found on the western part of the Gulf Coast. (Family *Anatidae*)

New Mexican Duck
Anas diazi novimexicana [133.1]

More resembling the Common Mallard Duck than any other, but with the forehead and crown black streaked with light pinkish brown. Sides of head and neck, same brownish color streaked with black. Throat, light pinkish brown, and unmarked. Breast black, mottled with rich brown, and shading to a vinaceous buff on the abdomen. Flanks, black marked with buffy. Back, wings, and upper tail coverts, black streaked and margined with buffy. Primaries, brown. Speculum (large patch in the wing), dull blackish violet, bordered first by a black and then by a white band. Feet and legs, bright orange. Bill, yellow.

DISTRIBUTION—"Rio Grande Valley from Albuquerque, New Mexico, to El Paso, Texas, and probably also Chihuahua [northern Mexico]. Casual in Nebraska and Colorado." (A.O.U. Check List). (Family *Anatidae*)

Red-legged Black Duck
Anas rubripes rubripes [133a]

Similar to the Common Black Duck, but larger, and with the dark crown edged with buff or grayish-white. The throat, spotted; the bill, yellow, and the legs, red.

DISTRIBUTION—Northern Quebec, northern Manitoba, and northern Ontario. In winter it is found in Arkansas and the Gulf States, and from the Great Lakes region and New England States southward along the coast into northern Florida. It is sometimes reported from Colorado. (Family *Anatidae*)

Ring-necked Duck
Nyroca collaris [150]

ADULT MALE—Back, and upper breast, black with greenish reflections. Head, except for a small white triangle on the chin, black with purplish reflections. A narrow chestnut brown collar about the neck. Wings, blackish

with blue gray speculum. Middle of abdomen, white; its sides a finely vermiculated gray. Under tail coverts, black. Bill, black, crossed near its end by a blue band.

ADULT FEMALE—Head, neck, and upper parts, dull brown; throat and face, whitish. Chest and sides of the body, fulvous. Abdomen, white.

LENGTH—16.75 inches.

DISTRIBUTION—It breeds from Minnesota and the Dakotas, northward, and in winter is found south as far as Guatemala. (Family *Anatidae*)

Ruddy Duck
Erismatura jamaicensis rubida [167]

ADULT MALE—Upper parts, throat, and the fore-neck, bright reddish-brown. Crown and nape, black. Sides of the head, and the chin, pure white. Upper breast washed with light reddish-brown; the rest of the under parts, pure glistening white. Tail, brownish-black, its separate feathers pointed and stiff. Wing without white marking.

ADULT FEMALE—Back, grayish-brown. Crown, dark sooty-brown. From below the eye to the back of the neck extends a white stripe. Under parts, dull ashy-white. Bill, broad and short.

LENGTH—15.00 inches.

DISTRIBUTION—Over the Western Hemisphere, from the region of Hudson Bay to northern South America, breeding locally throughout most of its range, but chiefly in the north. In winter it is found from New Jersey, southern Illinois, and California, southward.

The funny little Ruddy Duck sail about in small groups like little toys,

often with their tails cocked up over their backs—or at least held vertically —after the fashion of the Winter Wren. They are expert divers and swimmers, and disappear in a wink beneath the surface at the flash of a gun. Hunters aver that they see the flash, and dive before the shot has reached them. They are much like Grebes in this habit, and also in their submerging the body until only the head and neck are exposed, like the periscope of a submarine. They are difficult birds to flush, and prefer diving to flying. Their flight is labored, the short wings beating rapidly. (Family *Anatidae*)

Rufous-crested Duck

Netta rufina [145]

ADULT MALE—Back and scapulars, brown; the latter with white bases.

Speculum, white. Crown and nape, yellowish cinnamon; the head, crested. Lower face and throat, vinous chestnut. Hind neck, black. Breast, black; abdomen, brown; flanks, white. Bill, bright vermilion red.

ADULT FEMALE — Upper parts, brown; under parts, lighter. Crest, small; speculum, grayish white with dark border.

LENGTH—18.50 inches.

DISTRIBUTION—It has been "taken once in America . . . supposed to have been shot on Long Island." (Chapman). (Family *Anatidae*)

Tufted Duck

Nyroca fuligula [149.1]

ADULT MALE—Upper parts, black; the head and neck with purplish reflections. Speculum of wing, sides of the body, and the under parts, white. Bill, pale blue; legs and feet, dark blue.

ADULT FEMALE—Upper parts, dark brown; under parts, brownish gray.

LENGTH—17.00 inches.

DISTRIBUTION—This Old World and oriental species is reported as casual in Greenland, and also in Kurile and Pribilof Islands (St. Paul Island).

This European species, a regular breeder in the British Isles, inhabits

inland waters during the breeding season, and both inland waters and the sea during the winter. It feeds chiefly by night, and is relatively inactive by day. When arising from the water in flight, it gives voice to a harsh grating *quar-r-rk*. (Family *Anatidae*)

Western Harlequin Duck

Histrionicus histrionicus pacificus [155a]

Similar to the Eastern Harlequin Duck, but larger; with a heavier bill, and with the chestnut brown stripes on each side of the crown, shorter, not extending so far forward, and of a duller and paler tone.

DISTRIBUTION—Alaska, British Columbia, and Mackenzie, south in the mountains to Montana, Wyoming, and Colorado, and in the Sierra Nevada to central California; also in the Aleutian Archipelago, wintering from the Pribilof and Aleutian Islands to central California. In the interior of the continent it is a casual visitant as far south as Nebraska and Missouri. (Family *Anatidae*)

Wood Duck

Aix sponsa [144]

ADULT MALE—Upper parts, shining brown; wings, darker and in good light showing velvety purplish reflections. Bluish areas in the wings, and the feathers marked with white. Crown, shimmering metallic green, the feathers prolonged backwards into a purplish crest, with two narrow lines of pure white, one arising from near the base of the bill and passing over the eye. Sides of head iridescent black, with a white crescent. Throat, pure white, joining the white crescent and running around to the hind neck. Base of bill, reddish. Tail, dark, long, and fan-shaped. Upper breast, rich reddish chestnut brown with small white markings. In front of the bend of the wing (wrist) appears a broad, vertical black and white stripe. Flanks and sides, buffy brown, bordered above by

black and white feathers. Lower breast and abdomen, white. A patch of chestnut bronze on either side of the base of the tail. Under tail coverts, dusky. Legs and feet, brownish yellow.

ADULT FEMALE — Upper parts, brown; the wings much as in the male. Crown, blackish; sides of head, grayish brown. A white ring around the eye and a white patch behind it. Throat, pure white; breast, buffy mottled with light brown; sides of body similar. Abdomen, whitish. Bill, dark with a white lateral spot. Legs and feet, yellowish brown.

LENGTH—18.50 inches.

DISTRIBUTION—From Labrador and British Columbia southward to Florida, and across to Mexico, but locally absent. In winter it is found from British Columbia across to southern New Jersey, and south to Cuba and southern California.

The most beautiful of American waterfowl, found in woodland lakes,

ponds, forest streams, and swamps. They nest in hollow trees, and when disturbed and driven off, fly about with a plaintive *whoo-eeek*, a sort of whistled, sharp, whining note. Once threatened with extinction, because of ruthless slaughter, the birds are now carefully protected by state and federal laws. This, together with artificial rearing, is bringing back these lovely additions to our national scenery. (Family *Anatidae*)

DUNLIN

Dunlin

Pelidna alpina alpina [243]

Similar to the Red-backed Sandpiper, but less brightly colored and slightly smaller.

LENGTH—7.40 inches.

DISTRIBUTION—An Old World species of Sandpiper, occurring only cas-

ually in eastern North America. (Family *Scolopacidae*)

EAGLE

Golden Eagle

Aquila chrysaëtos canadensis [349]

ADULT MALE AND FEMALE—Plumage, sooty blackish or blackish brown; the feathers at the back of the head and on the nape, slightly longer and lighter brown (not "golden"). Legs feathered down to the toes with lighter feathers than those of the back. Tail crossed by indistinct grayish bands, or obscurely clouded by grayish markings.

LENGTH—32.50 inches. Female several inches longer than the male.

DISTRIBUTION—Throughout the northern portion of the Northern Hemisphere, southward into Mexico; more common in the Rocky Mountains, and the mountains of the Pacific Coast. Rare east of the Mississippi, though many have been seen in

recent years in migration at Hawk Mountain, Drehersville, Pennsylvania.

Golden Eagles nest high up among mountain crags, or more rarely in tall trees. They are birds of wild, mountainous regions, and formerly bred in the mountains of New England, the Catskills, and in the Adirondacks. Unlike the Bald Eagles, the Golden species is a fearless hunter, pursuing its prey with the velocity of the whirlwind, and striking its quarry in midair with the finality of a thunderbolt. It has been aptly called a "thunderbolt in feathers." That these birds may be more numerous east of the Mississippi than many suppose, is suggested by the fact that in one season

seventy-three were recorded migrating over Hawk Mountain, at Drehersville, Pennsylvania. A specimen was taken at Phillipsburg, New Jersey, in early November, 1943. (Family *Accipitridae*)

Gray Sea Eagle

Haliaeetus albicilla [351]

Similar to the Southern Bald Eagle, but with only the tail white.

DISTRIBUTION—In our part of the world the Gray Sea Eagle is a permanent resident in Iceland and Greenland. It is an accidental straggler off the coast of Massachusetts (one rec-

ord), and on the Aleutian Islands. (Family *Accipitridae*)

Northern Bald Eagle

Haliaeetus leucocephalus alascanus [352a]

Similar to the Southern Bald Eagle in all respects, but larger.

DISTRIBUTION—From northern Quebec, northwestern Mackenzie, and northwestern Alaska, southward into British Columbia and the Great Lakes. In winter it spreads southward into Washington, Montana, and in New England along the coast, sometimes as far south as Connecticut. (Family *Accipitridae*)

Southern Bald Eagle

Haliaeetus leucocephalus leucocephalus [352]

ADULT MALE AND FEMALE—Plumage, sooty brownish, but with the head, neck, and tail pure white. Bill, yellow.

LENGTH—32.85 inches. Female several inches longer than the male.

DISTRIBUTION—All over the United States and southern Canada, and extending into the central part of Mexico.

With its large wing-spread, which in the female may reach seven and a half feet, the Bald Eagle is truly a noble sight. This is the bird which was adopted as our National Emblem by act of the Second Continental Congress of 1782. It is, in the main, a harmless species. Its principal food is dead or dying fish. It seems to have little skill in capturing living fish, as does the Osprey or Fish Hawk, and when its taste inclines to such a delicacy, it pursues and hectors a successful Osprey until the latter drops its catch. Then the Eagle swiftly swoops below and snatches the falling fish before it reaches the ground or falls back into the water. Occasionally Eagles feed upon mice, rats, other small mammals, water-fowl, some very few game birds, and, very seldom indeed, young poultry. Reports represent it as attacking pigs, young lambs, and similar domestic animals, though attacks of this sort are so few as to be virtually negligible. No Eagle carries off young children, since it cannot rise from the ground with a weight greater than eight or ten pounds, and probably not even that. Experiments have demonstrated this conclusively. Eagles

almost never molest the smaller birds, with the exception of the Osprey. But even here the attack is not intended to do the Osprey harm. When once the tormented Osprey drops its fish, the Eagle pays no more attention to it. Eagles may often be seen, on broad wet tidal meadows, looking about on the ground for whatever they can find, or stalking slowly about on mud flats searching for clams, and other edible marine forms which have been left by the receding tide. In the air an adult Eagle may be recognized by the broad expanse of wing together with the pure white head and tail, which glisten like silver as the bird slowly wheels. Young birds are brown all over and show no white. The Bald Eagle, often also called the American Eagle, is now protected by Federal law (except in Alaska). It should be jealously guarded from molestation, and preserved as the living symbol of the spirit of majestic, free, aspiring America. (Family *Accipitridae*)

Steller's Sea Eagle
Thallasoaëtus pelagicus [352.1]

ADULT MALE AND FEMALE—Plumage, dark brown. Forehead, . wingcoverts, rump, tail, and flanks, pure white.

LENGTH—43.50 inches.

DISTRIBUTION — This Northern Hemisphere species occurs on the

Pribilof Islands, and on Kodiak Island, Alaska. (Family *Accipitridae*)

EGRET
American Egret
Casmerodius albus egretta [196]

ADULT MALE AND FEMALE—Pure white. When the Egret is breeding, about fifty long, finely dissected, filamentous "aigrette" plumes arise from between the shoulders, and extend out well beyond the tail. Legs and feet,

black; bill, yellow and blackish near its tip.

LENGTH—41.00 inches.

DISTRIBUTION—From Virginia, southern Illinois, and central California, south into the tropics. After the breeding season, some birds straggle as far north as New Brunswick, Canada, and westward into Minnesota, and Oregon. In winter it is not found north of the Gulf States or southern California.

Formerly almost exterminated by "plume hunters," these beautiful birds are now slightly on the increase, thanks to the enforcement of protective laws. In earlier days thousands upon thousands of Egrets occurred along the lake shores of Florida, and extended throughout the Gulf States. Some few birds bred as far north as New Jersey and Wisconsin. The birds breed in colonies, placing their large loose platforms of twigs close together in trees, usually overhanging the water of a lake or swampy lagoon. (Family *Ardeidae*)

Brewster's Egret
Egretta thula brewsteri [197a]

Similar in general to the Snowy Egret, but larger; with a longer bill, a longer tarsus, and with the entire leg very much stouter and heavier.

DISTRIBUTION — From Utah and California southward into Lower California. In the fall it migrates through Texas and Arizona into Mexico. In late summer and early autumn it is found casually as far north as Wyoming and Colorado, and in Alberta and British Columbia, Canada. (Family *Ardeidae*)

Dickey's Egret
Dichromanassa   rufescens   dickeyi [198a]

Resembles the Reddish Egret, differing chiefly from that bird in that the head and neck are much darker. The wings, body, and tail are a dark slaty gray.

DISTRIBUTION—Found in the peninsula of Lower California. (Family *Ardeidae*)

Reddish Egret
Dichromanassa   rufescens   rufescens [198]

ADULT MALE AND FEMALE—Plumage, dark slaty-bluish gray; the head and neck, dark chestnut brown, with purplish-red reflections. In the "white phase" of the plumage, the bird is entirely white, except the tips of the wings which are grayish. Long "aigrette" plumes springing from between the shoulders, reach out beyond the tail.

LENGTH—29.00 inches.

DISTRIBUTION — From the Gulf States and Lower California south-

ward into Central America and the West Indies. This species, now very rare, is found on the coasts of southern Florida. (Family *Ardeidae*)

Snowy Egret
Egretta thula thula [197]

ADULT MALE AND FEMALE—Pure white. From the region of the back between the shoulders, there arise about fifty long, upwardly-curved "aigrette" plumes. Bill, black. Legs, black; feet, yellow.

LENGTH—24.00 inches.

DISTRIBUTION—Eastern North America. Now extremely rare, but

formerly extended from Long Island, New York, westward to southern Illinois and California, and southward into the tropics. In winter it is not found north of the Gulf States or southern California.

After the breeding season some few individual Snowy Egrets wander north where they are striking objects in the dull-colored marshes. They closely resemble the immature Little Blue Herons, but possess yellow feet. (Family *Ardeidae*)

EIDER
American Eider
Somateria mollissima dresseri [160]

Similar to the Northern Eider, but with the bare spaces on each side of the base of the bill rounded at their posterior ends.

LENGTH—23.00 inches.

DISTRIBUTION—A northeastern North American bird, found from Labrador southward to Maine. In winter it is found eastward to the Great Lakes, and southward as far as the coast of New Jersey.

Like the Northern Eiders, the American Eiders are true ocean and sea dwellers, spending much of their time some distance offshore, where they dive for the mussels which constitute their chief food. Like other Eiders, the female lines her nest with soft breast-down, and builds this up at the side of the nest so that it can be pulled over the eggs for protection during incubation. The demand for eider-down in this country has been so great that our flocks of birds have become sadly depleted. Two or three broods may be raised each season, if the eggs are taken care of. It is said that the male contributes breast-down for the third lining. This denudation of the breast also serves to bring the hot "brood-spot" of the skin of this region into contact with the eggs for their more effective heating and incubation. The note of the bird is a

hoarse croaking quack. Many birds still breed in northern Quebec, in the region of Hudson Bay, and a few breed in northern Maine under the effective protection of our National

Audubon Society. Were it not for the work of this splendid organization, great numbers of many of our American bird species would long ago have trodden the path to extinction over which the Great Auk and Passenger Pigeon have passed. (Family *Anatidae*)

King Eider
Somateria spectabilis [162]

Similar in general to the American Eider, but differing chiefly in possessing more black on the back. The

feathers at the base of the bill do not extend as far as the nostril; the rump bears a white patch on each side; and the crown is grayish blue.

DISTRIBUTION—Labrador and Alaska, north to the Arctic Ocean and

Greenland. In winter it ranges south as far as New Jersey (sometimes slightly farther, and rarely into Georgia), and to the Great Lakes. (Family *Anatidae*)

Northern Eider

Somateria mollissima borealis [159]

Similar to the American Eider, but with the bare areas at the upper base of the bill pointed at their posterior ends.

DISTRIBUTION — From Greenland across to Labrador. In the winter it descends along the Atlantic coast of New England to Massachusetts. This species ranges farther to the north than the American Eider, and is the American representative of the common Eider Duck of northern Europe. (Family *Anatidae*)

Pacific Eider

Somateria v-nigra [161]

Similar to the Northern Eider (and hence also to the American Eider) but differing chiefly in possessing a black "V" on the throat.

DISTRIBUTION — From the Great Slave Lake, northern Canada, west-

ward to the North Pacific, and on the Aleutian Islands. (Family *Anatidae*)

Spectacled Eider

Arctonetta fischeri [158]

ADULT MALE—Back and lesser and middle wing coverts, white. Head and neck, white; the forehead region, nape, and cheeks, sea green. Large white areas ("spectacles") about the

eyes framed with black. Rest of the plumage, grayish black. Bill, orange; legs and feet, yellowish.

ADULT FEMALE—Variable, but in general entirely yellowish brown, finely cross-barred with black and brown, except on the head, which is streaked. Abdomen, plain brown.

LENGTH—22.00 inches.

DISTRIBUTION—In America on the Alaskan coast, and on the coast of the Bering Sea and adjacent Arctic Ocean. Also found on the northern coast of Siberia. In winter it migrates to the sea-surrounded and, hence, more temperate Aleutian Islands.

The Spectacled Eider is most frequently seen in Alaska near Norton Sound, where it breeds. When in flight it just skims the surface of the water or the shore, after the habit of the Emperor Goose. Its chief wintering grounds are on the Aleutian Islands, where the natives slaughter the bird in great numbers for food and for their skins. Except for the "spectacles" and the brown breast, the Spectacled Eider is similar to both the King and the American Eiders. Both these latter birds possess white breasts suffused

with pinkish brown. (Family *Anatidae*)

Steller's Eider
Polysticta stelleri [157]

ADULT MALE—Head, white; throat and band about neck, black. Forehead and nape, greenish. Middle of back, black; wings, black; the speculum, purplish blue. Breast, chestnut darkening below. Under tail coverts and tail, black.

ADULT FEMALE—Entire plumage, blackish and rusty brown; speculum of wing, purplish bordered with white.

LENGTH—18.00 inches.

DISTRIBUTION—In the Northern Hemisphere on the Arctic and adjacent coasts; on the Aleutian Islands

east to Unalaska and Kodiak Islands, and the Kenai Peninsula. (Family *Anatidae*)

powerful wings. They are extraordinarily keen of sight, and swift of flight. They are also fierce, powerful, fearless, and predaceous—qualities which made them so desirable in the

ancient (and recently revived) sport of falconry. They are not soaring Hawks, but make their way through the air with rapid wing-strokes, at a relatively low altitude. There are about fifty known members of this family, distributed from the icy polar circles to the tropics. Twenty *Falconidae* reside within the borders of our continent, confined to the genera *Polyborus* (two members) and *Falco* (eighteen members).

NESTING. The nests of Falcons are not so bulky as those of the other Hawks (Accipiters). Some species (e.g. our common Sparrow Hawk) utilize a deserted Woodpecker hole in a tree; others deposit their eggs on the bare rock of a cliff, or less commonly in a loosely built nest in trees. The eggs number two to four or five, and vary considerably in color among the species, being white, creamy, or dull yellowish-red or brownish, and variously speckled, spotted, and blotched with shades of brown.

FALCON FAMILY
Caracaras and Falcons
Falconidae

The members of this family have a strongly hooked and notched bill; large, strong feet with long, curved, sharp talons; and not very long tails; but especially, rather long, curved,

FALCON
Aplomado Falcon
Falco fusco-coerulescens septentrionalis [359]

ADULT MALE AND FEMALE—Upper parts, bluish gray; rump with fine whitish bars. Wings flecked with white; the secondaries with white tips, forming a single bar when the wing is closed. Tail narrowly barred with white. Side of head has broad black band through the eye, a white band over it, and a "mustache" marking from the base of the bill. Under parts, white; flanks and under tail coverts, orange-brown.

LENGTH — 15.00 inches. Female somewhat larger.

DISTRIBUTION—From southern Arizona, New Mexico and Texas, southward through Mexico.

The Aplomado Falcon is a bird of the open country and is found among the mesquites, yuccas, and cactuses; not in dense growths or in the mountains. While its actions are more lei-

surely and deliberate than those of the Sparrow Hawk, yet in its habits and food it somewhat resembles that species, but captures more small birds and mammals, some reptiles, and many insects. (Family *Falconidae*)

Peale's Falcon

Falco peregrinus pealei [356b]

Similar to the Duck Hawk, but much darker throughout.

DISTRIBUTION — "Breeds on the Queen Charlotte(?), Aleutian, and

Commander Islands. Transient in the Sitkan district, Alaska. South in win-

ter to Oregon." (A.O.U. Check List.) (Family *Falconidae*)

Peregrine Falcon

Falco peregrinus peregrinus [356]

Similar to the Duck Hawk, but with the under parts more heavily marked; the upper breast barred and spotted with blackish-brown.

DISTRIBUTION—A European Falcon, sometimes found in Greenland.

This famous Falcon is the "noble peregrine" of European falconry, and is the European counterpart of our own native Duck Hawk. (Family *Falconidae*)

Prairie Falcon

Falco mexicanus [355]

ADULT MALE—Upper parts, a pale clay-brown with dark grayish-brown markings. Sides of head, light pinkish brown with elongated dark patches. Chin, throat, and middle of under parts, almost white and lightly streaked or spotted. The sides of the body, especially the flanks, heavily blotched with dark grayish-brown. Tail crossed by many narrow, rather faint dark bars.

ADULT FEMALE—Somewhat similar to the male, but tail paler, tipped with whitish.

ʟᴇɴɢᴛʜ — 17.50 inches. Female somewhat larger.

Dɪsᴛʀɪʙᴜᴛɪᴏɴ—From the eastern borders of the Great Plains westward

to the Pacific Coast, and in the north from the Dakotas southward to Mexico. Sometimes found in Illinois. (Family *Falconidae*)

FAMILIES

In North America we number 75 families of birds. Some of these contain but a single species, as for example, the *Anhingidae* (Water Turkeys). The largest family is the *Fringillidae* (Sparrows, Buntings, Finches, Grosbeaks, Towhees, etc.), which numbers 217 species and subspecies. The *Compsothlypidae* (Wood Warblers) rank next, with 82 species and subspecies; and the *Anatidae* (Ducks, Swans, and Geese) third, with 78 species and subspecies.

FINCH FAMILY

Finches, Sparrows, Buntings, Siskins, Grosbeaks, Towhees or Chewinks, Redpolls, and Crossbills

Fringillidae

The Family *Fringillidae,* the largest of all bird families, contains some twelve hundred species and subspecies, distributed in almost every quarter of the globe, but most abundantly represented in the Northern Hemisphere. They possess twelve tail feathers, nine hand feathers, and stout, conical bills

useful in the cracking of tough seed-coats. In the Crossbills the tips of the mandibles are crossed over one another. The Sparrows are all dull-colored, brownish-streaked, "earthy" birds, the males and females being similar. But the Towhees, Grosbeaks, Crossbills, and the like, are bright-colored, strikingly patterned birds; the females being dissimilar and duller, often brownish streaked like the typical Sparrows. The whole family are primarily seed-eaters, with insects coming next in the dietary, and spiders, centipedes, small snails, and other small invertebrates forming a lesser proportion of the food. From the standpoint of general agriculture, the *Fringillid* birds are a most valuable group. Their actual cash value to the American farmer lies somewhere in the neighborhood of ninety millions of dollars per year. This service is rendered through their consumption of the seeds of pestiferous weeds.

Their value as insect destroyers may be at least half this sum. Of about twelve hundred of the world's *Fringillids,* two hundred and forty have been reported from North America, allocated to forty genera.

Nᴇsᴛɪɴɢ. Most of the *Fringillids* of North America nest either on the ground, in low shrubbery, or in trees. Some of the birds, like the Song Sparrow and Snow Bunting, may sink their nests in the soil or in the side of a bank; while others, going to the opposite extreme, like the Goldfinch, select a high branch as much as twenty or twenty-five feet from the ground. The Pine Siskin and the Red Crossbill build even higher, thirty feet or more; while the Purple Finch, nesting in a tall spruce, frequently builds at an elevation of fifty or sixty feet. The nests of *Fringillid* birds are cup-shaped, sometimes loose and bulky, sometimes very compact like that of the Goldfinch. The materials of their construction, while varying a good deal, are, in the main, small twigs, weed stems, grasses, leaves, rootlets; the hair of cattle or deer, etc.; soft weed bark, grape-vine bark, coarse and fine rootlets; soft plant fibers such as milkweed down, cattail down, or thistle down; human hair, feathers, mosses, and the like. The eggs vary greatly in coloration and pattern, but usually are either finely or heavily speckled, spotted, and blotched with shades of brown, black, gray, lilac, lavender, etc., on a ground color of white, pale bluish-white, greenish-blue, greenish, light creamy-brown, grayish, or pinkish white, etc. Often the spots are gathered together near the larger end, sometimes forming a sort of irregular wreath. From about four to six eggs are the average number in a clutch.

FINCH
Aleutian Rosy Finch
Leucosticte griseonucha [523]

Similar to the Gray-crowned Rosy Finch, but larger and darker, with

cheeks and throat, gray; and with a dark, rich-brown breast.

DISTRIBUTION—The islands of the Bering Sea, passing in winter to the Shumagin Islands, and to the southern part of Alaska and Kodiak Island. (Family *Fringillidae*)

Black Rosy Finch
Leucosticte atrata [525]

Similar to the Gray-crowned Rosy Finch, but in the male with the brown markings replaced by black, showing a brownish tinge in strong light; and in the female these markings exhibiting a decided grayish-brown hue.

DISTRIBUTION—This strikingly colored black-and-red Finch is found in Idaho and Wyoming, inhabiting the bleak upper reaches of the higher mountains. It spends its winters from this region southward to Colorado and Utah. (Family *Fringillidae*)

Brown-capped Rosy Finch
Leucosticte australis [526]

Similar in general to the Gray-crowned Rosy Finch, but with faint gray patches on the back of the head and nape, or lacking altogether. These areas are colored a blackish-brown into which the black of the crown passes imperceptibly.

DISTRIBUTION—The Brown-capped Rosy Finch is a mountain bird, found at an elevation of about 12,000 feet in the mountains of Colorado. In winter it descends nearer the base of the mountains, and winters southward as far as New Mexico. (Family *Fringillidae*)

California Purple Finch
Carpodacus purpureus californicus [517a]

Similar in general to the Eastern Purple Finch. The male, however, is darker, and the upper parts of the female are washed by a decided tint of olive green.

DISTRIBUTION—The Pacific Coast of North America, from British Columbia southward, and west of the Sierra Nevada Mountains into California. It spends its winters from central Oregon to the southern part of Arizona. (Family *Fringillidae*)

Cassin's Purple Finch
Carpodacus cassini [518]

Similar to the Eastern Purple Finch, but with a darker, more decidedly streaked back, and paler under parts. The female is much more heavily streaked with black than the female Eastern Purple Finch.

LENGTH—6.50 inches.

DISTRIBUTION—From British Columbia southward through all the western states, and along the entire width of the Rocky Mountain area east to its eastern border, and southward to New Mexico. (Family *Fringillidae*)

Common House Finch
Carpodacus mexicanus frontalis [519]

ADULT MALE—Upper parts, grayish-brown. Forehead, line over the eye, rump, throat, and breast, bright crimson, often with a flaming orange tinge. Abdomen, ashy white; its sides streaked with gray.

ADULT FEMALE—Upper parts, grayish brown. Under parts, whitish streaked with grayish-brown.

LENGTH—5.50 inches.

DISTRIBUTION — From the Great Plains to the Pacific Coast, and from southern Wyoming and Oregon southward to northern Mexico.

The House Finch, the commonest red bird of the western states, is generally as numerous throughout its territory as is the familiar Robin of the east. It nests intimately about houses and out-buildings, and while it is in some localities unfortunately regarded as a

nuisance because of its consumption of small cultivated fruits, yet the fact remains that its food is predominantly the seeds of noxious weeds—roughly

about eighty-five percent. Therefore the bird should be looked upon as a decided benefit to agriculture, and thus accorded complete protection. (Family *Fringillidae*)

Eastern Purple Finch
Carpodacus purpureus purpureus [517]

ADULT MALE—Head, throat, upper breast, and lower back, rich plum-colored purple. Back, brownish streaked with darker brown; wings, brownish gray with two indistinct bars. Abdomen, ashy white. Tail notched; bill rather short and heavy.

ADULT FEMALE—Upper parts, grayish-brown streaked with darker brown. A broad line of light gray extends backward from the eye. Under parts, grayish white prominently streaked with dark grayish-brown. Bill as in male.

LENGTH—6.22 inches.

DISTRIBUTION—From the northern regions of North America south to northern New Jersey and northern Illinois, and along the crests of the mountains into Pennsylvania, and westward to the Great Plains. In winter it spreads southward to the Gulf States.

The Purple Finch is one of our very few vinaceously colored birds, and in full sunlight on the topmost branch of a spruce tree—a favorite perch—is as striking a bird as the Cardinal or the

Scarlet Tanager. Both the male and the female sing. However, when a singing female is presumably seen, it may be a first-year male, since in this plumage the sexes are virtually indistinguishable in the field. The loud, rich, vigorous warble, frequently poured forth as the bird glides from a considerable height into the top of a tall spruce is one of the finest bits of bird music to be heard. (Family *Fringillidae*)

Gray-crowned Rosy Finch
Leucosticte tephrocotis tephrocotis [524]

ADULT MALE—Body, chestnut brown; crown, black. Hind-head and sides of head, gray. Back with fine streaks. Wings, rump, tail, and lower abdomen washed with bright pink. Bill, black.

ADULT FEMALE—Similar to the male, but more subdued in pattern and paler throughout.

LENGTH—6.70 inches.

DISTRIBUTION — Western and interior North America, from British Columbia southward along the Rocky Mountains and the high Sierra Ne-

vada Mountains into California. In winter it spreads eastward as far as Colorado, Nebraska, and Manitoba, Canada; and north to Saskatchewan, Canada.

The Gray-crowned Rosy Finch, often called the Gray-crowned Leucosticte, makes its home among the great peaks of our higher mountains, amid whistling icy winds, snow banks, and glaciers. Here, wherever there are bare rocks with a sprinkling of stunted spruces, mosses, lichens, and sparse patches of rocky soil, the birds may be found nesting, and singing their rather insignificant but sweet, twittering song. These hardy little mountaineers, which have been found at elevations ranging from 11,000 to 15,000 feet, subsist both upon minute insects borne

upward by the rising air currents from the valleys below, and upon larger forms swept skyward by fierce mountain gales. (Family *Fringillidae*)

Guadalupe House Finch
Carpodacus amplus [520]

Similar to the Common House Finch, but with a browner back, and a deeper red color.

DISTRIBUTION—As its name implies, this bird is restricted to Guadalupe Island off the coast of Lower California. (Family *Fringillidae*)

Hepburn's Rosy Finch

Leucosticte tephrocotis littoralis [524a]

Similar to the Gray-crowned Rosy Finch, but with gray cheeks, and the throat often gray.

DISTRIBUTION—Hepburn's Finch is found in northwestern North America, from Alaska southward into the high mountains of British Columbia and Washington. It spends its winters on the Pacific Coast as far north as Kodiak Island, and inland as far southwest as Colorado.

This rare Finch is found in the high mountains, feeding on large insects at the edges of glaciers and snow fields. (Family *Fringillidae*)

McGregor's House Finch

Carpodacus mcgregori [520.1]

Similar to the Common House Finch, but larger, with the upper parts grayer and more heavily streaked, and with the red color replaced by pale salmon, or oftentimes by a dull yellow.

DISTRIBUTION—McGregor's House Finch is restricted to San Benito Island off the coast of Lower California. (Family *Fringillidae*)

San Clemente House Finch

Carpodacus mexicanus clementis [519c]

Similar to the Common House Finch, but slightly darker, with the wings and tail shorter, and the bill and feet larger.

DISTRIBUTION—This subspecies is restricted to Todos Santos Island off the coast of Lower California. (Family *Fringillidae*)

San Lucas House Finch

Carpodacus mexicanus ruberrimus [519b]

Similar to the Common House Finch, but smaller, and with the red color

more extensive. In the male, the under tail coverts are also red.

DISTRIBUTION—The San Lucas House Finch is restricted to the southern part of Lower California. (Family *Fringillidae*)

Sierra Nevada Rosy Finch

Leucosticte tephrocotis dawsoni [524b]

Similar to the Gray-crowned Rosy Finch, but slightly smaller. Grayer in tone and less brownish.

DISTRIBUTION—In the Sierra Nevada of Eldorado and Tulare counties, California. (Family *Fringillidae*)

FLAMINGO FAMILY
Phoenicopteridae

Flamingos are closely allied to the Ducks and Geese (Family *Anatidae*). Their legs are extremely long, their

feet webbed, their wings pointed, their tails relatively short. The bill is peculiar, being bent downward and backward, so that in feeding, the tip of the upper mandible becomes the lower part of the bill and vice versa. This means that the tip is directed backward. The birds feed, therefore, with their bills "upside down" and "backside foremost." The bill is deep and its sides are fluted or serrated so that when it is closed, the muddy water is strained out, leaving safe in the bill cavity whatever food may be included. Flamingos feed thus upon any small creatures found in the soft mud and muddy waters of the shoals upon which they stalk about when feeding. Their food consists of water plants, small molluscs, frogs, etc. Their nests are tapering hillocks of mud about two feet high, with a depression at the top in which is laid one white egg—sometimes two. There are six species of Flamingos, four of them found in the Western Hemisphere, and one, the *Phoenicopterus ruber* or American Flamingo, occurring in the United States.

NESTING. These birds nest on desolate and remote islands, building up a truncated, conical structure of mud and marl to the height of a foot or more. At the base this nesting cone is about a foot and a half in diameter; and at the top, about a foot. In the top, a basin-shaped depression receives the one or two white eggs. The birds sit astride the nest, their legs extended down on each side.

FLAMINGO

Flamingo

Phoenicopterus ruber [182]

ADULT MALE AND FEMALE—Vermilion, with the shoulders somewhat lighter, and the larger wing feathers black. Bill, red with black tip. Under parts similar to the back, but paler. Bill, heavy with tips flattened and much decurved. Legs and neck, very long.

LENGTH—From tip of bill to tip of toes, 60.00 inches.

DISTRIBUTION—Breeds in the Bahamas, Cuba, Haiti, etc., and occurs rarely at the southern tip of Florida. Flamingos are exceedingly picturesque birds. An account of their structural peculiarities will be found under the heading FLAMINGO FAMILY. Those which reach the United States occur very sparingly on the southernmost Florida coast. They have been reported in earlier days as far north as South Carolina. Some few are now found on the Florida Keys. They were

formerly numerous there, as well as on the shoals and flats of this region. When in flight, their long necks and long legs are stretched straight out

in front and in back. Their notes are deep, and sound like the honking of the familiar Canada Goose. (Family *Phoenicopteridae*)

FLICKER

Cape Gilded Flicker

Colaptes chrysoides chrysoides [414]

Somewhat similar to the Northern Flicker, but with the crown light brown, and the under side of the wings and tail, yellow; and no red crescent on the nape. Mustache patches of the male, red.

DISTRIBUTION—"Central and southern Arizona, from latitude 34° to southern Sonora [northwestern Mexico] and Lower California south of latitude 30°." (A.O.U. Check List.)

This Flicker most often found in the region of the Giant Cactuses. (Family *Picidae*)

Guadalupe Flicker

Colaptes cafer rufipileus [415]

Similar to the Red-shafted Flicker, but with bill slightly longer; the wing somewhat shorter; the crown a cinnamon brown; and the rump a vinaceous white.

DISTRIBUTION—Found on Guadalupe Island off the coast of Lower California. (Family *Picidae*)

Mearns's Gilded Flicker

Colaptes chrysoides mearnsi [414a]

Similar to the Cape Gilded Flicker, but larger and paler. The black bars of the back are narrower; the head more reddish brown; the wings more marked with white; the gray of the throat and breast lighter; and the spots of the under parts usually somewhat smaller.

DISTRIBUTION—Extreme southwestern California, northern Lower California, and southern Arizona, southward into northwestern Mexico. (Family *Picidae*)

Northern Flicker

Colaptes auratus luteus [412a]

ADULT MALE—Crown and back of neck, ashy gray, with a scarlet crescent across the nape. Back, brownish gray barred with black; rump, white. Inner surface of wing feathers and their shafts, bright yellow. Tail, black above and below, yellow tipped with black. Sides of head, throat, and upper breast, vinaceous. A broad black stripe on the side of the throat from the base of the bill resembles a mustache. Breast crossed by a broad black crescent. Rest of under parts, vinaceous white spotted with black.

ADULT FEMALE—Similar to the male, but lacking the black mustache.

LENGTH—12.00 inches.

DISTRIBUTION—Over the whole of eastern North America, west as far as the Rocky Mountains, and extending up into Alaska.

This is the best-known member of the great Woodpecker family, if we may judge from its twenty or more vernacular names which include Yellowhammer, Clape, Wickup, High Holer, Golden-winged Woodpecker, Yellowshafted Woodpecker, and Wood Pigeon. Every type of country, except plains and dense forests, is inhabited by this adaptable species, and it is often found nesting in bird boxes close to windows or in city parks. Flickers have a large number of cries and calls.

The commonest, and one of the characteristic sounds of a quiet spring morning, is a clear, vigorous *wick, wick, wick, wick, wick,* and so on for a dozen or perhaps twenty repetitions, until the listener begins to wonder where the bird is getting its breath. During the mating season several birds together set up a conversational call of *wicker, wicker, wicker.* (Family *Picidae*)

Northwestern Flicker

Colaptes cafer cafer [413a]

Somewhat similar to the Red-shafted Flicker, but much darker and with a browner back.

DISTRIBUTION—From southern Alaska southward along the Pacific Coast to Oregon. In winter it spreads westward as far as northwestern California. (Family *Picidae*)

Red-shafted Flicker

Colaptes cafer collaris [413]

Somewhat similar to the Northern Flicker, but with a brownish crown, no red crescent on the nape, and [in the male] with a red mustache patch. The under sides of the wings and tail are reddish.

DISTRIBUTION—Along the western coast of the United States (except in the extreme north), and extending inland into the Rocky Mountains. In the eastern part of its range it apparently interbreeds with the Northern Flicker. (Family *Picidae*)

San Fernando Flicker

Colaptes chrysoides brunnescens [414b]

Similar to the Cape Gilded Flicker, but slightly smaller, and with the upper parts appreciably darker.

DISTRIBUTION—Occurs in the middle portion of the peninsula of Lower California, between the latitudes 28° and 30°. (Family *Picidae*)

San Pedro Flicker

Colaptes cafer martirensis [413b]

Similar in general to the Red-shafted Flicker, but slightly smaller, with a slenderer bill, and with the plumage showing a grayer, less vinaceous cast.

DISTRIBUTION—In the peninsula of Lower California, on the western slopes of the Sierra San Pedro Martir, and in winter extending outward [westward] to the coast. (Family *Picidae*)

Southern Flicker

Colaptes auratus auratus [412]

Similar to the Northern Flicker, but smaller.

DISTRIBUTION—Restricted to the southeastern states as far north as South Carolina. (Family *Picidae*)

FLYCATCHER FAMILY

Tyrannidae

Flycatchers are dull-colored birds, with large heads, wide mouths and bills from whose base there project several large "rictal" bristles. The feet are rather small. These birds sit upon some exposed perch, and from such

a point of vantage sally out and snap up flying insects on the wing, usually returning to the same perch. They are not classed among the true song-birds, though some of their notes are sweet and pleasing (e.g. those of the Eastern Phoebe, or of the Wood Pewee) and quite as musical as the insignificant insect-like buzzes of some of the so-called warblers (Family *Compsothlypidae*). Grays, olive-greens, olive-browns, and white are the chief colors of our native species. The American Flycatchers are not related to the Flycatchers of the Eastern Hemisphere. These latter are contained in the family *Muscicapidae*, and are true song-birds. The American *Tyrannidae* are sometimes called Tyrant Flycatchers. About seven hundred and fifty species and subspecies of Flycatchers have been listed in the Americas, chiefly in the tropics. Of these, forty-two are recorded from North America and are listed in eleven genera.

NESTING. Our Flycatchers are a varied group with respect to their nesting habits. Some species breed in trees, fashioning their nests out of small twigs, rootlets, weed stems, and the like, and lining them with feathers, hair, and often wool (e.g. the

Kingbird). Others, like the Phoebe, place their compact nests of mud, grasses, mosses, weed bark, other soft plant materials, feathers, and hair, in sheltered ledges of low cliffs along quiet streams, in caves, in old walls, under eaves, in old buildings, under porches, under bridges (a favorite situation), or in almost any protected spot. Others, like the Olive-sided Flycatcher and the Wood Pewee, saddle their nests on a large branch at heights from ten to fifty feet from the ground. The Yellow-bellied Flycatcher nests in the upturned roots of a fallen tree, in the side of a mossy, rocky bank, on the ground in a mass of mosses or lichens, or sometimes in a fallen and partially rotted log. The Crested Flycatcher, breeding in a hole in a stump, or more often in a deserted Woodpecker's hole, almost always twists a piece of soft cast-off snakeskin about the edge of the nest, or incorporates it into the lining near the top. Often this piece is so long that either by accident or design it hangs out of the entrance hole for a short distance. Forbush says, "Sometimes snakes' skins of various sizes make up almost the entire nest." The eggs of Flycatchers number from two to five or six (the Phoebe and Crested Flycatcher sometimes lay as many as eight) but three or four is most common. They are white and speckled, spotted, or blotched and splashed with various tones of brown, gray, lilac, lavendar, etc.

FLYCATCHER
Acadian Flycatcher
Empidonax virescens [465]

ADULT MALE AND FEMALE—Upper parts, grayish olive-green; wings and tail, darker and slightly brownish in cast, the former showing two whitish bars. Under parts, whitish, the breast tinged with olivaceous gray. Throat and middle of abdomen, pure white.

LENGTH—5.75 inches.

DISTRIBUTION—From northeastern Nebraska eastward to central New England, and south into Texas, the Gulf States, and Florida. It winters in northern South America.

Like the Yellow-bellied and Alder Flycatchers, this little species is a silent bird during its migrations, but on its nesting grounds utters one of the shortest of bird "songs"—an insignificant, almost insect-like *whi beet,* the

last note sharply accented. Its call note is an incisive *piit.* The Acadian Flycatcher is a bird of low, damp woodlands and swampy thickets in regions which are wild and unsettled. Here on a low-hanging limb in a forest clearing or old lumber road, it sits motionless on the watch for its insect prey, sailing out after it with a sharp snap of the bill in characteristic Flycatcher fashion. It is not strange that the bird is so little known when one recalls its unobtrusive coloration, diminutive size, modest utterance, quiet ways, and the nature of the country in which it is found. (Family *Tyrannidae*)

Alder Flycatcher
Empidonax trailli trailli [466a]

ADULT MALE AND FEMALE—Upper parts, dark olive-green, often tinged with brown. Wing bars, light grayish-brown. Under parts, white with grayish sides. Abdomen washed with yellow.

LENGTH—6.09 inches.

DISTRIBUTION—From New Brunswick, Canada, south to northern New Jersey, and west to Michigan. In winter it is found from Yucatan southward.

This bird, as its name implies, is frequently found in alder thickets along the borders of ponds, streams, and swamps, or on damp hillsides, where one may hear its characteristic song

while the singer remains concealed. Although the bird sings little on its nesting grounds, occasionally one will be found which utters its simple lay throughout the long hot summer. The bird's usual habit is to conceal its movements within the bosky screen of thickly leaved alder bushes, and then work upwards to the tip of some dead branch which rises above its leafy neighbors. From this perch it gives vent to its easily recognizable and comical little song resembling the syllables *jee jé eut,* the accent falling strongly on the second shorter note. In quality the song reminds one of the Phoebe's, but is harsher. With the head thrown back and the bill pointing upward, the syllables are jerked out with such apparent effort that the wings and tail tremble vigorously, as in a tiny sneeze. The call-note is a

sharp, clear, almost musical *peip.* (Family *Tyrannidae*)

Arizona Crested Flycatcher
Myiarchus tyrannulus magister [453]

Similar to the Great Crested Flycatcher, but slightly larger, and with the under parts paler.

DISTRIBUTION—From southern Arizona and southwestern New Mexico into western Mexico. In winter it moves southward into Mexico. (Family *Tyrannidae*)

Ash-throated Flycatcher
Myiarchus cinerascens cinerascens [454]

Somewhat similar to the Great Crested Flycatcher, but smaller, with an ashy white throat and upper breast, and a pale yellow abdomen. Wings with two white bars.

LENGTH—8.25 inches.

DISTRIBUTION—Colorado and Oregon to western Texas and Lower California. It winters in southern Mexico south into Central America. (Family *Tyrannidae*)

Beardless Flycatcher
Camptostoma imberbe [472]

ADULT MALE AND FEMALE—Upper parts, brownish-gray; wings edged with whitish. Under parts, soiled whitish, with a faint wash of yellow.

LENGTH—4.50 inches.

DISTRIBUTION—Extreme southwestern portion of Texas along the Rio Grande southward through Mexico into Central America. (Family *Tyrannidae*)

Buff-breasted Flycatcher
Empidonax fulvifrons pygmaeus [470a]

ADULT MALE AND FEMALE—Upper parts, dull grayish-brown; wings with two whitish bars. Under parts, pale buff, with a brownish cast on the breast and sides of the body.

LENGTH—4.92 inches.

DISTRIBUTION—From southwestern New Mexico and Arizona southwards into western Mexico. (Family *Tyrannidae*)

Coues's Flycatcher

Myiochanes pertinax pallidiventris [460]

ADULT MALE AND FEMALE—Upper parts, gray; crown, darker with a very slight crest. Under parts, light grayish fading to grayish-white on the under tail coverts.

LENGTH—7.70 inches.

DISTRIBUTION—From central Arizona southward into western Mexico, wintering south of the United States. (Family *Tyrannidae*)

Derby Flycatcher

Pitangus sulphuratus derbianus [449]

ADULT MALE AND FEMALE—Upper parts, brown, brightening on the wings

and tail. Top, sides of the head, and crown with a partially concealed yellow patch. Broad white line over the eye. Forehead, white. Throat, white; rest of under parts, sulphur yellow.

Bill, long and heavy; tail, shorter than the wings. Appears top-heavy when perched.

LENGTH—10.50 inches.

DISTRIBUTION—From the Lower Rio Grande of Texas southward into Central America. In winter it passes into northern South America.

This Flycatcher, presenting a rather ludicrous picture as it sits apparently top-heavily on an exposed twig watching for passing insects, is only a rare summer resident of the southern portion of the Rio Grande in Texas. (Family *Tyrannidae*)

Fork-tailed Flycatcher

Muscivora tyrannus [442]

Similar to the Scissor-tailed Flycatcher, but tail with less white; head with small yellow patch; and under parts, clear white.

DISTRIBUTION — From southern Mexico through Central America into South America, where it spreads over most of the continent. In the United States the bird is only an accidental straggler in the south. (Family *Tyrannidae*)

Gray Flycatcher

Empidonax griseus [469.1]

Similar to the Wright's Flycatcher, but slightly larger; the plumage grayer, the under parts, very faintly or not at all yellowish.

DISTRIBUTION—From Oregon and Colorado to southern Mexico, passing the winter from Arizona southward into west central Mexico. (Family *Tyrannidae*)

Hammond's Flycatcher

Empidonax hammondi [468]

ADULT MALE AND FEMALE—Upper parts, brownish gray with an olivaceous sheen in strong light. Wings with two whitish bars. Under parts, yellowish, grading to dark gray on the breast and fading out to a grayish white on the throat.

DISTRIBUTION—From the Lesser Slave Lake in Canada, and from the interior of Alaska south through the entire Rocky Mountain zone into the mountains of Arizona and New Mexico. In winter it is found in Lower California and southern Mexico.

This Flycatcher (to be distinguished by its notes from the Wright's and the Gray Flycatchers) may be found in the dense forests of Douglas Fir in Washington, Oregon, and in the Sierras, high up in the tops of the trees. It is also found in northern Idaho, among cottonwoods and willows along stream courses and in the edges of swamps. Hoffman says the "song" sounds like the syllables *sewip, tsurp, treep;* another utterance may be syllabified as *pee, pee, pée-wit, pée-wit.* (Family *Tyrannidae*)

Least Flycatcher
Empidonax minimus [467]

ADULT MALE AND FEMALE—Upper parts, brownish olive-green; the wings and tail, darker and grayer—the former with two grayish-white bars. Under parts, whitish shading to a yellowish-white on the abdomen.

LENGTH—5.41 inches.

DISTRIBUTION—From New Brunswick and the Great Slave Lake, Canada, south to eastern Colorado and western Texas, and east to Pennsylvania, and along the higher Allegheny Mountains as far south as North Carolina. In winter it is found in Central America.

This species, a diminutive member of the Flycatcher family, as its name implies, is often called the Chebec from its characteristic and easily remembered note *chi bíc, chi bíc.* The second syllable is strongly accented, and the whole "song" is jerked out with apparent effort—the wings and tail quivering at each repetition of the utterance. The favorite haunts of the Chebec are old orchards, tall trees in rather open country, around farm houses, in the trees of city parks, and occasionally along shady city streets.

Throughout the heat of summer the song resounds with tireless, and sometimes tiresome repetition. The "song" is entirely without melody or pleasing tone quality, but is, nevertheless, given with energy and cheer. The diminutive size of the bird, and its jerky dissyllabic song make the identification of this attractive little species easy. (Family *Tyrannidae*)

Little Flycatcher
Empidonax trailli brewsteri [466]

Similar to the Alder Flycatcher, but with browner upper parts.

DISTRIBUTION—In Canada from Alaska east to the Great Slave Lake region, south to western Texas and southern California, and east as far as Kansas. It winters south of the United States in the tropics. (Family *Tyrannidae*)

Lower California Flycatcher
Myiarchus cinerascens pertinax [454b]

Similar to the Ash-throated Flycatcher, but with a stouter, heavier bill.

DISTRIBUTION—From about latitude 28° 30′, in Lower California, southward to the Cape district. (Family *Tyrannidae*)

Mexican Crested Flycatcher
Myiarchus tyrannulus nelsoni [453a]

Similar to the Northern Crested Flycatcher, but with less brown in the tail. Back, grayer with no greenish tinge in strong light. Under parts, paler.

DISTRIBUTION—From the southern portion of the Rio Grande of Texas southward into Central America. (Family *Tyrannidae*)

Northern Crested Flycatcher
Myiarchus crinitus boreus [452a]

ADULT MALE AND FEMALE—Upper parts, grayish olive-brown shading to darker on the slightly crested crown. Tail, reddish brown. The outer vanes of the primaries are bordered with light reddish brown. Wing bars, yellowish. Throat and breast, grayish-white; abdomen, a bright sulphur-yellow.

LENGTH—9.01 inches.

DISTRIBUTION—From New Brunswick and Manitoba, Canada, south to Florida, and west to Texas and the Great Plains. In winter it is found from southern Florida to northern South America.

The loud, harsh, far-reaching, yet cheerful call of the Northern Crested Flycatcher is one of the characteristic sounds in an orchard on a hot summer day. It may be represented by the syllables *whreeep, whip, whip, whip.* Frequently only the first syllable, which is louder and in a slightly higher pitch than the succeeding ones, is given. Often it is the only part of the call clearly heard. On a quiet day this first loud shout may be heard over a distance of half a mile. The bird is more often heard than seen, for it frequents the middle portion or tops of tall trees in partly wooded, partly open country, and takes especial delight in orchards of large trees. It has the curious and rather startling

habit of lining its nest with a cast-off snake-skin, which is soft and dry, and

adapts itself well to forming a comfortable bed for the nestlings. (Family *Tyrannidae*)

Olivaceous Flycatcher
Myiarchus tuberculifer olivascens [455a]

ADULT MALE AND FEMALE—Upper parts, uniform olive brown; under parts, olive grayish.

LENGTH—7.15 inches.

DISTRIBUTION — Southwestern Arizona and northwestern Mexico. A small species, living in the brushy canyons of the southern Arizona mountains, and identifiable from its uniform dark olive color. (Family *Tyrannidae*)

Olive-sided Flycatcher
Nuttallornis mesoleucus [459]

ADULT MALE AND FEMALE—Upper parts, dark olive grayish-brown. Throat and a line through the middle of the under parts, whitish. Sides similar to the back, but with an olivaceous cast. No wing bars. Flanks with downy, yellowish-white patches of feathers, best seen in flight.

LENGTH—7.39 inches.

DISTRIBUTION—From Alaska south and east through the Rocky Mountains and the Pacific Coast ranges into Mexico; and into Minnesota, northern

New York State, Maine, and the mountains of northern and central New England. It winters in Central and South America.

The loud arresting "song" of the Olive-sided Flycatcher is its best identification in the field. The notes are loud, clear, and penetrating, and carry for a surprisingly long distance on a clear, quiet day. They may be

represented by *whip pee pée-oh,* or *pip pee pée-ah,* the final note falling in pitch. The whole song is given with loud and joyous vigor. Those who wish to construe bird notes into words might render the song thus: *see here; see me here!* There is little need for the bird to call attention to itself, for it habitually perches on an exposed dead limb of a tree, or chooses a bare elevated situation of some sort from which to ejaculate its vigorous song, and to watch for passing insects which it seizes awing. The alarm and call notes are sharp and penetrating: *pip-pip* or *pip, pip-pip.* The bird is essentially a denizen of wild country, frequently being found in forests where clearings have been made. On some of the mountains of New England, and along the coast of Maine, the loud cheerful call of the Olive-sided Flycatcher is one of the characteristic sounds of early summer days.

The bird is not at all shy, and may be approached quite closely before taking wing. (Family *Tyrannidae*)

San Lucas Flycatcher
Empidonax difficilis cineritius [464a]

Similar to the Western Flycatcher, but with the upper parts showing no yellowish cast, and almost no yellow below except on the throat and abdomen.

DISTRIBUTION—Upper portion of Lower California, sometimes occurring in southern California. (Family *Tyrannidae*)

Scissor-tailed Flycatcher
Muscivora forficata [443]

ADULT MALE—Ashy gray; throat, white; wings, dark slate gray. Under side of wings, and under tail coverts, salmon. Upper parts marked with red; crown with small partially concealed reddish patch. Very long and deeply forked tail, prominently marked with black and white.

ADULT FEMALE—Similar to the male but duller, smaller, and with a shorter tail.

LENGTH—13.50 inches.

DISTRIBUTION — From southern Kansas and western Louisiana southward through Texas and Mexico into Central America. It winters in Central America.

In the chaparral country of the southwest, this gorgeous Flycatcher is not uncommon, and excites admiration at once as it sits quietly atop some bush, its long tail slimly descending in a graceful sweep, and the pinkish salmon color of the sides of the body well set off by the dark color of its folded wings. Suddenly the bird launches outward and upward, turning quickly with open tail, and then rises by turns and jerks, opening and closing its graceful "scissors" as it goes. Bailey says of this astonishing aerial performance, that the bird flies ". . . with rattling wings, executing an aerial seesaw, a line of sharp-

angled VVVVVVV's. . . . As it goes up and down it utters all the while a penetrating scream, *ka-quee, ka-quee, ka-quee, ka-quee, ka-quee,* the emphasis being given each time at the top of the ascending line." (Family *Tyrannidae*)

Southern Crested Flycatcher

Myiarchus crinitus crinitus [452]

Similar to the Northern Crested Flycatcher, but slightly smaller, the bill slightly larger.

DISTRIBUTION—From South Carolina southward into Florida. (Family *Tyrannidae*)

Sulphur-bellied Flycatcher

Myiodynastes luteiventris swarthi [451]

ADULT MALE AND FEMALE—Upper parts, brown streaked with black. Crown of head with concealed yellow patch. Yellowish-white stripes over eye, and down the sides of the throat. Rump and tail, bright reddish brown. Under parts, yellow, the sides streaked with dusky. Throat, white, bordered on each side by a wide black stripe. Bill, broad.

LENGTH—7.87 inches.

DISTRIBUTION—From southern Arizona southward into Central America.

Tree-bordered stream courses are the favorite haunts of the Sulphur-bellied Flycatcher. Here it makes its nest in a hole in a sycamore. The habits of the bird are much like those of the

Northern Crested Flycatcher. Its notes are said to resemble the squeaking of a wheelbarrow. (Family *Tyrannidae*)

Vermilion Flycatcher

Pyrocephalus rubinus mexicanus [471]

ADULT MALE—Upper parts, dusky brown; top of head, flaming scarlet, and the feathers often raised into a crest. A black line runs from the base of the bill through the eye to the back of the head. Under parts, bright scarlet. Bill and feet, black.

ADULT FEMALE—Upper parts, including top of head, brown. Tail, blackish. Wings with two indistinct whitish bars. Under parts, white streaked with grayish-brown on the breast and upper abdomen, and flushed with salmon pink on the lower abdomen.

LENGTH—6.00 inches.

DISTRIBUTION—Southwestern Utah, southern New Mexico, Arizona, southwestern Texas, across to southern and

Lower California, and down into Central America.

In the cottonwoods and willows along stream courses, as well as in oak groves, this extremely brilliant little Flycatcher is most at home. Here, from some low, exposed perch, it watches for passing insects, and as it dashes out after its prey, its body

flames in the sunlight with a startling radiance. Often during the mating season, the male launches high into the air, expanding its feathers and fluttering at a height so that the female Flycatcher world can see. The bird does all this while uttering a subdued twittering chatter, before sailing gracefully back to earth. Hoffman says the bird's common notes sound like the syllables *pitt-a-see, pitt-a-see.* With each utterance the head is jerked upwards. (Family *Tyrannidae*)

Western Flycatcher
Empidonax difficilis difficilis [464]

Similar to the Yellow-bellied Flycatcher, but with the upper parts showing a yellowish cast; the under parts, brighter yellow; and the breast flushed with brownish.

DISTRIBUTION — From southern Alaska southward to Mexico, and eastward to about central South Dakota. (Family *Tyrannidae*)

Wright's Flycatcher
Empidonax wrighti [469]

ADULT MALE AND FEMALE—Upper parts, brownish-gray; the wings with two whitish bars. Ring around the eye, whitish. Under parts, light grayish-white.

LENGTH—6.07 inches.

DISTRIBUTION—From British Columbia, Canada; Oregon, and Montana, over the entire Rocky Mountain zone, and southward to Arizona and New Mexico. In winter it passes into Lower California and southern Mexico.

This trim, unobtrusively colored Flycatcher, a denizen of the sage brush, or the thick chaparral on the lower mountain slopes, is not apt to be encountered in forested regions. As a rule it prefers the vicinity of low damp situations, ponds, or streams. It is a difficult bird to identify, except from its notes. Hoffman describes its utterances as a series of three notes, built up into a number of varied combinations, as, for example, *psit hreek psit pseet.* Towards dusk the bird frequently says *tee, tee, tee-hick.* From such notes it may be distinguished from the Gray Flycatcher and from the Hammond's Flycatcher. (Family *Tyrannidae*)

Yellow-bellied Flycatcher
Empidonax flaviventris [463]

ADULT MALE AND FEMALE—Upper parts, dark olive-greenish-gray; the wings and tail somewhat darker, and the former with two whitish bars. Throat, breast, and sides, greenish-yellow; abdomen, bright yellow.

LENGTH—5.63 inches.

DISTRIBUTION—In Canada from Labrador westward; in the United States west to the Great Plains, and south into northern New England (in the mountains farther south), northern New York, and Minnesota. Along the Allegheny Mountains it reaches into Pennsylvania. In winter it migrates into Central America.

The Yellow-bellied Flycatcher is slightly more retiring and secretive than most Flycatchers, and this habit, together with its yellowish-green under parts (harmonizing effectively with the green leaves and greenish

lights of the forest interior) make it difficult to detect. Only as it dashes out from its perch after insects is it likely to attract notice. The notes of the species, heard commonly enough in the depths of wet coniferous and birch forests of the north, are of a plaintive, almost querulous quality, reminiscent of the notes of the Wood Pewee, though softer, and with a whispered character, best represented by the syllables *thoo wéep eh, thoo wéep eh*. To some ears the bird seems to be saying *she weeps, sir; she weeps, sir*. In precise contrast to this soft performance is its call note *pschee-ik*, often given over and over again with tiresome iteration, and is, as Dwight observes, "more suggestive of a sneeze on the bird's part" than of anything else. Unlike Flycatchers in general, the Yellow-bellied Flycatcher sinks its small nest of fine rootlets, grasses, mosses, and lichens, into a bank of damp, often almost wet moss on the forest floor. (Family *Tyrannidae*)

FOSSIL BIRDS

Extinct birds of North America, whose presence here is known only by their fossil remains, number roughly about 160 species. These are chiefly the water birds of various sorts, and the larger birds below the Order *Passeriformes*. The passeriform, or perching birds, are represented by only about half a dozen species.

FULMAR

Atlantic Fulmar
Fulmarus glacialis glacialis [86]

ADULT MALE AND FEMALE—Upper parts, slate gray; head, neck and under parts, white. In the dark phase, the entire bird is a dark slate gray.
LENGTH—19.00 inches.
DISTRIBUTION—In the North Atlantic, from the latitude of northern Greenland northward. In winter it descends as far as the latitude of Massachusetts. Occasionally it straggles south along the coast as far as Virginia.

The Atlantic Fulmars accompany whaling and sealing ships in the far

northern waters for the offal which is thrown overboard. The bird is known as the Mollimoke among sailors. (Family *Procellariidae*)

Pacific Fulmar
Fulmarus glacialis rodgersi [86.1]

ADULT MALE AND FEMALE—Upper parts, bluish-gray broken by a mixture of white; quills of the feathers, darker. Head, neck, and under parts, white.

LENGTH—18.00 inches.

DISTRIBUTION—In the north Pacific from Bering Sea southward to the middle of the California coast. (Family *Procellariidae*)

GADWALL

Gadwall

Chaulelasmus streperus [135]

ADULT MALE—Plumage finely mottled and marked with brown, giving an entire brown appearance at a distance, and a delicate barred and scaled

appearance at close range. A large area of chestnut and white in the wing. The rump, upper and under tail coverts, black. Under parts, grayish-white. Sides of the body finely marked with brown.

ADULT FEMALE—Somewhat similar to the male, but with the patterns larger, and the bird appearing paler. Speculum in the wing, grayish and white. Abdomen and under tail coverts, white.

LENGTH—19.50 inches.

DISTRIBUTION—From Minnesota, central southern Canada, and British Columbia northward to Alaska. In winter it is found from British Columbia to Virginia, and southward to South America. Along the Atlantic

coast to Labrador, it occurs only as a migrant.

The Gadwall is a fresh-water Duck, being found along the bushy and weedy shores of rivers, lakes, and ponds. It is a swift flier, producing a sharp whistling sound as it shoots through the air. Its flesh is highly esteemed by gourmets. (Family *Anatidae*)

GALLINULE

Florida Gallinule

Gallinula chloropus cachinnans [219]

ADULT MALE AND FEMALE—General color, dark bluish-slate; the back and scapulars, olive-brown. The sides of the body bear broad prominent white streaks. Abdomen, whitish; under tail coverts, white. Crown and forehead wear a bare bright red plate. Bill, bright red with yellowish tip. Tibia of legs, bright red; rest of legs, greenish.

LENGTH—13.50 inches.

DISTRIBUTION — From Montreal, Canada; Vermont, Minnesota, and northern California, southward to the West Indies, Lower California, Panama, and the Galapagos Islands. In winter it is found from the latitude of South Carolina and southern California southward. It has been reported from Quebec, Nova Scotia, New Brunswick, Maine, South Dakota, and Colorado.

The Florida Gallinule, like its purple relative, frequents the reedy, marshy shores of lakes, ponds, and sloughs, picking its way like a barn-yard fowl among the submerged vegetation, or stepping daintily along over floating aquatic plants, or swimming in little protected coves like a duck. Its notes resemble those of hens. At a distance it resembles a coot, but the bright red head-plate and bill readily proclaim its identity. Gallinules are very noisy birds and, even though usually hidden from view in the dense marshes, send forth a series of loud clucks, squawks, chucks, and other lower, purring hen-like sounds, as well as a note sounding like the word *ticket, ticket, ticket.* Another utterance seems to say *currit, currit.* Gallinules are difficult to flush. Their flight is weak, and they soon drop back into the friendly shelter of the

reeds and rushes. They thread the mazes of a marsh with great speed if alarmed. (Family *Rallidae*)

Purple Gallinule
Ionornis martinica [218]

ADULT MALE AND FEMALE—Back, lustrous olive-greenish; wings, light blue with greenish reflections. Forehead bears a bare, leaden-bluish horny plate. Head, dark purplish-blue. Under parts, rich purplish-blue; under tail coverts, white. Bill, carmine with a pale greenish tip. Legs, yellow or greenish yellow.

LENGTH—13.00 inches.

DISTRIBUTION—From Southern Illinois and South Carolina southward through subtropical and tropical America; sometimes straggling as far north as Wisconsin, and through New York and the New England States, sometimes as far as Maine. In winter it is found from southern Florida southward into South America.

This species is more brightly colored than its congener, the Florida Galli-

nule, and not so frequently seen in the north. The plate on its forehead is blue, instead of red, as in the Florida Gallinule, and the legs are a more decided yellow, rather than greenish. (Family *Rallidae*)

GANNET

Gannet
Moris bassana [117]

ADULT MALE AND FEMALE—Pure white; the primaries of the wing; black; head and neck, faintly suffused with yellow.

LENGTH—35.00 inches.

DISTRIBUTION—The North Atlantic Ocean, breeding in America on the

Bonaventure Islands, and on Bird Rock in the Gulf of St. Lawrence. In winter it is found off our Atlantic coast as far south as Florida.

The huge, pure white goose-like Gannets, with their silvery plumage and black wing-tips are splendid sights at sea. They are graceful birds, though heavy in flight, and make their way with surety over the waves, their long necks and tails giving them a sort of gull-like appearance. From a height of fifty to a hundred feet, these huge birds dive head foremost into the waves after fish, a habit shared with no other large birds in flocks. Their note is a harsh, deep, prolonged croak, *cor-r-r-r-rock*. (Family *Sulidae*)

GNATCATCHER
Black-tailed Gnatcatcher
Polioptila melanura californica [753]

Similar to the Plumbeous Gnatcatcher, but with darker upper parts, grayer under parts (the flanks washed with brownish), and with the outer vanes of the outermost pair of tail feathers black margined with white. DISTRIBUTION—From southern California southward along the coastal zone into the northern part of Lower California.

With a note like the mew of a tiny kitten, the little Black-tailed Gnatcatcher announces its presence from the midst of a thicket of sage, cactus, or sumach, where it slips and flits about, switching its tail sidewise, and acting much like our northern Catbird. (Family *Sylviidae*)

Blue-gray Gnatcatcher
Polioptila caerulea caerulea [751]

ADULT MALE—Upper parts, bluishgray, with the head somewhat brighter. Line across forehead, along the sides of the crown, and over the eyes, black. Wings, grayish-black edged with gray. Under parts, ashy white. Tail, black; its outer pair of feathers, white; the next pair with long white tips; and the third pair with short white tips.

ADULT FEMALE — Upper parts, brownish-gray, and lacking the line across forehead and over the eyes. LENGTH—5.00 inches.

DISTRIBUTION—Over the eastern part of the United States generally, from southern New Jersey and Ontario west to Colorado, and south to the Gulf States. Sometimes occurs irregularly as far north as Minnesota, and even Maine. It winters from the Gulf States southward.

The presence of the Blue-gray Gnatcatcher is apt to be announced by its loud penetrating unique note, *tingk!*, which sounds somewhat like a sharply

plucked banjo string, and carries to a surprising distance. Even more remarkable is the song of the bird—a long, complex, warbled strain; the notes clear, melodious, some rich and silvery, and the whole performance ethereal and beautiful. It is, however, given with so little volume and vigor as to be inaudible unless the bird is close at hand. The Gnatcatcher reminds one of a small edition of a Mockingbird with the admixed habits of a kinglet, warbler, and flycatcher. It is a slender, frail, graceful, fidgety, artless gray midget, not at all difficult to identify. It is a denizen of the upper branches of densely leafy trees of moderate height—a typical woodland bird, but more often found along the edges of woods, particularly in the neighborhood of streams, where thickets abound. (Family *Sylviidae*)

Margarita Gnatcatcher
Polioptila melanura margaritae [752b]

Similar to the Plumbeous Gnatcatcher, but with shorter wings, longer bill, the upper parts darker, and with a whitish crescentic patch behind the dark grayish auricular region.

DISTRIBUTION—Central Lower California. (Family *Sylviidae*)

Plumbeous Gnatcatcher
Polioptila melanura melanura [752]

In general similar to the Blue-gray Gnatcatcher, but chiefly different in

that the crown is jet black. The female lacks the black crown.

DISTRIBUTION—From California and Lower California east to western Texas, along the zone of the Mexican border. (Family *Sylviidae*)

San Lucas Gnatcatcher
Polioptila caerulea obscura [751a]

Similar to the Blue-gray Gnatcatcher of the East, but with the upper parts slightly grayer, less bluish, and with slightly less white in the tail.

DISTRIBUTION—The southwestern portion of the United States from California and Lower California, east-

ward into western Texas. (Family *Sylviidae*)

Western Gnatcatcher
Polioptila caerulea amoenissima [751b]

Similar to the Blue-gray Gnatcatcher, but with the upper parts a slightly duller gray.

DISTRIBUTION—Northern interior California, southern Nevada and Utah, and Colorado, southward to northern Lower California, and thence into Mexico. In winter it is found from southern California southward. (Family *Sylviidae*)

Xantus's Gnatcatcher
Polioptila melanura abbreviata [752a]

Similar to the Plumbeous Gnatcatcher, but with a decidedly shorter tail; a somewhat larger bill; the upper parts, a deeper gray; and the under parts, a slightly grayed white.

DISTRIBUTION — From La Paz, Lower California southward to the Cape district. (Family *Sylviidae*)

GOATSUCKER FAMILY
Whip-poor-wills, Nighthawks, etc.
Caprimulgidae

These curious birds are large-headed, long narrow-winged, small-footed creatures, with a very short insignificant bill, but with a deep wide mouth, which is cut back well under the eyes, and is capable of a surprisingly wide gape. Its base is fringed with

stiff long bristles, which, together with the huge mouth, form an excellent net for the capture of insects as the birds sweep and swoop through the twilight air. Their food is captured thus, and not secured by sucking the teats of goats, as the name implies. Gilbert White says of the English Goatsucker, the so-called Fern Owl: "The country people have a notion that the fern owl, or churn owl, or eve jar, which they also call a puckeridge, is very injurious to weanling calves, by inflicting as it strikes at them, the fatal distemper known to cow-leeches by the name of puckeridge. Thus does this harmless, ill-fated bird fall under a double imputation which it by no means deserves —in Italy, of sucking the teats of goats, whence it is called *caprimulgus;* and with us of communicating a deadly disorder to cattle." Over two hundred forms are known. Of these, about one half are in the Americas, and seventeen in North America in only four genera.

NESTING. Our native Goatsuckers (Chuck-will's-widow, Whip-poor-will, and Nighthawk) make no nest but deposit their eggs on the ground in any slight depression that will serve to keep them from rolling away. Thus the eggs may be laid in deep woods, pine groves, or swampy thickets. Our common Eastern Nighthawk places its "ovarian fruits" in open bare gravelly spots in fields, on hillsides, hilltops, ledges of rocks of high hills and mountains (not so commonly), and, rather surprisingly, on the gravelled flat roofs of high brick tenement buildings in large cities; though with the increasing popularity of roof-gardens, and playgrounds in these elevated situations, many birds are being forced again into their native wilds. The eggs of *Caprimulgid* birds are either unmarked white, creamy grayish-white, or dull-white, marked in a spotted, marbled, or blotched fashion with various shades of pale buff, gray, brown, black, purple, or lilac. Two is the normal number of eggs.

GODWIT
Bar-tailed Godwit
Limosa lapponica lapponica [250a]

ADULT MALE AND FEMALE—Upper parts, sooty brown with chestnut streakings. Head and lower neck, chestnut brown streaked with darker. Lower back and rump, white, sometimes sparsely streaked with brown. Upper tail coverts, white with brownish bars. Wing coverts and quills with white margins. Tail barred with white and brown. Under parts, chestnut brown. Bill, black and flesh-colored at its base.

LENGTH—16.50 inches.

DISTRIBUTION—This European Godwit has been reported from Cape Cod, Massachusetts; an accidental straggler. (Family *Scolopacidae*)

Black-tailed Godwit
Limosa limosa limosa [252]

Similar to the Bar-tailed Godwit, but with the lower back, plain brown; the upper tail coverts, white; and the tail, black. Much more white in the wing. Under parts, light reddish brown; the breast barred with black and the abdomen, white.

DISTRIBUTION—An accidental straggler to Greenland from Europe. (Family *Scolopacidae*)

Hudsonian Godwit
Limosa haemastica [251]

ADULT MALE AND FEMALE—Back, black or blackish spotted with buff. Head and neck speckled and streaked with buff and gray. Line over the eye, white or whitish. Chin, white; under parts, light chestnut brown barred with darker gray.

LENGTH—15.37 inches.

DISTRIBUTION—From the Arctic regions of North America, migrating southward through the United States, east of the Rocky Mountain region to southern South America.

Godwits are characterized by slightly up-curved, long bills, which are grooved almost to their tips. Hudsonian Godwits, which used to occur more often than now along the New England coast, are today among the rarest of our shore birds. Under the name of Goose Bird, it has been hunted almost to the point of extinction, or at any rate within sight of this calamity. The useful Hudsonian Godwit feeds to a very large extent upon horseflies and mosquitoes, and hence is more beneficial to mankind in this respect than as something to eat. The incubation is performed by

the smaller male birds, as is the case with the Phalaropes, and also with the rest of the Godwits. (Family *Scolopacidae*)

Marbled Godwit
Limosa fedoa [249]

ADULT MALE AND FEMALE—Plumage, light cinnamon-brown; the upper parts, heavily mottled or marbled with black. Breast, sides, and tail, finely barred with blackish. Throat and chin, white, the former streaked. Edge of wing, black.

LENGTH—16.50 inches.

DISTRIBUTION—Over almost the whole of North America. It nests from Manitoba, Saskatchewan, and British

Columbia to Iowa and Nebraska. In winter it is found in Guatemala, Trinidad, Yucatan, and Cuba.

The Marbled Godwits are birds of the seashore, where they follow the retreating surf, feeding as they go; and of moist meadows, prairies, and marshes. They are rare on the Atlantic coast. (Family *Scolopacidae*)

Pacific Godwit
Limosa lapponica baueri [250]

Similar to the Marbled Godwit, but with the upper parts less mottled; and with the head, neck, and under parts, plain cinnamon-brown. Tail barred with black and white.

LENGTH—16.00 inches.

DISTRIBUTION—On the Alaskan coast, and adjacent islands. In the United States it occurs only south of La Paz, Lower California. (Family *Scolopacidae*)

GOLDEN-EYE
American Golden-eye
Glaucionetta clangula americana [151]

ADULT MALE—Tail and middle of the back, black. Head, blackish with greenish reflections in strong light, and very slightly crested. A large, prominent spot in front of and slightly below the eye, white. Broad ring around the neck and the sides of the upper back, white. Under parts, white. Wing, black, covered with white feathers when folded, but showing a broad patch of white when spread. Bill, black. Legs and feet, orange.

ADULT FEMALE—Back and a band across the breast, dark dull grayish-brown. Head, dull reddish-brown, and without the white spot of the male. Ring around the neck, white. Under parts, white. Wing with much white both when folded and extended. Bill, yellowish-brown. Feet and legs, soiled yellow.

LENGTH—20.00 inches.

DISTRIBUTION—From the Arctic regions southward to Maine, Minnesota, and Alberta, Canada. In winter it is found from Maine, the Great Lakes, and southern Alaska southward into Mexico and Cuba.

The American Golden-eye, commonly called the Whistler, is with us chiefly an inshore duck, and extends up the lower reaches of tidal estuaries, small bays, and harbors, where it may be seen diving for its favorite foods of shellfish and all sorts of aquatic vegetation. Its flight, accompanied by a sharp hissing whistling sound, has given the bird its common name. The

small, trim, black head, with its prominent white spot identifies the male bird. The dull reddish-brown head makes the female appear quite similar

to the rather rare Redhead, but she exhibits white in the wing. The female Golden-eye also resembles somewhat the female of the two Scaup Ducks (Greater and Lesser), but may be distinguished from them by the absence of white about the base of the bill. Its food is crayfish, small fish, vegetation, and, in salt and brackish water, mussels. After feeding on fresh-water fare, its flesh is palatable. (Family *Anatidae*)

Barrow's Golden-eye
Glaucionetta islandica [152]

Similar in general to the American Golden-eye, but with the head a

purplish-blue, and with a larger white patch at the base of the bill, twice as high as it is wide.

DISTRIBUTION—From the mountains of Colorado and the St. Lawrence River northward, and into southern Greenland. In winter southward into Virginia, Illinois, and California. (Family *Anatidae*)

European Golden-eye
Glaucionetta clangula clangula [151a]

ADULT MALE—Head and neck, glistening glossy-green; feathers of the crown, slightly elongated. Bill, bluish-black, with a white patch at its base.

Back, black. Hind neck, scapulars, and speculum, white. Thighs, dark brown. Under parts, white. Legs and toes, yellow with dusky webs.

ADULT FEMALE—Upper parts, dark brown; white spot at base of bill absent. Under parts, white.

LENGTH—19.00 inches.

DISTRIBUTION—This European duck is casual on St. Paul Island in the Pribilof Group, Alaska.

The Golden-eye of Europe, while only a casual visitant to the extreme northwestern islands of our continent, is a regular winter visitant in the British Isles. During the summer it is found both on the sea and in inland waters; but in summer it is entirely an inland lake, pond, or river duck. When in flight the wings, beating with great rapidity, produce a loud hissing whistle. Its food consists of small fish, as well as insects, and other small aquatic invertebrates, together with the tender shoots of submerged plants, all of which it secures by diving. (Family *Anatidae*)

GOLDFINCH
Arkansas Goldfinch
Spinus psaltria psaltria [530]

Similar to the Eastern Goldfinch, but with back and cheeks, black; and the wings with broad white edgings.

DISTRIBUTION—Western and southwestern North America, from Colorado, New Mexico, and Texas, into Mexico, except the western and extreme southern counties. (Family *Fringillidae*)

British Goldfinch
Carduelis carduelis britannica [526.1]

ADULT MALE AND FEMALE—Back, cinnamon-brown; wings, black with very broad transverse yellow band, and with the tips of the prominent feathers, white. Tail, black, the inner

webs of the feathers tipped with white. Area about the base of the bill and including the eye, bright red. Crown, and irregularly narrowing band descending on the sides of the neck, black. Sides of head and neck, white. Under parts, white, the sides washed with cinnamon-brown.

LENGTH—5.50 inches.

DISTRIBUTION — Introduced from Europe into Hoboken, New Jersey, in 1878 and 1879. Scattered records of this lovely species exist for our north-

eastern states from the dates of its introduction down to 1932 in New Jersey, New York, Massachusetts, and Maine, and possibly other localities. Watch every flock of Goldfinches you see for *a Goldfinch with a red face!* (Family *Fringillidae*)

Eastern Goldfinch
Spinus tristis tristis [529]

ADULT MALE—Brilliant lemon yellow; the crown and forehead, solid black. Wings and tail, black marked with white.

ADULT FEMALE—Upper parts, olive yellowish-brown; wings and tail, brownish-black marked with white as in the male. Under parts, dull yellowish; grayish on the throat and upper breast.

LENGTH—5.10 inches.

DISTRIBUTION—Eastern North America from Labrador and Manitoba southward to Virginia and Missouri and west to the Rocky Mountains. In winter it is found spreading over the entire eastern and southern states from the Rocky Mountains.

Goldfinches are among the last birds of the season to nest, and protract this activity well into the last part of August. The nestlings are fed upon partially digested seeds by regurgitation from the bills of the parents. The process appears to be attended by no very pleasant sensations, if one may judge from the struggles and antics

of the young birds. Goldfinches are extremely gregarious birds; even during the nesting season small groups may be seen swinging over the fields, or caroling together in the tops of tall trees. The birds fly with a bouncing or undulatory flight, and at each dip utter a sweet *teé dee dee.* The song is rollicking and canary-like in character, with many repetitions of an upwardly slurred *swee-swee* syllable. (Family *Fringillidae*)

Green-backed Goldfinch

Spinus psaltria hesperophilus [530a]

Similar to the Arkansas Goldfinch, but with the black upper parts replaced by olive-greenish ones.

DISTRIBUTION—Southeastern North America from southern Oregon and Utah southward to the southern portion of Lower California, and southwestern New Mexico. It winters from

the central portion of California southward to the southern tip of

Lower California. (Family *Fringillidae*)

Lawrence's Goldfinch

Spinus lawrencei [531]

ADULT MALE—Crown, forehead, throat, and space between the eye and the bill, black. The rest of the bird, dark gray, with the middle of the

breast and upper abdomen, yellow. Wings and rump, dull yellowish-green.

ADULT FEMALE—Similar to the male, but duller, and lacking the black head and throat.

LENGTH—4.35 inches.

DISTRIBUTION—West of the Sierra Nevada Mountains in the northern part of California, and southward to Lower California. It spends the winter in the southern part of Arizona, and in New Mexico. (Family *Fringillidae*)

Pale Goldfinch

Spinus tristis pallidus [529a]

Similar to the Eastern Goldfinch, but larger and paler as its name suggests, and with more white in the wings and tail. The chief difference in color of the Pale and the Eastern Goldfinches is more noticeable in the winter than in the summer plumages.

LENGTH—4.65 inches.

DISTRIBUTION—Western North America, from British Columbia and Manitoba southward along the Rocky Mountain region, into northern and eastern Mexico. (Family *Fringillidae*)

Willow Goldfinch

Spinus tristis salicamans [529b]

ADULT MALE—Similar to the Eastern Goldfinch, but with slightly shorter wings and tail, slightly smaller black cap, and slightly paler yellow in the plumage. The wings show very little white.

ADULT FEMALE—Darker than the female Eastern Goldfinch, with a dull olive greenish-yellow throat.

DISTRIBUTION—Along the Pacific Coast of North America, from the State of Washington southward into Lower California. (Family *Fringillidae*)

GOOSE

Barnacle Goose

Branta leucopsis [175]

Similar to the Black Brant, but with the forehead, sides of the head, throat, and chin, white; and the lores, black.

LENGTH—26.00 inches.

DISTRIBUTION—This Old World species has been sparingly reported from Baffin Land, Labrador, James Bay, Quebec, Massachusetts, Ontario, Long Island, Vermont, and North Carolina.

The Barnacle Goose of Europe, called, because of its white cheeks, the White-cheeked Goose, is only a rare straggler to our shores. The Germans call it the Weisswangengans; the Italians, the Oca faccia bianca. It breeds in Spitz-

bergen and eastern Greenland, and migrates to Europe and the British Isles. (Family *Anatidae*)

Bean Goose

Anser fabalis [171.1]

ADULT MALE AND FEMALE—Upper parts, dark brown, the feathers with pale margins. Base of the bill sometimes whitish. Under parts, pale brown marked sparingly with black. Bill, pinkish to salmon-yellow. Legs and feet, black.

LENGTH—About 27.00 inches.

DISTRIBUTION—An accidental straggler in Greenland, having wandered over from northern Europe. (Family *Anatidae*)

Blue Goose

Chen caerulescens [169.1]

ADULT MALE AND FEMALE—Upper back, brownish-gray, the feathers margined with buffy. Lower back, and upper tail coverts, gray. Head and upper neck, white; the central part of the hind neck, sooty or blackish. Entire lower portion of the neck, above and below, brown. Wing coverts, brownish-gray or gray. Wing quills and terials, brown edged with whitish. Under parts, brownish-gray; the feathers edged with buffy, paling off sometimes to white on the lower abdomen.

LENGTH—28.50 inches.

DISTRIBUTION—Found in Canada in the general region of Hudson Bay. In winter it is found on the western coast of the Gulf of Mexico. Has been reported from Florida, Ohio, California, Maine, Massachusetts, Maryland, Virginia, North and South Carolina—but only rarely.

The wintering region of the Blue Goose was not discovered until 1910. And the region of its breeding grounds was unknown until as late as 1929. In

winter, in the delta of the Mississippi, Blue Geese are found in company with Brants, White-fronted, and Snow Geese. Huge flocks occur in winter along the western shores of the Gulf of Mexico. Their breeding and wintering ranges, and their intermediate passage between them, make an interesting study. Chapman says, "Why a species which makes a semi-annual journey over the 2,500 miles between Louisiana and Baffin Land, should be restricted to so small an area in winter, is a mystery." (Family *Anatidae*)

Cackling Goose
Branta canadensis minima [172c]

Similar to the Common Canada Goose, but much smaller; length about twenty-four inches; and with a black or blackish throat and a white collar about the lower part of the neck (similar to the White-cheeked Goose). (Family *Anatidae*)

Common Canada Goose
Branta canadensis canadensis [172]

ADULT MALE AND FEMALE—Back and wings, grayish-brown, the feathers narrowly edged with light-grayish. A broad bib of white from the sides of the head extends across the throat. Chin and head, black. Tail, and the shorter upper tail coverts, black; the longer ones on the side, white. Breast and upper abdomen, grayish, paling to white on the lower abdomen. Sides of body, brownish.

LENGTH—From 35.00 to 45.00 inches.

DISTRIBUTION—In the northern portion of North America, from Labrador, west to Minnesota and British Columbia northward to Alaska. In winter it migrates southward, and spends the colder months from Long Island Sound, New York; Illinois; and British Columbia, southward into Mexico, and across to southern California.

What the migrations of the Stork mean to the Europeans, the migrations of the Canada Goose mean to Americans. "The wild geese are going north," one neighbor will say to another, and immediately "spring fever," with its pleasing unrest and general agreeable disturbance of the whole routine of winter life and thinking, seizes the community. Known as the Wild Goose, the Canada Goose is firmly fixed in the affections of the American people who regard the bird highly both as a harbinger of spring and as an object of gustatory delight on the table. The Canada Goose is more often heard than seen, its deep resonant honking notes coming down out of the twilight sky. The familiar

V-shaped flight pattern is familiar to all watchers of the sky. Cormorants fly in the same way, as do some others. (Family *Anatidae*)

Emperor Goose
Philacte canagica [176]

ADULT MALE AND FEMALE—Plumage, bluish-gray, each feather bearing a small black bar and a white tip. Head and hind neck, white or whitish soiled with rusty-orange; chin and throat, a dusky brownish or blackish.

Tail, white. Bill, small and bluish or pinkish-white; feet, orange.
LENGTH—26.00 inches.
DISTRIBUTION—Along the coast of Alaska, being commonest in the region of Norton Sound and the lower part of the valley of the Yukon River. In winter it moves southward as far as Butte County, California, but is rare in the States. It is said to be the least known, but most beautiful of all the North American Geese. Their bodies are heavier and their necks shorter than those of other Geese, and in their quick wing strokes they resemble the Black Brant in flight. E. W. Nelson reports that as they fly they give voice to a harsh strident *kla-ha, kla-ha, kla-ha,* which is different from the notes of other Geese. The Aleuts of the Aleutian Islands call the birds Beach Geese, and use their skins in the manufacture of wind-proof parkas. (Family *Anatidae*)

Greater Snow Goose
Chen hyperborea atlantica [169a]

Similar to the Lesser Snow Goose, but roughly about ten inches longer.
DISTRIBUTION — In the Arctic regions of eastern North America,

spending the winter on the Atlantic coast from about Maryland south into Cuba. (Family *Anatidae*)

Hutchins's Goose
Branta canadensis hutchinsi [172a]

Similar to the Common Canada Goose, but about eight inches shorter.
DISTRIBUTION—Breeds in the Arctic regions of western North America, and spends its winters from British Columbia and Kansas southwards into Lower California and Mexico. (Family *Anatidae*)

Lesser Canada Goose

Branta canadensis leucopareia [172d]

Similar to the Hutchins's Goose, but without a white blotch before the eye. A white zone begins at the tail and extends forward to the breast. The feet are small.

DISTRIBUTION—From the Arctic shores of Alaska, Yukon, and Mackenzie to Southampton Island. In winter it is found from northern Washington to northern Mexico. (Family *Anatidae*)

Lesser Snow Goose

Chen hyperborea hyperborea [169]

ADULT MALE AND FEMALE—Entire bird, white, except for the primaries which are black, and the primary coverts which are ashy gray.

LENGTH—25.50 inches.

DISTRIBUTION—All along the Arctic coast of North America from east to west, and on the islands of the Arctic Ocean to the north. In winter it is found spread over the western United States west of the Mississippi, and from Illinois southward to the Gulf coast. More rarely it is found along the Atlantic coast from the St. Lawrence River to North Carolina.

This bird is similar to the Greater Snow Goose. In earlier days they were widely distributed over the prairies. Pioneers tell of huge flocks that appeared like local snowstorms in the sky, and whitened the fields over which they alighted. Although the bird is rarely met with on the Atlantic coast, they are common·on the Pacific side of the continent in winter. It is said to be à noisy bird in migration, with a high, rather cackling sort of honk. (Family *Anatidae*)

Pink-footed Goose

Anser brachyrhynchus [171.2]

Somewhat similar to the Bean Goose, but smaller, and grayer on the under parts. The wing coverts are also grayer, and the bill shorter. The legs and feet are pink.

DISTRIBUTION—This northern European species is reported as casual in

Greenland, and accidental in Massachusetts. (Family *Anatidae*)

Ross's Goose

Chen rossi [170]

Similar to the Greater Snow Goose, but very much smaller.

DISTRIBUTION—In Arctic America. In winter it is found along the Pacific

coast as far as southern California, and eastward as far as Montana. (Family *Anatidae*)

Tule Goose

Anser albifrons gambelli [171a]

Similar to the White-fronted Goose, but much larger.

DISTRIBUTION—The breeding range is unknown, but is probably in Arctic

America. It winters in the Sacramento Valley of California. (Family *Anatidae*)

White-cheeked Goose

Branta canadensis occidentalis [172b]

Similar to the Common Canada Goose, but with the throat, black or blackish, and with a white collar about the lower part of the neck.

DISTRIBUTION—"Pacific coast region from Sitka (Alaska), south in winter to California." (A.O.U. Check list.) (Family *Anatidae*)

White-fronted Goose

Anser albifrons albifrons [171]

ADULT MALE AND FEMALE—Upper parts and foreneck, grayish-brown,

marked on the back with light gray. Upper tail coverts like the back but with the longer side feathers, white. Forehead and region about the base of the bill, white. Breast, light grayish-brown, lower breast and abdomen cross-blotched with black. Lower abdomen, pure white. Bill, pink.

LENGTH—28.50 inches.

DISTRIBUTION—From Yukon River in extreme north, eastward to Mackenzie in Arctic America. In winter it is found in western United States from British Columbia south to Texas and

Louisiana, and into west central Mexico. Occurs casually on the Atlantic coast, from Labrador to South Carolina. (Family *Anatidae*)

GOSHAWK

Eastern Goshawk

Astur atricapillus atricapillus [334]

ADULT MALE AND FEMALE—Upper parts, bluish slate-gray; head, blackish. A white line extends over and behind the eye. Inner tail feathers similar in color to the back; the outer ones, brownish and lightly marked with blackish. Tip of tail, whitish. Under parts entirely and finely marked with irregular wavy lines and bars of gray and white. Throat and upper breast slightly streaked with blackish.

LENGTH—22.00 inches. Female slightly larger.

DISTRIBUTION—Confined in summer mostly to Canada, spreading south in winter to southern New Jersey (or rarely into Virginia along the mountains), Missouri, and Kansas; and northwestward into Oregon.

The bluish color of this fine Hawk, its finely marked under parts, its loud

piercing cries, and its swift dashing flight, combined with its rarity in the United States, all make it one of the most attractive subjects of study by students of bird life. Its prey is pursued through the air with dash and vigor, the Hawk turning, dropping, rising, and falling, and thus following precisely in the wake of its fleeing quarry. The chase is usually one of short duration, for few birds can hope to out-maneuver this thunderbolt in feathers. It is one of the most fearless of our birds of prey. (Family *Accipitridae*)

Mexican Goshawk
Asturina plagiata plagiata [346]

ADULT MALE AND FEMALE—Upper parts, ashy gray streaked or barred with blackish. Head, paler; rump, darker. Upper tail coverts, white. Tail,

blackish crossed by two or three wide white bars, and with a white tip. Chin and under tail coverts, white. Rest of under parts finely barred with gray and white.

LENGTH—17.00 inches.

DISTRIBUTION—From southern Arizona, southern New Mexico, and along the lower valley of the Rio Grande in Texas, southward into Guatemala.

This beneficial little Hawk is not a Goshawk at all, except in coloration. Its food consists of very few birds, but is made up chiefly of small injurious rodents and other mammals, as well as lizards, fish, and a goodly proportion of injurious large insects such as beetles and grasshoppers. It is a bird of open and broken country—not deep forests, or wastes and plains—and it seems to have a predilection for stream valleys and wet regions generally. (Family *Accipitridae*)

Western Goshawk
Astur atricapillus striatulus [334a]

Similar to the Eastern Goshawk, but with darker gray upper parts, and with the wavy lines of the under parts much darker and coarser.

DISTRIBUTION — From Alaska to California along the Pacific Coast, and eastward as far as Idaho. (Family *Accipitridae*)

GRACKLE
Boat-tailed Grackle
Cassidix mexicanus major [513]

Similar to the Purple Grackle, but bluish or purplish black, without iri-

descent bars or crescents on the upper parts. Wings and tail, more black. In the female the upper parts are washed with brown or rusty, and the under parts are much lighter.

DISTRIBUTION—From Virginia, southward along the coast into Florida, and westward along the coast to Texas.

A very large Grackle, much like other Grackles, but always found near water. (Family *Icteridae*)

Bronzed Grackle

Quiscalus quiscula aeneus [511b]

ADULT MALE—Plumage, black with iridescent bluish, greenish, and purplish reflections. Tail, long, the central pair of feathers projecting beyond the others.

ADULT FEMALE—Similar to the male, but the plumage washed with brownish. Somewhat smaller than the male.

LENGTH—12.75 inches.

DISTRIBUTION—From just north of Alberta and Saskatchewan, west to the Rocky Mountains, east to the Alleghenies, and southward to southern Texas. Also from Labrador southwest into central New England and New York, and along the Allegheny Mountains into Georgia. It winters in the southern states, mainly in the lower Mississippi Valley.

The Crow Blackbird, as the Grackle is often called, comes early in the spring in great flocks, together with

other members of its family, and gathering in the tree-tops sets up a great chorus of raucous cackling, squawking, and creaking notes. As the great flocks of birds fly high overhead, their call notes, *chucckk,* combine to form a wave of sound, like the rushing of a heavy rainfall. When in flight, the long, keel-shaped tails of Grackles are characteristic. On the ground, the birds walk with a stately tread, and appear much larger and longer, and more graceful than the Starlings. The Bronzed Grackle may be distinguished from its close relative, the Purple Grackle, by the uniform color of the back (without tiny iridescent bars), and by the way in which the head and neck are (in good light) marked off from the rest of the upper parts. Separation of the two subspecies in the field, however, is very difficult. The Bronzed Grackle ranges farther north, and breeds farther north than does the Purple Grackle. In summer, Purple Grackles are found in the central eastern states; and the Bronzed Grackles, from central New England northward. (Family *Icteridae*)

Florida Grackle

Quiscalus quiscula aglaeus [511a]

Similar to the Purple Grackle but smaller, the upper parts iridescent deep greenish, with faint iridescent barrings. Head and neck, deep purplish.

DISTRIBUTION—From Virginia, south along the coast into Florida, and westward along the coast to Texas. (Family *Icteridae*)

Great-tailed Grackle

Cassidix mexicanus mexicanus [513a]

Similar to the Boat-tailed Grackle, but still larger. The male is purplish about the head and neck, and greenish about the rump and abdomen. The female is blacker than the female Boat-tail.

DISTRIBUTION—From eastern Texas southward into Mexico.

Great-tailed Grackles, or Jackdaws as they are called in Texas, are fond of oak growths or "oak motts," where they set up a tremendous squawking, crackling, snapping, squeaking—but also indulge in a variety of sweetly whistled notes. The male often sits in the top of an oak, and there in full view spreads his wings and tail, turning and bowing to attract the attention of the females, and giving voice meanwhile to a crackling, harsh call, followed by several high squeals. (Family *Icteridae*)

Purple Grackle
Quiscalus quiscula quiscula [511]

Similar to the Bronzed Grackle, but head and neck not marked off from the rest of the upper parts, and with tiny iridescent bars or crescents on the back. The female is duller than the male.

DISTRIBUTION—From central New England east of the Allegheny Mountains as far as Georgia, and in the lower part of the Mississippi Valley. In winter it is found from Virginia southward, and in the southern Mississippi Valley.

In notes and habits, similar to the Bronzed Grackle. (Family *Icteridae*)

GRASSQUIT
Bahama Grassquit
Tiaris bicolor bicolor [603]

Somewhat similar to the Melodious Grassquit, but with the head and breast black or blackish; and the back, wings, and tail a dusky greenish.

DISTRIBUTION—This inhabitant of the Bahamas is accidental at Miami, Florida. (Family *Fringillidae*)

Melodious Grassquit
Tiaris canora [603.1]

ADULT MALE AND FEMALE—Upper parts, soiled greenish; under parts,

ashy. Cheeks, dusky. Breast displays a broken yellowish girdle.

LENGTH—About 5.80 inches.

DISTRIBUTION—This Cuban species occurs accidentally on Sombrero Key, off the coast of southern Florida. (Family *Fringillidae*)

GREBE FAMILY
Colymbidae

Grebes are rather small, somewhat duck-like birds, the largest of our North American species being about two feet long. The others are eighteen inches or less. Grebes also resemble squat blunt loons, but have less strikingly patterned plumage. The bills of Grebes are rather short, stout, pointed,

and flattened laterally. The wings are short and never show a bright colored patch or speculum. The tail is very short. The feet are peculiar, bearing three toes which are individually webbed and not joined together as are the toes of ducks and loons. The hind toe is set back from the others and is very small. The nails are short and round. Something over twenty kinds of Grebes are known, of which six occur in North America, allocated to three genera, *Colymbus*, *Aechmophorus*, and *Podylimbus*.

NESTING. The nest of Grebes is broad, shallow, and loosely built up of marsh grasses, rushes, reeds, and other similar marsh vegetation, and then lined with finer materials. Mud is sometimes added. The nest is located in swamps, or in the borders of watery marshes or grassy ponds, or concealed along the ragged edges of marshy lakes. Occasionally a nest is built up on a mass of floating vegetation near the shore. The eggs number from three to five, sometimes as many as seven, or, occasionally ten, according to the species. They are whitish, bluish-white, or grayish, sometimes stained by their contact with decaying vegetation.

GREBE

Eared Grebe
Colymbus nigricollis californicus [4]

ADULT MALE AND FEMALE—Back, blackish; head and neck, black. On each side of the head arises a fan-shaped tuft of soft yellowish-brown feathers. Sides of body, brown; under parts, pure white.

LENGTH—13.00 inches.

DISTRIBUTION—From southern Mackenzie southward over western

North America, east as far as the Mississippi River, and southward into Guatemala. (Family *Colymbidae*)

Holboell's Grebe
Colymbus grisegena holboelli [2]

ADULT MALE AND FEMALE—Back and wings, blackish; wings with a white patch; top of head and back of neck, black. Throat and sides of the head, a soiled or grayish white.

Upper part of neck, brownish-red, darkening on the sides. Breast, white spotted with reddish brown. Abdomen, clear white.

LENGTH—19.00 inches.

DISTRIBUTION—In North America over the entire northern portion as far

south as about the Canadian border, but in the interior only. In winter it is found from Maine and British Columbia to southern California, and across, through Nebraska, to South Carolina. (Family *Colymbidae*)

Horned Grebe
Colymbus auritus [3]

ADULT MALE AND FEMALE—Back and wings, blackish, the wings with a white patch. Top of head and back of neck, black. Back of the eye is a reddish-brown patch, and an extended broad tuft of feathers of the same color. Sides of head and throat, broadly black. Neck, upper breast, and flanks, rich reddish-brown. Abdomen, white. Tail, very short.

LENGTH—13.50 inches.

DISTRIBUTION—The Northern Hemisphere generally as far south in North America as eastern Quebec, northern Illinois and northwestward into British Columbia. In winter it is found in British Columbia across to

Maine, and southward into southern California and the Gulf States.

In the United States, the Horned Grebe is known chiefly as a migrant along the seacoast, and less commonly on inland waters. In all situations, it is not as frequently seen as the Pied-

billed Grebe, and in its winter plumage somewhat resembles this species. In breeding plumage, it is a strikingly lovely sight as it floats on a quiet body of water, whose smooth surface reflects the rich chestnut-and-black head and neck. (Family *Colymbidae*)

Mexican Grebe

Colymbus dominicus brachypterus [5]

ADULT MALE AND FEMALE—Back, dull greenish-black; top of head, chin, and throat, blackish. Sides of head and neck, leaden gray. Under parts mottled with blackish and silvery white. Bill, black tipped with white.

LENGTH—7.00 inches. The smallest of our American Grebes.

DISTRIBUTION—From Lower California and southern Texas, south to Panama.

A common Grebe on the ponds of southern Texas and Lower California, usually keeping close to the shore under cover of over-arching branches and among the sedges and water-lily pads. When fishing they spread out into the open water, where they bob up and down upon the little waves like so many fish-floats. They are fre-

quently called the Least, or Little Grebe. (Family *Colymbidae*)

Pied-Billed Grebe

Podilymbus podiceps podiceps [6]

ADULT MALE AND FEMALE—Top of head, back, wings, and tail, dark grayish-brown. Sides of head, gray. Neck and breast, brownish. Middle of throat, black. Bill, whitish with a black band encircling it. Abdomen, whitish. Neck, rather long; body, rounded; tail short.

LENGTH—13.50 inches.

DISTRIBUTION — Generally distributed through North America from northern Canada to Florida and Texas. In winter it is found from New York, New Jersey, and southern British Columbia southward. Occasionally it occurs in Bermuda.

The funny little Pied-billed Grebe (sometimes called the Hell-diver or Dabchick) breeds in quiet ponds, lakes, lagoons, the embayments of languid rivers, along the marshy shores, and among the sedges. In diving and swimming, it is most expert. It is claimed by many a hunter that the bird dives, and thus escapes the pursuing bullet, after the trigger has been

pulled. Fish constitute a large part of its diet, supplemented with crayfish, salamanders, small frogs, and aquatic insects. Grebes often sink their bodies in the water until only the head is visible, and thus quietly float or swim slowly and inconspicuously. (Family *Colymbidae*)

Western Grebe
Aechmophorus occidentalis [1]

ADULT MALE AND FEMALE—Back, slaty gray; top of head and a band

down the back of the neck to the back, black. Side of head and throat, neck, and under parts, pure glistening white. Head without crests; bill, long, slender, and sharp. A very graceful, slender, svelte bird.

LENGTH—26.50 inches.

DISTRIBUTION—From British Columbia and Alberta southward to central Mexico, and from the Pacific Coast eastward to Manitoba. (Family *Colymbidae*)

GROSBEAK
Alaska Pine Grosbeak
Pinicola enucleator alascensis [515c]

Similar to the Canadian Pine Grosbeak, but larger, with a shorter bill, and with paler plumage throughout.

DISTRIBUTION—The Alaska Pine Grosbeak is found in the interior of Alaska during its breeding season, but with the approach of winter it passes into the region of eastern British Columbia and Montana. (Family *Fringillidae*)

Black-headed Grosbeak
Hedymeles melanocephalus melanocephalus [596]

ADULT MALE—Upper parts, black, with a broad collar, rump, streaks on the back, a line behind the eye, and through the crown, all cinnamon-brown. Wings, black mottled with white and bearing two white bars. Tips of outer tail feathers, white. Under parts, cinnamon-brown, shading to a lemon-yellow on the abdomen. Bill, large, heavy, and conical.

ADULT FEMALE — Upper parts, blackish-brown streaked with pale brown; collar, whitish brown. Under parts, light brown with a yellowish wash. Sides of the body, dark streaked.

LENGTH—8.10 inches.

DISTRIBUTION — From the Great Plains westward, and from British Columbia and North Dakota south to Mexico. It winters in Mexico.

In call-notes and habits the Black-headed Grosbeak is similar to the eastern Rose-breasted Grosbeak, but its

song, while in general like the Rose-breast's strain, is fuller, clearer, slightly more rapid, and on the whole, more melodious. (Family *Fringillidae*)

California Blue Grosbeak
Guiraca caerulea salicaria [597b]

Similar in general to the Eastern Blue Grosbeak.

DISTRIBUTION—Common in central and Lower California in the willows along streams. (Family *Fringillidae*)

California Pine Grosbeak
Pinicola enucleator californica [515b]

In general similar to the Canadian Pine Grosbeak. The upper parts of the male are a uniform unmarked gray, and the red portions of the plumage are more brilliant. In the female, the greenish hue on the rump is faint, or is lacking altogether.

In habits, and notes, the California Pine Grosbeak resembles closely the other members of its genus. (Family *Fringillidae*)

Canadian Pine Grosbeak
Pinicola enucleator leucura [515]

ADULT MALE—Rosy red plumage, brightest on the head and rump. Middle of the back marked with black. Wings, slaty brown with two white bars; tail, brownish and prominently notched. Bill, short and thick.

ADULT FEMALE—Grayish plumage, with head, breast, and rump, grayish-green. Wings, tail, and bill as in the male.

LENGTH—9.08 inches.

DISTRIBUTION—Northeastern North America south as far as New Brunswick, Canada, and northern New England. It straggles irregularly southward in winter, reaching the southern parts of New England and New York, and is also found infrequently in Manitoba, Canada; Ohio; Kansas; and as far south as Washington, D. C.

Large, heavy, and deliberate in all their movements, the Pine Grosbeaks move gravely about in small flocks among the twigs and branches, especially of coniferous trees, in search of buds, small fruits, or the seeds of cones. In such situations the brilliant rosy red of the males shows startlingly against the dark green of spruces or pines. Here also, the subdued colors of the females render them particularly inconspicuous. Pine Grosbeaks are singularly unwary birds, and allow the close approach of an observer. While feeding they utter to one another a continuous, sweet, subdued, ingenuous twitter; but when alarmed, give vent to an abrupt whistled call,

whee-tee; whee-tee tee, a note used also during flight. When flushed, they launch into the air to the accompaniment of an abrupt, trilled *prrrt.* Another common note is a loud *teeurr,* like the suppressed call of a Blue Jay.

On the sides of the higher mountains of New England, and on their

more northern breeding grounds, Pine Grosbeaks give forth a sweet, prolonged, warbled strain, reminiscent of the song of the Purple Finch. (Family *Fringillidae*)

Eastern Blue Grosbeak
Guiraca caerulea caerulea [597]

ADULT MALE—Deep indigo blue (appearing black in most lights). Blackish about the sides and base of the bill. Back marked with irregular black streaks. Wings, blackish, the feathers edged with blue and bearing one wide and one narrow brown bar. Bill, short, heavy, and conical.

ADULT FEMALE—Upper parts, grayish-brown, sometimes washed on the head, rump, and shoulder (or wrist) region with bluish. The wings bear two light buffy bars. Under parts, light brownish-gray.

LENGTH—7.00 inches.

DISTRIBUTION—Over the eastern portion of the United States from the latitude of Maryland and southern Illinois, to the Gulf of Mexico. It sometimes straggles as far north as Quebec, and has been recorded on the mountains of New England. It winters in Mexico and Central America.

Blue Grosbeaks often sit motionless for long periods of time on the topmost twig of a bush or low tree, somewhat

after the manner of Cowbirds, and when in such situations, and seen against the bright white light of the sky, reveal not a vestige of their deep indigo color. Because their general appearance is like that of Cowbirds, they may often be mistaken for them. Blue Grosbeaks haunt bushy country, thickets, and the alders and low willows along streams, or may be found on mountain sides among scrubby growths, or in old forest clearings where sproutlings are repopulating the lumbered areas. The song of the Blue Grosbeak is reminiscent of the Purple Finch, but is fainter, sweeter, clearer, with fewer overtones, and on the whole is more pleasing and melodious. (Family *Fringillidae*)

Eastern Evening Grosbeak

Hesperiphona vespertina vespertina
[514]

ADULT MALE—Upper parts, olive-brownish with a yellowish wash on the rump. Forehead, and line over the eye, yellow. Shoulders (wrists), lower breast, and abdomen, bright yellow. Wings, black; the ends of the secondaries showing pure white; tail, black. Bill, unusually large, heavy, and a dull yellow.

ADULT FEMALE—Duller than the male. The head, grayish; the throat, white. Abdomen, white; rest of the under parts, grayish-yellow. Bill, similar to that of male.

LENGTH—8.00 inches.

DISTRIBUTION—Northwestern North America, in the Rocky Mountain area of British Columbia. In winter the birds pass southward to region of the upper Mississippi Valley, sometimes to Ohio, and sometimes straggling east into New York and New England.

During their winter visits to the United States, the Evening Grosbeaks are quiet, unsuspicious birds, usually keeping together in small flocks and appearing day after day in the same

locality where food is abundant. Their large size, yellow plumage, and huge beaks, make them very showy and attractive birds. (Family *Fringillidae*)

Kamchatka Pine Grosbeak

Pinicola enucleator kamtschatkensis
[515f]

In general coloration similar to the Canadian Pine Grosbeak, but with the feathers of the upper breast not quite so rosy, or the effect somewhat subdued by the fact that the feathers are enclosed by narrow borders of ashy gray. The rosy color does not extend as far as to the sides of the abdomen.

DISTRIBUTION—Occurs as an accidental visitor on St. George Island, in the Pribilof Group, Alaska. (Family *Fringillidae*)

Kodiak Pine Grosbeak

Pinicola enucleator flammula [515d]

Similar to the Canadian Pine Grosbeak, but with a shorter bill—its upper mandible with a more pronounced hook at the tip. The wings and tail are a grayish brown.

DISTRIBUTION—This Grosbeak is confined to the Kodiak Island, and ranges southward on the coast as far as Sitka, Alaska. (Family *Fringillidae*)

Queen Charlotte Pine Grosbeak

Pinicola enucleator carlottae [515e]

The smallest and darkest of all the American Pine Grosbeaks, and with a much shorter tail.

DISTRIBUTION—On the Queen Charlotte Islands of British Columbia. (Family *Fringillidae*)

Rocky Mountain Grosbeak

Hedymeles melanocephalus papago [596a]

Similar to the Black-headed Grosbeak, but larger. Wings and tail longer, bill heavier, and stripe back of the eye usually absent.

DISTRIBUTION—In western North America from the southern part of Saskatchewan, southeastward to eastern Idaho, Nevada, and south to western Arizona, western Texas, and northern Mexico. East to Nebraska, North Dakota, and Kansas. (Family *Fringillidae*)

Rocky Mountain Pine Grosbeak

Pinicola enucleator montana [515a]

Similar to the Canadian Pine Grosbeak, but larger and somewhat darker,

and with the red bearing a deeper carmine tinge.

DISTRIBUTION—From Montana and Idaho southward through the Rocky Mountain region, as far as New Mexico. (Family *Fringillidae*)

Rose-breasted Grosbeak

Hedymeles ludovicianus [595]

ADULT MALE—Head, throat, and upper back, black. Wings and tail, black spotted with white. Lower back, white. Breast, bright rosy red; abdomen, white. The lining of the wings shows a pinkish flush when the bird is in flight. The bill is unusually thick and heavy, hence the name Grosbeak.

ADULT FEMALE—Brown where the male is black, with back and breast heavily streaked with dark brown. Line over the eye, and wing-bar, white. Line through center of the crown, white. Lining of the wings tinged with orange-pink. Bill is same as in the male, but lighter in color.

LENGTH—8.12 inches.

DISTRIBUTION — Eastern North America, from Nova Scotia and Manitoba west to the Great Plains, and south to northern New Jersey, northern Ohio, and northern Indiana, and southward along the higher Allegheny Mountains into North Carolina. It winters in Central and South America.

The contrast between jet black, clear white, and bright rosy red, which this lovely Grosbeak exhibits in full sunlight, causes even experienced observers to exclaim with delight. The birds fly with a heavy, flippy, labored motion, and in the spring often remain together in small flocks. They take kindly to the tall trees of city parks, and are altogether one of our most desirable urban birds. This is especially true in consideration of their song, which is a loud, cheerful lay, poured forth from the top of some tall tree, and resembling somewhat the song of the Robin, but not so perceptibly divided into phrases and given as an almost continuous, loud, clear, rapid, heavy warble. Burroughs has described

the bird, in its singing, as a "glorified Robin," and this happy characterization cannot be amended. The call note is peculiar—a sharp, high squeak, like the sound made by a pair of large rusty shears. (Family *Fringillidae*)

Western Blue Grosbeak

Guiraca caerulea interfusa [597a]

Similar to the Eastern Blue Grosbeak, but with the male bird larger, and a brighter blue; and with the female grayer.

DISTRIBUTION—In western United States, from Kansas, southern Nebraska, Colorado, and northern California, southward into Mexico. It winters in Mexico and Central America. (Family *Fringillidae*)

Mexican Evening Grosbeak

Hesperiphona vespertina montana [514a]

Western Evening Grosbeak

Hesperiphona vespertina brooksi [514b]

These two Grosbeaks, confined to the extreme western states and the Pacific Coast, are virtually similar to the eastern species. (Family *Fringillidae*)

GROUSE FAMILY
Grouse and Ptarmigans
Tetraonidae

The members of this large family are all "hen-like" birds; terrestrial; with short stout bills possessing a rounded upper edge or culmen; with stout legs and feet, the hind toe being short and elevated above the ground. When flushed they spring up into the air and dart away with amazing speed for such heavy birds. As they go, the rapid vibration of their short, stiff, rigid, rounded wings produces a startling, almost machine-like *whirrrrrrrrr*. The young, upon hatching, are thickly covered with fine heavy down, protectively colored, and run about ac-

tively shortly after their emergence from the shell, zealously guarded by the female. *Tetraonid* birds are distributed over the northern portions of both eastern and western hemispheres. In North America there are seven members of the genus *Dendragapus;* five of the genus *Canachites;* six of the genus *Bonasa;* twenty of the genus *Lagopus;* four of the genus *Tympanuchus;* three of the genus *Pediocetes;* and one of the genus *Centrocus*—forty-six representatives of the family in all.

NESTING. Grouse and Ptarmigans nest on the ground, on a slight depression, the nest itself being composed either of only a few feathers, grasses, etc., lining the depression; or else a somewhat thicker structure made with the addition of a few sticks, leaves, weed stems, and the like.

The eggs are numerous, from six to twelve, fifteen, or more; sometimes plain in color, sometimes (as in the Ptarmigans) blotched or spotted.

GROUSE
Alaska Spruce Grouse
Canachites canadensis osgoodi [298b]

Similar to the Hudsonian Spruce Grouse, but with the feathers of the upper back margined with light brownish-gray. The female is paler throughout.
DISTRIBUTION—Confined to Alaska. (Family *Tetraonidae*)

Canada Ruffed Grouse
Bonasa umbellus togata [300a]

Similar to the Eastern Ruffed Grouse, but a darker gray—less brown—on the upper parts; the tail similar, and the bars on the under parts darker and more prominent.
DISTRIBUTION—Found in the spruce forests of Nova Scotia, New Brunswick, Maine, northern New Hampshire, also on the higher mountains of New England where spruce forests occur, and in northern New York. This subspecies is the typical grouse of these northern regions, where wilder more forested country is found. Westward it ranges to the eastern slopes of the Coast Ranges in British Columbia, Washington, and Oregon. (Family *Tetraonidae*)

Canada Spruce Grouse
Canachites canadensis canace [298c]

The male is similar to the male of the Hudsonian Spruce Grouse, but the female has rustier brown upper parts, with the brown bars darker in color and more prominent on the back and on the flanks.
DISTRIBUTION—From Nova Scotia

and Quebec westward to northern Minnesota, and southward into north-

ern New England and northern New York. (Family *Tetraonidae*)

Columbian Sharp-tailed Grouse
Pedioecetes phasianellus columbianus [308a]

Similar to the Northern Sharp-tailed Grouse, but with the upper parts more generally light yellowish-brown or buffy.
DISTRIBUTION — "Northwestern United States; south to northeastern California, northern Nevada and Utah; east to Montana and Wyoming, west to Oregon and Washington; north, chiefly west of the Rocky Mountains, and through British Columbia to central Alaska (Fort Yukon)." (Bendire.) (Family *Tetraonidae*)

Dusky Grouse
Dendragapus obscurus obscurus [297]

ADULT MALE—Upper parts dusky slate-color, with a bluish cast, finely mottled with grays and browns. Wings lighter, and browner, the hinder scapulars somewhat spotted and streaked with white. Tail, blackish, its tip bearing a wide bluish gray band. Under parts slaty-brown or gray, marked with white on the sides of the neck, sides of the upper breast, and flanks.
ADULT FEMALE—Similar to the male, but smaller. The upper parts, breast, and sides of the body are mottled with dark brown and light yellowish-brown.

LENGTH—21.50 inches.

DISTRIBUTION—From Idaho and Montana southward along the Rocky Mountains into Arizona and New Mexico, and from the East Humboldt Mountains of Nevada eastward to the Black Hills of South Dakota.

Like the Canada Spruce Grouse, this present bird is singularly unsuspicious

and trustful of human beings. Among local hunters, this characteristic has earned for the unfortunate bird the name of "Fool Hen." (Family *Tetraonidae*)

Eastern Ruffed Grouse
Bonasa umbellus umbellus [300]

ADULT MALE—Upper parts, reddish-brown or grayish-brown streaked with black. The sides of the neck bear large tufts of glossy greenish or bluish-black feathers. Tail, broad, reddish-brown or grayish-brown, and crossed near its tip by a broad band of black. Before and behind this band is a light grayish or whitish one. Throat, buffy; the rest of the under parts, white tinged with buffy and barred with blackish-brown. Sides of the body more heavily barred with the same color.

ADULT FEMALE—Similar to the male, but smaller. Neck tufts much reduced or virtually absent.

LENGTH—17.00 inches.

DISTRIBUTION—From Massachusetts westward to New York, Michigan, Wisconsin, and Minnesota, and south to eastern Kansas and northern Arkansas, to Missouri, Tennessee, and Virginia, and along the higher Appalachian Mountains into northern Georgia and northern Alabama.

The Ruffed Grouse, or Partridge as it is familiarly called in New England, is perhaps our most celebrated game bird. It is strictly a forest bird, seldom or never appearing in the open, broken, farmland country. It is at home in mountains, swamps, extensive forests, and in moderate woodlands. Its startling, thunderous WHUR-R-R-R-R-RRRR, as it springs aloft from the side of the forest trail, has caused many a heart to skip a beat, and many a breath to remain for a moment undrawn. The female often flops, tumbles, and limps away

with shrill whining cries if the young are too closely approached, a ruse which often succeeds in luring the walker away from her silent cowering bevy of yellowish-brown downy chicks. The drumming of the male—his call to a mate—is a deep, booming roll, that thumps upon the ears like great heartbeats, increasing in rapidity until, with a soft subdued, continuous deep tremor of sound, it trembles into silence. The sound is produced by the bird's wings beating the air, and thus setting vibrations in sequence—not by the wings striking an object. This seductive drum-beat is given usually from some favorite perch, commonly the top of a large prostrate log, and is sent forth upon the vibrant air not only in spring, but also—though less frequently—in the autumn and winter. Grouse roost in trees, and in the winter sometimes burrow beneath the soft snow for warmth and protection from high chilling winds. The female bird, as well as the male, gives voice to numerous mewing, clucking sounds, not unlike those uttered by barnyard fowls. (Family *Tetraonidae*)

Fleming's Grouse
Dendragapus obscurus flemingi [297d]

Similar to the Richardson's Grouse, but without the terminal tail band, and with the general coloration darker in tone than that of the Sooty Grouse.

DISTRIBUTION—Southern portion of Yukon territory, northern British Columbia, and into southwestern Mackenzie. (Family *Tetraonidae*)

Franklin's Grouse
Canachites franklini [299]

Similar to the Hudsonian Spruce Grouse, but with the tail lacking the brown tips, and sometimes tipped with white.

DISTRIBUTION—From the Pacific Coast of southern Alaska southward through the northern Rocky Mountains to northwestern Montana and the Coast Ranges of Oregon and Washington. (Family *Tetraonidae*)

Gray Ruffed Grouse
Bonasa umbellus umbelloides [300b]

Similar to the Eastern Ruffed Grouse, but very much grayer on the upper parts, including the crown.

DISTRIBUTION—From about the middle portion of Alaska eastward to Mackenzie and western Manitoba, and down along the Rocky Mountains to Colorado. (Family *Tetraonidae*)

Hudsonian Spruce Grouse
Canachites canadensis canadensis [298]

ADULT MALE—Upper parts wavily barred with black and gray. Tail, black with a broad terminal band of orange-brown. Shoulders and wing coverts marked with white. Head and neck, gray; lores, white; a patch of bare skin over the eye, bright yellow or reddish. Chin and throat, broadly jet black bordered with white. Breast, same. Abdomen, white with broad markings of black.

ADULT FEMALE — Upper parts, brown marked with yellowish-brown and transversely barred with black. Lores and throat patch, whitish. Under parts, whitish mixed with yellowish-brown, especially on the breast, and marked with wavy black bars. Flanks and sides of body streaked with white. Tail mottled with light yellowish-brown, and narrowly tipped with orange-brown.

LENGTH—17.00 inches.

DISTRIBUTION—From the eastern side of the Rocky Mountains of Alberta eastward to Labrador, also in Alaska from Prince William Sound, southern Alaska, northward to Bristol Bay, north of the Alaskan Peninsula.

The Hudsonian Spruce Grouse has been hunted so persistently that it is now restricted to the northern wildernesses. It occurs in only a few of our northern states, in most of which it is now almost, if indeed not quite extinct. It bears the unenviable distinction of being our stupidest bird. Forbush writes of it, "In its native wilds this bird exhibits the most charming confidence in mankind. The hunters know it as the champion fool among birds. The Indian boy shoots it with a blunt-headed arrow, or even knocks it down with a stick as it walks by unconcernedly or sits on a limb regarding the intruder with happy curiosity. Full grown birds have been

caught in the hand or beheaded with a switch. As civilization approaches, the Spruce Partridge disappears, for man destroys every wild creature that confides in him." (Family *Tetraonidae*)

Mount Pinos Grouse

Dendragapus fuliginosus howardi [297f]

Similar to the Sierra Grouse, but with the upper parts paler, and more dis-

tinctly barred, and with less white on the flanks.

DISTRIBUTION—In southern California on Mt. Pinos, and eastward through Tehechapi Range, and north through the Sierra Nevada to about

the region of Capital Peak (latitude 36°). (Family *Tetraonidae*)

Northern Sharp-tailed Grouse

Pedioecetes phasianellus phasianellus [308]

ADULT MALE—Upper parts, brown irregularly marked and barred with black. Neck tufts absent. Outer side of primaries spotted with white. Middle tail feathers about an inch longer than the lateral ones, and marked with brown and black. Throat, light brownish; breast marked with black V's. Sides of body irregularly spotted and barred heavily with black and brown. Middle of abdomen white.

ADULT FEMALE—Similar to the male but smaller, and with the middle tail feathers shorter.

LENGTH—17.50 inches.

DISTRIBUTION—From the central portion of Alaska to Manitoba, and

eastward to northern Quebec; southward to Lake Superior, and the Parry Sound district of Ontario. Occurs casually eastward as far as the Saguenay River, Quebec.

The Northern Sharp-tailed Grouse, also called the Pin-tail, Sprig-tail, or Spike-tail, is the darker, more northern representative of the Sharp-tails, with habits similar to those described for the Prairie Sharp-tailed Grouse. (Family *Tetraonidae*)

Nova Scotia Ruffed Grouse
Bonasa umbellus thayeri [300d]

Similar to the Canadian Ruffed Grouse, but with the upper parts less grayish, darker, and with a more sooty tone; and with the entire under parts (except the throat) heavily and regularly banded with dusky.

DISTRIBUTION—"Nova Scotia and probably eastern New Brunswick." (A.O.U. Check List.) (Family *Tetraonidae*)

Oregon Ruffed Grouse
Bonasa umbellus sabini [300c]

Similar to the Eastern Ruffed Grouse, but with the upper parts a much darker, rustier brown.

DISTRIBUTION—From British Columbia southward through the Coast Ranges as far as the latitude of Cape Mendocino, Humboldt County, northern California. (Family *Tetraonidae*)

Prairie Sharp-tailed Grouse
Pedioecetes phasianellus campestris [308b]

Similar to the Northern Sharp-tailed Grouse, but with the prevailing hue of the upper parts a more bright rusty brown.

DISTRIBUTION—Found in the plains and prairie regions of the United States and Canada, from Manitoba, Wisconsin, and northern Illinois, west to eastern Colorado, and southward into the eastern portion of New Mexico. (Family *Tetraonidae*)

Richardson's Grouse
Dendragapus obscurus richardsoni [297b]

Similar to the Sooty Grouse, but with the tail band either absent or very faint, and never showing beneath.

DISTRIBUTION — Rocky Mountain region (chiefly eastern slopes) from British Columbia to central Montana, northern Wyoming, and southeastern Idaho. (Family *Tetraonidae*)

Sierra Grouse
Dendragapus fuliginosus sierrae [297c]

Somewhat similar to the Dusky Grouse, but the back not so black, and more heavily marked with browns and grays; the white tufts on the neck are either very inconspicuous, or absent altogether, and the feathers on the sides of the body, the flanks, and the under tail coverts show less white. The middle tail feathers are more heavily marked with gray or brownish-gray, and the band across the end of the tail is narrower and more speckled with blackish.

DISTRIBUTION—From central Klamath County (just north of Klamath Lake), southern Oregon, southward through the Sierra Nevada as far as Mt. Pinos in southern California. (Family *Tetraonidae*)

Sitka Grouse
Dendragapus fuliginosus sitkensis [297e]

The male of this subspecies is not appreciably different from the male of the Sooty Grouse, but the female differs in being more of a reddish-brown in the general tone of the plumage.

DISTRIBUTION—Restricted to various islands off the southeastern coast of Alaska (with the exception of Prince of Wales Island), Queen Charlotte and Porcher islands. (Family *Tetraonidae*)

Sooty Grouse
Dendragapus fuliginosus fuliginosus [297a]

Similar to the Dusky Grouse, but somewhat darker, and with the grayish band of the middle tail feather less than an inch in width.

DISTRIBUTION—"Northwest Coast

Mountains from California to Sitka [Alaska], east to Nevada, western

Idaho, and portions of British Columbia." (A.O.U. Check List.) (Family *Tetraonidae*)

Valdez Spruce Grouse
Canachites canadensis atratus [298d]

Similar to the Alaskan Spruce Grouse, but with the plumage in general uniformly darker; the white markings not so extensive; the black ones expanded; and with the grays suffused with a more olive tone.

DISTRIBUTION—Along the coastal region of southeastern Alaska. (Family *Tetraonidae*)

Yukon Ruffed Grouse
Bonasa umbellus yukonensis [300e]

This is the largest and palest of all the Ruffed Grouse group. It is most nearly like the Gray Ruffed Grouse in coloration, but the general tone of the light-colored parts of the plumage is more ashy, and the pattern of the dark markings is finer.

DISTRIBUTION—From Alaska southeastward into the interior of Yukon Territory, Canada. (Family *Tetraonidae*)

GUILLEMOT
Black Guillemot
Cepphus grylle grylle [27]

ADULT MALE AND FEMALE—Upper parts, sooty black with faint greenish reflections. Lesser wing coverts, and terminal halves of the greater coverts, white. Basal half of the greater coverts, black. Under parts, sooty and slightly lighter than the upper parts. Feet, webbed.

LENGTH—13.00 inches.

DISTRIBUTION—From central Labrador south to Nova Scotia and Maine. In winter it is found from Cumberland Sound to Cape Cod, and, casually, to the coast of New Jersey.

The Black Guillemot or Sea Pigeon may be recognized, as it sits upright and squatted on its broad webbed feet and short tail, by the large area of white in the upper or "shoulder" portion of the wing. In the United States it is found on rocky islands off the northern coast of Maine. In winter it

spreads slightly southward along the New England coast. It floats on the water in a duck-like manner, diving now and then, and at this season at a distance the general effect is white or whitish, the black bill being very conspicuous. (Family *Alcidae*)

Mandt's Guillemot
Cepphus grylle mandti [28]

Similar to the Black Guillemot, but with the bases of the greater wing covert feathers white instead of black.

DISTRIBUTION—From the coasts and islands of the Arctic regions southward to the northern part of Hudson Bay, James Bay, and to Siberia. In winter it occurs from the Arctic Ocean southward, casually to Norton Sound, southern Quebec, and to Lake Ontario, and accidentally to New Brunswick. (Family *Alcidae*)

Pigeon Guillemot
Cepphus columba [29]

ADULT MALE AND FEMALE—Entire plumage, black, except at the base of the wing, where a large white patch partially encloses a black triangle. Feet, bright red; bill, black.

LENGTH—13.50 inches.

DISTRIBUTION—From the Aleutian Islands southward along the Pacific Coast of North America as far south as southern California.

Pigeon Guillemots squat like ducks on the rocks, motionless, until as a bird wheels in from the sea they rise, open their bills, and welcome the voyager with a whistling cry. Bailey reports

that Nelson, in Alaska, "found the Pigeon Guillemot one of the most abundant of the larger water birds, occurring wherever the coast was bordered by bold headlands, or where there were precipitous islands. He says that their bright red legs and white wing patches make them very conspicuous. They are graceful swimmers,

and have the amusing habit of putting their heads under water and paddling along their headless bodies." (Family *Alcidae*)

GULL FAMILY
Gulls and Terns
Laridae

This large family contains about one hundred species, of which roughly half are Gulls and half are Terns. Terns are slender, long-winged, long-tailed

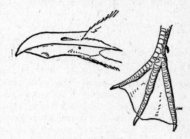

birds with slender pointed bills, and are graceful and light in the air— some species being known as sea-swallows. Their plumage is chiefly gray and white, with some black. Terns are birds of the seacoasts and are seldom found far from land. Some species nest inland, however, and are found on lakes.

Gulls are heavier-bodied and larger than Terns. Their bills are heavy, strong, and hooked. Like the Terns, their feet are webbed. The wings are long and slender, and the plumage chiefly white, gray, brown, with some black. Their tails are square. Unlike Terns they often roost on the water in large, closely-compacted flocks. Unlike Terns they do not plunge into the water to secure living prey with their bills, but feed from the surface upon any sort of soft organic matter which they can suck down. They are birds of oceans and bays, often following ships for long distances feeding upon whatever is edible that is thrown overboard. In our bays they form a most valuable corps of scavengers, keeping the surface of the water free from offensive offal. They also feed upon the eggs and young of other birds, which nest near them. Some gulls are found on inland bodies of water. Of the one hundred or so species of Gulls and Terns distributed throughout the world, twenty-seven species and subspecies of Gulls are found in North America, contained in five genera. Nineteen species and subspecies of Terns are similarly found, contained in six genera.

NESTING. These birds nest on the ground, on cliffs, sandy beaches, flats, or bars, or in a salt marsh, or along the marshy borders of a lake; and infrequently in trees. The nests themselves are composed of seaweeds, rushes, splinters, sticks, weed stems, and materials of this general nature, and are lined with mosses, lichens, grasses, and sometimes a few feathers, and are either bulky or scanty in volume. The Bonaparte's Gull's nest is in a tree from four to twenty feet high, or less commonly on a stump or log, or in low bushes; and is composed of sticks, twigs, and leaves, lined with moss and feathers. The eggs of *Larids* are from one to three, sometimes four, rarely five. They are creamy brown, greenish, or bluish, to olive and darker brown, and spotted, scrawled, or blotched with various shades of grays, browns, olives, chestnut, or lavender.

GULL
Black-headed Gull
Larus ridibundus ridibundus [55.1]

Similar to the Bonaparte's Gull, but larger, with a slightly paler back, a grayish wash on the under side of the wings, and a red bill. Sometimes the birds exhibit a rosy suffusion on the breast.

DISTRIBUTION—A European Gull, breeding "from the Faroes and Scandinavia east to western Siberia, and south to the Mediterranean. Winters in North Africa, the Canaries, the Azores, India, China, Japan, and the Philippines. Casual in Iceland; accidental in Greenland, Massachusetts, . . . Mexico, . . . and Barbadoes." (A.O.U. Check List.)

Black-headed Gulls are usually found, on our side of the Atlantic, in company with flocks of the Bonaparte's Gulls. (Family *Laridae*)

Bonaparte's Gull
Larus philadelphia [60]

ADULT MALE AND FEMALE—Head black; back and wings pearl gray, the outer wing feathers white almost to

their tips; tips black. Tail and under parts white. Bill black. Feet deep orange-red.

LENGTH—14.00 inches.

DISTRIBUTION—From northwestern Alaska and northern Mackenzie south to British Columbia and central Alberta. In winter it is found from Maine and Massachusetts to Florida; along the Gulf coast as far south as Yucatan; and along the Pacific coast from southeastern Alaska to Lower California, and to western Mexico.

This graceful and dainty little gull often feeds in small flocks, fluttering about lightly and easily, more after the manner of a tern than of a heavy gull. It is far less wary than the Herring or the Ring-billed Gulls, and like these is often seen on lakes and rivers as well as on freshly plowed fields; in the latter situations searching for insects. In its breeding plumage the black head distinguishes it from all other gulls except the Laughing, the Franklin's, and the Sabine's Gulls. From these it may be separated by its white, black-tipped outer wing feathers. (Family *Laridae*)

California Gull

Larus californicus [53]

Similar to the Ring-billed Gull, but larger, and bearing a larger white spot on the outer primary, nearer its tip. Also shows a red spot near the tip of the lower mandible.

LENGTH—21.50 inches.

DISTRIBUTION—In western North America from Alaska south into Mexico.

This is more of an inland Gull than our common Herring Gull, and frequents lakes and rivers, more often than seashores. Hundreds of them have been seen following ploughs, to feast on the larvae of beetles, and other forms turned out into the light of day. (Family *Laridae*)

Franklin's Gull

Larus pipixcan [59]

Similar to the Laughing Gull, but with a well-defined, uneven black band across the tip of the wing (i.e. across the tips of the first five primaries). In the Laughing Gull the black tip of the wing grades evenly into the gray of the rest, without definite demarcation.

LENGTH—14.25 inches.

DISTRIBUTION—In the interior prairie regions of North America, from south central Manitoba, Sas-

katchewan, and Alberta, southward to Minnesota, Utah, and formerly Iowa. In winter it is found along the coast from Louisiana to Chile. "Accidental in Colorado, Ontario, Ohio, Illinois, Michigan, Massachusetts, New Brunswick, California, Lesser Antilles, and Hawaii." (A.O.U. Check List.) Rarely occurs on the coasts, except the Pacific Coast of South America in winter. (Family *Laridae*)

Glaucous Gull

Larus hyperboreus [42]

ADULT MALE AND FEMALE—Back and wings, pale pearl gray; primaries, light gray. Head, neck, tail, and under parts, white. Bill, rather large.

LENGTH—28.00 inches.

DISTRIBUTION—Northern parts of North America, south to the latitude of Labrador. In winter it is found as far south as Long Island, the Great Lakes, and middle California. It is not common in the United States.

From the Iceland Gull, which the present species closely resembles, it may be distinguished by its somewhat

greater size, but principally by its longer and heavier bill. The Glaucous Gull might also be termed the raucous gull, for its voice is loud and harsh. (Family *Laridae*)

Glaucous-winged Gull
Larus glaucescens [44]

ADULT MALE AND FEMALE—Back, light pearl gray; primaries, slightly darker gray with white tips. Head, neck, tail, and under parts, pure white.

LENGTH—25.72 inches.

DISTRIBUTION—Bering Sea. In winter it migrates southward as far as the southern coast of California, and to Japan.

In winter the Glaucous-winged Gulls are common in San Francisco and Monterey bays, California. They often fly far up the rivers during the season when salmon are running, to feed on the dead fish, and also congregate about the salmon canneries to feed on the offal. (Family *Laridae*)

Great Black-backed Gull
Larus marinus [47]

ADULT MALE AND FEMALE—Back and wings, dark slate-color, almost black. Wing feathers tipped with white. Head, neck, tail, and under parts, pure white.

LENGTH—29.00 inches.

DISTRIBUTION—From Iceland and the central part of Greenland southward to the British Isles, Nova Scotia, and the Maine coast, also to north

Europe. In winter it is found from southern Greenland southward as far as the Great Lakes, and to Delaware

Bay, sometimes farther south along the coast.

This great Gull is a sort of more northern, larger, blacker-backed representative of the Herring Gull. Its head and bill are appreciably large and heavy, and its flight heavier and more labored. Its voice is correspondingly louder and harsher. It is a very wary bird. (Family *Laridae*)

Heermann's Gull
Larus heermanni [57]

ADULT MALE AND FEMALE—Back, sooty gray; primaries of the wing, black; secondaries, gray tipped with white. Tail, black tipped with white. Head and upper neck, white; under parts, dark gray. Feet, and a ring around the eye, red. Bill, bright red with a black tip.

LENGTH—19.25 inches.

DISTRIBUTION—Along the Pacific Coast from British Columbia southward to Panama.

Bailey writes of this species, "Heermann's Gulls are generally common winter visitors in southern California. Mr. Grinnell says that on the coast near Los Angeles where the fishermen draw their seines along the beaches, clouds of gulls are usually attracted, about half of the flocks being Heermann's, and a quarter Western Gulls." The cries of the Heermann's Gull are low, mellow, and with a musical quality usually absent from the notes of the *Laridae*. (Family *Laridae*)

Herring Gull
Larus argentatus smithsonianus [51a]

ADULT MALE AND FEMALE—Back and wings, pearl gray. Ends of primaries, black; the two outer ones black for about seven inches of their length, and spotted near the ends with white, and with white tips. Head, neck, tail, and under parts, pure white. Bill, yellowish. Legs and feet, flesh-color, pinkish, or salmon.

LENGTH—24.00 inches.

DISTRIBUTION—From extreme northern North America south to Maine, the Great Lakes, Minnesota, and British Columbia. In winter it is found south as far as Lower California and Cuba.

The Herring Gull is the common large gull of our lakes, shores, and harbors. Off the coast of Maine they breed in

large colonies, and spread southward along the Massachusetts coast in summer and early fall. They are also found on inland lakes. The birds spend most of their time floating about in duck-like fashion on the water; rising together to fly here and there after floating refuse. When the tide goes out they congregate on the lower rocks, and exposed flats, in search of whatever soft organic matter they can find. Their notes are loud, and somewhat raucous, *cack, cack, cac-cac-cac-cac;* or sometimes a querulous scream, *kuh-r-e-e-e-e, kuh-r-r-e-e-a-a-ah,* mingled with cluckings and subdued hen-like gobblings. As with most of our Gulls, the young are dark, mottled brownish or grayish-brown. (Family *Laridae*)

Iceland Gull
Larus leucopterus [43]

Similar to the Glaucous Gull, but smaller.

LENGTH—25.00 inches.

DISTRIBUTION—Breeding in Greenland, this Gull is found in the Atlantic; it winters southward to the Great Lakes, and rarely to Long Island, New York. (Family *Laridae*)

Ivory Gull
Pagophila alba [39]

ADULT MALE AND FEMALE—Entire bird, pure ivory white. Bill, yellow; feet, black.

LENGTH—17.00 inches.

DISTRIBUTION—From the Arctic regions, south in winter to British Columbia, and the Great Lakes; rarely found as far east as Massachusetts.

The beautiful Ivory Gull in summer is said to spend most of its time floating about amid the pack ice of the Arctic regions. It is our only pure white gull with black legs. Although in color the Ivory Gull is the embodiment of purity, and in flight the embodiment of delicacy, in its feeding habits it diverges far from all that these attributes suggest, gorging itself

upon the putrid blubber of whales, and the decaying flesh of seals, and even sitting near a seal-hole in the ice, with the object of securing a tidbit in the form of seal excrement. (Family *Laridae*)

Laughing Gull
Larus atricilla [58]

ADULT MALE AND FEMALE—Back and wings, dark pearl gray. The two outer primaries, solid black; the rest, black with small white tips. Entire head, and throat, dark slate gray, appearing black at a distance. Rest of plumage, pure white. Breast sometimes suffused with a faint peachy-pink flush. Bill, dark reddish, its tip bright red.

LENGTH—16.50 inches.

DISTRIBUTION—From Nova Scotia and Maine southward along the coast (rare in the interior) to Florida and Texas. In winter it is found from South Carolina south to northern South America.

The Laughing Gull takes its name from its long, derisive, though far from unpleasant *ha-ha-ha-ha-ha - ha - ha.* Some observers call the sound "demoniac" or "lunatic" laughter. To the

writer's ears it is the joyous, buoyant, free laugh of the open sea. This is the commonest Black-headed Gull on our eastern coast in summer. Another Black-head (north of Cape Cod) is the Bonaparte's Gull, which differs from the Laughing Gull in having the primaries white, with black tips—an easily recognized characteristic. In winter the head of the Laughing Gull is white with dark markings. (Family *Laridae*)

Lesser Black-backed Gull
Larus fuscus graellsi [50]

Similar to the Great Black-backed Gull, but smaller, the back paler, and with the legs greenish instead of flesh-colored or pinkish.

DISTRIBUTION—An Old World form, accidental in Greenland. (Family *Laridae*)

Little Gull
Larus minutus [60.1]

Somewhat similar to the Bonaparte's Gull, but smaller, and with plain gray wings with no black tips. The under surface of the wings is sooty, or washed with dark grayish.

LENGTH—11.00 inches.

DISTRIBUTION—Europe, with but few records in North America from the coasts of Maine, Long Island, Staten Island, New York, and New Jersey. (Family *Laridae*)

Ring-billed Gull
Larus delawarensis [54]

Similar to the Herring Gull, but with yellowish or greenish-yellow legs and feet, and a black ring around the bill. Its smaller size is a good field help when the bird is seen in company with its larger relative.

LENGTH—18.50 inches.

DISTRIBUTION—From the extreme northern parts of North America south to Newfoundland, southern Minnesota, and British Columbia. It winters

from Nova Scotia and British Columbia to Cuba and Lower California. (Family *Laridae*)

Ross's Gull
Rhodostethia rosea [61]

ADULT MALE AND FEMALE—Back and wings, soft pearl gray. Outer margin of outer primary, black, except the tip. Tail, white tinged with pink. Head, neck, and underparts, delicate rosy-pink. Black band around the neck.

LENGTH—13.50 inches.

DISTRIBUTION—"Arctic regions; erratic and irregular. Breeds in. . . . northeastern Siberia. . . . Migrates to

Kamchatka, the Arctic coast of Alaska, and the west coast of Greenland . . ." (A.O.U. Check List.) (Family Laridae)

Sabine's Gull
Xema sabini [62]

ADULT MALE AND FEMALE—Back and wings, slaty gray. Middle of wing, white; the outer quills, black; their inner webs and tips, white. Head and

upper neck, dark leaden-gray bordered by a black collar below. Under parts, white. Bill, black with yellow tip. Tail, conspicuously forked.

LENGTH—13.50 inches.

DISTRIBUTION—In the Arctic regions of North America, passing south in winter to Peru. Uncommon in the United States, but has occurred in many localities, among them Maine, Massachusetts, New York, Kansas, Iowa, and Utah. This is our only American gull showing a forked tail. (Family *Laridae*)

Short-billed Gull
Larus canus brachyrhynchus [55]

ADULT MALE AND FEMALE—Back, light pearl gray. Outer primary, chiefly black with a large white spot near its tip; second primary marked with gray on the inner web, a smaller white spot near the end, and a white tip; third primary with a large white spot on the inner web between the black and the gray, and with a white tip. Head, neck, tail, and under parts, white. Feet and legs, greenish. Bill, greenish tipped with yellow.

LENGTH—17.25 inches.

DISTRIBUTION—From Alaska and the interior of northern British Columbia, southward in winter along the Pacific coast of British Columbia as far as southern California. (Family *Laridae*)

Slaty-backed Gull
Larus schistisagus [48]

Somewhat similar to the Great Black-backed Gull, but with a lighter, more slaty-colored back.

DISTRIBUTION — Confined to the North Pacific Ocean, mainly on the Asiatic side; "Herald Island, Arctic Ocean, and the Alaskan coast of the Bering Sea." (A.O.U. Check List.) (Family *Laridae*)

Thayer's Gull
Larus argentatus thayeri [51b]

Similar to the Herring Gull, but with gray wing tips instead of black, and with the bill, seen from the side, slenderer.

DISTRIBUTION—In Arctic regions of North America west of Greenland, spending the winter on the Pacific coast down to British Columbia. Casually occurs as far east as Quebec, Illinois, and south to New Jersey. (Family *Laridae*)

Vega Gull
Larus argentatus vegae [52]

Similar to the Herring Gull, but with a darker back, and with the legs and feet yellow.

DISTRIBUTION—In the Bering Sea and vicinity, passing south in winter to the coast of California, and to Japan. (Family *Laridae*)

Western Gull
Larus occidentalis occidentalis [49]

ADULT MALE AND FEMALE—Back, dark slate-gray. Primaries, and inner webs of the first, second, and third feathers, black with white tips. Head, neck, tail, and under parts, white. Bill and feet, yellow or yellowish.

LENGTH—25.50 inches.

DISTRIBUTION—Along the Pacific coast from British Columbia southward to about Cape St. Lucas, Lower California.

This Gull is very common at all seasons along the California coast. Great flocks rest on the water, or fly back

and forth over harbors, where they form a highly efficient corps of cleaners. So valuable are they as scavengers, that in some harbors they are protected by law. They often descend in a flock close about fishing boats to secure the refuse thrown overboard by the fisherman. (Family *Laridae*)

Wyman's Gull
Larus occidentalis wymani [49b]

Similar to the Western Gull, but with darker upper parts, and with the four outer primaries, black and lacking the gray markings.

DISTRIBUTION—Along the Pacific coasts of California and Lower California, from Monterey County southward, including the Santa Barbara Islands, to about Ascension Island, Lower California. (Family *Laridae*)

Yellow-footed Gull
Larus occidentalis livens [49a]

Most nearly resembles the Western Gull, but possesses a darker, more leaden-hued mantle on the upper parts, and shows slightly more black in the primaries.

DISTRIBUTION—The Gulf of California. It is a casual visitant at Hyperion, Los Angeles County, California. In winter it is distributed south along the Mexican coast to about latitude 20°. (Family *Laridae*)

GYRFALCON
Asiatic Gyrfalcon
Falco rusticolus uralensis [354c]

Similar to the other dark Gyrfalcons, but with the outermost, or first primary equal to or shorter than the fourth primary, instead of decidedly longer, as in the other races of these birds. It is similar in general to the Black Gyrfalcon, but somewhat paler in general tone, with the head more uniformly colored.

DISTRIBUTION — A Siberian form, occurring on the islands of the Bering

Sea, and on the Bering Sea coast of Alaska. In winter it is occasionally found as far south as Washington. (Family *Falconidae*)

Black Gyrfalcon
Falco rusticolus obsoletus [354b]

ADULT MALE AND FEMALE—Upper parts, dark slaty grayish-brown, sometimes almost black. Plumage, very variable. Edges of the feathers zoned

with lighter shades. Under parts similar, or with feather edges broader and lighter; sometimes white streaked and spotted with black.

LENGTH — 21.00 inches. Female somewhat larger.

DISTRIBUTION — "Northern North America from Point Barrow to Labrador. South in winter to Nova Scotia, Quebec, and Maine, casually to New York, New Hampshire, Massachusetts, Rhode Island, and Connecticut; also probably to South Dakota, Kansas, Minnesota, Ohio, and Pennsylvania, although some of these records probably represent the gray phase of the [White Gyrfalcon] *Falco rusticolus candicans*." (A.O.U. Check List.)

This Gyrfalcon is similar in habits to the White Gyrfalcon. (Family *Falconidae*)

White Gyrfalcon
Falco rusticolus candicans [353]

ADULT MALE AND FEMALE—Upper parts, white; the plumage finely streaked (on the head and neck), cross-barred, or spotted more heavily (on the back) with slate color and brownish-gray. Under parts usually unmarked white, sometimes finely spotted on the sides of the body with dusky.

LENGTH — 22.00 inches. Female slightly larger.

DISTRIBUTION—Greenland, and probably eastern Arctic America, sometimes straggling in winter to British Columbia, Montana, Ontario, Quebec, Nova Scotia, and Maine.

There are very few white birds of prey, but the White Gyrfalcon is one of these. Unfortunately this beautiful and graceful bird is only an extremely rare visitor to us in winter. There seems to be no reason to doubt that unusually severe winters in its northern range might force the bird to descend in some numbers into our northwestern states. Several individuals have

been recorded (but not taken) flying over the Kittatinny Ridge in Pennsylvania. Gyrfalcons as a whole are among the most adept fliers known, taking their rapid course through the air in periods of sailing on set wings and alternating this with rapid flapping. Their food consists of grouse, ptarmigan, murres, puffins, ducks, geese, guillemots, dovekies, gulls, and terns, together with various species of shore birds. In their dietary are also largely represented lemmings, hares and rabbits, meadow mice, shrews, and other small mammals. These magnificent falcons appeal strongly to students and lovers of all that is splendid in nature. Their very great beauty should protect them at all times from the gunman; for lovers of wild nature should surely be accorded a voice in this matter. (Family *Falconidae*)

HAWFINCH
Japanese Hawfinch
Coccothraustes coccothraustes japonicus [514.2]

ADULT MALE—Upper parts, reddish-brown; wings, darker marked with white and grayish. Nape, gray. Face and throat, black or blackish. Under parts, brownish-purple or grayish.

LENGTH—7.00 inches.

DISTRIBUTION—An accidental visitor to St. Paul Island in the Pribilof Group, Alaska. (Family *Fringillidae*)

HAWK FAMILY
Eagles, Kites, Goshawks, Hawks, and Ospreys
Accipitridae

Hawks exhibit great diversity of habit and of form. Their beaks are strongly hooked; their talons long, curved, and sharp; their feet stout and powerful; their wings either long and broad, or short, rounded and broad; their powers of vision unsurpassed. Their voices are loud, piercing, often harsh

and screaming. They strike their prey with their powerful feet, and carry it in the same members, using their beaks to tear it in pieces, which are swallowed in large fragments. The bones, fur, scales, and other indigestible parts are rolled up by the muscles of the

stomach into longish, compact pellets, which are ejected through the mouth. An examination of these pellets gives one an excellent idea of the nature of the food. In North America, at least, Hawks, hitherto much misunderstood, and wrongly persecuted birds, are now known to be for the majority of the species, among the best friends of the farmer and the sportsman, and in most states are protected accordingly. Intelligent persons who are willing to read and inform themselves about our native Hawks, invariably are soon found on the side of the birds' protectors. Hawks should not be confused with Falcons which belong to another, though closely allied family, the *Falconidae*. The Vultures or Condors or Buzzards are contained in still another, also closely related family, the *Cathartidae*. These three families: *Accipitridae, Falconidae,* and *Cathartidae,* contain those birds usually referred to as "birds of prey." To this category also, Owls are often assigned by popular terminology. With the exception of the Vultures, the feeding habits of the "birds of prey" are all quite similar. About 260 members of *Accipitridae* exist, distributed widely over the globe. Of this number, thirty-five species and subspecies are found in North America, included in fifteen genera.

NESTING. The members of this large family all construct large, coarse, bulky nests of sticks, twigs, pieces of bark, leaves, sometimes moss, and other plant materials, and place the whole structure high up in trees, or sometimes on a shelf of rock in a cliff. When the nest is thus placed it is apt to be less bulky. The Golden Eagle nests usually in such a situation, and less commonly in a tall dead tree. The Bald Eagle's habit is the reverse. The Marsh Hawk, on the other hand, fashions its large round nest of fine dried grasses, which it places directly on the ground, either among large tufts of tall grasses, in a weed tangle, or among grassy hummocks. The eggs of our *Accipiters* number from two to four, to five or six (sometimes eight or nine in the case of the Marsh Hawk). The Eagles lay two or three. In color they are white (unmarked in the Golden Eagle), buffy white, pale greenish, or bluish white, and are spotted, blotched, and otherwise marked with various shades of brown, lavender, etc., the markings often gathered together more thickly near the larger end.

HAWK
American Rough-legged Hawk
Buteo lagopus sancti-johannis [347a]

ADULT MALE AND FEMALE—*In the light plumage phase:*—Upper parts, dark grayish-brown, the feathers margined with whitish and light reddish brown. Basal half of tail, white or buffy; the end with two or three whitish or grayish bars. Under parts varying from white to reddish buff, streaked and spotted with black. On the abdomen these markings fuse more or less, sometimes forming an irregular transverse band. The front of the tarsi are entirely feathered, this con-dition giving the bird its name. *In the dark plumage phase:*—Entire bird, black or blackish, the primaries and the tail crossed by whitish or grayish bars.

LENGTH—22.00 inches.

DISTRIBUTION—The Rough-leg breeds in Canada, and descends into the United States only in winter, when it is found spread as far south as Virginia, and westward through Missouri to central California.

This rather rare Hawk, both because it is with us in the States only in winter, and because it is chiefly a crepuscular hunter, is seldom seen by the casual observer. It is a heavy, sluggish bird, circling and soaring with much flapping of wings, apparently with considerable effort. Unlike our other native Hawks, the Rough-leg is active chiefly during the twilight

(In light plumage phase)

hours, and throughout moonlight nights. It is a relatively silent bird, rarely uttering its note except during the nesting season. It is unfortunate that this valuable Hawk is not represented by greater numbers, for it is one of the farmers' most faithful allies against meadow mice. During its winter residence with us it feeds on little else. (Family *Accipitridae*)

Black Pigeon Hawk

Falco columbarius suckleyi [357a]

Similar to the Eastern Pigeon Hawk, but darker. The back is almost black, and the under parts marked with

deeper, broader, sharper stripings. Throat, sharply streaked.

DISTRIBUTION—From British Columbia, and perhaps Vancouver Island, southward in winter rarely to the northern portion of California. (Family *Falconidae*)

Broad-winged Hawk

Buteo platypterus platypterus [343]

ADULT MALE AND FEMALE—Upper parts, dark grayish-brown, the feathers more or less margined with reddish-brown and whitish. Tail, reddish-brown with about two broad whitish bars, which show fairly prominently when the bird is in flight high above the observer. Tip of tail with a narrow grayish-white or white band. Under parts heavily barred with light reddish-brown.

LENGTH — 16.00 inches. Female slightly larger than the male.

DISTRIBUTION—Over the whole of eastern North America from New Brunswick and Saskatchewan westward to the Great Plains, and southward to the Gulf Coast. It spreads in winter from about central New Jersey southward to the northern portion of South America.

The Broad-winged Hawk might very well be called the Gentle Hawk, for of all our northern birds of prey it is the most unsuspicious and forbearing. It very rarely molests small birds, and will not attack humans who intrude upon its nesting domains. Its voice, too, is soft and pleasing, being a faint musical scream, somewhat like the magnified call of the Wood Pewee. It is a bird of high wooded hills and mountainous country, and disappears if the region is cleared of trees. In wild wooded places it may be observed with ease as it sits motionless in the top of a dead tree, small bush, or even upon a log or stone, near some stream or bog; where in immobile patience, it watches for its humble quarry. Every effort should be extended for the protection of this valuable Hawk. With a dietary almost three-quarters of which is made up of various species of

mice, and other destructive rodents and insects, it appears in the light of an undoubted friend of the farmer. Reptiles, frogs, toads, and salamanders —as well as enormous numbers of the injurious caterpillars of large moths— form an important element of its yearly food. (Family *Accipitridae*)

Cooper's Hawk

Accipiter cooperi [333]

Similar to the Sharp-shinned Hawk, but some four inches longer, and with a blackish crown, and rounded, instead of square-tipped tail.

DISTRIBUTION—From Canada southward into the southern portion

of Mexico, spending its winters from central New England, Missouri, and Oregon southward.

A larger edition of the Sharp-shinned species, feeding on larger birds. (Family *Accipitridae*)

Desert Sparrow Hawk

Falco sparverius phalaena [360a]

Similar to the Eastern Sparrow Hawk, but slightly larger and paler.

DISTRIBUTION—From British Columbia and western Montana southward into northwestern Mexico. (Family *Falconidae*)

Duck Hawk

Falco peregrinus anatum [356a]

ADULT MALE AND FEMALE—Upper parts, dark bluish-slaty-gray; the primaries barred with light reddish-brown. Dark "moustache" markings at the base of the bill. Tail faintly barred with black and tipped with white. Under parts, creamy or yellowish-buff, barred and spotted with black, except on the breast.

LENGTH — 16.50 inches. Female somewhat larger.

DISTRIBUTION—From Norton Sound, Alaska, southward to central Lower California, northeastward to Connecticut, and Massachusetts; through the mountains of Tennessee. In winter it is found as far south as the West Indies and South America.

In its powers of flight the Duck Hawk is probably unequalled by any other living bird. It can with ease overtake the swiftest fliers, and it is only by means of quick twists and dodgings that its proposed dinner may hope to elude its impetuous rush. Rising high above its intended quarry, the Duck Hawk glances downward with hissing velocity, striking with its closed fist a lightning-like, mortal blow, that sends its victim hurtling dead to earth. Or it

may swoop alongside of, or ahead of, some bird in the full headlong flight of terror, and suddenly reaching out, snatch its victim out of mid-air with one foot. One grip of those powerful, sharp, curved talons is abrupt death. Whether it strikes a blow or grasps, the Duck Hawk's killing is instantaneous and merciful. There is nothing cruel in its hunting. It hunts for food, not for sport, and does not wound and allow its intended meal to escape. Moderate-size and larger birds, sometimes ducks and other game birds form its chief dietary. (Family *Falconidae*)

Eastern Pigeon Hawk

Falco columbarius columbarius [357]

ADULT MALE AND FEMALE—Upper parts, slaty blue, with an irregular buffy collar about the neck streaked with the same color. Primaries barred

with white. Tail tipped with white and crossed by three or four grayish bars. Under parts varying from a creamy-buff to a reddish-brown, streaked with blackish, except the throat which is often white or whitish.

LENGTH — 10.50 inches. Female slightly larger than the male.

DISTRIBUTION — From Newfoundland, Nova Scotia, northern Maine, Ontario, northern Michigan, and southern Manitoba, westward to the foothills of the Rocky Mountains. It spends its winters in the Gulf States, Central America, and the West Indies.

The favorite hunting grounds of the Pigeon Hawk are along the edges of woods, in more or less open country, and along the shores of bodies of water. Its name is derived not from any predatory association with pigeons, but from the resemblance which its contour and flight habits bear to those birds. Small birds form the bulk of its diet. Its powers of flight are remarkable, nearly equal to those of the Duck Hawk and Goshawk. The fact that it pursues and captures dragonflies on the wing, bears witness to the rapidity and flexibility of its flight. (Family *Falconidae*)

Eastern Red-tailed Hawk

Buteo borealis borealis [337]

ADULT MALE AND FEMALE—Upper parts, dark grayish or fuscous-brown, the feathers irregularly edged with shades of reddish-brown, buff, and white. Upper surface of tail, silvery gray. Upper breast heavily streaked with grayish-brown and buff; lower breast lightly streaked with same colors, or not at all. Upper abdomen streaked, spotted, or barred with blackish, the markings often forming a broken band. Lower abdomen usually white and unmarked.

LENGTH — 20.00 inches. Female slightly larger.

DISTRIBUTION—From the extreme northern parts of Canada, west to the Great Plains of the United States, and southward to the Gulf of Mexico; in winter its northern limit is central New England, Illinois, and South Dakota.

With widely expanded wings and tail the Red-tail sails in ever enlarging circles higher and higher, until, becoming a mere speck in the blue, it finally passes from sight. It has been recorded by Blanchan that one of these tireless hawks was seen to soar continuously ". . . without once alighting, from seven in the morning until four in the afternoon." During such times of soaring, the Red-tail is not on a hunt for prey. When feeding, it sits motionless on some dead limb, or other elevated perch of vantage and watches for its quarry to come within range; then suddenly dashes down

and strikes. The notes of the Red-tailed Hawk are of a screaming and querulous character, sounding like the syllables *peee errr, peee errr*. The cries are uttered with a pitch and vigor which remind one of escaping steam. This species is one of our most valuable hawks, and not at all a "hen hawk." The larger soaring hawks (Red-tailed, Broad-winged, Red-shouldered, and similar species) are useful. The smaller hawks (except the Sparrow Hawks), such as the Sharp-shinned and Cooper's Hawks, are the destructive species, as far as poultry is concerned. In their native wilds no hawks are detrimental. (Family *Accipitridae*)

Eastern Sparrow Hawk
Falco sparverius sparverius [360]

ADULT MALE—Back, rich reddish-brown somewhat barred with black. Tail similar, tipped first with a white, then with a broader black band. Head, slate-blue; crown, reddish-brown. Ear coverts, white marked before and behind with black. Wings, slate-blue;

the primaries barred with white. Under parts varying from creamy-buff to light reddish-brown. Sides of breast and abdomen prominently spotted with black.

ADULT FEMALE—Back, tail, and wing coverts, reddish-brown barred with black. Head similar to that of the male. Under parts more or less heavily streaked with reddish-brown.

LENGTH—10.00 inches.

DISTRIBUTION—From Hudson's Bay to the Gulf of Mexico, and westward to the Rocky Mountains. In winter it is restricted to the region from New Jersey and southern Illinois, southward.

This diminutive and most brilliantly colored of our native Hawks may be seen almost any day during the year in the Eastern States—except during the winter in New England. It is the commonest of our Hawks. One of its favorite perches is a telephone wire (or top of the pole) where it watches

for its chief quarry, grasshoppers, crickets, and meadow mice. Frequently it may be seen poised fixed in the air, its body held perfectly motionless by the rapid and regular beating of its long pointed wings. Suddenly it drops lightly and swiftly down upon its victim. Its high-pitched ringing call of *killy, killy, killy* has earned for it the name of Killy Hawk. (Family *Falconidae*)

Ferruginous Rough-legged Hawk
Buteo regalis [348]

Somewhat similar to the American Rough-legged Hawk, but lighter and

rustier; and lighter below; also slightly larger.

DISTRIBUTION—Over the whole of western North America from Saskatchewan southward into Mexico, and from the Great Plains to the Pacific, sometimes straggling as far east as Illinois. (Family *Accipitridae*)

Florida Red-shouldered Hawk
Buteo lineatus alleni [339a]

Similar to the Northern Red-shouldered Hawk, but smaller; upper parts, much grayer; no brownish on the head; under parts, much paler.

DISTRIBUTION—Southern part of Oklahoma, Arkansas, Alabama, Louisiana, South Carolina, and Florida, and along the coast to the eastern part of Texas. (Family *Accipitridae*)

Florida Red-tailed Hawk
Buteo borealis umbrinus [337f]

Similar to the Eastern Red-tailed Hawk, but darker, the tail bearing

broken dark brown bands. The throat and middle of the abdomen show heavy broad stripes and bands of chocolate-brown.

DISTRIBUTION — Restricted to the southern portion of Florida, the Isle of Pines, and Cuba. (Family *Accipitridae*)

Harlan's Hawk
Buteo borealis harlani [337d]

Similar to the Eastern Red-tailed Hawk, but with darker grayish-brown upper parts, the tail thickly mottled with blackish, brownish, and whitish, and with the under parts, white or whitish; more or less spotted on the abdomen with grayish-brown.

DISTRIBUTION—From Pennsylvania, Illinois, Iowa, and Kansas, south and east to the Gulf of Mexico, and into Georgia and Florida.

This darker form of the common Red-tailed Hawk is more widely dis-

tributed throughout the south than the Florida Red-tailed Hawk. (Family *Accipitridae*)

Harris's Hawk
Parabuteo unicinctus harrisi [335]

ADULT MALE AND FEMALE—Plumage, dark sooty-brown with a lighter brownish reflection. Shoulders and thighs, chestnut-brown; rump, slightly darker. Upper and under tail coverts, basal part of tail, and its tip, white. Space before the eye, and cere, lemon-yellow. Legs and feet darker yellow. LENGTH—20.50 inches.

DISTRIBUTION—From southeastern California, southern Arizona, southern

New Mexico, southern Texas, Louisiana and Mississippi, southward through Mexico to Panama. A friendly, unsuspicious hawk, feeding largely on offal, small mammals, reptiles, and only occasionally on birds. (Family *Accipitridae*)

Insular Red-shouldered Hawk
Buteo lineatus extimus [339c]

Similar to the Northern Red-shouldered Hawk but with upper parts grayer and somewhat darker; no brownish on the head; under parts slightly paler. Slightly smaller than the Northern Red-shoulder.

DISTRIBUTION — On the Florida Keys. (Family *Accipitridae*)

Krider's Hawk
Buteo borealis krideri [337a]

Similar to the Eastern Red-tailed Hawk, but with almost entirely white under parts.

DISTRIBUTION—From Minnesota to Texas, wandering irregularly eastward

about as far as Iowa and Illinois. (Family *Accipitridae*)

Little Sparrow Hawk
Falco sparverius paulus [360c]

Similar to the Eastern Sparrow Hawk, but smaller and darker. The wings and tail are shorter, and the bill relatively larger and heavier.

DISTRIBUTION—From the central part of Alabama south into the southern zone of the Gulf States, and down in Florida. (Family *Falconidae*)

Marsh Hawk
Circus hudsonius [331]

ADULT MALE—Upper parts, ashy-gray tinged with brownish. Upper tail coverts, white, forming a conspicuous patch when the bird is in flight. Tail, silvery gray, irregularly crossed by five or six blackish bars. Upper breast, pearl gray; lower breast and abdomen, white spotted or barred with reddish-brown.

ADULT FEMALE—Upper parts, brownish; head and neck streaked with light brown. Upper tail coverts, white, as in the male. Middle tail feathers barred with ashy-gray and black, the others with yellowish-brown and black. Under parts yellowish-brown streaked with dark grayish-brown.

In the "light phase" of plumage, the birds may be almost white, and in this condition remind one of large white gulls.

LENGTH—19.00 inches. Female slightly larger than the male.

DISTRIBUTION—From the northern portions of Canada southward over the United States, spending the winter from southern New York northwestward into British Columbia, and southward into Central America.

The Marsh Hawk, or Harrier, is a bird of meadows, marshes, low pastures, or wide salt-marsh reaches, flying low over the ground, veering and

tilting in a graceful manner as it follows the undulations of the terrain in its constant search for its chief article of diet, the meadow mouse. Its cries are sharp and short, resembling the syllables *geg, geg, geg.* It is one of the few birds of prey to nest on the ground. (Family *Accipitridae*)

Mexican Black Hawk
Urubitinga anthracina anthracina [345]

ADULT MALE AND FEMALE—Plumage, very dark slate, almost black; wings, black; the primaries mottled with brown. Tail marked at the base with white, crossed by a broad band of white, and tipped with a narrow

band of white. Cere, legs, and feet, yellow; bill, black.

LENGTH—22.50 inches.

DISTRIBUTION—Extreme southern Arizona and the lower Rio Grande

Valley of Texas, southward through Mexico and Central America to extreme northern South America. (Family *Accipitridae*)

Northern Red-shouldered Hawk
Buteo lineatus lineatus [339]

ADULT MALE AND FEMALE—Upper parts, reddish-brown, the feathers more or less edged with darker grayish-brown, yellowish-brown, and white. Four outer primaries barred with black and white; shoulder (i.e. wrist) patch, reddish-brown, richer in color than the back, and not very conspicuous. Tail, blackish or dark grayish-brown with four or five white cross-bars and a white tip. Under parts, brown or grayish-brown, everywhere barred with white and light gray. Throat streaked with blackish.

LENGTH — 18.30 inches. Female slightly larger than the male.

DISTRIBUTION—The whole of the eastern United States, from Maine south and west to eastern Nebraska and Kansas, and into Oklahoma; and east and south into southern Florida.

Falling from out the azure depths of the quiet summer sky comes the faint, musical *kee-yoo, kee-yoo* of the

Red-shouldered Hawk—one of the characteristic sounds of midsummer, and one of the most pleasing utterances of all our birds of prey. It is quite similar to the call of the Blue Jay, and less so to the call of its near relative the Northern Red-tailed Hawk. The Red-shoulder is a bird of rich, low woodlands, in which streams and marshes abound, though it is sometimes, but rarely, found in high mountains and hills. Perched upon a stump or a dead limb, not far above the ground, it remains motionless for long periods of time, watching for its lowly quarry, and at such times it may be quite closely approached before taking flight. Like the Red-tailed and Broad-winged Hawks, it is much given to high soaring. Mice and large insects form the

chief food elements of this very valuable species of Hawk. It is not at all a "hen hawk," and should be given every protection by the farmer. (Family *Accipitridae*)

Red-bellied Hawk

Buteo lineatus elegans [339b]

Similar to the Northern Red-shouldered Hawk, but with a light reddish-brown, unstreaked or unmarked, breast.

DISTRIBUTION—From British Columbia southward along the coastal region to Lower California; rarely

extending its range eastward to Colorado and western Texas. (Family *Accipitridae*)

Richardson's Pigeon Hawk

Falco columbarius richardsoni [357b]

Similar to the Eastern Pigeon Hawk, but much lighter, and more like the Merlin. In fact it is often called the Pale Merlin.

DISTRIBUTION—From southern Alberta and Saskatchewan, to northern Montana and northwestern Dakota. In winter it spreads southward through Colorado, New Mexico, and western Texas, and down into northwestern Mexico. (Family *Falconidae*)

San Lucas Sparrow Hawk

Falco sparverius peninsularis [360b]

Similar to the Eastern Sparrow Hawk, but smaller and paler throughout, and with a proportionately larger bill.

DISTRIBUTION—Restricted to the southern part of the peninsula of Lower California. (Family *Falconidae*)

Sennett's White-tailed Hawk

Buteo albicaudatus hypospodius [341]

ADULT MALE—Upper parts, slaty bluish-gray. Shoulders, reddish-brown. Rump and tail, white; sometimes

faintly and narrowly barred with blackish. Tail with a narrow white tip, followed by a broader blackish band. Under parts, white crossed by faint narrow dark bars. Legs and feet, yellowish.

ADULT FEMALE—Darker than the male, with more brown on the shoulders.

LENGTH—23.50 inches.

DISTRIBUTION—From lower central Texas southward through Mexico and Central America into the extreme northern portion of South America (Colombia). (Family *Accipitridae*)

Sharp-shinned Hawk

Accipiter velox velox [332]

ADULT MALE AND FEMALE—Upper parts, slaty gray; the primaries barred with blackish. Tail, ashy gray crossed with blackish bars; tip, whitish, and nearly square. Throat, white with blackish streaks; the rest of the under parts barred with white and light reddish-brown.

LENGTH—11.25 inches. Female slightly larger than the male.

DISTRIBUTION—Over the whole of North America, wintering from central New England and extreme northwestern United States southward.

"Feathered Lightning" is a term often applied to this little Hawk. It is found in all types of country, wooded and open, but is rare or absent in dense forests or high mountains. Its flight is easy and graceful, and consists of short periods of gliding, alternating with periods of rapidly beating wings. When in pursuit of prey, it dashes rapidly this way and that, following exactly in the wake of its falling quarry, and often plunging fearlessly into a dense thicket in the exuberance of its chase. Almost seven-eighths of its food consists of small birds, yet because of its "weeding-out" of the weak, ailing, and diseased, it is ac-

counted, biologically, a valuable bird. In the vicinity of chicken yards, it becomes a great pest. (Family *Accipitridae*)

Short-tailed Hawk

Buteo brachyurus [344]

ADULT MALE AND FEMALE—Upper parts, dark slaty-brown; forehead, whitish. Tail with black bars and a narrow white tip. Sides of neck and upper breast sparingly marked with reddish-brown. Under parts, white, unmarked.

LENGTH—17.00 inches.

DISTRIBUTION—From Florida and eastern Mexico southward to Central

and South America. (Family *Accipitridae*)

Swainson's Hawk

Buteo swainsoni [342]

ADULT MALE AND FEMALE—*Light phase:* Upper parts, dark grayish-

brown; the edges of the feathers, light yellowish-brown. Forehead, light. Tail with many narrow faint whitish bars, and a narrow white tip. Upper breast, light or dark reddish-brown. Rest of under parts, white or pale flesh color barred with brownish, especially on the sides. Chin and throat, white. *Dark phase:* Entire bird mantled with deep dusky-brown. The plumage of this Hawk is very variable, and all gradations between light and dark phases occur. The birds found in the Northeastern States are usually in the dark phase.

LENGTH—22.50 inches.

DISTRIBUTION—From the Arctic regions of North America, chiefly through western United States, to the Pacific coast (though some straggle to the northeast) and southward to Argentina. One of the commonest, if not the commonest Hawk of the wide wastes and table-lands of the west, with habits similar to those of the Red-shouldered and Red-tailed Hawks. (Family *Accipitridae*)

Texas Red-shouldered Hawk

Buteo lineatus texanus [339d]

Similar to the Red-bellied Hawk, but with the breast more heavily spotted with buffy, and with the head and back a more reddish-brown tone.

DISTRIBUTION — From southern Texas south into Tamaulipas, northeastern Mexico. (Family *Accipitridae*)

Western Pigeon Hawk

Falco columbarius bendirei [357c]

Similar to the Eastern Pigeon Hawk, but with the upper parts lighter. The tail is black with three bands of grayish-white.

DISTRIBUTION—From northwestern Canada and Alaska southward into the mountains of northern California. In winter it is found from California and New Mexico into Lower California, and northwestern Mexico. Seldom occurs in Louisiana, Florida, North and South Carolina. (Family *Falconidae*)

Western Red-tailed Hawk
Buteo borealis calurus [337b]

Somewhat similar to the Eastern Red-tailed Hawk, but paler in general tone, the tail bearing two or three faint dark bars, and the under parts darker with more pronounced markings. In the dark phase of plumage, the entire tones of the plumage are deeper.

DISTRIBUTION—From British Columbia southward to Central America, along the Pacific Coast eastward to the Rocky Mountains. (Family *Accipitridae*)

Zone-tailed Hawk
Buteo albonotatus [340]

ADULT MALE AND FEMALE—Plumage, blackish-brown or black. Forehead, whitish. Tail crossed by three

broad dull grayish-white bands or zones. Legs and feet, bright lemon-yellow.

LENGTH—20.50 inches.

DISTRIBUTION—From extreme southern California, southwestern New Mexico, Arizona, and Texas, south-

ward through Mexico and Central America to extreme northern South America. (Family *Accipitridae*)

HEN

Heath Hen
Tympanuchus cupido cupido [306]

Similar to the Greater Prairie Chicken, but with the scapulars broadly tipped with buffy. The feathers of the neck

tufts are pointed instead of being rounded, and are less than ten for each tuft.

DISTRIBUTION—Formerly occurred on Cape Ann and Martha's Vineyard, Massachusetts; southern New Hampshire; Long Island, New York; on the Pocono Plateau of Pennsylvania; on Schooly's Mountain and in the Pine Barrens of New Jersey; and probably also on the shores of Chesapeake Bay in Maryland and Delaware; finally restricted to Martha's Vineyard, Massachusetts.

The Heath Hen, now extinct, the last birds having passed into the realm of historical record from Martha's Vineyard some years ago, was a bird in appearance and habits much like the Prairie Chicken. Prior to the year 1800 the bird was common, but between that year and 1896 its gradual extermination on the mainland was accomplished, and only a few surviving representatives of the bird could be found on the Island of Martha's

Vineyard. Here it was protected by law, and studied, and every effort made to preserve it from extinction. Now the bird is known only from museums, from photographic film, and from numerous drawings, paintings, and field notebooks. (Family *Tetraonidae*)

Sage Hen

Centrocercus urophasianus [309]

ADULT MALE—Upper parts mottled with light brown and gray, spotted and barred with black and brown. The shoulders bear tufts of white downy feathers, mixed with black wiry plumes. Yellow distensible air sacs spring from each side of the throat. Upper breast, black with wiry feathers

springing from the transverse band which is black but worn off during breeding season, leaving upper breast white.

ADULT FEMALE—Similar to the male but without the air sacs or plumes. Throat, white; band across the upper breast, speckled white, or grayish.

LENGTH—28.00 inches; female about 22.00 inches.

DISTRIBUTION—From west central Canada and British Columbia to Utah, Nevada, and California, and from the Sierra Nevada and Cascade ranges east to the Black Hills; Nebraska, Colorado, and in the sagebrush plains. (Family *Tetraonidae*)

HERON FAMILY
Herons and Bitterns
Ardeidae

Herons and Bitterns are tall, gaunt, long-billed, long-necked, long-bodied, long-legged, long-toed birds. It is lamentable that their wings and tails

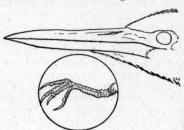

cannot be long instead of short. However their patience is very long, as any observer of their fishing habits can well attest. In their fishing and general habits they are solitary birds, but many species are gregarious in their nesting habits, and nest in large colonies. There are about one hundred species and subspecies of *Ardeidae*, widely distributed over the world, but more numerous in the tropical and subtropical regions. About twenty-five members are found in the Western Hemisphere, and of this number twenty-four are recorded in North America, distributed among eleven genera.

NESTING. The nests of *Ardeid* birds are usually very bulky structures, placed high in trees, in swampy regions, or near water, often in large colonies, rookeries, or heronries. Sometimes they are mere platforms of sticks. The tree nests are composed of sticks and twigs, often with the addition of weed stalks, rushes, and some grasses. Some species nest on or near the ground among reeds and rushes in swamps or sloughs, or along the marshy borders of streams, lakes, or ponds, fashioning their simple nests out of local materials, i.e., reed stems, rushes, and the like. Often these elements are soft and decomposing. The eggs number from two or three to four or six, and are mostly bluish-green of varying depths of color. Others are bluish-white, dull bluish, greenish-white, pale sea-green, blue, grayish-blue, green, or brownish-gray. All are unmarked. Young Herons and Bitterns are awkward, straddly birds, with very alert eyes and faces, but comical in their expressions and attitudes. Sometimes, when the nest is attacked or approached too closely, the young birds reach out over its edge, and greet the intruder with a deluge of regurgitated stomach contents.

HERON
Anthony's Green Heron
Butorides virescens anthonyi [201c]

Similar to the Little Green Heron, but larger and lighter in general tone, with more light streakings on the throat, neck, and wings.

DISTRIBUTION—From Oregon to the northern portion of Lower California, southern Arizona, and southward into the northwestern part of Mexico. In winter it is found from southern California, southern Arizona, northern Lower California, as far south as southern Mexico, and through Nicaragua as far as central Costa Rica. (Family *Ardeidae*)

Bancroft's Night Heron
Nyctanassa violacea bancrofti [203a]

Similar to the Yellow-crowned Night Heron, but larger, and with a larger, heavier bill.

DISTRIBUTION—In southern Lower California, south of about latitude 28°, i.e., the southern half of the peninsula, and along the Pacific Coast southward to Salvador. (Family *Ardeidae*)

Black-crowned Night Heron
Nycticorax nycticorax hoactli [202]

ADULT MALE AND FEMALE—Upper parts, black; wings and tail, gray; crown, black, with two or three white plumes about eight inches long. Lores, greenish-yellow. Rest of plumage, white. Bill, dark; legs and feet, yellow.
LENGTH—24.00 inches.
DISTRIBUTION—From New Brunswick, Canada, westward to Oregon and south to the Gulf of Mexico. In winter it is not found north of the Gulf States or California.

The Black-crowned Night Heron feeds chiefly at dusk along the mud flats and tidal estuaries, and nests in large

colonies, sometimes far inland. As it flies over, just after the sun has set, it utters now and then a single hoarse deep *quowk*, a note which has given the bird one of its names, Night Quawk. The young are brown, dark-streaked birds, somewhat similar to the adult American Bitterns, but are a more grayish-brown, and more marked with white. No evening picture of our New England tidal marshes would be complete without a solitary Night Heron dignifiedly flapping its darkling way overhead, ejaculating "quowk" every now and then as it disappears in the gloom. (Family *Ardeidae*)

California Heron

Ardea herodias hyperonca [194d]

Similar to the Great Blue Heron, but decidedly larger.

DISTRIBUTION—From western Oregon to northern Lower California, west of the Cascade Mountains, and the Sierra Nevadas. In winter it spreads southward to Guadalupe Island, off the coast of Lower California. (Family *Ardeidae*)

Eastern Green Heron

Butorides virescens virescens [201]

ADULT MALE AND FEMALE—Wings, back, and tail, glossy greenish—the green being appreciable only in good light. The long flight feathers of the

wing show a bluish tinge. Top of head, shining greenish-black. Sides of throat and neck, rich chestnut-brown. Middle of the neck with a narrow stripe of black and white. Under parts, grayish-brown.

LENGTH—17.00 inches.

DISTRIBUTION—From Nova Scotia and Manitoba south to the Gulf States. In winter it is found from the Gulf States to northern South America.

The little Green Heron, Quak, or Shitepoke, is a common bird along stream courses, rivers, ponds, swamps, tidal marshes, and estuaries. As it flies it somewhat resembles a crow, but its tail is shorter, and its wing strokes are slower and heavier. The long neck is bent back into an "S" curve and concealed in the long feathers. Its commonest note is a short, hoarse *quak*. Boys along the seashore in Connecticut call the bird the Minnow Fisher or Kelly Fisher. (Family *Ardeidae*)

Espíritu Santo Heron

Ardea herodias sancti-lucae [194e]

Similar to the Great Blue Heron but uniformly much paler in coloration.

DISTRIBUTION—This eminently scriptural bird—according to its scientific name, the Heron of St. Luke; or according to its vernacular appellation, the Heron of the Holy Spirit—is found ranging in southern Lower California from San Jose Island to San Jose del Cabo. (Family *Ardeidae*)

European Heron

Ardea cinerea cinera [195]

Similar in general to the Great Blue Heron of North America, but differing from that species chiefly by the possession of white instead of brownish feathers on the upper part of the legs.

LENGTH—36.00 inches.

DISTRIBUTION—This European species occurs as a rare straggler in the southern part of Greenland. (Family *Ardeidae*)

Frazar's Green Heron

Butorides virescens frazari [201a]

Similar to the Little Green Heron, but larger, with a more purplish sheen on the neck feathers, the upper parts darker, and with fewer buffy streaks on the throat and neck.

DISTRIBUTION — Restricted to the peninsula of Lower California. (Family *Ardeidae*)

Great Blue Heron
Ardea herodias herodias [194]

ADULT MALE AND FEMALE—Back and tail, gray, the wings edged broadly with black. Crown, black with broad

white stripe through its center, and with a black lengthened crest. Throat, white; neck, pale brown with a narrow line of white, brown, and black down its center below. Long feathers at the base of the neck. Under parts streaked with black and white; sometimes pale brown. Shoulder, chestnut-brown. Leg feathers, dusky brown. Bill, very long and heavy; dull olive-yellow above and yellower below. Lores, bluish-gray. Legs and feet, black.

LENGTH—About 46.00 inches.

DISTRIBUTION—Widely distributed in the Americas, from the Arctic regions southward into the northern parts of South America.

The Great Blue Heron, perhaps our stateliest bird, is a fairly familiar sight to dwellers near the coast or near inland waters. The bird is found standing quietly at the edges of ponds, lakes, and streams; sometimes on the sand-bars or shoals of broad rivers, or less often along beaches. It is apt to be very common in salt marshes and along the muddy banks of tidal estuaries, two situations common along our Atlantic Coast. It is a wary bird, rising heavily long before the observer is near enough to see it well, except with glasses. With its long neck in a graceful crook, and its long legs extending out straight backward, it slowly and aristocratically flaps off, its great wings bearing it along with ease and considerable speed. Its spread of wing is almost equal to that of the Bald Eagle. Its food consists of almost any animal it can secure with its powerful beak: frogs, salamanders, tadpoles, fish, crayfish, small snakes; and in the marshes, meadow mice, shrews, and the like. This bird is a magnificent addition to our natural scenery. (Family *Ardeidae*)

Great White Heron
Ardea occidentalis [192]

ADULT MALE AND FEMALE—Pure white. During the breeding season, long stiff feathers arise from the lower

part of the neck, from between the shoulders, and two from the back of the crown.

LENGTH—About 50 inches.

DISTRIBUTION—On the southern

tip of Florida, the Keys, Cuba, and Jamaica.

The largest of the White Herons, which should not be confused with the "aigrette"-bearing White Heron, the Egret. This Heron is as large as our familiar Great Blue Heron, but a much more striking figure. Its white plumage makes it appear a larger bird. (Family *Ardeidae*)

Little Blue Heron

Florida caerulea caerulea [200]

ADULT MALE AND FEMALE—Slaty bluish-gray, with the head and neck a rich maroon-chestnut-brown. Long narrow feathers between the shoulders and on the lower part of the long neck. Legs and feet, black.

LENGTH—22.00 inches.

DISTRIBUTION—From Virginia and Illinois south through the eastern states into tropical America. After the breeding season it may wander as far north as Nova Scotia and Montreal.

The Little Blue Heron, common in Florida and elsewhere in the south,

wanders north after the breeding season is over. The immature birds are pure white, and make striking objects standing in the bleak brown of some New England marsh in the fall. The legs and feet are a dusky greenish or dirty yellowish-green. The adults resemble the adult Little Green Heron, but have black instead of yellowish legs. Their notes, like Heron notes in general, are hoarse croaks or squawks. (Family *Ardeidae*)

Louisiana Heron

Hydranassa tricolor ruficollis [199]

ADULT MALE AND FEMALE—Upper parts, dark bluish-slate-gray, with pale grayish-brown "aigrette" plumes, extending down to the tail. Back of head and upper part of neck with long chestnut-brown and white feathers.

Lower back and rump, white. Throat, white; neck, bluish-slate, with thin brownish line down its center. Under parts, white. Base of bill and lores, bluish-slate. Legs and feet, black.

LENGTH—26.00 inches.

DISTRIBUTION—From the Gulf States southward into Central America and the West Indies. Wanders north in late summer as far as Indiana, Long Island, New York, and southern Connecticut.

These graceful and beautiful birds are common in the Southern States, nesting in large colonies in wooded swamps, and on wooded islands in the midst of inaccessible bogs. Their pure white under parts look almost silvery in the sunlight, and form an excellent recognition mark for the species. They are larger than the Little Blue Herons. (Family *Ardeidae*)

Northwestern Coast Heron

Ardea herodias fannini [194a]

Similar to the Great Blue Heron, but much darker.

DISTRIBUTION—Along the Pacific Coast from Sitka, Alaska, to Vancouver Island, British Columbia. (Family *Ardeidae*)

Treganza's Heron

Ardea herodias treganzi [194c]

Similar to the Great Blue Heron, but with the neck and upper parts much paler in color.

DISTRIBUTION—From southern Wyoming, southern Idaho, and eastern Washington southward to the region of the Slaton Sea, southern California, northern Lower California, northwestern New Mexico, and through southern New Mexico to western Texas, and up through central Colorado. In winter it is found from Texas, southern California, and Arizona south into Mexico. (Family *Ardeidae*)

Ward's Heron

Ardea herodias wardi [194b]

Similar to the Great Blue Heron, but larger, with a darker neck and whiter under parts.

LENGTH—52.00 inches.

DISTRIBUTION—Along the coast from South Carolina, Florida, the Keys, to Georgia, Alabama, Indiana, Illinois, Iowa, Kansas, Oklahoma, and the Gulf coast of Texas. Winters in southern Florida, Alabama, Texas, and southward into Mexico. (Family *Ardeidae*)

Yellow-crowned Night Heron

Nyctanassa violacea violacea [203]

ADULT MALE AND FEMALE—Upper parts, bluish-gray; the long feathers on the upper wings and between the shoulders, bluish-gray and black. Crown of head, white or buffy yellowish-white, with two or three very long plumes. Ear coverts, white or yellowish-white; rest of head, upper neck, and throat, black. Under parts, bluish-gray. Iris of eyes, orange-red; legs, greenish or yellowish-gray.

LENGTH—23.00 inches.

DISTRIBUTION—From South Carolina, southern Illinois, and Lower California southward into subtropical and tropical America. After the breeding season it straggles irregularly as far north as central New England and westward to Colorado.

These beautiful Herons sometimes wander northward in late summer and early fall. The young birds are similar

to the young of the Black-crowned Night Herons, common along the New England coast, but appreciably darker. (Family *Ardeidae*)

HONEY CREEPER FAMILY
Coerebidae

Honey Creepers are small, short-tailed, slender-billed birds—the bill being decurved like our common Brown Creeper's. The plumage shows bright greens, yellows, blues, and also grays, olives, and black. Their tongues are brushy for the securing of nectar from flowers. The birds also feed upon soft fruits. They are most abundant in the Amazon Valley, and occur also in less numbers in Ecuador, Columbia, the Bahamas, and the West Indies. A few species are found as far north as Mexico, and one reaches the Florida Keys. About seventy-five birds make

up this family. The only North American representative is the Bahama Honey Creeper (*Coereba bahamensis*).

NESTING. The nests of these little birds are usually well-made structures composed of small strips of bark, small twigs, and neatly lined with grasses and rootlets. They are roughly dome-shaped, and about five inches broad and about six inches high. The usual location is in a bush or tree, but not infrequently they may be found between two beams of an old building, or on some sill or shelf. In such cases the shape of the nest accommodates itself to the exigencies of the situation. The eggs, normally three in number, are a dull white, thickly spotted with shades of brown.

HUMMINGBIRD FAMILY
Trochilidae

Hummingbirds are the smallest birds in the world—that is to say, the smallest are found within this family. They range in size from the Giant Hummer of the higher Andes Mountains of South America (eight and a half inches in length—about two inches or so larger than our common English Sparrow), to the little Fairy Hummingbird of Cuba, barely two and a quarter inches long, and the smallest known bird. The nest of this little feathered midget is only three-quarters of an inch in diameter across the nest-cavity, and the eggs are about a quarter of an inch in length. The young are smaller than many small insects. It is interesting to picture to oneself the minuteness of the complex systems of the body within so tiny a creature: the four-chambered heart, the thousands upon thousands of blood-vessels which ramify throughout the body, the complex digestive system, reproductive system, respiratory system, nervous system, and the rest; to say nothing of the muscular system and the very complex skeleton—all within the body of a creature which itself is contained within a quarter-of-an-inch egg! The bills of Hummingbirds are long and slender, though

here there is great diversity, some being but a quarter of an inch long, while others reach a length of five inches. Some are straight, and some are much decurved. The plumage of these birds is the most brilliant in the world; gorgeous red, violet, yellow, orange, emerald green, sapphire blue, often changeable from one hue to another, and due both to pigments and to the structure of the feathers, which refract these colors to the eye. This latter mode of color production gives to most hues their metallic, scintillating, iridescent quality, and has earned for Hummingbirds as a group the name of "feathered gems." "Glittering fragments of the rainbow," Audubon called them. The breastbone of these birds possesses a deep keel, to which heavy wing muscles are attached. The wings are well adapted for flight, and are moved with such velocity, that, in the smaller species, they produce only a blur to the eye, and a buzzing or humming to the ear. The feet are very small, and delicate; the birds rarely using them for support upon the ground. They frequently perch upon small twigs, or wires. In general they are extremely fearless, aggressive birds, not hesitating to attack, upon the slightest provocation, birds many times their size. Even Hawks are not immune to their impetuous onslaughts. Hummingbirds are birds of forest clearings, less often of deep forests, and are found wherever blossoms open their chalices. The food of Hummingbirds consists chiefly of small insects, and secondly of the nectar (not honey) of flowers. Besides insects, some minute spiders are also eaten. In their visits from blossom to blossom Hummingbirds perform the very valuable service of cross-fertilization in the transference of pollen grains. The Hummingbirds of the world are entirely confined to the Western Hemisphere, ranging from Alaska to the southern tip of South America, but occurring in the greatest numbers in the Andean Mountain regions of Colombia and Ecuador. About seven hundred and fifty species and subspecies are now known. Of these, nineteen species and subspecies occur in North America. Only one, the Ruby-throated Hummingbird (*Archilochus colubris*) penetrates into the Northern States. The North American forms represent eleven genera.

NESTING. The nests of Hummingbirds vary considerably, but in general are neat, small, cup-shaped structures attached like a knot or a knob to the upper sides of branches or twigs. They are compactly composed of various fine, soft materials, such as plant downs, fine soft bits of weed bark, and pieces of silky tissue, decorated exteriorly with bits of mosses, lichens, and tiny fragments of bark, overlaced and bound firmly together with long plant down, or often with spider-web silk. The eggs are extremely small, in some cases being no larger than the smallest of the small white baking beans. They are pure unmarked white, and usually two in number; rarely one.

HUMMINGBIRD
Allen's Hummingbird
Selasphorus alleni [434]

ADULT MALE—Upper parts, bright metallic-green. Tail, brown. Throat, bright red; breast, whitish; abdomen, reddish-brown.

ADULT FEMALE—Tail tipped with black and white; throat spotted with gray; abdomen, whitish; sides, reddish-brown.

LENGTH—About 4.00 inches.

DISTRIBUTION—From British Columbia southward into California. In winter it passes through southern California and Arizona to Mexico. (Family *Trochilidae*)

Anna's Hummingbird
Calypte anna [431]

ADULT MALE—Upper parts and the central tail feathers, metallic bronze or greenish; tail, forked. Top of head, gorget, and long ruff, shimmering, flashing, metallic, deep rose-pink with greenish and bronze reflections. Under parts, white washed with greenish.

ADULT FEMALE—Similar to the male, but with crown like the back, and with the throat usually speckled with rosy-pink.

LENGTH—3.40 inches; female slightly larger.

DISTRIBUTION—In central and southern California, mainly west of the mountains, in southern Arizona, and in Lower California.

In late summer many of these brilliant Hummingbirds may be seen in southern California especially, hovering about the flowers of the tar weed, or among sunflowers. In early winter they are found among the blossoms of the eucalyptus trees; later among the

blooms of the manzanitas; and still later, in early spring, among currant bushes and in orange groves. (Family *Trochilidae*)

Arizona Blue-throated Hummingbird

Lampornis clemenciae bessophilus [427]

ADULT MALE—Upper parts, dull bronzy-green, grading to purplish-black on the upper tail coverts and on the tail. Outer tail feathers tipped with white. Gorget, brilliant azure-blue. Streak from the base of bill to the back of eye, white.

ADULT FEMALE—Similar to the male, but with the throat gorget, buffy instead of blue.

LENGTH—4.95 inches.

DISTRIBUTION—From the western part of Texas to southern Arizona, and in the mountains and tablelands of Mexico, and south to Oaxaca.

These Hummingbirds are sombre-colored and quiet; not like the agitated, restless, brilliant Hummers commoner in the United States, but rare across our Mexican border. They often climb about among the flowers of a big agave, much like orioles. (Family *Trochilidae*)

Black-chinned Hummingbird

Archilochus alexandri [429]

ADULT MALE—Upper parts, greenish. Upper portion of the gorget, opaque velvety-black; lower portion, a scintillating flashing metallic violet, reflecting iridescent blue, purple, and peacock-green lights. Under parts, soiled white; the sides of the body washed with green.

ADULT FEMALE—Upper parts, bronze with greenish reflections. Tail, rounded; central feathers, green; the next two, green tipped with black; and the outer three tipped with white.

LENGTH—3.52 inches; female somewhat longer.

DISTRIBUTION — From British Columbia southward into Lower California, and from Texas and the Rocky Mountain region westward to the Pacific. In winter it migrates into Mexico.

In Los Angeles County, California, the Black-chinned Hummingbirds are found in summer, spread from the lowlands at sea level up to the tops of the high mountains. They are most abundant, however, during the breeding season among the foothills, where in the canyons, they nest sometimes by the thousands. They have been found feeding voraciously on the nectar of the flowers of the desert Fouquieria.

The metallic colors of the gorget of this Hummer, I think, are among the

most brilliantly iridescent colors to be found in the plumage of our native birds. In contrast to the rich velvety, almost plush-black of the upper portion of the gorget, the colors of the under portion flash out with startling brilliance—shooting forth rays of living pulsating fire, now violet, now blue, now purple, now green—a play of vibrating, coruscant rays of fiery color. This is all due, of course, not to the presence of pigments, but to the structure of the feathers which refract the white light of the sun into its components, with some modification of dull brown and black pigments beneath. (Family *Trochilidae*)

Broad-billed Hummingbird

Cynanthus latirostris [441]

ADULT MALE—Entire body, metallic green; sometimes with a wash of bronze iridescence on the back. Gorget, brilliant peacock-blue. Tail, bluish-black tipped with gray and deeply emarginate. Bill, wide at its base.

ADULT FEMALE—Upper parts, green shading to gray on the forehead.

Tail with its central feathers and the basal half of its outer ones, green; the corners bluish-black tipped with gray. Behind the eye, a whitish streak; below it, a dusky one. Under parts, soiled grayish. Tail, less emarginate than that of the male.

LENGTH—3.62 inches; female slightly longer.

DISTRIBUTION—From the mountainous regions of southern Arizona and of southwestern New Mexico southward into Mexico about as far as Mexico City.

Broad-billed Hummingbirds prefer water, and may be found along streams in the high mountain canyons. They perch high on exposed twigs of trees, preferably sycamores. Their

notes are described as "flat," and differ from those of Hummingbirds in general. (Family *Trochilidae*)

Broad-tailed Hummingbird

Selasphorus platycercus platycercus [432]

ADULT MALE—Back and middle tail feathers, and top of the head, bronzy-green. Gorget, deep metallic rose-pink. Outer tail feathers, purplish, some of them edged with reddish-brown. Under parts white; sides of the body glossed with shining green.

ADULT FEMALE—Upper parts, bronzy-green. Throat, whitish with a few dark speckings, and sometimes bearing a few central feathers similar to the gorget of the male. Under parts, whitish; sides of the body, brownish. Tail marked with greenish, reddish-brown, and white.

LENGTH—4.12 inches; female slightly larger.

DISTRIBUTION — Rocky Mountains from Idaho and Wyoming to the mountains of Arizona and New Mexico, and west to the Sierra Nevada. In winter it migrates to Guatemala. (Family *Trochilidae*)

Buff-bellied Hummingbird
Amazilia yucatanensis chalconota [439]

ADULT MALE AND FEMALE—Upper parts, light greenish-bronze. Upper tail coverts, bright green. Tail, brown; the feathers tipped with bronze or violet, and forked. Throat, bright green. Breast and abdomen, buffy brown.

LENGTH—4.25 inches.

DISTRIBUTION — From the lower portion of the valley of the Rio Grande in Texas, southward in winter as far as the eastern part of Mexico.

Of this beautifully colored little Hummer, Bailey writes, "The Buff-bellied Hummingbird proves to be an abundant summer resident, and I have nowhere found it so abundant as on the military reservation at Fort Brown. Here it seems perfectly at home among the dense tangled thickets, darting rapidly among the bushes and creeping vines. . . . A rather noisy bird, its shrill cries usually first attract one's attention to its presence. (Dr. Merril, quoted by Bendire)." (Family *Trochilidae*)

Calliope Hummingbird
Stellula calliope [436]

ADULT MALE—Upper parts, golden-green. Throat, grayish-white with lilac speckles, the lance-shaped feathers at its sides with brilliant lilac tips. Under parts, white; the flanks washed with dull greenish. Upper mandible, black; lower mandible, flesh color.

ADULT FEMALE—Upper parts, slightly duller than in the male. Throat, white with dusky speckles. Under parts, pale reddish-brown, darker on the flanks. Tail, greenish, its base a reddish-brown; beyond, barred with black and tipped with a narrow white band. Slightly larger than the male.

LENGTH—Barely 3.00 inches.

DISTRIBUTION—In the mountains of the western part of the United States and Canada, from British Columbia, Montana and Idaho, to eastern Oregon and eastern California, but rarely found on the coast. In winter it passes into Mexico, as far as the mountains of Guerrero.

The little Calliope Hummer enjoys the distinction of being the smallest Hummingbird, and hence the smallest of all birds within the borders of the

United States. Its tiny body is barely three inches long, and of this, about half is accounted for by the length of the bill and tail. When plucked of its feathers, its minute body proper is about the size of the first joint of a lady's thumb. It is interesting to imagine the size of the heart, the circulatory system, the digestive, respiratory, muscular, reproductive, nervous, and skeletal systems, all packed into so small a space. (Family *Trochilidae*)

Costa's Hummingbird
Calypte costae [430]

ADULT MALE—Back, rump, and central tail feathers, green or greenish-bronze; outer ones, dusky-purple; tail, only slightly forked. Head, gorget, and long wide flaring ruff, a shimmering, scintillating metallic amethyst-violet, changing to green and to blue. Under parts, whitish; abdomen washed with green.

ADULT FEMALE—Upper parts and central tail feathers, bronzy-green; the outer feathers near tip, black terminated by white. Throat, whitish and more or less spotted with iridescent purple. Rest of under parts, whitish; the sides of the body greenish.

LENGTH—3.00 inches; female somewhat longer.

DISTRIBUTION—From south Utah and New Mexico to southern California, in winter passing to western Mexico, and Lower California. This species is chiefly a denizen of the deserts. (Family *Trochilidae*)

Heloise's Hummingbird
Atthis heloisa heloisa [435]

ADULT MALE—Head, crown, neck, and rump, shimmering greenish-gold. Wings, brownish-purple, narrow and crescentic. Throat and upper neck marked with iridescent violet spots. Neck with a white collar. Under parts, ruby-red with violet and vinaceous reflections. Flanks, rusty-yellow. Tail feathers, rounded, the two middle ones greenish-gold tipped with black; the outer ones, first brownish-red, then dull black, then tipped with snowy-white.

ADULT FEMALE—Upper parts, greenish-gold. Under parts, whitish. Violet spottings on the neck replaced by brown.

DISTRIBUTION—Central and southern Mexico; occurring casually in southern Arizona. (Family *Trochilidae*)

Lucifer Hummingbird
Calothorax lucifer [437]

ADULT MALE—Upper parts, rich bronzy-green. Tail, deeply forked; its narrow outer feathers, purplish-black; its four middle feathers, green. The gorget is a beautiful metallic shimmering violet-purple or lilac with a touch of vinaceous, and elongated into two points on the sides. Bill, long and slightly decurved. Middle of the under parts, white; sides of the body, green and brown.

ADULT FEMALE—Similar to the male, but with the upper parts duller bronzy-green. Tail not so deeply forked as in the male; the three outer feathers, brownish at their bases and white at their tips. Under parts, pale brown.

LENGTH—3.50 inches.

DISTRIBUTION—From southern Arizona and western Texas southward as far as the City of Mexico, and Puebla.

In June the Lucifer Hummingbird is common in the Chisos Mountains of western Texas, feeding among the big agaves which are in full bloom at this season. (Family *Trochilidae*)

Rieffer's Hummingbird
Amazilia tzacatl tzacatl [438]

ADULT MALE AND FEMALE—Entire bird, rich dark peacock-green; wings, purplish. Tail, chestnut-brown; the feathers, marked with bronze and square at tip. Upper tail coverts, chestnut-brown. Abdomen, brownish-gray. Bill, nearly an inch long.

LENGTH—4.00 inches.

DISTRIBUTION—From the lower portion of the Rio Grande, Texas, southward through Central America, and into Ecuador.

This deeply and richly colored Hummer is a Central American bird, and occurs in the United States as a straggler across the Mexican-Texas boundary. (Family *Trochilidae*)

Rivoli's Hummingbird

Eugenes fulgens [426]

ADULT MALE—Upper parts, bronzy-green. Top of head, glistening metallic purple. Gorget, iridescent emerald-green. Under parts, blackish-green or dull bronze with greenish reflections. Breast usually appears black. Tail, slightly forked. Bill flattened and slightly widened at its base.

ADULT FEMALE—Upper parts, bronzy-green. Top of head, dull brownish. Behind the eye, a small white spot. Under parts, brownish-gray; sides of the body washed with greenish. Outer tail feathers deeply tipped with pale gray or white.

LENGTH—4.75 inches.

DISTRIBUTION—In southeastern Arizona and the tablelands of Mexico and Nicaragua. Always among mountains.

This curious little Hummer may often be seen buzzing about among the tops of dead trees, catching insects after the manner of a Flycatcher. They have been recorded in the Chiricahua Mountains at elevations as high as 9,500 feet. (Family *Trochilidae*)

Ruby-throated Hummingbird

Archilochus colubris [428]

ADULT MALE—Upper parts, metallic greenish; wings, slightly darker. Throat, brilliant ruby-red (at the proper angle of light). Breast, whitish; abdomen, grayish with a greenish flush on the sides. Tail, forked.

ADULT FEMALE—Upper parts, duller; throat-patch, lacking. Under parts, grayish-white. Tail, not forked and its three outer feathers tipped with white.

LENGTH—3.75 inches.

DISTRIBUTION—From Labrador and the Hudson Bay region south to Florida and eastern Mexico, and west to about the central portion of South Dakota. In winter it is found from southern Florida to Central America.

This, the smallest bird of our Northern States, hovers before open flowers with wings vibrating so rapidly as to produce only the effect of a dull blur over the back. The male's bright red throat is not always visible, since the color is produced by the refraction of light from the feathers. Only occasionally does the brilliant ruby-red glisten with a live metallic sheen as the bird darts here and there. The female is decidedly a dull colored bird, and is often mistaken for a large moth —or rather, for certain large moths such as the sphinx or hummingbird moths. The only notes of the species are a series of short high squeaks, given when the bird is excited, either by love or anger. The food of the Hummer is not only nectar (not honey) of flowers, but also small insects, which latter are fed to the young by regurgitation, that is, by being pumped into the stomach of the young bird through the inserted bill of the parent. Hummingbirds may very often be seen perched on a thin twig, or more commonly on a wire stretched over the garden. They may be attracted to windows by small bottles filled with sugar-water, and adorned with some red substance, as a frill of red flannel. Red or orange are colors which strongly attract the birds. They are less responsive to others. (Family *Trochilidae*)

Rufous Hummingbird
Selasphorus rufus [433]

ADULT MALE—General color, bright reddish-brown, with the crown and sometimes the back showing bronzy-green reflections. Whitish near gorget and on the abdomen. Tail feathers, brown with dark medial streaks. Central tail feather, broad and pointed near the tip; second from the central

one, deeply notched on its inner web, and sinuated on its outer web. Gorget, brilliant flaming-red, orange, and metallic green.

ADULT FEMALE — Upper parts, bronzy becoming brownish on the rump and upper tail coverts. Tail feathers, brownish at their bases; the central ones, green almost to their bases. Outer feathers, blackish near their white tips. Under parts, soiled white, the throat sometimes showing a few flashing feathers. Sides of body washed with reddish-brown.

LENGTH — 3.50 inches; female slightly longer.

DISTRIBUTION — From the high mountains of southern California and Arizona north into Alaska. During its migrations it is found as far east as Montana, Wyoming, Colorado, New Mexico, and western Texas. It spends its winters in southern Mexico.

Rufous Hummingbirds are extremely active, vigorous, pugnacious little mites, found commonly on Mt. Shasta among the tiger lilies, painted cups, and columbines. On San Francisco Mountain, Arizona, they feed commonly from the scarlet pentstemons. In southern California they may be found among the wild gooseberry bushes in the chaparral, and among the blossoming orange trees. Their notes are a series of sharp squeaks. (Family *Trochilidae*)

Salvin's Hummingbird
Amazilia salvini [439.1]

ADULT MALE—Upper parts, dark shining green; head, iridescent blue; tail, dark shimmering green; the outer pair of feathers broadly tipped with drab. Throat, light brownish-white, its sides spotted with blue. Under parts, soiled white; the sides of the breast, greenish-blue; and the sides of the abdomen, brilliant green.

ADULT FEMALE—Similar in general to the male, but duller.

LENGTH—3.90 inches.

DISTRIBUTION—In the Huachuca Mountains, southern Arizona, and in eastern Sonora, Mexico. Exceedingly rare. (Family *Trochilidae*)

Texas Blue-throated Hummingbird
Lampornis clemenciae clemenciae [427a]

ADULT MALE—Upper parts, slaty gray with brownish and faint dull bronzy-greenish reflections. Chin and throat, iridescent and lustrous azure-blue. Wings and tail darker than back. Outer tail feathers deeply tipped with white. Under parts similar to the upper parts, but paler and duller. Under tail coverts, light gray.

ADULT FEMALE—Similar, but with buff colored throat.

LENGTH—5.00 inches.

DISTRIBUTION—From the extreme western part of Texas southward to central and southern Mexico.

A larger, darker Hummingbird, similar in general to the Blue-throated Hummingbird, and with similar habits. (Family *Trochilidae*)

White-eared Hummingbird

Hylocharis leucotis leucotis [440.1]

ADULT MALE—Upper parts, bronzy greenish-brown; forehead and chin, a deep rich blue. Behind the eye extends a prominent white stripe. Tail largely sooty or blackish. Throat and upper breast, flashing metallic emerald-green.

ADULT FEMALE—Head as in the male; under parts, gray spotted with green. Central tail feathers, wholly green or bronzy; the others black; outer feathers tipped with grayish.

LENGTH—3.32 inches.

DISTRIBUTION—From southeastern Arizona, among the mountains, southward into Nicaragua.

The White-eared Hummingbird has been found among the wild honeysuckle bushes in the Chiricahua Mountains. (Family *Trochilidae*)

Xantus's Hummingbird

Hylocharis xantusi [440]

ADULT MALE—Upper parts, greenish; chin, forehead, and cheeks, black. A wide white streak behind the eye. Tail, rusty brown. Throat, green with shimmering reflections. Under parts, whitish; sides of body washed with brownish.

ADULT FEMALE—Similar to the male, but with the outer tail feathers only, rusty brown, and the under parts, dull brownish.

LENGTH—3.60 inches.

DISTRIBUTION—Found in Lower California from about latitude 29° southward, but most common in the Cape region. (Family *Trochilidae*)

IBIS FAMILY
Ibises and Spoonbills
Threskiornithidae

Ibises are long-necked, long-legged, long-billed birds; the bill, possessing narrow grooves which extend from the nostrils to the tip. At its base the bill is very heavy and as large as the forepart of the head from which it arises, but it tapers and is curved downward near the tip. Ibises live in

flocks and feed along the shores of lakes, lagoons, salt-water embayments, and tidal mud flats. In flight, the neck is not pulled in and bent into a crook, as is the case with Herons and Bitterns, but is extended straight forward. Ibises inhabit the warmer parts of the earth, and number about thirty species. The most famous member of the family is the great sacred Ibis of the Egyptians, represented largely in the art of that ancient land. Its name in Lower Egypt is picturesque and poetic, Abou-Mengel, or "Father of the Sickle," in allusion to its long, decurved bill. Of the thirty extant species of Ibises, three species and one subspecies are found in North America, in the genera *Plegadis* and *Guara*.

Spoonbills, like Ibises, are found in the warm parts of the globe. Their habits are in general like those of Ibises, except that in feeding they swing their queer spoon-shaped bills (see illustration under Spoonbill) from side to side just under the surface of the water, to capture their minute prey. Spoonbills number six species. Only one of these, the Roseate Spoonbill (*Ajaia ajaja*) is found in our continent.

NESTING. Ibises and Spoonbills breed in colonies. Our native Ibises place their nests cozily down in among reeds and rushes, or bushes, customarily in wet swampy situations. The nests themselves are large and composed of reeds, weed stalks and the like, or of twigs from the bushes in which they are located (e.g., the White Ibis). The eggs, from three to five in number, are whitish, grayish-white, bluish-white, spotted with shades of brown and yellow (White Ibis), or plain deep bluish-green (Glossy Ibis and White-faced Glossy Ibis). The Roseate Spoonbills nest also in colonies, placing their shallow platform of sticks in cypress trees and mangrove bushes from ten to twenty-five feet from the ground, in dense tropical marshes. The eggs number three or four, and are white or dull buffy, spotted and blotched with various shades of brown.

IBIS
Eastern Glossy Ibis
Plegadis falcinellus falcinellus [186]

ADULT MALE AND FEMALE—Plumage, rich chestnut-brown; the upper parts with purplish and greenish iridescence. Lores, blackish. Under tail coverts like the back. Bill, long (five inches) and decurved. Tail, short.
LENGTH—24.00 inches.
DISTRIBUTION—In the Southeastern States this Ibis is of rare and local occurrence. It appears more frequently in subtropical and tropical America, and seldom straggles north as far as Illinois and Massachusetts. (Family *Threskiornithidae*)

Scarlet Ibis
Guara rubra [185]

ADULT MALE AND FEMALE—Plumage, scarlet; the tips of the large flight feathers, black.
LENGTH—24.00 inches.

DISTRIBUTION—"Tropical South America. Casual in the West Indies and Central America, and recorded

as an accidental straggler in New Mexico, Texas, Louisiana, and Florida." (A.O.U. Check List.) (Family *Threskiornithidae*)

White Ibis
Guara alba [184]

ADULT MALE AND FEMALE—Plumage, white; face, bright red; the four

outer primaries deeply tipped with black. Bill, long (about five inches).
LENGTH—25.00 inches.

DISTRIBUTION—From Lower California, southern Indiana and Illinois, and South Carolina, southward into tropical America. An accidental straggler as far north as South Dakota, Connecticut, and Long Island, New York. (Family *Threskiornithidae*)

White-faced Glossy Ibis
Plegadis guarauna [187]

Similar to the Eastern Glossy Ibis, but with the lores reddish instead of blackish. Usually in this species the feathers about the base of the bill are white.

DISTRIBUTION — From California, Texas, and Kansas, seldom east to

Florida; and southward through subtropical into tropical America. (Family *Threskiornithidae*)

Wood Ibis
Mycteria americana [188]

ADULT MALE AND FEMALE—Pure white. Head and neck, bare, with wrinkled dark, heavy skin. Tail, glossy black. Primaries and secondaries of wing, same. Bill, heavy at its base, and long and tapering.

LENGTH—40.00 inches.

DISTRIBUTION — From the Gulf States southward into subtropical and tropical America. After the breeding season it wanders irregularly northward and may be seen as far north as New York, Wisconsin, and California. It has even been reported in northern New England (Vermont).

This huge, stork-like bird, with its ugly, naked head, and ungainly bill

is known as the Iron Head or Goard Head, and is common in the Big Cypress Swamp of southern Florida. They nest in large colonies, and, like so many of their relatives (the Herons) are seized with a wanderlust after the cares of housekeeping and family-rearing are over, and "take a vacation" with a trip north! In the United States it has been reported as far north as Vermont, and in Canada, as far as Ontario, and even New Brunswick. (Family *Ciconiidae*)

JAÇANA FAMILY
Jacanidae

Jaçanas are rather like Rails in general appearance, except for enormously large feet, and long claws at the end of the toes. The claw of the hind toe is longer than the toe which bears it. This great spread of foot enables a Jaçana to walk with ease over the floating leaves of water lilies, and other aquatic plants. Jaçanas inhabit marshy ponds, swamps, and sluggish streams, where they make their way over the surface of the water on the floating vegetation in search of food: small frogs, insects, snails, seeds, soft bits of vegetation, and small crustaceans. The bend of the wing (wrist) is armed with a sharp spur. The colors of Jaçanas are yellow, white, brown, and a glossy black which shows purplish, bluish, and greenish reflections. Jaçanas are tropical birds, numbering about twelve species. One of these, the Mexican Jaçana (*Jacana spinosa gymnostoma*), occurs in the Central American region and southern Texas.

NESTING. The Jaçanas fashion very simple nests of reeds and the like, in

marshy spots, sometimes on the ground near, but usually on floating masses of vegetation anchored among rooted and growing rushes and weeds. The four eggs are a beautiful glossy yellowish-brown, also buff of a light olive color; sometimes plain and unmarked, but usually thickly spotted with brown.

JAÇANA
Mexican Jaçana
Jacana spinosa gymnostoma [288]

ADULT MALE AND FEMALE—Plumage, rich purplish-chestnut-brown; the head and neck, greenish-black; the quills of the wing feathers, greenish-yellow with darker tips. Sharp spur on the bend of the wing (wrist). A

broad, irregular, leaf-like, yellowish plate arises from the base of the bill and extends back over the forehead. Feet broad and spready; toes very

long and slender, and armed with long, slender, sharp claws. The claw on the hind toe is straight and is longer than the toe itself. Tail, very short.

LENGTH—8.50 inches.

DISTRIBUTION—From the lower Rio Grande Valley in Texas south to Central America, Cuba, and Haiti.

The habits of this bird are described under the heading of its family, *Jacanidae*.

JAEGER FAMILY
Skuas, and Jaegers
Stercorariidae

Jaegers and Skuas may be termed the pirates among birds. Their flight is strong, fierce, and hawklike. They outfly the swiftest Terns and Gulls, and force them to give up their lawfully caught prey. On the wide tundras of the North, where they nest, they feed upon the eggs and nestlings of other neighboring birds, and also prey upon mice, and lemmings. Their plumage is in general dark sooty brown and black above, and white or light-colored below, sometimes with markings. The wings are relatively long, and slender. The bill is hooked, and the toes, though webbed and gull-like, are armed with strong, curved, sharp talons. They might be well described as a sort of hawk-gull. Some of their popular names reflect the nature of this dual life, i.e., Robber Gulls, Gull Hawks, Teasers, Sea Hawks. After the nesting season is over, they become birds of the ocean, but occasionally are found on large bodies of inland waters. There are seven known members of the family. Three of these are found on the Antarctic seas; the other four breed in the northern parts of the Northern Hemisphere. Three species of Jaegers occur in North

America, all of the genus *Stercorarius.* Two species of Skuas occur here, contained in the genus *Catharacta.*

NESTING. These birds nest on rocky cliffs, tundras, or marshes. The nest is merely a depression in the moss or soil, sometimes with a very meager lining, or surrounded by a few bits of grass, moss, or leaf fragments. The two or three eggs are pale olive, or gray, ranging from these colors to dull greenish or brown, spotted and blotched with various shades of brown, drab, lilac, etc.

JAEGER
Long-tailed Jaeger
Stercorarius longicaudus [38]

Similar to the Parasitic Jaeger, but with a longer central pair of tail feathers—as long again as the rest of the tail.

DISTRIBUTION—Over the Northern

Hemisphere, breeding in the Arctic regions, and wintering mainly at sea. Southward as far as the Gulf of Mex-

ico, and across the Atlantic to Gibraltar. There is one record from the coast of California. (Family *Stercorariidae*)

Parasitic Jaeger
Stercorarius parasiticus [37]

ADULT MALE AND FEMALE—Back, wings, and tail, brownish slate-gray; the top of the head and the lores, darker, almost black. Sides of head and hind neck, straw-yellowish, sometimes extending down the sides of the neck and throat. Breast and abdomen, white. Sides of breast, flanks, lower abdomen, and under tail coverts, brownish-slate. Middle tail feathers, pointed and longer than the others, extending out about three inches be-

yond the next pair. (A dark phase of the plumage also occurs, in which the whole tone is much darker.)

LENGTH—17.00 inches.

DISTRIBUTION—Over the Northern Hemisphere, breeding in the Arctic regions and migrating out to sea for the winter. Ranging from Massachusetts and California southward to the coasts of South America.

The Parasitic Jaeger, with habits similar to those of the Pomarine, may be distinguished from that species by its central tail feathers, which are pointed instead of broad and oar-like. (Family *Stercorariidae*)

Pomarine Jaeger
Stercorarius pomarinus [36]

ADULT MALE AND FEMALE—Similar to the Parasitic Jaeger, but with the upper parts so much darker as to be almost black. Central tail feathers, broad. (A dark phase of the plumage also occurs, in which the entire bird is a dark slaty-brown.)

LENGTH—22.00 inches.

DISTRIBUTION—The Pomarine Jaeger is a bird of both oceans of the Northern Hemisphere, breeding north of latitude 70°. It spends its winter mainly at sea, ranging southward to South America, and crossing the oceans to southern Africa, and Australia.

The commonest Jaeger off the New England coast is the Pomarine, which appears in almost every possible plumage variation of light to dark. This interesting bird, known as the Jiddy Hawk among fishermen, pursues smaller Gulls and Terns, hectoring them until they drop the food they are carrying, which is at once seized upon and swallowed by the Jaeger. Sometimes the victim of a Jaeger's pursuit disgorges a mass of partially digested food—perhaps to lighten the body, perhaps to divert the attention and satisfy the voracity of the pursuer, and so bring the chase to an end. Although the Pomarine Jaeger is often thought of as a coward and a bully of smaller

birds, yet Forbush has noted that it does not hesitate to attack Gulls of all sizes in its quest for food, attacking even the large Glaucous Gull and the Great Black-backed Gull. The impetuosity of its dash seems to catch the

larger Gulls off their guard. The Jaegers are the true pirates of the bird world, carrying on their buccaneering on the high seas. This is merely in a manner of speaking, however, for birds know naught of right or wrong, and merely fulfill their instincts. (Family *Stercorariidae*)

JAY

Alaska Jay
Perisoreus canadensis fumifrons [484b]

Similar to the Canada Jay, but with the forehead showing a yellowish wash.

DISTRIBUTION — "Alaska; interior and west to Cook Inlet, north of southern coast region." (Chapman.) (Family *Corvidae*)

Arizona Jay
Aphelocoma sieberi arizonae [482]

ADULT MALE AND FEMALE—Upper parts, dull blue; the back with a grayish cast, sometimes brownish between the shoulders. Under parts, dull white with grayish or brownish cast; tail, rounded.

LENGTH—12.25 inches.

DISTRIBUTION—From southern New Mexico and Arizona south into northwestern Mexico. During the breeding season, on mountains, in the live-oak zones, from 3,000 to 7,000 feet. (Family *Corvidae*)

Belding's Jay
Aphelocoma californica obscura [481b]

Similar to the California Jay, but smaller and darker.

DISTRIBUTION—Southern coast region of California southward to Lower California. (Family *Corvidae*)

Black-headed Jay
Cyanocitta stelleri annectens [478c]

ADULT MALE AND FEMALE—Head, black; back, slaty blue. Forehead with bluish white. A small white spot over the eye. Somewhat similar to the Steller's Jay.

LENGTH—13.12 inches.

DISTRIBUTION—From Alberta and British Columbia southward through the northern Rocky Mountain region to northern Utah and southern Wyoming. (Family *Corvidae*)

Blue-fronted Jay
Cyanocitta stelleri frontalis [478a]

Similar to the Steller's Jay, but with the back less blue, the forehead with more blue, the rump and abdomen a more intense iridescent blue.

DISTRIBUTION — "Southern coast ranges and Sierra Nevada of California and western Nevada, from Fort Crook south to northern Lower California." (A.O.U. Check List.) (Family *Corvidae*)

California Jay
Aphelocoma californica californica [481]

ADULT MALE AND FEMALE—Upper parts, blue; middle of back and shoulders, brown. Under parts, white. Throat streaked with blue, and upper

breast with a bluish and brownish necklace. Sides of head, black bearing a white line over the eye.

LENGTH—11.87 inches.

DISTRIBUTION—From the Columbia River southward along the coast, and spreading over the zones of the Cascade and Sierra Nevada mountains south into the northern part of Lower California.

The California Jay, known commonly as the Blue Squawker, is more a bird of the lowlands and moderate foot-

hills, than its relative, the Blue-fronted Jay, and is common where oak trees and chaparral country occur. (Family *Corvidae*)

Canada Jay
Perisoreus canadensis canadensis [484]

ADULT MALE AND FEMALE—Upper parts, gray, darkening on the nape and back of the head, and lightening to whitish and then white on the forepart of the head. Wings and tail, gray; the majority of the feathers finely tipped with white. Under parts, ashy gray fading to white on the sides of the neck and throat.

LENGTH—12.00 inches.

DISTRIBUTION—In eastern North America from Newfoundland and the Hudson Bay region to New Brunswick and Nova Scotia, and southwestward through northern New England and New York, across into northern Minnesota, and thence westward to the Rocky Mountains of Alberta.

The familiar Whiskey Jack of the north woods, also called the Moose Bird, Meat Hawk, Grease Bird, Venison Jay, and Camp Robber, is, despite

the disparagement implied by these uncouth names, a cheerful rascal, and one who does much to relieve the tedium of life in the north country. Thief, he undoubtedly is about the camp, yet, as Gladden happily remarks, ". . . the man who doesn't enjoy being robbed by such a thief had better stay home and sit in the parlor." His notes are various and diverting (except when one is still-hunting!) and consist of numerous screams, squawks, rolling whistles, and many nasal notes. In his demure dress of gray, black, and white, he does not at all resemble the other members of his flamboyant family. (Family *Corvidae*)

Coast Jay

Cyanocitta stelleri carbonacea [478e]
Similar to both the Steller's Jay and the Blue-fronted Jay, but intermediate in size and coloration.

DISTRIBUTION — "Humid Pacific Coast strip from northern Oregon to the Santa Lucia Mountains, California; east to the Gabilan and Mt. Diabolo ranges, and the mountains on the western side of the Napa Valley." (A.O.U. Check List.) (Family *Corvidae*)

Couch's Jay

Aphelocoma sieberi couchi [482a]

ADULT MALE AND FEMALE—Upper parts, bright azure-blue; the back and scapulars dulled with grayish. Throat, whitish; breast, brownish-gray; abdomen and under tail coverts, pure white.

LENGTH—11.50 inches.

DISTRIBUTION—From western Texas south into eastern Mexico. In the United States (Texas) the Couch's Jay is found only in the Chisos Mountains. (Family *Corvidae*)

Florida Jay

Aphelocoma coerulescens [479]

ADULT MALE AND FEMALE—Back, pale brownish-gray; crown, sides of the head, neck, wings, and tail, grayish-blue. Under parts, grayish-white,

indistinctly streaked on the throat and breast with gray. Band across the breast, and sides, obscure grayish-blue.

LENGTH—11.50 inches.

DISTRIBUTION—The central portion of Florida, mainly along the coasts, from about the latitude of St. Augustine south to the latitude of Lake Okeechobee.

A bird not to be confused with the Florida Blue Jay, which is of a different genus (*Cyanocitta*). The Florida Jays travel in flocks, and inhabit scrub growths, chiefly along the coastal zones, where they feed on or near the ground. (Family *Corvidae*)

Florida Blue Jay
Cyanocitta cristata florincola [477a]

Similar to the Northern Blue Jay, but smaller, with the upper parts showing a slightly more purplish cast, and with the wings slightly less prominently marked with black and white.

DISTRIBUTION—From Florida, westward along the Gulf Coast to southeastern Texas. (Family *Corvidae*)

Gray Jay
Perisoreus obscurus griseus [485a]

Similar to the Canada Jay, but larger, and a deeper gray with less brownish. Under parts also grayer and less brownish.

DISTRIBUTION—From British Columbia south through Washington and Oregon, east of the Cascade Mountains, and into northern California. (Family *Corvidae*)

Green Jay
Xanthoura luxuosa glaucescens [483]

ADULT MALE AND FEMALE—Upper parts, bluish-green with a pale bluish cast. Middle tail feathers, bluish-green; outer ones, pale yellow. Top of head, bluish-purple; sides of head marked with same color and black. Forehead with small white patch. Throat and sides, under auricular region, black, which extends down into the upper breast and is sharply de-

fined. The most strikingly colored of the Jays.

LENGTH—11.50 inches.

DISTRIBUTION—From the region of the lower Rio Grande in Texas southward into northeastern Mexico.

The Green Jay is a bird of thorny thickets, and in good light a striking and colorful bird. (Family *Corvidae*)

Long-crested Jay
Cyanocitta stelleri diademata [478b]

Similar to the Steller's Jay, but with upper parts less blue; the rump and abdomen, a more intense iridescent blue; the forehead bearing pale bluish-white streaks; and a white spot over the eye. Crest, longer.

DISTRIBUTION—From southern Wyoming, eastern Utah, and the higher mountains of northwestern Arizona, south to New Mexico. (Family *Corvidae*)

Long-tailed Jay
Aphelocoma californica immanis [481c]

Similar to the California Jay, but larger.

DISTRIBUTION—In the valleys of Oregon, between the Cascade Mountains and the Coast Ranges; in extreme southern Washington; and in the valleys of the Sacramento and San Joaquin rivers, in California. (Family *Corvidae*)

Nicasio Jay
Aphelocoma californica oocleptica [481d]

Similar to the California Jay, and sometimes called the Swarth California Jay.

DISTRIBUTION—In California from the region of Humboldt Bay southward, and west of the Coast Ranges along the coast from the eastern side of San Francisco Bay. (Family *Corvidae*)

Northern Blue Jay
Cyanocitta cristata cristata [477]

ADULT MALE AND FEMALE—Upper parts, grayish-blue; wings and tail, bright blue marked with narrow black bars and broad white spots. Head, crested. Throat, gray; irregular collar about breast and neck, black. Abdomen, white.

LENGTH—11.74 inches.

DISTRIBUTION—The whole of eastern North America, from Labrador and the Hudson Bay region south to Georgia and northern Texas, and west to the Great Plains.

The familiar "Jay Bird" ranges over a greater area than any other member of this large group, and is a familiar sight to the dwellers of lumber camps, farms, and towns. Their notes are numerous, some raucous, others distinctly musical. The commonest call is a harsh, nasal *jaay, jaay;* another less common one is similar to the scream of the Red-shouldered Hawk, *tee-aare, tee-aare;* and a still less common one, an utterance quite unlike any of the bird's other calls, is a pleasingly musical, rolling, flute-like, *kerdle, kerdle, kerdle,* or *too-weedle, too-weedle, too-weedle.* The Blue Jay has been called "The Planter of Oak Forests," since it hides acorns in all sorts of places, or loses them from its bill in flight—in most cases never retrieving the nut, which may spring up where it falls. Insects of the larger

sort, small amphibians, all sorts of small invertebrates, seeds, and nuts form a large percentage of the food of the jay. It also takes a considerable

number of eggs and nestlings. Even this does a good service, as it is one of Nature's devices for maintaining the proper balance of life. Blue Jays come readily to winter feeding stations, where their attractive colors, active movements, and loud cheerful voices add much to brighten the dreary days of winter. (Family *Corvidae*)

Oregon Jay
Perisoreus obscurus obscurus [485]

Similar to the Canada Jay, but with less white on the forehead; the shafts

of the back feathers, whitish; and the under parts, white.

DISTRIBUTION—From southern British Columbia along the coast southward into northern California. (Family *Corvidae*)

Piñon Jay
Cyanocephalus cyanocephalus [492]

ADULT MALE AND FEMALE—Entire bird nearly uniform grayish-blue, the color brightening somewhat on the head, which is not crested. Throat marked with white streaks. The tail is cut square across, and is much shorter than the wings. Claws, long and curved.

LENGTH—11.37 inches.

DISTRIBUTION—In the western portion of North America from southern British Columbia, eastward to the Rocky Mountains, westward to the Sierra Nevada and Cascade mountains, and southward to New Mexico and Lower California.

Piñon Jays are found characteristically among the Piñon Pines of the western mountains, actively flying about, usually in small flocks, feeding on their

staple, the piñon nuts. These gregarious birds often breed in colonies, and after the young are out of the nest, band together in great companies and go trouping about the country, their flocks resembling the great ragged aggregations of Grackles and other Blackbirds that one often sees in the East. Their flight is somewhat similar to the Crow's, and as they go they utter a crow-like *cahw, cahw*, higher in pitch and less vigorous than the note of their blacker and larger cousin. (Family *Corvidae*)

Queen Charlotte Jay
Cyanocitta stelleri carlottae [478d]

Similar to the Steller's Jay, but darker.

DISTRIBUTION—Restricted to the Queen Charlotte Islands, British Columbia. (Family *Corvidae*)

Rocky Mountain Jay
Perisoreus canadensis capitalis [484a]

Similar to the Canada Jay, but with the gray at the back of the head lighter and more restricted, and the head white.

DISTRIBUTION — In the Rocky Mountain region, from Montana and Idaho south to New Mexico and Arizona. (Family *Corvidae*)

Santa Cruz Jay
Aphelocoma insularis [481.1]

Similar to the California Jay, but larger; the upper parts, a darker, more intense blue. The notes of this species are similar also to those of the California species, but harsher.

DISTRIBUTION—Restricted to the island of Santa Cruz, twenty-five miles out from Santa Barbara, California. (Family *Corvidae*)

Semple's Blue Jay
Cyanocitta cristata semplei [477b]

Similar to the Northern Blue Jay, but with the upper parts a paler, duller blue; the under parts, whiter; and the lower part of the throat, less bluish.

DISTRIBUTION—Confined to central and southern Florida. (Family *Corvidae*)

Steller's Jay
Cyanocitta stelleri stelleri [478]

ADULT MALE AND FEMALE—Whole head, neck, upper back, and breast, dull blackish. Lower back, upper tail coverts, and abdomen, pale blue. Wings and tail, purplish-blue barred with blackish.

LENGTH—12.50 inches.

DISTRIBUTION—From Cook Inlet, Alaska, and Vancouver Island southward along the Pacific Coast to Monterey, California, spreading east to the Cascade Mountains.

In the deep dank forests of the Puget Sound region, as well as among the

great redwood forests of California farther south, the Steller's Jay is found in abundance. It is without doubt the most strikingly colored of any member of its family. In general habits it is similar to its far eastern cousin, the Northern Blue Jay, but its notes are harsher, like the syllables *checker, checker, checker, check.* (Family *Corvidae*)

Texas Jay
Aphelocoma californica texana [480.2]

Similar to the Woodhouse's Jay, but with a distinct whitish line over the eye. Throat and part of upper breast with faint streaks; rest of under parts

a pale brownish-gray; under tail coverts, white.

DISTRIBUTION — The southeastern portion of Texas. (Family *Corvidae*)

Woodhouse's Jay
Aphelocoma californica woodhousei [480]

ADULT MALE AND FEMALE—Middle of back and scapulars, slate gray; rest of upper parts, dull blue. Tail, blue. Under parts, gray; throat and part of upper breast, white or whitish streaked irregularly with dark gray. Under tail coverts, blue. Bill, heavy and about an inch long.

LENGTH—12.12 inches.

DISTRIBUTION — In the western United States chiefly in the Great Basin country.

A bird quite similar to the California Jay, but inhabiting the region to the east of the Sierra Nevada Mountains instead of to the west. In good light

the Woodhouse's Jay appears slightly the grayer bird of the two. (Family *Corvidae*)

Xantus's Jay
Aphelocoma californica hypoleuoa [481a]

Similar to the California Jay, but much paler; under parts, whiter.

DISTRIBUTION—Restricted to the southern portion of Lower California south of the Sebastian Vizcaino Bay. (Family *Corvidae*)

JUNCO

Arizona Junco
Junco phaeonotus palliatus [570]

Similar to the Slate-colored Junco, but with the back, shoulders (wrists), and tertial wing feathers, reddish-brown; and with grayish-white under parts.

DISTRIBUTION—From the mountainous regions of southern Arizona southward, probably as far as northern Mexico. (Family *Fringillidae*)

Baird's Junco
Junco bairdi [571]

Similar to the Slate-colored Junco, but with the head gray, the throat and breast grayish-white, and the sides of the body washed with light brown.

DISTRIBUTION — Restricted to the southern portion of Lower California. (Family *Fringillidae*)

Carolina Junco
Junco hyemalis carolinensis [567e]

Similar to the Slate-colored Junco, but larger; the slaty-gray plumage showing no trace of a brownish cast.

DISTRIBUTION—Along the higher Allegheny Mountains from Virginia to Georgia. (Family *Fringillidae*)

Gray-headed Junco
Junco caniceps [570b]

Similar to the Slate-colored Junco, but with the whole head, breast, and sides

of the body, ashy-gray; and with a large bright reddish-brown back patch.

DISTRIBUTION—In the high mountains in the southern part of Wyoming, Utah, Colorado, Nevada, and New Mexico. (Family *Fringillidae*)

Guadalupe Junco
Junco insularis [572]

Similar to the Pink-sided Junco, but smaller, and with a darker head and breast.

DISTRIBUTION—Restricted to Guadalupe Island off the coast of Lower California. (Family *Fringillidae*)

Hanson Laguna Junco
Junco oreganus pontilis [567j]

Resembles the Townsend's Junco, but with the back slightly browner, and the head and throat a darker slate color.

DISTRIBUTION—In the Sierra Juarez, of northern Lower California. (Family *Fringillidae*)

Montana Junco
Junco oreganus montanus [567f]

Similar to the Slate-colored Junco, but with a decidedly browner back, and with the sides of the body exhibiting a broad pinkish-brown suffusion.

DISTRIBUTION—From the latitude of Alberta southward to northern Idaho, northeastern Montana, and along the higher mountains. In winter it spreads southward as far as Mexico, and occasionally straggles eastward as far as the Mississippi River, and northward, rarely, into Maryland and even Massachusetts. (Family *Fringillidae*)

Oregon Junco
Junco oreganus oreganus [567a]

ADULT MALE—Whole head, neck, and upper breast, very dark slate-gray. Patch in middle of back, dark brown. Abdomen, white. Sides of body, a brownish flesh color. Outer pair of

tail feathers, pure white; the two succeeding pair, partly white.

ADULT FEMALE—Paler than the
male, with the nape and back more
brownish.

LENGTH—6.00 inches.

DISTRIBUTION—Along the Pacific
Coast of North America, from Alaska

southward as far as northern British
Columbia, and in winter spreading
southward to California. (Family
Fringillidae)

Pink-sided Junco
Junco mearnsi [567g]

ADULT MALE—Whole head, neck,
and breast, light gray; the back, grayish brown. Sides of the body broadly
washed with pink. Abdomen, white.

ADULT FEMALE—Similar to the
male, but with the nape and crown

also brownish, and the sides of the
body a much paler pink.

LENGTH—6.20 inches.

DISTRIBUTION—In the southern
parts of Montana and Idaho, spreading southward in winter into Wyoming and Colorado, and as far as the
northern portion of Mexico. (Family
Fringillidae)

Point Pinos Junco
Junco oreganus pinosus [567d]

Similar to the Slate-colored Junco, but
with a pale, flesh-colored brown back,
and a gray throat and breast.

DISTRIBUTION—Restricted to the
Santa Cruz region of the coast of
southern California, and in winter
spreading eastward to the Santa Clara
and the San Benito valleys. (Family
Fringillidae)

Red-backed Junco
Junco phaeonotus dorsalis [570a]

Similar to the Slate-colored Junco, but
with a reddish-brown back patch, and
grayish-white under parts.

DISTRIBUTION—In the high mountains of central Arizona, and in New
Mexico, spreading southwestward in
winter as far as western Texas and
northern Mexico. (Family *Fringillidae*)

Shufeldt's Junco
Junco oreganus shufeldti [567b]

Similar to the Oregon Junco, but
larger, and showing a paler brown
back patch.

DISTRIBUTION—The Pacific Coast
of North America, from British Columbia south to Oregon; spreading in
winter southward as far as the northern portion of Mexico. (Family *Fringillidae*)

Slate-colored Junco
Junco hyemalis hyemalis [567]

ADULT MALE—Upper parts, throat,
and breast, dark slate-gray, sometimes

appearing almost black. Abdomen, white, sharply marked off from the rest of the dark plumage. Two outer tail feathers, and a part of the third, white, showing conspicuously in flight. Bill, pinkish or flesh-color, prominent against the dark head.

ADULT FEMALE—Upper parts, dull brownish-gray. Under parts as in the male, but the throat and breast, paler gray. Bill as in the male.

LENGTH—6.27 inches.

DISTRIBUTION—In eastern North America from Labrador and Alaska south to northern New England, northern New York, northern Minnesota, and extending southward along the higher Allegheny Mountains into Pennsylvania. In winter it spreads downward into the lowlands from the mountains where it has been nesting (within the borders of the United States), and winters from central New England southward as far as the Gulf of Mexico.

The Junco, or Snowbird, is one of the commonest of our winter birds, and may almost invariably be found wherever there are weed patches rising above the snow. The birds characteristically fly just ahead of the walker along country roads, particularly where there are bushes and weeds bordering wide fields, showing promi-

nently their white outer tail feathers as they go. On their nesting grounds, in the mountains of New England, and in the cool coniferous forests of

the north, the Juncos give voice to a soft, sweet, trilled song, similar to that of the Chipping Sparrow, but richer and more melodious. When flocks of the birds rise together and whisk away over some winter field, they utter a sharp tinkling *titit*, or *tit-it-it*, as they pass over, in a sort of careless, flippy flight. Sixteen members of the genus *Junco* are found in North America, all with somewhat similar coloration and habits. (Family *Fringillidae*)

Thurber's Junco

Junco oreganus thurberi [567c]

Similar to the Slate-colored Junco, but with the back a light flesh-colored brown.

DISTRIBUTION—In the western mountains of southern Oregon, south-

ward to northern California; spreading eastward as far as western Nevada. (Family *Fringillidae*)

Townsend's Junco

Junco oreganus townsendi [567i]

Similar to the Slate-colored Junco, but with the back slightly paler, and showing a more brownish cast.

DISTRIBUTION—Among the mountains of the northern section of Lower California. (Family *Fringillidae*)

White-winged Junco
Junco aikeni [566]

Similar to the Slate-colored Junco, but larger; the upper parts, a lighter gray; the wings showing two white bars; and the tail showing slightly more white.

DISTRIBUTION—Wyoming and western North Dakota, passing in winter to Colorado and western Kansas, and occasionally to Indiana and Wisconsin. In the mountains of Colorado this hardy little bird, while found commonly in the lowlands, ascends to the surprising winter altitude of about eight thousand feet, where the conditions are anything but mild. (Family *Fringillidae*)

KESTREL
Kestrel
Falco tinnunculus tinnunculus [359.1]

In general similar in coloration to the Eastern Sparrow Hawk, but larger; with the tail, slaty-blue, less bluish on

the wings, and fewer dark markings about the head.

LENGTH—About 13.50 inches.

DISTRIBUTION—This European species, so common in England where it

is often called the Windhover, occurs as a rare straggler in Greenland, and once in Massachusetts. In habits it is similar to our various North American Sparrow Hawks. (Family *Falconidae*)

KINGBIRD
Arkansas Kingbird
Tyrannus verticalis [447]

Upper parts, ashy gray; wings, brownish; tail, black with white edges. The male alone bears a crown-patch of orange-red feathers. Throat, ashy

white; breast, light gray; abdomen, sulphur-yellow. Slightly larger than the Eastern Kingbird.

DISTRIBUTION—From southern British Columbia, Assiniboia, and southern Alberta, east to the longitude of central South Dakota, and west to the Pacific. It winters in Mexico and Central America. (Family *Tyrannidae*)

Cassin's Kingbird
Tyrannus vociferans [448]

Upper parts, slate-gray with an olive cast; the wings with a brownish cast. Tail in spring and winter edged on its sides and tip with gray. Chin, white; throat and breast, dark gray; abdomen, sulphur-yellow. The male alone possesses a crown-patch of orange-red feathers, as in the Eastern Kingbird.

DISTRIBUTION—From southern Wyoming south and west to western Texas, New Mexico, Arizona, and northwestern Mexico. (Family *Tyrannidae*)

Couch's Kingbird
Tyrannus melancholicus couchi [446]

ADULT MALE—Upper parts, gray with a greenish tinge in strong light. Wings and notched tail, brown; the feathers edged with whitish. Crown bears a concealed orange patch. Throat, white, grading through greenish-gray to brilliant lemon-yellow on the abdomen. Under tail coverts, white.

ADULT FEMALE—Similar to the male but smaller, with a smaller crown patch, and a less deeply notched tail.

LENGTH—9.50 inches.

DISTRIBUTION—From the lower portion of the Rio Grande in Texas southward through Mexico to the central portion of Central America. (Family *Tyrannidae*)

Eastern Kingbird
Tyrannus tyrannus [444]

ADULT MALE AND FEMALE—Upper parts, slaty gray, shading to blackish on the crown and upper tail coverts. The crown bears a partially concealed crest of orange-red feathers. Wings with a brownish cast; tail tipped with a conspicuous band of pure white. Breast, white, slightly washed with grayish; abdomen, white.

LENGTH—8.51 inches.

DISTRIBUTION—From New Brunswick and Manitoba south to Florida, and from western British Columbia to Utah, Nevada, northeastern California, and to eastern Texas. It winters in Mexico, through Central America into South America.

From an elevated perch such as the tip of a dead branch, the top of a mullein stalk, telegraph pole, or fence post, the Kingbird, with wings stiffly and rapidly quivering, sallies out after passing insects. With true Flycatcher precision the insect is snapped up, and the bird returns to its perch. Just before alighting, it spreads out its blackish tail, displaying the pure white terminal band. Kingbirds pursue

Crows and Hawks with unusual pertinacity, often for long distances; sometimes in their headlong fury descending upon their heads and backs to tweak out a billfull of feathers. The notes of the species are of a quivering and spasmodic character, quite in accord with the bird's characteristic flight, and may be represented by the syllables *kitter, kitter, kitter*. Although not a true songbird, the Kingbird occasionally utters a sweet, rather jittery sort of song, which is low and pleasing in quality, and given forth only during the early morning hours, often before sunrise. The orange-red feathers of the head bear a distant resemblance to a royal crown. These are usually concealed, except when the crest-feathers are raised in anger or alarm, when they are visible only from above. (Family *Tyrannidae*)

Gray Kingbird
Tyrannus dominicensis dominicensis [445]

Somewhat similar to the Eastern Kingbird, but a trifle larger, and with no white terminal tail band. Ear coverts, black; under wing coverts, yellowish.

DISTRIBUTION—From South Carolina along the Atlantic Coast to Florida, and into the West Indies. It win-

ters in Mexico, Central America, and the Lesser Antilles. (Family *Tyrannidae*)

Lichtenstein's Kingbird

Tyrannus melancholicus chloronotus [446a]

This species, similar in general to the Couch's Kingbird, ranges from southern Mexico southward. It has been reported as an accidental straggler in Maine. (Family *Tyrannidae*)

West Mexican Kingbird

Tyrannus melancholicus occidentalis [446b]

In this subspecies, the upper tail coverts are a light grayish, and the under parts a very pale yellow.

DISTRIBUTION—Found in western Mexico, and also as an accidental straggler in Jefferson County, Washington. (Family *Tyrannidae*)

KINGFISHER FAMILY
Alcedinidae

Kingfishers form a large family of more than two hundred and fifty species and subspecies. Most of them are found in the Malayan Archipelago and in the islands of the Pacific. Some are very brilliantly colored. In this family, while there are some exceptions, the head is large and crested, the bill very heavy and long, the body and tail short and stout, and the feet very small and weak. The colors represented in the plumage are chiefly greens, blues, and chestnuts, with white. Only four members of this great family are recorded in North America in the genera *Megaceryle* and *Chloroceryle*.

NESTING. Our Western Hemisphere Kingfishers excavate horizontal tun-

nels in sand banks, at the end of which a roundish chamber is formed for the reception of the eggs which are deposited upon the bare soil. They number from five to eight, and are pure white.

KINGFISHER
Eastern Belted Kingfisher
Megaceryle alcyon alcyon [390]

ADULT MALE—Upper parts, grayish-blue, the feathers of the wing tipped with white, and a white spot before the eye. Tail feathers, narrowly barred with white. Collar, white; band across the breast, bluish-gray. Lower breast and abdomen, white. The feathers of the head are long, and frequently raised in a prominent crest. Bill, long and heavy. Feet, small and weak.

ADULT FEMALE—Similar to the male in pattern, but with an additional chestnut band across the breast, and with the sides of the body chestnut-brown.

LENGTH—13.02 inches.

DISTRIBUTION—Over almost the entire continent, from the Arctic regions to the Gulf of Mexico. In winter it is found from Virginia, Kansas, and southern California southward into northern South America.

The Belted Kingfisher is a peculiar looking bird. As it sits on an exposed perch over the water, its heavy crested

head, large bill, small feet, and relatively short tail give it a "top-heavy" appearance. Suddenly it drops from its perch and plunges headforemost into the water with a great splash, emerging a moment afterwards with a fish in its bill. Frequently its nest is built far from its fishing grounds—wherever a sand-bank offers an opportunity for the bird to excavate its long tunnel inward to the depth of two or three feet. The note of the Kingfisher is unmistakable—a loud, harsh rattle, sometimes repeated several times as the bird flies upstream. Kingfishers prefer lakes, ponds, and streams, and are seldom found along the seacoast, except where estuaries penetrate the land. (Family *Alcedinidae*)

Ringed Kingfisher
Megaceryle torquata torquata [390.1]

ADULT MALE—Upper parts, bluish-gray streaked with blackish. Tail spotted with white. Throat and collar, white; the breast and abdomen, a reddish-brown. Under tail coverts, white.

ADULT FEMALE—Similar to the male, but with bluish-gray breast bordered below by white. Under tail coverts, reddish-brown.

LENGTH—16.25 inches.

DISTRIBUTION—Confined to tropical America, except for the West Indies. Occurs sometimes in the southern part of the Rio Grande Valley in Texas. (Family *Alcedinidae*)

Texas Kingfisher
Chloroceryle americana septentrionalis [391]

ADULT MALE—Upper parts, greenish; the wings spotted with white. Upper breast with a broad band of chestnut-brown, bordered below by a zone of green spots. Throat, collar, and abdomen, pure white.

ADULT FEMALE—Similar to the male, but lacking the chestnut-brown

breast-band, and with two bands of green spots crossing the breast. The heads of the birds are not crested.

LENGTH—8.00 inches.

DISTRIBUTION—From southern Texas and Mexico to Panama. (Family *Alcedinidae*)

Western Belted Kingfisher
Megaceryle alcyon caurina [390a]

Similar to the Eastern Belted Kingfisher, but larger, especially the wings.

DISTRIBUTION—In northwestern North America and California. (Family *Alcedinidae*)

KINGLET FAMILY
Kinglets, Warblers, and Gnatcatchers
Sylviidae

This large family comprises the Old World Warblers (not to be confused with our native Wood Warblers of the Family *Compsothlypidae*), the Kinglets, and Gnatcatchers. Of the

Old World Warblers, over five hundred species and subspecies are known. Of these, but two are reported from North America, the Kennicott's Willow Warbler (*Acanthopneuste borealis kennicotti*), and the Middendorff's Grasshopper Warbler (*Locustella ochotensis*). Kinglets are tiny birds, less than five inches long; grayish olivegreen, with small golden or orange "crowns." Their motions are quick and agitated, and as they move, their wings are constantly flitted. Gnatcatchers are small, grayish, long-tailed birds, and resemble miniature Mockingbirds. Seven North American Gnatcatchers are recorded, in the genus *Polioptila;* and six Kinglets, of the genera *Regulus* and *Corthylio*.

NESTING. The nests of *Sylvids* are small, neat cup-shaped structures, about one-and-a-half to four-and-a-half inches in diameter, built up of mosses, and lined with weed bark, fine rootlets, hair, soft grasses, sometimes with milkweed or cattail down, and a few feathers, often decorated with lichens. They are placed usually in a coniferous tree, from twenty-five to sixty feet from the ground, either saddled on a branch, or pensile, or nearly so. The eggs number from four to five

up to ten in some species, and are a dull creamy or buffy white, or a greenish or bluish white, with fine spots, speckles, or blotches of pale brown, chiefly about the larger end.

KINGLET
Dusky Kinglet
Corthylio calendula obscurus [749b]

Similar to the Eastern Ruby-crowned Kinglet, but with the upper parts a darker, more leaden gray; the bill larger; and the wings and tail somewhat shorter.

DISTRIBUTION—Found on Guadalupe Island off the coast of Lower California. (Family *Sylviidae*)

Eastern Golden-crowned Kinglet
Regulus satrapa satrapa [748]

ADULT MALE—Similar to the adult male Eastern Ruby-crowned Kinglet, except that the crown patch is orange in its center, bordered first by yellow and then by black, giving the whole patch a much more golden-yellow appearance. Line over the eye, white.

ADULT FEMALE—Crown patch, yellow only, bordered by black.

LENGTH—4.07 inches.

DISTRIBUTION—From the Northern States northward into Canada, and southward following the Rocky Mountain zone into Mexico and the Allegheny Mountains into North Carolina. It spends its winters in the Southern States and in Mexico.

This diminutive little mite in feathers, ranking among our smallest birds, is, in general respects of habit, food, and breeding, essentially similar to the Eastern Ruby-crown. In the Eastern States in winter, it appears among our bushes, coppices, and cedars, usually in small flocks, and may be seen agitatedly searching for its winter food of scale insects and aphid eggs. Old orchards are one of its favorite haunts, especially in spring when it hovers about near the tips of twigs, where leaf and flower buds are beginning to expand. It is more a bird of twig-tips than its Ruby-crowned cousin. Its call note, a characteristic sound of winter

in some localities, though so thin and fine as to be inaudible except to keen ears, sounds like the syllables *tsee, tsee, tsee,* a sibilous, lisping note. Its song is not warbled and varied like that of the Ruby-crown, but is a series of variants of the call which is sweeter and delivered with more power: *tsee, tsee, tsee, tsee, tsee, ti ti ti ti ti ti ti,* in an ascending and descending cadence. There are several variations of this song, and — very infrequently — the bird breaks out into a more varied strain, faintly reminiscent of the song of the Ruby-crown. (Family *Sylviidae*)

Eastern Ruby-crowned Kinglet
Corthylio calendula calendula [749]

ADULT MALE—Upper parts, greenish-gray, decidedly greenish in strong light; wing bars, whitish. Top of head with a small brilliant orange-red crown patch, partially concealed except when the bird excitedly raises the crown feathers. Under parts, grayish-white.
ADULT FEMALE—Similar, but lacking the bright crown patch.
LENGTH—4.41 inches.
DISTRIBUTION—From the Northern States northward into Canada; south-

ward along the Rocky Mountain zone into Arizona, and along the Sierra Nevada Mountains into California; into the high mountains of New England. It spends the winter from the latitude of South Carolina and Oregon southward as far as Central America.

Ruby-crowns are birds of the edges of woods, where smaller trees and bushes abound; or of pastures overgrown with this same kind of vegetation. They are fond of cedars and of coniferous trees in general, moving restlessly about among the branches and twigs in search of minute insects. As they go they continually flit the wings in a nervous manner. This distinctive habit, together with their small size and agitated ways, proclaims them to be Kinglets; while their harsh gritty call note (like the squeaky grating of a pair of tiny rusty scissors) serves to

identify them as Ruby-crowns. The song of the bird is remarkable. It commences with several thin, high, wiry notes; and then expands into a warbled melody—sweet, intricate, loud, long-protracted, and uttered with a resounding vigor quite surprising for so diminutive a performer. Both the Ruby and the Golden-crowned Kinglets are extremely beneficial birds among trees, since their diet consists almost wholly of insects which are detrimental to the leaf and blossom buds, as well as of aphids, bark beetles, scale insects, grasshoppers, and various species of small bugs. Insect eggs are also eaten. (Family *Sylviidae*)

Sitka Kinglet

Corthylio calendula grinnelli [749a]

Similar to the Eastern Ruby-crowned Kinglet, but smaller and darker, and with the bill appreciably larger.

DISTRIBUTION—From Prince William Sound and Skaguay, Alaska, to British Columbia, along the Pacific Coast. In winter it is found as far south as the middle portion of California. (Family *Sylviidae*)

Western Golden-crowned Kinglet

Regulus satrapa olivaceus [748a]

Similar to the common Eastern Golden-crowned Kinglet, but with the plumage much brighter, and the upper parts more olivaceous, especially on the rump and the tail.

LENGTH—4.07 inches.

DISTRIBUTION — From Kodiak Island and the Kenai Peninsula, Alaska, southward to the San Jacinto Mountains of California, and New Mexico. In winter it is found from British Columbia to the highlands of Mexico, and southward into Guatemala. (Family *Sylviidae*)

Western Ruby-crowned Kinglet

Corthylio calendula cineraceus [749c]

Resembles the Eastern Ruby-crowned Kinglet, but is larger, paler, grayer in color, and shows less yellowish tinge.

DISTRIBUTION—In the Siskiyou Mountains and the Sierra Nevada, southward, and less commonly in the San Jacinto, San Gabriel, and San Bernardino mountains, California; also in Idaho. It winters in southern California, and in the interior in sheltered valleys west of the Sierra Nevada, and in Lower California. (Family *Sylviidae*)

KITE

Everglade Kite

Rostrhamus sociabilis plumbeus [330]

ADULT MALE—Plumage, dark (almost black) slate-blue. Head and upper back, lighter gray. Tail coverts, markings near base of tail, and tips of tail feathers, white. Bill slender, very sharply pointed, very much decurved, and black. Area about base of bill, as well as legs and feet, orange.

ADULT FEMALE—Upper parts, rusty black. Sides of the head sparingly marked with white or whitish. Tail, brown tipped with white. Under parts streaked and mottled with lighter and darker shades of brown, and whitish.

LENGTH—17.50 inches.

DISTRIBUTION—Florida, and south into Cuba, eastern Mexico and Central America. In winter it is not found north of the central part of Florida.

This strikingly colored Kite is found only in the region of large fresh-water marshes and lagoons, and along the

swampy shores of lakes, where it feeds apparently exclusively upon a single genus of large fresh-water snails. It flaps and sails, in the same leisurely manner as the Marsh Hawk, closely above the tops of rushes and along the shores, in its ceaseless search for its lowly prey. Its slender, sharp, much decurved bill is well adapted for extracting the snail's soft body from its shelly housing. (Family *Accipitridae*)

Mississippi Kite

Ictinia misisippiensis [329]

ADULT MALE AND FEMALE—Plumage, bluish-gray. Head, neck, and secondaries of wing, much lighter. Shoulders and primaries of wing, dark bluish-gray streaked with chestnut. Tail, black, cut almost square across. Legs and feet, yellow-orange or orange-red.

LENGTH—15.00 inches.

DISTRIBUTION—This rare Kite, becoming rarer and in danger of extinction unless vigorously protected, used to breed over a large part of the central United States, and eastward through Mississippi to South Carolina. Now it is found breeding only in parts of South Carolina, Kansas, Oklahoma, Tennessee, and the Gulf States. It has occurred as an accidental visitant in Colorado, Nebraska, Wisconsin, Pennsylvania, and New Jersey. In winter it is found in southeastern Texas, and down through Mexico, sometimes as far as Guatemala; and in Florida.

The Mississippi Kite resembles the Swallow-tailed Kite in its general habits. It feeds upon insects, small

reptiles, salamanders, frogs, toads, and the like, but does not attack mammals nor small birds. Like the Swallow-

tailed Kite it carries its prey firmly gripped in its talons, often tearing it in pieces which it swallows while in flight. (Family *Accipitridae*)

Swallow-tailed Kite

Elanoïdes forficatus forficatus [327]

ADULT MALE AND FEMALE—Upper parts, black with bronzy, purplish, and greenish reflections. Head, neck, rump, and under parts, pure white. Wings,

very long, narrow, pointed, crescentic; and when folded, extending to the tip of the tail. Tail, long, slender, and very deeply forked.

LENGTH — 22.50 inches. Female somewhat longer than the male.

DISTRIBUTION—While this species ranges northward, it is found chiefly in the Gulf States of Louisiana, and along the Gulf Coast to Florida, Georgia, and South Carolina. It migrates into Central and South America in winter.

This aristocratic and beautiful species is one of America's most graceful aerial performers. In the air it resembles an enormous black and white Barn Swallow, but handles itself in the Swallow's own element with even more assured elegance. Its whole dietary seems to be made up of insects, hence the bird is entirely beneficial. (Family *Accipitridae*)

White-tailed Kite
Elanus leucurus majusculus [328]

ADULT MALE AND FEMALE—Upper parts, light gray fading to white on the head. Wing coverts, black. Tail, white. Under parts, pure white. Tail cut nearly square across, not deeply forked.

LENGTH—15.50 inches.

DISTRIBUTION—From South Carolina, southern Illinois, western Texas,

Arizona, and central California, southward into Argentina. It is seldom found east of the Mississippi. (Family *Accipitridae*)

KITTIWAKE
Atlantic Kittiwake
Rissa tridactyla tridactyla [40]

ADULT MALE AND FEMALE—Back and wings, soft pearl-gray. Outer web of the first primary feather, and about three inches of the ends of the first and second primaries, black. Third, fourth, and fifth primaries with black ends and white tips. Head, neck, tail, and under parts, silvery-white. Bill, yellow; feet, black.

LENGTH—16.00 inches.

DISTRIBUTION—In the eastern Arctic regions, and the North Atlantic. From Greenland to the Gulf of St. Lawrence. In winter it is found south as far as the Great Lakes, along the Long Island coast, and rarely to Virginia.

The Kittiwake is not often seen on the beaches, or in the harbors as is the Herring Gull. It searches for its food

well out at sea. They are extremely graceful Gulls, and often follow steamers for long distances, for the sake of the food refuse thrown overboard; diving oftentimes from a considerable height. From the Herring Gull and Ring-billed Gull, the Kittiwake may be distinguished by its more graceful flight, smaller size, and black feet. When seen at close range, the black wing markings are distinctive. The loud cheerful cry of this Gull, from which it derives its name, sounds like the syllables *kitt, kitt; wake wake*. (Family *Laridae*)

Pacific Kittiwake
Rissa tridactyla pollicaris [40a]

Similar to the Atlantic Kittiwake, but with a more developed hind toe, and the black tips of the three outer primary feathers, three inches or more in length.

DISTRIBUTION—Found in the North Pacific and in the Bering Sea. In winter it spreads southward, casually as far as the coast of southern California. (Family *Laridae*)

Red-legged Kittiwake
Rissa brevirostris [41]

Similar to the Atlantic Kittiwake, but with a shorter bill, with the back and the inner webs of the primaries darker, and with red legs. (The vernacular name of the bird calls attention to its red legs, and the scientific name to its short bill.)

DISTRIBUTION—Found on the coasts and on the islands of the Bering Sea. (Family *Laridae*)

KNOT
American Knot
Calidris canutus rufus [234]

ADULT MALE AND FEMALE—Upper parts, gray spotted with reddish-brown and black; the rump and the base of the tail somewhat lighter. Sides of head, pale brown; under parts same.

LENGTH—10.50 inches.

DISTRIBUTION—All over the Northern Hemisphere, breeding within the Arctic Circle, and wintering from Florida to South America. It is rare on the Pacific Coast, migrating chiefly along the Atlantic Coast.

On the mud-flats, sand-bars, and the outer beaches, one sees the Knot busily engaged in searching for whatever

small forms of life these situations afford, calling as it goes *whuit whuit,* a soft little whistle, which sounds like a small boy calling his dog. It is a common migrant along the New England coast in May, and again in late summer and early fall. (Family *Scolopacidae*)

Eastern Asiatic Knot
Calidris tenuirostris [234.1]

ADULT MALE AND FEMALE—Upper parts, pale brownish-gray, mottled and variable. Wings more decidedly brownish. Under parts, whitish; the throat and breast spotted or mottled with brown. Bill, slender.

LENGTH—About 10.00 inches.

DISTRIBUTION—An oriental Sandpiper, accidental at Cape Prince of Wales, Alaska. (Family *Scolopacidae*)

LAPWING
Lapwing
Vanellus vanellus [269]

ADULT MALE AND FEMALE—Upper parts, deep metallic-green with purplish reflections; wing quills, black. Tail, white, terminated by a broad black band. Crown, and long crest, greenish-black. Sides of the neck, white or ashy white. Face, throat, and upper breast, bluish-black. Lower breast and abdomen, white. Tail coverts, fawn-brown.

LENGTH—12.50 inches.

DISTRIBUTION—Of this European species Chapman says, ". . . is casual in Greenland, Baffin Land, Newfoundland, Labrador, Maine, New Brunswick, Nova Scotia, Maine, Long Island, New York. . . . North Carolina, the Bahamas, and Barbadoes. Prior to 1927 there were records of the occurrence of only eight individuals of this species in North America, but in December, 1927, high easterly winds in Great Britain drove large numbers of Lapwings westward and they occurred by hundreds in Newfoundland whence many wandered southward. . . ."

Who has not sung,
  "Thou green-crested Lapwing thy
    screaming forbear"?
not thinking perhaps, that this Scottish bird of "Sweet Afton" had actually occurred on our shores, and in

considerable numbers. The Lapwing, Green Plover, or Pewit, as the bird is variously called in Great Britain, is one of the most beautiful of all the

long-legged tribe, and it is a pity that it has not been naturalized here. In its habits it is similar to our Killdeer Plover, and would probably accommodate itself to our biological situation very well indeed. Like our Killdeer, too, the Lapwing is exceedingly vociferous, and as it sails overhead it gives forth a wailing, feline, cry—the "screaming" alluded to in Burns's song. Its sudden, zigzag dashes downward from a great height are one of the astounding feats of aerial wing power and dexterity among birds. (Family *Charadriidae*)

LARK FAMILY
Alaudidae

Larks are rather dull-colored, brownish birds, with lighter under parts, sometimes streaked. They are found

in flocks, except during the breeding season. The claw of the hind toe is much elongated; the bill short, rather stout, and pointed; and the head bears

"horns" or tufts of longish feathers. The birds walk rather than hop, and sing while on the wing. The most noteworthy member of this family is the Skylark, made famous by the English poets. More than two hundred and fifty Larks are known, of which seventeen are recorded from North America, one of these being the English Skylark. Our native American Larks form one species, represented by sixteen subspecies.

NESTING. The nests of Larks are placed directly on the ground amid grasses and rushes, sometimes at the base of a prominent tuft, in wide open places such as fields. They are simple, broad, open, cup-shaped structures, composed of grasses, plant stems, weed bark, a few feathers, leaves, etc. The eggs are of varying ground colors: grayish, pale greenish, etc., and are thickly marked with spots of darker gray, drab, olive, brown, or lavender, in considerable variation. Our native Larks lay from three to five eggs.

LARK
California Horned Lark
Otocoris alpestris actia [474e]

Similar to the Northern Horned Lark, but browner on the upper parts, with the nape, shoulders, and rump, pinker. The yellow head and throat markings are somewhat paler than in the Northern Lark.

DISTRIBUTION—The Mohave Desert, Owen Valley, and San Joaquin Valley, and southern California. (Family *Alaudidae*)

Desert Horned Lark
Otocoris alpestris leucolaema [474c]

Similar to the Prairie Horned Lark, but generally paler throughout, with the upper parts a plainer more uniform pinkish-brown.

DISTRIBUTION—Found over the Great Plains, and in the Great Basin of the United States, spreading in winter as far south as the northern portion of Mexico. (Family *Alaudidae*)

Dusky Horned Lark
Otocoris alpestris merrilli [474i]

Similar to the Prairie Horned Lark, but with a faintly yellowish band over the eye, and with the upper parts a darker brown.

DISTRIBUTION—From British Columbia southward, between the Rocky Mountains and the Cascade Ranges, spreading in winter still farther south into California and eastward into Nevada. (Family *Alaudidae*)

Hoyt's Horned Lark
Otocoris alpestris hoyti [474k]

Similar to the Northern Horned Lark, but with paler, grayer upper parts; white instead of yellow about the head; forehead, a grayish-greenish-white; and throat, yellow. The yellow throat of the female is much paler than is the male's.

DISTRIBUTION—District of Mackenzie, Canada, to the west shore of Hudson Bay, and southward to the northern portions of Alberta, Saskatchewan, and Manitoba. In winter it spreads southward into the United States, into Nevada, Utah, Kansas, Michigan, Ohio, New York, and as far east as Connecticut. (Family *Alaudidae*)

Island Horned Lark
Otocoris alpestris insularis [474m]

Similar to the Northern Horned Lark, but darker; back heavily streaked with black; the under parts washed with yellow.

DISTRIBUTION—Restricted to the Santa Barbara Islands of California. (Family *Alaudidae*)

Magdalena Horned Lark
Otocoris alpestris enertera [474n]

Similar to the Mohave Horned Lark, but smaller; with paler, more grayish upper parts. The nape, bend of the wing (wrist), and upper tail coverts are more pinkish.

DISTRIBUTION — Throughout the central portion of the peninsula of Lower California, from the region of Santa Rosalia Bay to Magdalen Bay. (Family *Alaudidae*)

Mohave Horned Lark
Otocoris alpestris ammophila [474o]

Similar to the California Horned Lark, but with much paler upper parts.

DISTRIBUTION — In the Mohave Desert, and to Owens Valley, California. In winter it spreads to southern California and Nevada. (Family *Alaudidae*)

Montezuma Horned Lark
Otocoris alpestris occidentalis [474l]

Similar to the Prairie Horned Lark, but with the upper parts showing a reddish hue.

DISTRIBUTION—From central Arizona eastward into central New Mexico, passing in winter into northwestern Mexico, and thence southeast into Texas. (Family *Alaudidae*)

Northern Horned Lark
Otocoris alpestris alpestris [474]

ADULT MALE—Back of head, back, and rump, pinkish-brown; the tail darker and with its outer pair of feathers edged with white. Forehead region over the eye, and a patch behind it, yellow. Two "horns" of black feathers form a crescent on the crown, and project backward from the head. Line from the base of the bill down along the sides of the throat, and a wide band across the upper breast, black. Throat, bright yellow; lower breast and abdomen, white; the sides, pink-ish-brown.

ADULT FEMALE—Similar to the male, but smaller; the black a more grayish hue; throat, dull yellow; sides of the body showing little if any pink-ish-brown.

LENGTH—7.75 inches.

DISTRIBUTION—Over the whole of eastern North America, breeding in the region from Hudson Bay east to the Atlantic. In winter it spreads southward mostly along the coast, as far as South Carolina, and westward to Illinois.

When on the ground, the Horned Larks run about like little chickens; when they spring into the air, their long, pointed, graceful wings carry them with a soft easy flight, as they

rise often high in the air, and circle about, returning to the same spot. When flying, they utter short, sweet, whistled calls, *see see te-ree*. From the Prairie Horned Larks they may be distinguished by their yellow, instead of white, foreheads and region over and behind the eye. (Family *Alaudidae*)

Pallid Horned Lark

Otocoris alpestris articola [474a]

Similar to the Northern Horned Lark, but larger, and without yellow in the plumage; with the back darker, and with grayish edges to the feathers.

DISTRIBUTION—In the interior of Alaska, passing south in winter into Oregon, Utah, and Montana.

The Pallid Horned Lark is the largest of the Horned Larks. (Family *Alaudidae*)

Prairie Horned Lark

Otocoris alpestris praticola [474b]

Similar to the Northern Horned Lark, the chief difference being that the region of the forehead, and over and behind the eye are white, not yellow, and that the throat is either very pale yellow, or whitish.

LENGTH—7.25 inches.

DISTRIBUTION—From Quebec and Ontario down the Mississippi Valley to southern Illinois and Missouri, eastern Nebraska; eastward through northern Pennslyvania, northern New Jersey, central New York, into west-ern and northern New England. In winter it spreads southward as far as Texas, Kentucky, and South Carolina.

Like his celebrated English cousin, the Skylark, our Prairie Horned Lark mounts into the air by stages, singing as he goes a song consisting of a series of sharp little *tsits,* followed by a broken trill. Arriving at a considerable height above the ground the song be-comes sweeter and more varied, though still far inferior to that of the Skylark, and shorter. Often the bird starts to descend, and then, with a second burst of vigor, ascends again, and continues its rather weak, almost unmusical song. Sometimes an individual, espe-cially gifted, renders a song very little inferior to the Skylark's, but shorter. On the cold heaths in the north of Scotland, I have often heard the Eng-lish bird sing almost an exact replica of our own Lark's song. The Prairie Lark, as it used to be called, is gradu-ally invading the east, as the great forests of former days give way to open farming country. It nests on the ground, often sinking its nest to ground level, and sometimes lays its eggs while the snow is thick all about its grassy cup. It is often found in company with its congener, the Northern

Horned Lark, and in winter and early spring is also seen in flocks of Snow Buntings. Larks do not perch in trees or even bushes, but sometimes alight on a fence-post, rail fence, or large stone. (Family *Alaudidae*)

Ruddy Horned Lark
Otocoris alpestris rubea [474f]

Similar to the Northern Horned Lark, but with the back of head and nape, rich reddish-brown. Upper parts washed with the same color.

LENGTH—6.75 inches.

DISTRIBUTION—Restricted to the Sacramento Valley of California. (Family *Alaudidae*)

Scorched Horned Lark
Otocoris alpestris adusta [474h]

Similar to the Northern Horned Lark, but with back more brownish, the feathers edged with pinkish and not quite so streaked; the head markings, faint yellowish or white.

DISTRIBUTION—From central southern Arizona southward into Mexico. (Family *Alaudidae*)

Sonora Horned Lark
Otocoris alpestris leucansiptila [474j]

Similar to the Northern Horned Lark, but with the upper parts pale grayish-brown; the feathers edged with lighter gray; the nape, a pale pinkish-brown; and the head markings only faintly washed with yellow.

DISTRIBUTION — "Region immediately adjacent to the head of the Gulf of California, Mexico." (Oberholzer.) (Family *Alaudidae*)

Streaked Horned Lark
Otocoris alpestris strigata [474g]

Similar to the Northern Horned Lark, but with the back heavily streaked with blackish, and with the back of head, upper back, and sides of body more pronouncedly and deeper pinkish-brown. Breast flushed with light yellow.

LENGTH—7.00 inches.

DISTRIBUTION—From British Columbia southward along the coastal region to California. (Family *Alaudidae*)

Texas Horned Lark
Otocoris alpestris giraudi [474d]

Similar to the Northern Horned Lark, but smaller and paler. Breast of male usually washed with lemon-yellow.

DISTRIBUTION—Texas, from the Rio Grande along the coast to Galveston. (Family *Alaudidae*)

LIMPKIN FAMILY
Courlans and Limpkins
Aramidae

The Courlans are large birds with long legs and long bills somewhat resembling large rails (Family *Rallidae*). Their habits, however, are distinctly Heron-like. The wings are broad and

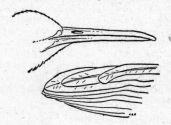

rounded, and the general color of the plumage is brown or dusky, with the admixture of some white. These birds inhabit swamps; damp woods, where streams are found; the bushy borders of ponds and streams; and infrequently higher drier ground. Among their favorite foods are certain land snails into whose spiral shells the birds insert their beaks to extract the soft body. The tips of Limpkins' bills are slightly deflected to one side, and permanently deformed, it is said, as a result of the birds' vigorous efforts to force the mandibles as far as possible into the spirals of the shells. The Family *Aramidae* contains but a single genus, *Aramus*, which in turn contains two species, one of which the Limpkin (*Aramus pictus pictus*) occurs within the borders of the United States.

NESTING. The single representative of this family in North America, the Limpkin or Courlan, nests on the ground, usually near water, sometimes in a tangle of vines. The nest is composed of leaves, grasses, fine vine stems, rootlets, moss, and miscellaneous dead vegetation. In this nest are deposited from four to seven buffy-brown, grayish-brown, or olive-brown eggs, splotched and spotted with browns and grays. Limpkins nest in numbers in the Everglades of Florida, and prefer a swampy tract, often along a river, where the stumps of cut trees have become covered with a dense tangle of vines. In these vines the birds build their nests. Nests are also placed in great bunches of swamp grass, or in custard-apple bushes in the Everglades.

LIMPKIN

Limpkin

Aramus pictus pictus [207]

ADULT MALE AND FEMALE—Plumage, shining olive-brownish; the wings and tail with metallic bronzy reflections. Narrow white stripes on the head and neck, and broad ones on the body.

LENGTH—28.00 inches.

DISTRIBUTION—From South Carolina (rarely), south in the Okefinokee Swamp of Georgia, and down into Florida.

The large, long-billed Limpkin is now a rare bird in Florida and the Okefinokee Swamp of Georgia. Formerly it was more widely distributed in the large swamps. It is a brownish, bittern-like bird, but 'with longer, very

slightly decurved bill, longer neck, and longer legs. The latter hang down below the bird as it flies. The white-spotted appearance is very pronounced. (Family *Aramidae*)

LIZARD-TAILED BIRD

Lizard-tailed Bird

Archaeopteryx lithographica

Archaeopteryx siemensi

Though not a North American bird, the famous *Archaeopteryx*, or Lizard-tailed Bird, is of supreme interest to students of bird life as being at present the oldest recorded bird in the world, and while not perhaps the ancestor of modern birds, it is at least, the most ancient relative of them, and is very much like what the ancestors of our present-day birds might have been. Therefore like Adam, the Ark, the Pyramids, and Socrates, the *Archeopteryx* belongs to all lands and all people. Two specimens of this bird have been found, one in 1863; the other in 1877, in the lithographic slate deposits of Solenhofen, Bavaria. So well and so completely have the remains been fossilized, that many of the feathers, even, are perfectly preserved. The two specimens thus far found have been assigned to two separate species, *Archaeopteryx lithographica* and *Archeopteryx siemensi,* and are closely similar. *Archeopteryx* is about as large as a Crow—that is, about 18 inches, and possesses reptilian characteristics, as well as bird-like ones. Thus the

wings show well-developed hands, with long claws on the fingers; the jaws are armed with long sharp teeth (there is no beak); and the tail is very long, consisting of about twenty vertebrae, supporting long lateral feathers. *Archaeopteryx* probably lived in trees, climbing about by means of its hands and feet; and, though its powers of flight were not remarkable, yet it could probably fly at least as well as some of our present-day barnyard fowl. This is about as much as we know, at this distance of time, about *Archaeopteryx,* for it lived about the year one hundred and thirty million B.C., in the period known to geologists as the Jurassic. It probably was voiceless, as are the reptiles of today, or, if it had a "song," it was of a character which bred no envy in others. The writer had the privilege, several years ago, of going over with

some care the specimen in the British Museum in London. The feathers and some other features of the skeleton are bird-like; many characters of the skeleton are reptilian; and thus, although the creature possesses structures peculiar to both the birds and the reptiles, it stands much nearer to the birds than to the reptiles. Knowlton says of it, "It is clearly a connecting link between the two classes [reptiles and birds], and yet we are undoubtedly still very far from the original point where the branch was made from the reptilian stem."

LONGSPUR

Alaskan Longspur
Calcarius lapponicus alascensis [536a]

Similar to the Lapland Longspur, but with the feathers of the back margined with a paler, light brownish-gray. In the winter plumage the nape is a more creamy light brown. The bird appears decidedly paler, especially in its winter plumage. In summer it shows less of the rusty tinge than the Alaskan subspecies, and the black streaks are narrower.

LENGTH—6.15 inches.

DISTRIBUTION—This bird, breeding in Alaska, migrates in winter to the United States, and is found in western Kansas, Colorado, and Nevada. (*Family Fringillidae*)

Chestnut-collared Longspur
Calcarius ornatus [538]

ADULT MALE—Upper parts streaked with brown, black, and buffy; shoulder patch, black tipped with white. Crown, black; sides of head, white marked with black. Nape, bright rufous-brown. Throat, white or buffy white. Under parts, black, sometimes washed with reddish-brown. Abdomen, white. Bases of all tail feathers except the middle pair, white.

ADULT FEMALE — Upper parts, buffy-brownish streaked with black. Under parts sometimes lightly streaked with blackish.

LENGTH—5.62 inches.

DISTRIBUTION—A bird of the Great Plains of North America, from Saskatchewan southward to central Kan-

sas and eastern Colorado. In winter it is found from Nebraska and eastern Colorado south into Mexico. (Family *Fringillidae*)

Lapland Longspur

Calcarius lapponicus lapponicus [536]

ADULT MALE—Upper parts streaked with brown, black, and buffy-white. Wings, grayish-brown; the feathers with brown and white edgings. Tail largely dark sooty-brown. Foreparts, black; a white or whitish line extends from the eye backward to the side of the hind neck. Nape patch, bright rufous-brown. Lower breast and abdomen, white. Inner webs of the outer tail feathers, grayish; the middle ones, black. The hind claw is long and nearly straight, giving this genus of birds its name. Longspurs run; never hop.

ADULT FEMALE—Similar to the male, but smaller; the black of the foreparts more restricted, and the hind neck streaked with blackish. The rufous nape patch is much restricted and more or less obscured by whitish, and streaked. Sides of head, buffy-brown.

LENGTH—6.24 inches.

DISTRIBUTION—A bird of northern Europe, found also in the northeastern part of North America, southward into northern Labrador. In winter it is an irregular visitant in the United States along the New England coast, and irregularly southward as far as South Carolina. Westward it reaches Kentucky, Kansas, Colorado, and Manitoba, and extends also into Texas.

In winter these beautiful birds are among the loveliest sights of our "wide open spaces," as well as of the more restricted regions in New England and along the coast. Their plumage at this season is not as striking as in summer, but is still provocative of expressions of admiration, as their hues of orange-brown, black, and white flash in the winter sun. Longspurs move about in large flocks often in company with Snow Buntings and Horned Larks. As they fly they give voice to a sweet *to-eee, to-eee,* a plain-

tive note, and also to a harsh *churrr.* Their flight song, on the breeding grounds, is similar to that of the Horned Larks. (Family *Fringillidae*)

McCown's Longspur

Rhynchophanes mccowni [539]

ADULT MALE—Back, brownish-gray streaked with black; shoulder patch, reddish-brown. Crown, black. Line over the eye, pure white. Sides of head and throat, white or whitish, with a black streak from the base of the bill along the sides of the throat. The upper breast bears a prominent black crescentic patch. Rest of under parts, white or whitish, more or less marked with blackish; these marks increasing on the sides of the body.

ADULT FEMALE—Upper parts, grayish-brown; under parts, white or buffywhite.

LENGTH—5.48 inches.

DISTRIBUTION—Found on the plains in the interior of North America, from Saskatchewan southward to eastern Nebraska. In winter it spreads south through Texas and Arizona into northern Mexico.

During the mating season, the Mc-Cown's Longspur gives voice to a flight song as it hovers in the air with its graceful wings pointed almost straight upward over its back. In general habits, the bird is similar to the other Longspurs. (Family *Fringillidae*)

Smith's Longspur
Calcarius pictus [537]

ADULT MALE—Upper parts streaked with brown, black, and buffy; hind neck, buffy-brownish streaked with black. Top and sides of the head, black marked with three white stripes. Under parts, buffy-brownish. Inner webs of the outer tail feathers, largely white.

ADULT FEMALE—The black of the head is replaced by brownish and streaked with blackish; throat and upper breast, somewhat streaked. Colors, pale and grayish, not sharply defined.

LENGTH—6.00 inches.

DISTRIBUTION—Found over the interior portion of North America generally, from the Arctic Ocean southward (in migration), as far as southern Arizona and Texas. (Family *Fringillidae*)

LOON FAMILY
Gaviidae

Loons are relatively large birds, of primitive structure, inhabiting the northern parts of the Northern Hemisphere. Their wings are short, narrow, and pointed. Their tails are short, pointed, and stiff. Their bills are very stout and heavy, but long, straight, and very sharp, with a sharp edge— a formidable weapon for defence, and

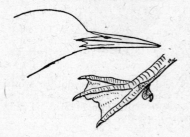

an effective implement for securing food. The toes are four in number, the foremost three being webbed together, the hinder one free, flat, and very short. The plumage is very compact and firm, so that the bird in the hand has a hard feeling. Six Loons are found on our continent, contained in the single genus *Gavia*.

NESTING. Loons nest along the rushy and bushy shores of wild, large freshwater ponds or lakes, or in swamps and marshes. The nests of all species are more or less similar, being sometimes a mere depression in the soil perhaps with a few sticks or rushes about the margin, or a loosely made structure of weed stems, mosses, or marsh vegetation, sometimes hidden from view either by a growth of reeds, or concealed beneath overhanging shrubs or at the base of a tussock of drooping grasses. Sometimes the nests are in shallow pools. The eggs are usually two in number, and in color vary from sepia or olive to brown, or some darker neutral shade;

spotted and blotched with drab hues, browns, and blackish.

LOON

Common Loon

Gavia immer immer [7]

ADULT MALE AND FEMALE—Back, black spotted with white. Head and throat, black; the throat and back of the neck marked with small white streaks. Under parts, white. Bill, long, heavy and sharp. Tail, short.

LENGTH—32.00 inches.

DISTRIBUTION — From Greenland and Alaska south to Maine, northern Illinois, Minnesota, and northern California. In winter from the latitude of Illinois southward to the Gulf of Mexico, mainly along the coasts.

Loons are remarkable for their great skill in diving and swimming, and when under water, shoot here and there with amazing rapidity, aided

both by their feet and wings, the latter being used as a sort of submarine pair of oars. So rapid is their progress that they are able to overtake fish, which they capture with their long sharp bills. Their motions are so quick when disturbed, and their dive so instantaneous, that hunters often aver that they "dodge the shot" after it has left the gun-barrel. During the nesting season Loons are to be found in north-

ern lakes and large ponds. Their weird laughing calls (easily imitated by the female human voice) are characteristic sounds of the wilder lakes. During the winter many migrate to sea. Their manner of submergence is peculiar, the body being depressed beneath the surface until only the head and neck are visible—like the periscope of a miniature submarine. Soon they drop beneath the surface of the water with not a ripple. (Family *Gaviidae*)

Green-throated Loon

Gavia arctica viridigularis [10a]

In general similar to the Pacific Loon, but with the throat, when seen in strong light, a dusky velvet olive-green.

DISTRIBUTION—This rare species is an occasional visitant to the coast of Alaska, as far as the region about Victoria, British Columbia. (Family *Gaviidae*)

Lesser Loon

Gavia immer elasson [7a]

Similar to the Common Loon, but smaller.

DISTRIBUTION—From Manitoba and British Columbia southward to northern California, North Dakota, and northern Wisconsin. (Family *Gaviidae*)

Pacific Loon

Gavia arctica pacifica [10]

ADULT MALE AND FEMALE—Upper parts, black; middle of back bearing rows of large square white spots. Top of head, nape, and back of neck, gray. Throat, black with purplish reflections, streaked on its sides with white. Bill, jet black. Under parts, white.

LENGTH—23.00 inches.

DISTRIBUTION—Alaska to Lower California along the coast, and eastward to Hudson Bay.

The Pacific Loon may be distinguished from the Common Loon chiefly by its

smaller size. As they fly, their necks and legs are bent slightly downward, giving them a bow-shaped appearance. (Family *Gaviidae*)

Red-throated Loon

Gavia stellata [11]

ADULT MALE AND FEMALE—Back, sooty grayish-brown flecked with whitish. Top of head and back of neck, streaked black and white. Rest of head and neck, a leaden gray. Throat bears a large patch of rich chestnut-brown. Under parts, white.

LENGTH—25.00 inches.

DISTRIBUTION—Across the Northern Hemisphere from Greenland to Alaska. In winter it is found as far south as South Carolina and southern California.

The Red-throated Loon is the handsomest of our common Loons, with its

sleek, smooth gray neck and cheeks, black-and-white streaked top of head

and back of neck, and its rich reddish-brown (not red) throat. (Family *Gaviidae*)

Yellow-billed Loon

Gavia adamsi [8]

Similar to the Common Loon, but larger, and with the bill, yellow, yellowish-white, or almost white.

DISTRIBUTION — Northern Asia across to Arctic America, west of Hudson Bay. (Family *Gaviidae*)

MAGPIE

American Magpie

Pica pica hudsonia [475]

ADULT MALE AND FEMALE—Wing patches, and abdomen, pure white; the rest of the plumage, black with a bronze iridescence. Tail, long; the central feathers longest, the rest graduated, giving the tail a wedge-shaped outline when spread in flight. The skin about the eye is bare of feathers, and black. Bill, black and heavy.

LENGTH—17.50 inches.

DISTRIBUTION—From the Hudson Bay region west to Alaska, south to the northern parts of Arizona and New Mexico; and from the western part of Nebraska westward as far as the eastern borders of the Sierra Nevada and Cascade mountains.

Magpies are a striking sight as they fly away from an observer, displaying their vivid black and white pattern, and their long tails extended straight out behind. They are sociable birds, and if encouraged will come close about buildings to feed. Although they are thievish and sometimes troublesome, yet their antics are diverting, and their cheerful noisy ways add a pleasing stir of life to the scene. They are birds chiefly of low bushes and the ground, and spend much of their time in small flocks, preferring the neighborhood of water. Their notes are many and expressive. The commonest call is a rapidly repeated *check check check check*. Often, when in flocks, they "converse" together in a variety of whistles, clucks, chatters, and whines, and often give voice to a loud nasal *maaagg*, as though pronouncing the

first syllable of their name. The food of the Magpie is varied and consists of such items as small birds, eggs, small mammals, crawfish, a few leaves, and small fruits; but mainly of noxious insects, such as grasshoppers, crickets, and the like. (Family *Corvidae*)

Yellow-billed Magpie

Pica nutalli [476]

Similar to the American Magpie, but smaller. The bare skin of the eye region and the bill are bright yellow, instead of black.

LENGTH—17.00 inches.

DISTRIBUTION—In California, from the valley of the Sacramento River south to the region of Los Angeles, and west of the Sierra Nevada Mountains. (Family *Corvidae*)

MALLARD

Common Mallard

Anas platyrhynchos platyrhynchos [132]

ADULT MALE—Upper part of back, dark grayish-brown; rump and upper tail coverts, black. The four central tail feathers are curved upward. Speculum, rich glossy purple, with a basal border and tip of black and white. Head and throat, glossy greenish or bluish-black. Neck with a white ring. Breast, rich chestnut-brown; abdomen, whitish marked with fine wavy black lines. Bill, yellow or greenish-yellow; legs and feet, orange.

ADULT FEMALE—Brown marked with black; speculum of wing as in the male. Under parts, light yellowish-brown mottled with dusky brown. Bill and feet, dull yellowish.

LENGTH—23.00 inches.

DISTRIBUTION—In America from Alaska and Labrador, across to Greenland; and in Indiana, Iowa, and California. In winter it is found from British Columbia, southwestward to Kansas and across to New Jersey, and southward to Central America and the West Indies.

The Mallard Duck is said to be the most domesticated animal in the world. It has been bred in China from immemorial ages, and is now spread over the globe. It is a familiar sight on

most American farms where Ducks of any sort are raised. Its loud cheerful *quack* is as familiar a sound to rural ears as is the crowing of chanticleer. Great hordes of wild Mallards winter in our southern states. Very few breed in the east, though a great many winter with us, and pass down the coast on their migrations. The wild Mallard is slightly larger than its domesticated cousin. In flight, its wing strokes are somewhat slower than those of the Black Duck, which it resembles in the air, when the colors cannot be seen. The Mallard's white neck-ring, and rich chestnut breast distinguish it from other Ducks. (Family *Anatidae*)

Greenland Mallard

Anas platyrhynchos conboschas [132a]

Similar to the Common Mallard, but, in the male, the wing coverts are grayer, and the markings on the sides of the body are grayer and heavier. The margin of the breast-shield shows black markings. The female shows grayer upper parts than the female Common Mallard, with the markings a reddish instead of a grayish-brown.

DISTRIBUTION—On the eastern and western coasts of Greenland. Chapman says, "Apparently resident, but may migrate locally." (Family *Anatidae*)

MAN-O'-WAR-BIRD FAMILY
Fregatidae

Two species of Man-o'-war-birds are known, inhabiting tropical and subtropical oceans. They are characterized by short legs; very long, deeply forked

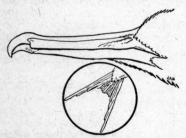

tails; excessively long slender wings; and long, hooked bills. For their body-weight they possess the greatest wing-spread of any known bird, and are not surpassed (or hardly equalled) by

any bird in powers of sustained flight. The one species which reaches the coast of the United States is the *Fregata magnificens*.

NESTING. Our Man-o'-war-birds or Frigate Birds nest in colonies, on tropical and subtropical islands, sometimes on the ground, and sometimes in low bushes. The nests are loose structures of small sticks and twigs, and herein we find the one, sometimes two, or perhaps three plain white eggs, about the size of those of the domestic hen. Frigate Birds are said not to breed within the limits of the United States, but it may be that they occasionally do off the coast of Louisiana.

MAN-O'-WAR-BIRD
Man-o'-war-bird

Fregata magnificens [128]

ADULT MALE—Upper parts, glossy shining black; under parts, similar but slightly duller. Bill, very long; its mandibles enlarged and somewhat hooked at their tips. Throat pouch, during the breeding season, deep red or brilliant orange, and dilatable. Wings, long and pointed; tail, long and very deeply forked.

ADULT FEMALE — Similar to the male, but in general, a rusty dull brown, with the breast and upper abdomen, white or whitish.

LENGTH—40.00 inches, of which 17.00 inches is tail.

DISTRIBUTION—In North America, found off Florida, the Bahamas, Venezuela, the islands of the Caribbean Sea, and off the west coast of Mexico. Has been recorded also as an accidental straggler along the north Atlantic coast at various points, and also inland.

The Man-o'-war-bird is, I believe, the most graceful bird of all the world. Floating high in the air, and buoyed up by rising currents, it sometimes

sails, or hangs motionless for long
periods of time; then slowly slides
down, down, and levels off again, without a perceptible motion of its long
slender wings. It possesses the greatest expanse of wing, in proportion to
its body-weight, of any living bird.
Its food is captured in its long bill, the
bird dashing down in lightning-like

curves and snatching fish from the
surface of the water. Sometimes (after
the manner of the Bald Eagle) a Man-
o'-war-bird attacks gulls and terns in
mid-air, forcing them to drop their
catch, which is snatched up by the
aggressor before it reaches the water.
Often flying-fish, which have burst out
of one wave and are gliding into the
next oncoming one, are snatched up
in mid-air during the passage. There
are two species of Man-o'-war-birds,
of the Family *Fregatidae*. They are
entirely ocean birds, nesting along the
coasts, but often sailing out far from
land, riding the air-currents sometimes
even above the storm clouds.

MARTIN
Cuban Martin
Progne cryptoleuca [611.1]

The male of this species is similar to
the male Purple Martin, but with white
markings on the under parts. The female bears a sooty brownish wash on
the breast and flanks. This species is
slightly smaller than the Purple Martin.

DISTRIBUTION — Southern Florida;
passing south in winter into Cuba.
(Family *Hirundinidae*)

European Martin
Chelidonaria urbica urbica [615.2]

ADULT MALE AND FEMALE—Upper
parts, lustrous shining black with violet reflections; rump, pure white. Under parts, pure white. Tail, deeply
forked.

LENGTH—5.50 inches.

DISTRIBUTION—Occurs as an accidental visitor in Greenland. The European Martin, beloved by Gilbert White
of Selborne, has much the same habits
as our Cliff or Eave Swallow, and
when perched resembles our Tree
Swallow. It is widely diffused in
Europe and the British Isles, and regarded with much affection. (Family
Hirundinidae)

Gray Breasted Martin
Progne chalybea chalybea [611.2]

The male of this subspecies resembles
the female Purple Martin, but the
nape lacks the collar, and the upper
parts are a more uniform, steel blue.
The female resembles the female Purple Martin, but with the upper parts
a brighter, clearer gray; without a collar; with the abdomen whiter and
lacking black streakings.

DISTRIBUTION—From the lower portion of the Rio Grande in Texas
southward into southern Brazil. (Family *Hirundinidae*)

Purple Martin
Progne subis subis [611]

ADULT MALE—Entire body, iridescent purplish-black; wings and tail,
duller with a slightly brownish cast.

ADULT FEMALE—Most of the upper
parts, wings and tail, dark brownish;
the head and back, however, glossy

purplish-black. Throat and forehead, gray; breast, brownish-gray. Abdomen, whitish or light gray.

LENGTH—8.00 inches.

DISTRIBUTION—Over the whole of North America, except the arctic north and the Pacific Coast. In winter it migrates south of the United States and Mexico into the tropics.

The Purple Martin, appearing like a "large black swallow," is irregularly distributed as a breeding bird throughout its range. Formerly it was a much more common bird, but of late years

it has steadily decreased in numbers in many localities, probably because of the appropriation of its nesting sites, first by the ubiquitous House Sparrow, and later by the Starling. This is to be lamented, for the Martin is one of our largest and most powerful fliers (among the perching birds). Its graceful and attractive flight, its interesting habits, its loud musical notes, and its decided value as an insect-destroyer make it a pleasing and desirable adjunct to rural and suburban life. Its natural nesting site is in a cavity of a tree, cliff, or building; or in "martin-boxes"—in which it is especially fond of nesting in large colonies. It prefers to breed near wide open valleys watered by sluggish streams, or in the neighborhood of salt meadows near the shore, or near lakes. Its notes are sweet, loud, and chittering. One common call sounds like the syllables *peeyou, peeyou, pee-*

you; another is a short whistled, or squeaked note, which some hearers liken to the call of the Rose-breasted Grosbeak. (Family *Hirundinidae*)

Western Martin

Progne subis hesperia [611a]

The male of this species is similar to the male Purple Martin; the female is similar to the female of that species, but with a whiter abdomen, and with a lighter gray forehead.

DISTRIBUTION—From Washington, along the Pacific Coast to the northern portion of Lower California, passing southward into the tropics for the winter. (Family *Hirundinidae*)

MEADOWLARK

Eastern Meadowlark

Sturnella magna magna [501]

ADULT MALE AND FEMALE—Upper parts streaked with chestnut, black, and buff. *Under parts, bright yellow with a large black, upper-breast crescent. Outer tail feathers, white,* prominent in flight. Tail and legs, short; body, rounded; bill, heavy, sharp, and rather long, giving the head an elongated appearance.

LENGTH—10.70 inches.

DISTRIBUTION — Eastern North America, west as far as central Nebraska, and north to Minnesota and New Brunswick, Canada. Winters southward from Illinois and Massachusetts.

Damp meadows and fields with long grass are the favorite haunts of the Meadowlark. Here it builds on the ground a large domed nest, with an opening at one side. To judge from the number of Meadowlarks singing about any one field, these nests must be numerous, but they are cleverly concealed and difficult to discover. The song of the bird is one of the cheeriest sounds of spring—a loud flutelike whistle, clear and free. *Heeeere, way up heeeere,* it seems to pipe; the first and last notes being slurred downwards. Chunky and large-footed, the Meadowlark walks, not hops, and both in this respect and in build of body somewhat resembles its close relative, the ubiquitous European Starling. He might much more

fittingly be called the "meadow starling." In spite of the termination of his name, he is in no way related to our Horned Lark, nor to the famous European Skylark. Nearly 99 percent of the food of this valuable bird consists of such injurious insects as grasshoppers, crickets, cutworms, and hairy caterpillars of various species. In winter its food of injurious weed seeds constitutes approximately one-third of its total diet. No bird deserves better care at the hands of the farmer. It should be rigorously protected. (Family *Icteridae*)

Rio Grande Meadowlark

Sturnella magna hoopesi [501a]

Similar to the Western Meadowlark, but with the yellow restricted entirely to the throat and upper breast, paling on the rest of the under parts.

DISTRIBUTION — From Arizona, southern New Mexico, and southeastern Texas, and thence southward into northern Mexico. (Family *Icteridae*)

Southern Meadowlark

Sturnella magna argutula [501c]

Similar to the Eastern Meadowlark, but darker throughout, and somewhat smaller.

DISTRIBUTION—Florida, and along the coast to Louisiana. (Family *Icteridae*)

Western Meadowlark

Sturnella neglecta [501.1]

Similar to the Eastern Meadowlark, but paler; the yellow on the throat extending more to the sides; the middle tail feathers distinctly barred.

DISTRIBUTION — From Canada southward to Lower California and northern Mexico, between Wisconsin, Illinois, Texas, and the Pacific Coast.

This fine bird is one of the best singers of the West. Over the rolling fields its notes ring out, reminding one somewhat of the eastern bird's song, but longer, more varied, and clearer and sweeter in tone. In other respects it is close to its eastern relative. (Family *Icteridae*)

MERGANSER

American Merganser

Mergus merganser americanus [129]

ADULT MALE—Middle of back, black; tail, gray. Head and neck, black with strong glossy greenish reflections in strong light. Head, smooth and lacking any trace of crest. A broad white collar about the neck. Sides of upper back and entire under parts, white, showing a faint salmon tint in strong light. Wings, white and when spread showing black quill feathers and a black bar. Bill and feet, orange-red.

ADULT FEMALE—Upper parts and tail, gray. Wings, black with a white patch. Throat, white; rest of head and neck, reddish-brown. Feathers of back part of the head elongated into a short ragged crest. Under parts, white. Bill, reddish-brown; legs and feet, orange.

LENGTH—25.00 inches.

DISTRIBUTION—In North America generally, from the far northern borders of the continent southward to New Brunswick, Canada (rarely the mountains of Pennsylvania), eastward to Minnesota, the mountains of Colorado, and California. In winter it is spread from Maine and British Columbia, southward to South Carolina and across to southern California.

The Merganser, or Sheldrake, is one of our handsomest water fowl. Whether alight or aflight, its strong contrasting patterns and pure silvery white sides and under parts secure for it the admiration of all who see it. It is a most adroit diver, pursuing and capturing small fish with ease. These birds are often seen together

in pairs—a pleasing picture. The flesh of the Merganser is rancid, fishy, and strong. (Family *Anatidae*)

Hooded Merganser

Lophodytes cucullatus [131]

ADULT MALE — Neck and back, black. Breast and abdomen, white; sides of the breast with a black band; sides of the abdomen, cinnamon-brown finely barred with black. Large upright circular crest, black with great white area.

ADULT FEMALE—Back, brownish-gray; head, neck, and upper breast,

grayish-brown washed with reddish-brown. Small crest, reddish-brown. Throat, white. Lower breast and abdomen, white; sides of body, grayish-brown.

LENGTH—17.50 inches.

DISTRIBUTION—Locally distributed through North America from Labrador and Alaska southward to Lower California and Cuba. Breeds locally

but chiefly in the interior regions of Canada. In winter it is found spread from Massachusetts, Illinois, and British Columbia southward.

The Hooded Merganser is a denizen of the secluded quiet waters of ponds, sloughs, and lakes. It is a very rapidly flying bird, and slants down into a hidden pool with the speed of an arrow, and is soon lost to view among a tangle of reeds or bushes near the water's edge. The male is sometimes confused with the Bufflehead, but can be distinguished by its slender bill and larger crest. (Family *Anatidae*)

Red-breasted Merganser

Mergus serrator [130]

Similar to the American Merganser, but with long crest feathers; the upper breast, brownish, speckled; the sides of the body, white and finely vermiculated with black.

LENGTH—22.00 inches.

DISTRIBUTION—In America, from Alaska and New Brunswick, to Greenland and south as far as Illinois. In winter it is found from these southern

limits south into Lower California and Cuba. (Family *Anatidae*)

MERLIN
Merlin
Falco aesalon aesalon [358.1]

Similar to the Eastern Pigeon Hawk, but, in the male, with a broad black band near the tip of the tail, and about six narrow transverse bars. Under parts, light brown streaked with darker. In the female, the upper parts are brownish; under parts as in the male, but lighter.

LENGTH—12.00 inches.

DISTRIBUTION—This Old World bird may be an accidental visitant in Greenland. (Family *Falconidae*)

MIMID FAMILY
Mimidae

The Mimids are restricted to the Americas, and comprise the Catbirds, Mockingbirds, and Thrashers. They are fairly large birds, eight inches or more in length, with long slender bodies, long slender tails, and rather long slender (often decurved) bills. Their colors are never brilliant, being confined to grays, browns, and white, often streaked. Their deficiency of bright hues, however, is more than compensated for by excellence of voice, for the Mimids are famous for their vocal powers; one of them, the Mockingbird, rivalling the famed Nightin-gale of Europe, at least in the multiplicity of notes. There are about sixty *Mimidae* described from the Western Hemisphere, of which eighteen inhabit North America, allocated to the genera *Mimus, Dumetella, Toxostoma,* and *Oreoscoptes.*

NESTING. The nests of Mimids (Catbirds, Mockingbirds, and Thrashers) are rather bulky, large structures, composed of twigs, rootlets, weed stems, sometimes grapevine-bark, lined with fine black rootlets, grapevine or weed bark, and grasses. They are placed in a thick tangle of bushes or of vines. (The thorny intricacies of catbriar tangles are favorite spots for the nests of the Catbird.) In every case the nests are located in situations difficult of access for enemies of the

nest. The eggs are deep bluish-green (Catbird), or greenish-white, speckled and spotted, sometimes thickly, with browns and lavenders. Two to six eggs are deposited.

MOCKINGBIRD
Eastern Mockingbird
Mimus polyglottos polyglottos [703]

ADULT MALE AND FEMALE—Upper parts, light ashy-gray; the primary coverts of the wing, white, forming, when the bird is in flight, a conspicuous white bar. Three inner tail feathers, black or blackish; the outer pairs, white. Under parts, white, often tinged with a light pearl-gray. (In the female the white markings of the wings and tail are often slightly smaller.)

LENGTH—10.50 inches.

DISTRIBUTION — Southeastern United States (and the Bahama Islands), from southern New Jersey to northeastern Texas and southern Illinois. In winter it is found from the lower part of the Mississippi Valley and Virginia southward.

Reports of recent years indicate that the Mockingbird is gradually spreading its range farther and farther into the northeastern states, until it is now

found in progressively diminishing numbers up through the New England States, and even as far north as Quebec. In respect to the variety and multitude of its notes, this songster is without a peer in our continent. In its song (in form similar to that of the Brown Thrasher and Catbird, q.v.), the notes of scores of birds, as well as the sound of barking dogs, barnyard fowls, farm animals of all sorts, the notes of insects, and many other sounds within reach of the bird's mimetical powers, are all unmistakably recognizable. Forbush, that veteran observer, gives a list of "39 bird songs, 50 bird calls, and the notes of a frog and a cricket, all imitated by one Mockingbird in the Arnold Arboretum in Boston." In the South, it seems that the bird sings even more

exuberantly than in the North, often prolonging its music until far into the night, and sometimes during the entire night when the moon is full. The Mockingbird may be identified as a large Catbird, pale, with white under parts, and white in the wings and tail. (Family *Mimidae*)

Western Mockingbird

Mimus polyglottos leucopterus [703a]

Similar to the Eastern Mockingbird, but with slightly more white in the wings, and somewhat grayer under parts.

DISTRIBUTION — New Mexico to southern Mexico, and from the Gulf Coast of Texas west to the Pacific, and in Lower California.

Of this western cousin of our eastern bird, Bailey says, "In Texas the birds are so common and their mimicry so perfect, that it is positively tormenting to the ornithologist. They imitate everything from the *squack* of the Blue Jay, the varied notes of the Cassin Kingbird, the Shrike, and the Gnatcatcher, to the shrill call of the Rock Squirrel. Whenever you hear a new bird, and hurry through brush and briars to see it, at the end of your heated search there sits a calm mocker! As the birds are omnipresent, and always singing somebody else's song, they sadly interfere with the ornithologist's serenity of spirit!" (Family *Mimidae*)

MURRE

Atlantic Murre

Uria aalge aalge [30]

ADULT MALE AND FEMALE—Upper parts, dark sooty-brown; secondaries tipped with black. Neck, dark sooty-brown; breast and abdomen, white. Sides of body more or less streaked with blackish.

LENGTH—16.00 inches.

DISTRIBUTION—From southern Greenland to Nova Scotia, on the coasts and islands of the North Atlantic. In winter it is found as far south as the coast of Maine, and casually to Massachusetts.

The common note of these curious birds is a low, muttered, guttural *mur-r-r-r*—whence the name Murre. When riding on the water, Murres

closely resemble Ducks, but with a shorter neck and a more pointed bill. They nest on the ledges of cliffs, often in densely packed masses of thousands of birds. Their most famous nesting site is along the chalk cliffs of the North Sea coast of England, where the famous "egging" by local collectors is carried on. Because of their varied markings, the eggs of the Guillemots (as the birds are called in England) are much prized by collectors. They are also eaten. A fried Guillemot's egg is a pretty, though rather startling, sight, for its yolk is red, and its "white" a delicate sky-blue. (Family *Alcidae*)

Brünnich's Murre
Uria lomvia lomvia [31]

ADULT MALE AND FEMALE—Upper parts, sooty black; secondaries tipped with white. Foreneck, sooty brownish. Under parts, white. Bill with the upper mandible rounded outward beyond the edge of the lower one, and greenish in color.

LENGTH—16.50 inches.

DISTRIBUTION—On the islands of the eastern Arctic seas and northern Greenland, southwards to the Gulf of St. Lawrence. In winter it is found from southern Greenland and Hudson's Bay southward to Long Island, New York, and also casually to South Carolina. (Family *Alcidae*)

California Murre
Uria aalge californica [30a]

Similar to the Atlantic Murre, but larger.

DISTRIBUTION—Along the Pacific Coast of North America southward to southern California.

The California Murre rookeries on the Farallone Islands, off the coast of California, have become famous, at least on the west coast, by reason of the tremendous expansion which egging assumed in the middle eighteen hundreds. Between the years 1850 and 1856 it was estimated that between three and four millions of eggs were brought to the San Francisco markets, where they sold for a little less than hens' eggs. Bryant says that in the eighties the number of eggs marketed annually averaged 180,000 to 228,000. (Family *Alcidae*)

Pallas's Murre
Uria lomvia arra [31a]

Similar to the Brünnich's Murre, but larger. Nelson states that the bird utters a "peculiar growling, or hoarse chattering note."

DISTRIBUTION—"Breeds from Kodiak, Aleutian, and Commander islands, and islands in the Bering Sea and in the Arctic Ocean (Wrangel and Herald islands and Koliuchin Island, Siberia) to Kotzebue Sound, Alaska; also reported in summer from Kamchatka, the Kurile Islands, and Japan. Winters in the open sea about the Aleutian and Commander islands south to Japan. Casual at Point Barrow, Alaska. (Family *Alcidae*)

MURRELET
Ancient Murrelet
Synthliboramphus antiquus [21]

ADULT MALE AND FEMALE—Back, slaty gray; sides of the body, black. Head and neck, black; the sides of the neck showing a large conspicuous white patch. The back edge of the crown bears a wide stripe of white

filamentous feathers, and scattered white filaments occur over the back of the neck. Under parts, white. Bill, small and short.

LENGTH—10.15 inches.

DISTRIBUTION—On the islands and along the coasts of the North Pacific, southward as far as Monterey Bay, California.

On the Commander Islands of the Bering Sea, where these curious little Murrelets are common in summer, the rocks seem literally alive with birds: Murrelets, Petrels, and Auklets. Because of the scattered white filaments about the head, the bird is known locally as the Old Man. The name Ancient Murrelet indicates also its archaic mien. It might well be called the Ancient Mariner, even though it lacks the "glittering eye." It is an excellent swimmer and diver, moving beneath the water with lightning-like rapidity in its pursuit of small fish. The white head filaments are lost in the winter plumage. (Family *Alcidae*)

Craveri's Murrelet
Endomychura craveri [26]

ADULT MALE AND FEMALE—Upper parts, slaty or brownish-black. Under parts, white; sides of the body, slaty gray. Inner webs of outer primaries, white. Bill, slender and dark.

LENGTH—10.00 inches.

DISTRIBUTION—In the Gulf of California, where it breeds on many of the islands. After breeding it spreads out on the ocean from Monterey Bay, California, and southward in the Pacific to Lower California. (Family *Alcidae*)

Kittlitz's Murrelet
Brachyramphus brevirostris [24]

ADULT MALE AND FEMALE—Upper parts, gray mottled with buff. Breast and sides mottled with black and buff; abdomen, white. Bill, short.

LENGTH—9.50 inches.

DISTRIBUTION—From the Aleutian Islands eastward to Glacier Bay and Point Barrow, Alaska; also Kamchatka. In winter it is found from Kamchatka to the Kurile Islands. (Family *Alcidae*)

Marbled Murrelet
Brachyramphus marmoratus [23]

ADULT MALE AND FEMALE—Upper parts, dusky; the back and sides of

the body finely barred with deep brown. Under parts, white mottled or marbled with blackish-brown. (Figure shows the bird in winter plumage.)

LENGTH—9.75 inches.

DISTRIBUTION—Along the Pacific coast from western Alaska southwards to southern California.

An extremely shy little Murrelet, diving, instead of taking wing, at the slightest alarm. (Family *Alcidae*)

Xantus's Murrelet

Endomychura hypoleuca [25]

ADULT MALE AND FEMALE—Upper parts, uniform dark slaty-gray. Under parts, white.

LENGTH—10.00 inches.

DISTRIBUTION—From the Aleutian Islands along the coast of the Pacific to southern California. (Family *Alcidae*)

MYNAH
Crested Mynah

Aethiopsar cristatellus cristatellus [493.1]

A Starling-like bird, with bright black and yellow plumage, a large naked area about the eyes, and a moderate crest. The bill is not as long as in our common Starling, and is slightly decurved. The tail is short, and wedge-shaped, and the sexes are alike in coloration.

DISTRIBUTION—This inhabitant of the lowlands of southern China has been introduced into Vancouver, British Columbia, and is spreading up the Frazer River Valley and beyond.

Like the common Starling, the Mynah, or Mina (Hindustani for Starling) makes its nest in holes in trees, or in any convenient and sufficiently deep cavity. The birds are sociable, and go about in small flocks, uttering harsh chattering notes. (Family *Sturnidae*)

NIGHTHAWK
Cherrie's Nighthawk

Chordeiles minor aserriensis [420f]

Similar to the Eastern Nighthawk, but smaller and much lighter in general tone.

DISTRIBUTION—From south central Texas southward into Tamaulipas, Mexico. In winter it migrates southward at least as far as Costa Rica. (Family *Caprimulgidae*)

Eastern Nighthawk

Chordeiles minor minor [420]

ADULT MALE—Upper parts, a speckled mixture of grays, black, and buffy browns. The middle pair of tail feathers is similar; the rest tipped with black and crossed near their tips by a white band. A broad white band crosses the throat and extends backward to the gape of the mouth. Bill, short; mouth wide and gaping, and beset with long basal bristles. Breast, blackish speckled with gray. Abdomen, grayish finely barred with black, and sometimes suffused with buff. Wings, near their tips, with a transverse band of white, which shows prominently from below when the bird is in flight.

ADULT FEMALE—Similar to the male, but with the throat band buffy instead of white, and lacking the white in the tail.

LENGTH—10.00 inches.

DISTRIBUTION—Over the eastern part of North America from Labrador to Florida, extending northwestward to northern California, British Columbia, and Alaska. It winters in Mexico, and south of the United States.

The Nighthawk is a common bird of both country and city districts, for its eggs are deposited as well upon the flat surfaces of high gravelled roofs, as upon the bare ground or flat rocks of hillsides, mountains, and rocky pastures. Flying high in the air with a sweeping and graceful, but somewhat erratic and bouncing flight, these birds are characteristic and pleasing sights of a summer twilight sky. The bird's call note is a sharp, nasal *peeent*, which, to New England ears, sounds

like the word *beans!* Occasionally a deeper note is heard, resembling the word *pork*, a booming sound produced by the resistance offered to the air by the stiff primary feathers of the wings, as the bird darts downward from a height, and then turns upward in an abrupt curve. From the Whip-poor-will, the Nighthawk may be distinguished by its broad white throat-patch, and by the bars of white near the tips of the wings. (Family *Caprimulgidae*)

Florida Nighthawk
Chordeiles minor chapmani [420b]

Similar to the Eastern Nighthawk, but somewhat smaller, and with the upper parts more thickly mottled with white and creamy buff markings.
LENGTH—8.60 inches.
DISTRIBUTION—From southern Illinois, central Arkansas, and eastern Texas, through the Gulf States as far north as central North Carolina. (Family *Caprimulgidae*)

Howell's Nighthawk
Chordeiles minor howelli [420e]

Somewhat similar to the Sennett's Nighthawk, but with a paler and de-

cidedly browner cast; less grayish, and with the lighter markings more buffy in tone. Under parts also more buffy.
DISTRIBUTION—Found in the southern portion of the Great Plains, and in the central Rocky Mountain region; migrating in the fall through Nicaragua, and wintering probably in South America. (Family *Caprimulgidae*)

Pacific Nighthawk
Chordeiles minor hesperis [420d]

Similar to the Eastern Nighthawk, but with the wings slightly grayer, and with larger white patches on the throat, wings, and tail.
DISTRIBUTION—Southeastern British Columbia across Alberta into southwestern Saskatchewan, central Montana, central Utah, and northwestern Wyoming; thence southward along the Pacific coastal strip to northern California, and in the Sierra Nevada southward in southern California to the San Bernardino Mountains. It migrates in the fall through Nicaragua, and probably into South America. (Family *Caprimulgidae*)

San Lucas Nighthawk
Chordeiles acutipennis inferior [421a]

Similar to the Texas Nighthawk, but somewhat smaller.
DISTRIBUTION—Restricted to about the southern half of the peninsula of Lower California. (Family *Caprimulgidae*)

Sennett's Nighthawk
Chordeiles minor sennetti [420c]

Similar to the Eastern Nighthawk, but with the wing coverts and scapulars largely whitish, and with the plumage less brownish. It is the palest of all our Nighthawks.

DISTRIBUTION—From northern North Dakota and northeastern Montana, southward into eastern Wyoming, northwestern Iowa, and northern Nebraska. In winter it migrates through Oklahoma and Texas, probably into South America. (Family *Caprimulgidae*)

Texas Nighthawk

Chordeiles acutipennis texensis [421]

ADULT MALE—Upper parts, dull mottled-gray, much streaked with blackish. A white band in the wing, the space between this and the primary coverts spotted with brown. Throat, white; rest of under parts finely barred with white, buffy, and blackish. Tail band, white.

ADULT FEMALE—Similar, but with the tail band restricted or absent, and wing band buffy, instead of white.

LENGTH—8.50 inches.

DISTRIBUTION — From Texas to southern California, and from Nevada and Utah southward to the tip of Lower California and Veragua.

The Texas Nighthawks fly low, pursuing their insect prey only a few feet from the ground. Their calls are said to be "bubbling cries," and they do not give voice to the booming sound, nor to the nasal *"beans"* call of our New England species. (Family *Caprimulgidae*)

Western Nighthawk

Chordeiles minor henryi [420a]

Similar to the Eastern Nighthawk, but with the upper parts a more decided brown, and more thickly marked. Abdomen washed with rusty brown.

DISTRIBUTION — Throughout western United States, east to the Great Plains. It winters south of the United States, probably in South America. (Family *Caprimulgidae*)

NIGHTINGALE

Greater Kamchatka Nightingale

Calliope calliope camtschatkensis [764.1]

ADULT MALE AND FEMALE—Upper parts, brown; a line over the eye, light brownish or brownish-white. Chin and throat, reddish. Under parts, brownish-white.

LENGTH—About 7.25 inches.

DISTRIBUTION — This northeastern Asiatic form has been reported as

casual on Kiska Island, in the Aleutian Chain, Alaska.

This Greater Kamchatka Nightingale is also known as the Ruby-throated Nightingale. (Family *Turdidae*)

NUTCRACKER

Clark's Nutcracker

Nucifraga columbiana [491]

ADULT MALE AND FEMALE—Body, light gray; region about the base of the bill, white. Wings, black with prominent white patches. Middle tail feathers, black; outer ones, white. Bill, long and heavy; wings, long and pointed. Claws, heavy, curved, and sharply pointed.

LENGTH—12.50 inches.

DISTRIBUTION—From northern Alaska southward in the mountains of western North America as far as northern Lower California, Arizona, and New Mexico; sometimes wandering eastward into the Mississippi Valley.

These black and white **crow-like birds** (often called Clark Crows) are found on the higher mountains near the edge of a timber line from 6000 to 9000 feet, and usually stay in the zone of the alpine hemlocks and dwarf pines.

Their notes are long-drawn-out, harsh *kaaaaah* sounds, somewhat similar to the notes of Jays, but higher in pitch and more grating. Their flight habits are unusual and startling. Often a bird will be seen dropping from a rocky peak with closed wings and rapidly gaining momentum. For a thousand feet this black and white bullet in feathers plummets downward, until, suddenly spreading its wings with a sound like a small gun, it swoops upward, and then repeats the performance, sliding down each time to a lower elevation. (Family *Corvidae*)

NUTHATCH FAMILY
Sittidae

Nuthatches are like feathered mice in the bird world, in that they are able to crawl about among the branches, and on the trunks of trees, either head upward or downward, as the exigencies of the situation or desire dictate. Their bills are relatively long, straight, and sharp; their tails, short and square; and their toes and claws, well developed for their peculiar mode of progression. They are small birds, not much more than six inches in length, with gray upper parts. Their voices are nasal and trumpet-like. Of the approximately eighty species and subspecies, thirteen are found in North America, contained in the single genus *Sitta*.

NESTING. The nests of Nuthatches are to be found either in small natural cavities in tree trunks and the larger limbs, in dead stumps, or in a deserted Woodpecker's hole. The birds prefer woodlands, though they often show a partiality to old orchards where cavities of all kinds occur in the old, gnarled, partly-decayed trees. Such an orchard should be a part of every nature-lover's estate, for while it may not bear much of a crop of fruit, yet its blossoms are equally lovely with those of a well-kept, well-pruned orchard, and its crop of Nuthatches, Wrens, Woodpeckers, Chickadees, Bluebirds, and other hole-nesting birds, is a constant delight all through the spring and summer months. To return to the Nuthatches: often these

birds may be induced to nest in a nesting box, if it is properly constructed of old, weathered, rough boards. The height of the Nuthatch's nesting site varies from two or three to sixty feet or more from the ground. The nest itself is composed of coarse and fine grasses, weed bark, shreds of tree bark, leaves, and miscellaneous plant fibre; and is lined with a few fine grasses, some soft cottony plant down, fur (often the rabbit's), sheep wool, hair, some feathers, and the like; the materials varying somewhat with the species. Some species which nest habitually in coniferous trees smear pitch about the entrance hole of the cavity, and make no nest within, but lay the eggs on a bed of small soft chips at the bottom of the cavity. Nuthatch eggs vary in number from four to eight (rarely nine or ten) —four or five is the usual clutch. They are either white, grayish-white, light flesh-color, or creamy, and speckled with browns, grays, and various shades of lilac or lavender.

NUTHATCH
Black-eared Nuthatch
Sitta pygmaea melanotis [730b]

Similar to the Pygmy Nuthatch, but with the top of the head and the nape much darker, and with a less brownish cast. Line through the eye, broader and often nearly black.

DISTRIBUTION—From southern British Columbia, northern Idaho, and eastern Washington southward through the Rocky Mountain region to the Mexican border; and along the Sierra Nevada of California south to the San Bernardino Mountains. The bird occurs casually in South Dakota and Nebraska. (Family *Sittidae*)

Brown-headed Nuthatch
Sitta pusilla pusilla [729]

ADULT MALE AND FEMALE—Upper parts, bluish-gray; the top and back of the head, grayish-brown; and the nape bearing a whitish patch. Middle tail feathers, bluish-gray; outer tail feathers, black tipped with grayish. Under parts, grayish-white; the breast tinged with buffy. Sides of body, gray.

LENGTH—4.50 inches.

DISTRIBUTION—From Delaware (accidentally, New York) and rarely Missouri, south through the South Atlantic and Gulf States.

This little acrobat is similar in its habits to the common Red-breasted

Nuthatch, and like it possesses a "tin trumpet" voice, higher in pitch, and sounding like *tney-tney-tney,* or again

nee-nee-nee. Brown-headed Nuthatches are characteristic birds of the pine woods of the South. (Family *Sittidae*)

Florida Nuthatch
Sitta carolinensis atkinsi [727b]

Similar to the White-breasted Nuthatch, but slightly smaller, and lacking the whitish markings in the wings.

DISTRIBUTION—South Carolina, along the coast into Florida. (Family *Sittidae*)

Gray-headed Nuthatch
Sitta pusilla caniceps [729a]

Similar to the Brown-headed Nuthatch, but with the upper parts and head paler in color, and the wings shorter.

DISTRIBUTION—Florida and the Bahamas. (Family *Sittidae*)

Inyo Nuthatch
Sitta carolinensis tenuissima [727e]

Similar to the Slender-billed Nuthatch, but larger; the back, darker; the flanks, paler; and the bill, much longer and slenderer.

DISTRIBUTION—Found in the Panamint, and the White Mountains of California. (Family *Sittidae*)

Pygmy Nuthatch

Sitta pygmaea pygmaea [730]

ADULT MALE AND FEMALE—Upper parts, bluish-gray; top of head, brownish-gray. Nape patch, white. Basal portion of middle tail feathers, white;

outer feathers marked with white. Line through eye, black; chin, white; the rest of the under parts, whitish tinged with buffy.

LENGTH—4.17 inches.

DISTRIBUTION—From British Columbia southward through western North America east of the Rocky Mountains, to Mexico.

A denizen of pines and other conifers, the little Pygmy Nuthatch never fails to attract attention by reason of its diminutive size, its mouse-like habits of crawling about the branches, and its high nasal notes. (Family *Sittidae*)

Red-breasted Nuthatch

Sitta canadensis [728]

ADULT MALE—Top of head, black; a broad white stripe over the eye, and a broad black one through it. Upper parts, bluish-gray; wings, the same uniform color. Outer tail feathers, black with white patches near their tips; middle tail feathers, bluish-gray. Throat, white; the rest of the under parts, chestnut or orange-brown. The name "red-breasted" is a misnomer.

ADULT FEMALE—Similar to the male, but with the top of the head and the eye-stripe, bluish-gray instead of black. Under parts, light yellowish-brown or pale orange-brown.

LENGTH—4.62 inches.

DISTRIBUTION—From the far north in Canada and Alaska southward into the Northern States, and still farther southward along the high Allegheny Mountains into Virginia; along the Rocky Mountains into Colorado; and along the Sierra Nevada Mountains into California. It spends its winters as far south as Arizona and the Gulf States.

Red-breasted Nuthatches are more commonly found among coniferous trees than among deciduous ones, creeping over the bark, crawling about the cones, head upwards or downwards indifferently. It does not take an observer long to note that they are more acrobatically inclined birds than their White-breasted relatives. No bird is more leisurely alert, more filled with a nervous yet restrained vigor than this comical little inspector of nooks

and crannies. As a result of this tireless searching, there is constantly disappearing down the throat of the bird an interminable procession of insect adults, larvae, pupae, and eggs, which if unmolested would result in great injury to the trees which harbored them. The notes of the Red-breast resemble the protracted blasts from tiny tin trumpets, a leisurely, nasal, somewhat musical *waank, waank, waank,* more languid than the notes of the White-breasted Nuthatch, and slightly higher in pitch. Like other nuthatches it is the forester's ally in its destruction of insects injurious to trees, especially conifers. (Family *Sittidae*)

Rocky Mountain Nuthatch
Sitta carolinensis nelsoni [727c]

Similar to the Slender-billed Nuthatch, but slightly larger, and with more white markings in the outer tail feathers, and slightly more brownish flush on the flanks and abdomen.

DISTRIBUTION—From Arizona, New Mexico, Colorado, and northward; south into the mountains of northwestern Mexico. (Family *Sittidae*)

San Lucas Nuthatch
Sitta carolinensis lagunae [727d]

Somewhat similar to the Slender-billed Nuthatch, but with shorter wings and tail, and with less black on the tips of the outer tail feathers.

DISTRIBUTION—Restricted to the high mountains of the southern portion of Lower California. (Family *Sittidae*)

San Pedro Nuthatch
Sitta carolinensis alexandrae [727f]

Similar to the Slender-billed Nuthatch, but with much longer bill, wings, and tail; also with more white in the wings and tail, and with the upper parts slightly darker.

DISTRIBUTION—In the pine belt of the Sierra San Pedro Martir of Lower California. (Family *Sittidae*)

Slender-billed Nuthatch
Sitta carolinensis aculeata [727a]

Similar to the White-breasted Nuthatch, but with a greenish cast to the blackish head, and with grayish-black instead of black tertials.

DISTRIBUTION—From British Columbia southward and west of the

Rocky Mountains into Lower California. (Family *Sittidae*)

White-breasted Nuthatch
Sitta carolinensis carolinensis [727]

ADULT MALE—Top of head and neck, black; the rest of the upper parts, bluish-gray; the wings bearing whitish markings. Outer tail feathers, black with white near their tips; middle tail feathers, bluish-gray like the back. Sides of head and under parts, white, except the lower abdomen and under tail coverts, which are brown and white.

ADULT FEMALE—Similar to the male, but with the top and back of the head washed with bluish-gray.

LENGTH—6.07 inches.

DISTRIBUTION—From New Brunswick and Minnesota, west to the Rocky Mountains, and south into the Gulf States.

"Wank, wank, wank" trumpets this little acrobat of the bird world, as it crawls, often head-downward, over the trunks and branches of large trees. It is one of our commonest birds, especially in winter, because of the diminution of other bird life at this season. Yet because of its unobtrusive habits, and rather subdued nasal notes, it is not often noticed. It is more apt to be found in old orchards, along quiet village streets, sometimes in parks, or in the country where large trees abound. It is a ubiquitous

bird, however, and is quite as likely to be encountered in the depths of a forest as in one's own dooryard. Nuthatches do not use their tails as props, as do Woodpeckers, but rely both for support and progression upon their large, strong feet. In the spring, Nuthatches give joyous voice to a series of musically nasal notes many times

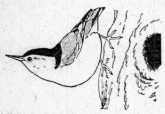

rapidly repeated, like the syllables *wank, wank, wank, wank, wank, wank, wank, wank.* This is their nearest approach to a song, and announces the advent of the mating season. Nuthatches are active birds, being constantly on the move, crawling, swinging, hitching, flying, or hammering to open or "hatch" an acorn or small nut or seed. (Family *Sittidae*)

White-naped Nuthatch

Sitta pygmaea leuconucha [730a]

Similar to the Pygmy Nuthatch but with a grayer crown, a grayer back, a more prominent nape-patch, a longer bill, and whiter under parts.

DISTRIBUTION—Restricted to Lower California. (Family *Sittidae*)

OLD-SQUAW

Old-squaw

Clangula hyemalis [154]

ADULT MALE—Head, neck, back, breast, and upper abdomen, sooty-black; the feathers of the back margined with reddish-brown. A patch in front of the eye is gray, and a smaller patch behind it is white. At a distance the whole side of the head

about the eye appears bearing a broad patch of white. Lower abdomen, white. The two middle tail feathers are black, and much elongated and narrow. The base of the bill is black, its tip is yellow, and the region between is pinkish or pinkish-brown. Legs and feet, pale slaty-bluish or gray.

ADULT FEMALE—Head, neck, and under parts, largely white. Crown, and the sides of the neck, dark dusky. Upper parts, dusky-brown marked with darker. Upper breast, dusky. Central tail feathers not elongated, making bird shorter.

LENGTH — 21.00 inches; female some five inches shorter.

DISTRIBUTION—From northern Labrador and the shores of Hudson Bay westward over northern Canada to the Aleutian Islands, and northward to the shores of the Arctic Ocean. In winter it is found as far south as Virginia, the upper portion of the Mississippi Valley, and California. Occurs rarely in Florida and Texas.

Along the coast of New York and New England, the Old-squaw is a common winter resident from October to May. In the surf of the outer beaches one

may see flocks of them feeding, or they may be observed farther out from the shore, floating about in great "rafts," looking almost like small dark islands. The Old-squaw is a constant "gabbler." Its notes are liquid and pleasing, and are best represented by the syllables of Sanford, as *honk, honk-a-link, honk-a-link.* Sometimes they seem to say *oh come here, oh come here, e-waanky, e-waanky*. When the male elevates its long tail feathers, it makes the bird a conspicuous object as it rides gracefully over the waves. It is one of the most rapidly flying of our sea birds. (Family *Anatidae*)

ORDERS

North American birds still existent are contained in 20 orders. The largest is the Order *Passeriformes*, with 27 families; the next in size is the Order *Charadriiformes*, with 10 families. The other 25 orders contain from one to six families each. The Order *Passeriformes* contains the families of smaller, perching birds; the Order *Charadriiformes* includes the families of Sandpipers, Plovers, Gulls, Terns, Auks, Oystercatchers, etc.

North American birds known from fossil remains are contained in 19 orders. The largest of these is the Order *Anseriformes* (Ducks, Geese, etc.).

ORIOLE
Arizona Hooded Oriole
Icterus cucullatus nelsoni [505a]

Similar to the Sennett's Oriole, but with yellow replacing the orange of that species.

DISTRIBUTION—From southwestern New Mexico, Arizona, and southern

California, and west of the Sierra Nevada into Lower California and

northwestern Mexico. In winter it passes farther into Mexico. (Family *Icteridae*)

Audubon's Oriole
Icterus melanocephalus auduboni [503]

ADULT MALE AND FEMALE—Upper parts, lemon-yellow or yellowish-green, variable. Whole head and upper

breast, jet black. Wings, black with white edgings to the feathers, and yellowish-green shoulders (wrist). Tail, black, narrowly tipped with grayish.

LENGTH—8.82 inches.

DISTRIBUTION—From the southern half of Texas southward into eastern and central Mexico. (Family *Icteridae*)

Baltimore Oriole
Icterus galbula [507]

ADULT MALE—Upper back, whole head and throat, wings and tail, jet black. Wing feathers edged with white. Outer tail feathers, yellow-orange for about half their length, graduated toward the middle. Rest of plumage, flaming reddish-orange.

ADULT FEMALE—Upper parts, brownish; wings, darker. Throat sometimes spotted with dark grayish. Rest of plumage, greenish-yellow.

LENGTH—7.53 inches.

DISTRIBUTION—The eastern portion of North America, from New Brunswick and Saskatchewan southward into Florida and eastern Texas, and west to the Rocky Mountains. In winter it passes into Central and South America.

The "Fire Hang Bird" is a familiar sight to dwellers of country and town alike. Its long, gray, pendant nest dangles from scores of drooping elm branches along country roads, city streets, parks—wherever there are long, sweeping branches. The bird keeps well to the tops of the trees, however, where its startlingly flaming colors flash out in the bright sunshine. Its song is a clear, loud, rich whistle: *Oh here hère; see me up hère;* or

again, in shorter form, *Johnny, Joe,* and *Jim.* Both sexes sing during the mating season; the song of the female being shorter than that of the male, and not quite so loud. (Family *Icteridae*)

Bullock's Oriole
Icterus bullocki [508]

ADULT MALE—Upper back, crown, line through eye, and throat, jet black. Wings, black marked with white; tail with middle feathers, black. Rest of plumage, bright orange.

ADULT FEMALE—Upper parts, olive or olive-brown, streaked. Under parts, yellow, graying on the lower abdo-

men; throat, black or blackish. Wings marked with white.

LENGTH—7.17 inches.

DISTRIBUTION — British Columbia and its region to Mexico, east as far as western Texas, and west to the Pacific Coast. In winter it is found in Mexico. With its bright orange, black, and pure white, this Oriole is the most strikingly colored of our native Orioles. (Family *Icteridae*)

Orchard Oriole
Icterus spurius [506]

ADULT MALE—Upper portion of back, whole head, and throat, jet black. Tail, nearly black; wings, dark brown. Lower back, breast, and abdomen, rich chestnut-brown.

ADULT FEMALE—Upper parts, greenish and brownish-yellow, brightening on the lower back and rump; wings, slightly darker. Tail, brownish washed with greenish. Under parts, yellow.

LENGTH—7.30 inches.

DISTRIBUTION—The eastern half of the continent, from central New England across to Michigan, Ontario, North Dakota, and the Great Plains. It winters in Central America, and in northern South America.

The Orchard Oriole, as its name implies, is most often found in orchards or groves of low trees, where its rich, throaty, musical notes are sure to attract admiring attention. The tones are whistled, and seem, at times, almost clear through a rich film of overtones, which renders the performance unlike that of any other neighboring bird. To some ears the quality of the notes is reminiscent of that of the

Purple Finch. The richness of song, and the rich chestnut coloring of the male bird, are a harmonious consociation. The rich coloration of the cock bird shows at its best only in strong sunlight. (Family *Icteridae*)

San Lucas Hooded Oriole

Icterus cucullatus trochiloides [505b]

Similar to the Arizona Hooded Oriole, but with a longer bill, and with the orange in the plumage duller, and washed with yellowish.

DISTRIBUTION—The southern half of Lower California. (Family *Icteridae*)

Scott's Oriole

Icterus parisorum [504]

Somewhat similar to the Audubon's Oriole, but with black of head region more extended down the back, and with more white in the wings. The female is yellowish, the back brownish-yellow, and only a small patch of black on the throat.

LENGTH—7.85 inches.

DISTRIBUTION — From western Texas, west to California, and from

south Utah and Nevada southward

into Lower California and Mexico. (Family *Icteridae*)

Sennett's Oriole

Icterus cucullatus sennetti [505]

ADULT MALE—Face, throat, back, wings, and tail, jet black. Wings marked with white. Rest of plumage, deep rich yellow.

ADULT FEMALE—Upper parts, grayish; under parts, yellowish.

LENGTH—7.36 inches.

DISTRIBUTION—The southwestern portion of Texas along the Rio Grande Valley, southward into Mexico.

The Sennett's Oriole is an inhabitant of the yucca region of the lower Rio Grande Valley, among the dense impenetrable tangles of cactus and dwarf yuccas. (Family *Icteridae*)

OSPREY

Osprey

Pandion haliaëtus carolinensis [364]

ADULT MALE—Upper parts, dark grayish-brown; the head and nape marked with white. Tail crossed by six or eight narrow light bars. Under parts, white; the breast sometimes lightly spotted with grayish-brown.

ADULT FEMALE—Similar to the male, but with the breast always spotted with grayish-brown.

LENGTH—23.10 inches.

DISTRIBUTION—Over the whole of North America, but in winter restricted to the region from South Carolina and the lower section of the Mississippi southward to northern South America.

The Osprey, or Fish Hawk as it is more commonly called, secures its food by diving head first into the water, and gripping its finny prey with

its powerful talons. Although the bird may nest many miles inland, it is most frequently seen along the coasts, and in the region of large lakes and rivers. It is a gentle Hawk, never molesting small birds, and intent only on its fishing excursions, and the duties of nesting and the rearing of its young. It is often confused with the Bald Eagle, but from that bird it may be distinguished by its smaller size, and chiefly by its *white under parts* —those of the Bald Eagle being dark, like the back. The voice of the Osprey, not very often heard, seems ridiculously small and out of proportion to so majestic a bird, and consists of a shrill, high-pitched, screaming whistle. When heard at a distance it sounds like the peeping of a baby chick. Nests of the Osprey look like bushel baskets of sticks, placed high in dead trees, on the rocky ledges of

cliffs, on deserted buildings, or even on the cross-arms of telegraph poles. Sometimes the birds nest on platforms provided for them. (Family *Accipitridae*)

OVEN-BIRD

Oven-bird
Seiurus aurocapillus [674]

ADULT MALE AND FEMALE—Upper parts, medium brown; the center of the crown bearing a light orange or orange-brownish stripe, edged on each side by a narrow black line. Under parts, white streaked with black on the breast, on the sides of the abdomen, and on the throat.
LENGTH—6.17 inches.

DISTRIBUTION — Eastern North America, from Labrador and northwestern Alaska southward, west of the Rocky Mountains, to Virginia and Kansas. It spends the winter from Florida southward through the West Indies into Central America.

The Oven-bird is a forest dweller, frequenting moderately heavy growths, but being absent or nearly so in the

deep evergreen forests. Its loud ringing crescendo song is familiar to all who wander among the trees, though the singer is not easy to locate. Sometimes the bird says *te'a cher, te'a cher, te'a cher, te'a cher*—with the accent falling on the first syllable; but more often the stress falls on the second syllable. When singing, the bird sits motionless on a horizontal limb, usually back among the leaves, and about fifteen or twenty feet from the ground, and from this situation pours forth its loud and penetrating song, the notes of which are often ventriloquial in character. When on the ground (for the bird is one of the ground warblers, like the two so-called water thrushes), it walks (not hops) about tilting its tail upwards in the daintiest manner. Among the dry leaves its sombre colors afford it excellent obliteration. When disturbed, instead of taking flight, it often slips away among the debris of the forest floor, threading its way quickly like a tiny mouse. The evening flight song of the Oven-bird compares favorably with the famous flight song of the European Skylark, and usually ends with a few *teacher* notes as the singer drops back among the leaves of the forest. (Family *Compsothlypidae*)

OWL FAMILY
Typical Owls, Horned Owls, Screech Owls, Hawk Owls, etc.
Strigidae
(See also Barn Owl Family)

The Typical Owls (differing somewhat from the Barn Owls) are distributed over almost the whole globe. They range from very small (as the Elf Owl) to large (as the Great Horned Owl). The face is circular, not oval or heart-shaped. When the feathers of the leg are present, they are directed downward. The bills of Owls are short, but strong and hooked, and often almost concealed by feathers. The head is capable of being turned so that the birds can look almost straight backwards between their shoulder blades. The eyes are large, and especially keen-sighted, and the ears extremely sensitive to the faintest sounds. The plumage is soft and fluffy, and the birds are able to fly and to swoop upon their prey with hardly a sound. The feet are large and strong, and the claws extremely long, curved, and as sharp as daggers. Owls are unable to

see when there is no light (light is the prerequisite of vision in any animal), but they are able to see very well in twilight and in moonlight, and it is during such times that the birds engage in their silent hunting. Bones, fur, feathers, and the like are ejected from the mouth in the form of pellets. This prevents their passing down through the rest of the alimentary tract and clogging it with useless indigestible matter. Over five hundred members of this family are known, spread all over the world, with few regions uninhabited by them. In the Western Hemisphere about one hundred and seventy-five species and subspecies are found, and fifty-five are recorded from North America, contained in eleven genera. Of these, there are seventeen species and subspecies of Screech Owls; ten species and subspecies of Horned Owls; and six of the little Pygmy Owls. Owls feed upon small mammals (such as several species of mice, shrews, rabbits, squirrels, and the like) as well as upon frogs, toads, large insects, and small birds. The larger Owls take some of the large birds, such as quail, grouse, and ducks, but on the whole they are an extremely beneficial group because of their destruction of injurious rodents, and of weak and diseased animal forms of all kinds.

NESTING. The Strigid or Typical Owls breed in a great variety of situations. Some lay their eggs in a hollow tree or on a bed of soft chips. The Barred Owl usually nests so. The Screech Owl utilizes either a deeper hollow, a deserted Woodpecker's hole, some convenient crevice in an old building, or a bird box (one usually intended for a Flicker). Others fashion a large nest of sticks, twigs, rootlets, weed stems, bits of bark, and the like, lining it with fine grasses, leaves, feathers, and sometimes mosses and lichens, and placing it in a tree (often an evergreen), from ten to fifty feet or so from the ground (e.g., the Long-eared Owl). Still others, like the Short-eared Owl, place a flimsy nest of sticks and grasses on the ground in a clump of grass or reeds, or at the base of a small bush. The Great Horned Owl and others which make large nests of sticks frequently appropriate to their needs the deserted nest of a crow, hawk, osprey, or eagle, adding to the structure a few extra sticks or a lining of rootlets and feathers. The Great Horned Owl, in some parts of its range, breeds in a cave, on a cliffy ledge, or in a hollow tree, depositing its eggs amid a rubble of fur, feathers, bones, dried bits of skin—the relics of former feasts. The great Snowy Owl lays its eggs in a depression in the ground, on a scanty lining of grasses and a few feathers. The Burrowing Owl utilizes the burrow of a skunk, fox, badger, or prairie dog, laying its eggs deep within the tunnel, from five to ten feet from the entrance hole, on a collection of miscellaneous rubble of weed stems, grasses, fragments of dried horse or cow dung, bones, feathers, bits of dry skin, and other similar trash. The eggs of our Strigid Owls are white, unmarked, and with sometimes a smooth, and sometimes a slightly chalky or dull surface.

OWL
Aiken's Screech Owl
Otus asio aikeni [373g]

Similar to the Eastern Screech Owl, but much grayer, and with the upper and under parts bearing more black markings.

DISTRIBUTION—From Colorado southward into New Mexico and northeastern Arizona (Family *Strigidae*)

American Hawk Owl
Surnia ulula caparoch [377a]

ADULT MALE AND FEMALE—Upper parts, dark grayish-brown; the top of the head and neck, finely speckled with white. Tertials, heavily spotted with white. The tail bears about seven fine white bars, and is long (for an Owl), being about half as long as the body proper, and rounded at its tip. Sides of neck and upper breast, streaked with dark grayish-brown; the breast and abdomen, white thickly barred with brown. Facial discs, white, bordered on the sides with black. Eyes, rather small for an Owl; yellow irises. Bill, yellow, set off by a blackish patch beneath. No ear tufts. Female usually slightly larger than the male.

LENGTH—About 16.00 inches.

DISTRIBUTION — In the extreme northern parts of North America, southward to Newfoundland and northern Montana, but seldom found on the Pacific Coast. In winter the bird straggles into our northernmost states, sometimes as far south as southern New York, Connecticut, and the northern hill region of New Jersey, and into northern Illinois.

As its name suggests, the Hawk Owl is, in appearance at least, partly a Hawk and partly an Owl. It is not at all a wary species, and may be approached quite closely before taking wing. As it flies it shows a long pointed tail and falcon-like wings. Its high squealing flight-call reminds one

of the cry of the Osprey, sounding like the syllables *pi-reek, pi-reek*. Other notes include a varied series of whines, whistles, and screams. (Family *Strigidae*)

Arctic Horned Owl

Bubo virginianus subarcticus [375b]

Similar to the Great Horned Owl, but paler; almost white.

DISTRIBUTION—In the central portion of arctic North America, from

Hudson Bay to the Rocky Mountains. In winter it very infrequently straggles

down into our northern states. (Family *Strigidae*)

Barn Owl

Tyto alba pratincola [365]

ADULT MALE AND FEMALE—Upper parts, buffy yellow finely marked with black, white, and gray. Tail, yellowish or whitish flecked with black, and sometimes bearing three or four indistinct black bars. Under parts, white or straw-yellow sprinkled with fine black dots. Facial discs, whitish or yellowish, deepening to light brown around the eyes, and outlined with deep yellowish-brown. Iris of eye, and bill, black. Female usually larger than the male; rarely smaller.

LENGTH—About 18.00 inches.

DISTRIBUTION—From central New England and Long Island, Minnesota, southern Ontario, and Oregon, south to the Gulf States, wintering as far south as Mexico.

The Barn or Monkey-faced Owl is seldom seen in daylight, except as it may be chanced upon, roosting in the dark corner of some old building or among the thick foliage of an evergreen. When disturbed, it makes off clumsily and in an uncertain and erratic flight, as though bewildered both by the intrusion and by the light into which it has been driven. At night, however, the bird is anything but uncertain or bewildered. Possessed of unusually acute night vision, and served by large and especially sensitive ears, it glides swiftly, noiselessly, and unerringly upon its prey, aided in this sort of spectral locomotion by its extremely light and downy plumage which enables it to fly without a sound, and free from the noise of whistling pinions which stiffer feathers would occasion. This eerie flight and the habit of nesting in deserted buildings, old towers, steeples, and ghostly ruins, have resulted in the bird's being taken more than once for the "haunt" or spirit of such localities, more especially since one of its common flight notes is a weird, subdued, hissing

scream. Its consumption of harmful rodents makes it one of our most valuable birds of prey. After a kill the quarry is usually borne to the nest in the mouth rather than carried by the powerful talons. (Family *Tytonidae*)

Brewster's Screech Owl

Otus asio brewsteri [373j]

Similar to the Kennicott's Screech Owl, but somewhat smaller, and with the plumage less brownish in general tone.

DISTRIBUTION—In Oregon, and in Washington west of the Cascade Mountains and Chelan County, southward in California as far as Humboldt County. (Family *Strigidae*)

California Pygmy Owl

Glaucidium gnoma californicum [379a]

Similar to the Rocky Mountain Pygmy Owl, but slightly darker, and with the upper parts spotted with brownish instead of whitish.

DISTRIBUTION—From British Columbia southward, and along the coastal zone of California as far as Monterey. (Family *Strigidae*)

California Screech Owl

Otus asio bendirei [373c]

Similar to the Eastern Screech Owl, but darker, and with under parts more heavily barred.

DISTRIBUTION—Restricted to the region between southern Oregon and California. (Family *Strigidae*)

California Spotted Owl

Strix occidentalis occidentalis [369]

Somewhat similar to the Northern Barred Owl, but with the head and neck thickly spotted with white, and

with prominent white tips on the primary wing feathers.

DISTRIBUTION—From southern Colorado, New Mexico, and California, southward into Lower California and into south central Mexico. (Family *Strigidae*)

Coast Pygmy Owl

Glaucidium gnoma grinnelli [379c]

Similar to the California Pygmy Owl, but with the general tone of the plumage much browner.

DISTRIBUTION—From the southeastern portion of the Alaskan coastal district southward as far as about Monterey County, California, and eastward as far as the western slopes of Mt. Shasta and to Lake County, California. It occurs casually to eastern Washington. (Family *Strigidae*)

Dusky Horned Owl

Bubo virginianus saturatus [375c]

Somewhat similar to the Great Horned Owl, but darker, with heavier dark markings on the breast.

DISTRIBUTION—Along the Pacific Coast from Alaska southward into California, also eastward to Labrador. (Family *Strigidae*)

Dwarf Horned Owl

Bubo virginianus elachistus [375e]

Similar to the Great Horned Owl, but much smaller and much darker, resembling in this respect more the color of the Dusky Horned Owl.

DISTRIBUTION—Restricted to Lower California. (Family *Strigidae*)

Eastern Screech Owl

Otus asio naevius [373m]

ADULT MALE AND FEMALE—*In the gray phase:* Upper parts, brownish-gray delicately streaked with black and finely flecked with yellowish-white. Under parts, white sparsely marked with broad streaks of black, and finely barred with the same color. *In the brown phase:* Gray everywhere re-placed by reddish-brown. Facial discs not prominent. Ear tufts prominent and rising toward the sides of the head, and not directly over the eyes. Iris of eye, yellow; bill, yellowish. Female larger than the male.

LENGTH—About 8.50 inches.

DISTRIBUTION—Widely distributed over the whole of eastern North America from New Brunswick, Ontario, and Minnesota south to Florida, and west to the Great Plains.

This friendly little Owl occurs in the rural suburbs of towns, in small villages, and farming districts generally. It seems to take kindly to man's occupation of the land, and to breed and

thrive in the near vicinity of his dwellings, in spite of the injudicious warfare that is sometimes waged against it. Screech Owls often will nest in a bird house, if the opening is large enough. The bird's common note is one of the most plaintive and doleful of all bird utterances—a tremulous, wailing cry, suggestive of the prolonged subdued whinny of a horse, quavering and sepulchral in character, yet with a pleasing musical quality. To some it is a sound inducive of a pleasant melancholy; to others, the weird and ghostly tremolo is prophetic of disaster or death. It may be written *whe-e-e-e-e-o-o-o-o-oh*, with a slight fall of pitch at its close. The bird rarely "screeches." The name "Screech Owl," taken from the European species, is inappropriate to our form. Screech Owls often take smaller birds, but their chief food is rodents and large insects, hence their value to the farmer. (Family *Strigidae*)

Ferruginous Pygmy Owl
Glaucidium brasilianum ridgwayi [380]

Similar to the Rocky Mountain Pygmy Owl, but with the upper parts brighter, varying from a grayish-brown to a rather bright reddish-brown. The sides of the breast are plain and unmarked, and vary from brown to reddish-brown. The bars on the tail vary in color from whitish to reddish-brown.
LENGTH—6.75 inches.
DISTRIBUTION—From Arizona, New Mexico, and Texas, south through Mexico as far as southern Brazil.
Its note is a loud *cuck,* rapidly repeated. (Family *Strigidae*)

Flammulated Screech Owl
Otus flammeolus [374]

Somewhat similar to the Eastern Screech Owl, but smaller; with shorter ear-tufts; and with a generally more rusty-brown tone.
DISTRIBUTION—From Colorado and California southward through Mexico into the mountains of Guatemala. A very rare species. (Family *Strigidae*)

Florida Barred Owl
Strix varia alleni [368a]

Similar to the Northern Barred Owl, but somewhat smaller and darker, with black bars on the breast. Toes not feathered.
DISTRIBUTION—From South Carolina southward along the Florida coast, and along the Gulf Coast to Texas. (Family *Strigidae*)

Florida Burrowing Owl
Speotyto cunicularia floridana [378a]

Similar to the Western Burrowing Owl, but slightly smaller and paler, with more white spots on the upper parts.
DISTRIBUTION—In the interior region of the southern part of Florida. (Family *Strigidae*)

Florida Screech Owl
Otus asio floridanus [373a]

Similar to the Eastern Screech Owl, but darker, and with heavier markings on the under parts.
DISTRIBUTION—From South Carolina southward along the coast to Florida, and along the Gulf Coast westward as far as Louisiana. (Family *Strigidae*)

Great Gray Owl
Scotiaptex nebulosa nebulosa [370]

ADULT MALE AND FEMALE—Upper parts, dark brownish slaty-gray, mottled with white. Under parts, white, heavily streaked on the breast, and heavily streaked and barred on the abdomen with dark brownish-gray. Facial discs, white, heavily concentrically ringed with zones of black. Iris of eye and the bill, yellow. The head and face are much larger, in proportion to the body, than in other Owls. The head is rounded, with no ear-tufts.
LENGTH—About 28 inches.
DISTRIBUTION—The arctic portion of North America, wintering south to our northernmost states, and infrequently found in winter in New Jersey, Illinois, Minnesota, Idaho, and sometimes as far west as northern California.

With a wing-spread of from four to five feet, and an enormous head and face, the Great Gray Owl presents an appearance of unequalled majesty. Its great size, however, is due to the extremely puffy character of its plumage —its body is not large, sometimes weighing even less than that of the

Barred Owl. Jencks says of it, ". . . it is the most bird for the least substance we ever examined." The great puff of feathers with which its body is invested, is an adaptation for retaining the body heat; the bird ranges north as far as trees will grow, and where temperatures under fifty degrees below zero are not unknown.
"St. Agnes' Eve—Ah, bitter chill it was!
The owl, for all his feathers, was a-cold."
The Great Gray Owl inhabits dense low wilderness forests, or wooded mountain slopes, and rarely straggles southward except when forced to do so by unusually heavy snows in its northern home. In the United States the bird is not numerous enough to exert any appreciable effect upon our agricultural economy. (Family *Strigidae*)

Great Horned Owl

Bubo virginianus virginianus [375]

ADULT MALE AND FEMALE—Upper parts mottled with light brownish,

yellowish, white, and black. Throat, white; the rest of the under parts, yellowish-white finely and heavily barred with black. The upper breast bears about six heavy irregular black streaks. Facial discs light brown edged with black. Ear tufts, long and prominent; bill, black. Iris of eye, deep yellow.

LENGTH—About 22 inches.

DISTRIBUTION — Through eastern North America, from Labrador to Central America.

The more unsettled parts of our country where impenetrable swamps, deep lowland forests, and wild wooded mountains and hills abound, are the common domain of the Great Horned Owl. This is the species most often called the "Hoot Owl" by hunters. Its notes are all on the same pitch, deep and booming, being among the lowest notes heard in the forest. Usually they are uttered without a definite

rhythm, as *hoo, hoo, hoo, hoo, hoo;* but are sometimes grouped and accented thus: *hoo-hoo, h'oo-hoo;* or *h'oo hoo h'oo, hoo-hoo.* In addition, the bird infrequently emits a loud terrifying scream, as of a soul in dire anguish, a sound which if once heard in the midnight forest is not soon forgotten! This great Owl, with a wingspread which in large specimens may reach to sixty inches, is the most fearless of our birds of prey. It attacks even the Bald Eagle, the skunk, porcupines (when pressed by severe hunger), dogs, and even man himself. Any moving object would seem to be the prey of this intrepid feathered monster. In its own haunts the Great Horned Owl forms a valuable check upon the undue increase of diseased and weak creatures, and should never be shot in its native wilds. (Family *Strigidae*)

Hasbrouck's Screech Owl
Otus asio hasbroucki [373i]

Similar to the Texas Screech Owl, but decidedly larger, darker, and with the under parts more heavily marked, their transverse bars being broader and more numerous. Legs marked with a much darker brown than in the Texas form.

DISTRIBUTION—Restricted to central Texas. (Family *Strigidae*)

Hoskins's Pygmy Owl
Glaucidium gnoma hoskinsi [379.1]

Similar to the California Pygmy Owl, but smaller and paler; the head showing more white.

DISTRIBUTION—Restricted to the southern part of Lower California. (Family *Strigidae*)

Kennicott's Screech Owl
Otus asio kennicotti [373d]

Similar to the Eastern Screech Owl, but larger and much darker, being the darkest of the Screech Owls.

DISTRIBUTION—Along the Alaskan Coast into Oregon. (Family *Strigidae*)

Labrador Horned Owl
Bubo virginianus heterocnemis [375f]

Similar to the Great Horned Owl, but in general a much darker bird, the prevailing color being a sooty or dusky brown.

LENGTH—About 22.00 inches.

DISTRIBUTION—Nova Scotia, Newfoundland, northern Quebec, and Labrador. In winter it moves westward to Ontario, and in severe winters may be forced down into the northern states, and New England, where it has been reported as far south as Connecticut. (Family *Strigidae*)

Long-eared Owl
Asio wilsonianus [366]

ADULT MALE AND FEMALE—Upper parts, grayish-brown marked with whitish and yellowish-brown. Breast, whitish with heavy streaks of dark brownish-gray. Abdomen and sides heavily streaked and cross-barred with this same color. The conspicuous ear-tufts, an inch or so long, are blackish bordered by yellowish-brown and white. Facial discs, reddish-brown bordered with black. Iris of eye, yellow; bill, black. Female slightly larger than male.

LENGTH—About 15.00 inches.

DISTRIBUTION—North America generally, from Nova Scotia, Manitoba, and British Columbia, southward as far as Mexico.

This Owl is one of our slenderest and most graceful species. When in flight, its long wings and tail make it appear a much larger bird than it actually is, particularly when one sees it in the twilight hours. It is almost exclusively a nocturnal hunter, and seldom flies except at night, or in the deep dusk of morning or evening twilight. During the day it remains concealed amid dark foliage, usually in a grove of coniferous trees, and if disturbed does not ordinarily take flight at once, but draws the feathers tightly about the body and stands stiffly erect—a habit which, together with its obliterative coloration, gives it the appearance of a broken, upright stub. Long-eared Owls nest in deep woodlands, preferably coniferous ones, from which situations they give forth their various cries, the commonest being a long, snarling, cat-like *eeeeaaaaoooow!* Another note, often heard, is a thin, nasal, querulous *eeeeuuuh!* During the

mating season a frequent call is a deep, soft *Hoo-oo.* Because of the enormous quantities of field mice and large noxious insects which this Owl consumes, it is ranked as among the best friends of the farmer. The bird makes a very amusing pet, and is easily tamed. (Family *Strigidae*)

MacFarlane's Screech Owl
Otus asio macfarlanei [373h]

Somewhat similar to the Eastern Screech Owl, but larger and darker.
DISTRIBUTION—From British Columbia southward into the eastern parts of Washington and Oregon, and westward into western Montana. (Family *Strigidae*)

Mexican Screech Owl
Otus asio cineraceus [373f]

Similar to the Eastern Screech Owl, but somewhat smaller; with the upper

parts grayer, and with more thickly barred under parts.
DISTRIBUTION—"New Mexico, Arizona, Lower California, and western Mexico." (A.O.U. Check List.) (Family *Strigidae*)

Mexican Spotted Owl
Strix occidentalis lucida [369b]

Similar to the California Spotted Owl, but darker; with a less yellowish-brown suffusion throughout; and with the white markings in the plumage larger, and of a purer white.
DISTRIBUTION — Colorado, New Mexico, and western Texas, through the mountains of Arizona to the mountains of central Mexico. (Family *Strigidae*)

Montana Horned Owl
Bubo virginianus occidentalis [375j]

Similar to the Pacific Horned Owl, but appreciably larger.
DISTRIBUTION—From Minnesota, South Dakota, Nebraska, and Kansas, westward to Nevada, the southeastern portion of Oregon, the northeastern corner of California, and to Wyoming, Montana, and northward into central Alberta. In winter it is found as far south as Iowa. (Family *Strigidae*)

Northern Barred Owl
Strix varia varia [368]

ADULT MALE AND FEMALE—Upper parts, dark grayish-brown, marked with a multitude of small bars of white or yellowish-white. Under parts, buffy white, finely cross-barred on the throat and breast, and heavily streaked on the abdomen with dark grayish-brown. The facial discs are concentrically ringed with the same color. Ear tufts absent. Iris of eye, dark brown; bill, yellow. Female slightly larger than the male.

LENGTH—20.50 inches.

DISTRIBUTION — From Manitoba and Nova Scotia, west to Colorado, and southward, except along the coast of the Gulf of Mexico. The individuals in the extreme north move slightly southward at the approach of winter.

The Barred Owl is a bird of dense wooded swamps, deep forest solitudes, and bosky ravines; but sometimes, unknown to its human neighbors, it nests close by man's dwelling in a

thick grove of trees. From such situations its loud, reverberant *hoo*-ing notes boom forth on spring and summer nights with such power that frequently they may be heard for a distance of a mile or more when the air is still and moist. The notes are uttered usually in the earlier half of the night, and again in the early morning hours, in monotonous iteration. Among country dwellers the Barred Owl is known as the Swamp Owl, or more commonly as the Eight-Hooter from the number of notes in its commonest call. This may be rendered thus: *hoo-ho'o, hoo-ho'o; hoo-hóo hoo-hoóoaaww.* The last note is slurred downward. To some ears the Owl says *Oh who are you; oh who are you-all!* Besides these notes, the Barred

Owl gives vent to numerous croaks, clucks, cackles, and snarls, and to a high-pitched scream, heard with dread by many, who suppose it to be an augury of impending death. Because of its consumption of many injurious rodents and large insects, the Barred Owl should be given complete protection. (Family *Strigidae*)

Northern Spotted Owl
Strix occidentalis caurina [369a]

Similar to the California Spotted Owl, but uniformly darker in tone. The white spots on the head and neck are greatly shrunken and inconspicuous; the white tips on the primaries are virtually obsolete.

DISTRIBUTION—From British Columbia to western Washington. (Family *Strigidae*)

Northwestern Horned Owl
Bubo virginianus lagophonus [375i]

Similar to the Pacific Horned Owl, but larger and darker.

DISTRIBUTION—From Idaho, eastern Washington, through northeastern Oregon, and on through the eastern and central portions of British Columbia, as far as Cook Inlet, and into the interior of Alaska. Sometimes it is found in winter as far south as Colorado. (Family *Strigidae*)

Pacific Horned Owl
Bubo virginianus pacificus [375d]

Similar to the Great Horned Owl, but whiter, less brownish, and smaller.

DISTRIBUTION — From California (except along the coast) eastward as far as Arizona. (Family *Strigidae*)

Pasadena Screech Owl
Otus asio quercinus [373k]

Similar to the California Screech Owl, but paler and ashier in tone, and with the under parts exhibiting sharper black markings. It possesses very little or no reddish-brown cast on the upper breast, around the facial discs, or on the ear tufts.

DISTRIBUTION—From southern California west of the desert region, and along the western flank of the Sierra Nevada, northward to Mt. Shasta; also on the Pacific side of northern Lower California in the northern quarter of the Peninsula (north of Rosario). (Family *Strigidae*)

Queen Charlotte Owl

Cryptoglaux acadica brooksi [372a]

Similar to the Saw-whet Owl, but darker throughout.

DISTRIBUTION—Found on Queen Charlotte Islands, British Columbia. (Family *Strigidae*)

Richardson's Owl

Cryptoglaux funerea richardsoni [371]

ADULT MALE AND FEMALE—Upper parts, grayish-brown, distinctly spotted with white. Tail, grayish-brown, crossed by four or five imperfect white bars. Under parts, white, streaked deeply and heavily with grayish-brown. Legs and feet densely feathered, and white or whitish crossed by bars of gray or brown. Iris of eye, yellow.

LENGTH—10.00 inches.

DISTRIBUTION—A northern North American form, found from the Gulf of St. Lawrence, and the central portion of Manitoba northward. In winter it descends into our northern states, casually appearing in Massachusetts, Connecticut, Iowa, and Colorado.

A completely nocturnal Owl is the rare Richardson's Owl. During the day it remains concealed amid thick evergreen foliage, or within the dusky confines of a dense bush, or other convenient retreat. It is so helpless as regards accurate vision in the bright

light, that many individuals have been captured in the hand. Fisher writes of the notes of this bird, "The song of this Owl, according to Dr. Merriam, is a low liquid note that resembles the sound produced by water slowly dropping from a height." Richardson's

Owl resembles the Saw-whet Owl, but is larger, its facial discs (large areas of feathers about the eyes) are bordered with black, and its bill is yellowish or yellow. While it is sometimes recorded in New England, it cannot be called a common species with us. (Family *Strigidae*)

Rocky Mountain Pygmy Owl

Glaucidium gnoma pinicola [379]

ADULT MALE AND FEMALE—Upper parts, dark sooty or slaty gray; or with an olive-brownish or dark rusty-brownish cast. Head finely speckled with white; tail, blackish-brown barred with white. Under parts, white, heavily and thickly streaked with dark grayish-brown. Sides of the body, light brownish faintly spotted with lighter tones of yellowish or grayish-brown.

LENGTH—7.00 inches.

DISTRIBUTION—From British Columbia southward through the mountain regions of western United States (except in the humid Pacific coastal region) as far as the Sierra Madre of Mexico.

Although this little Owl is more frequently seen in the dusky hours of morning and evening twilight, yet it commonly flies about during the day even in the bright sunlight. It is said to be very tame and unsuspicious, and may be attracted toward an observer by an imitation of its notes, which are of a low cooing character, somewhat resembling those of the Mourning Dove. It feeds chiefly on large insects, such as grasshoppers, together with some mice and lizards. (Family *Strigidae*)

Rocky Mountain Screech Owl
Otus asio maxwelliae [373e]

Somewhat similar to the Eastern Screech Owl, but pale grayish above, with pale brownish cast, and paler below. This Owl is the lightest colored of the genus.

DISTRIBUTION—Foothills of the Rocky Mountains, and plains, from Montana southeastward into Colorado. (Family *Strigidae*)

Sahuaro Screech Owl
Otus asio gilmani [373l]

Somewhat similar to the Mexican Screech Owl, but smaller, and with the general tone of the bird paler. The black markings are more shrunken and less pronounced.

LENGTH—10.00 inches.

DISTRIBUTION—Found in southeastern California, Arizona, and probably also in New Mexico. (Family *Strigidae*)

St. Michael Horned Owl
Bubo virginianus algistus [375g]

Somewhat similar to the Pacific Horned Owl, but larger, and with the under parts a more intense tawny-brown color.

DISTRIBUTION—An extreme northern form of the Horned Owl, ranging from the coastal region of northern Alaska, from Bristol Bay and the delta of the Yukon River, northward. (Family *Strigidae*)

Sanford's Elf Owl
Micropallas whitneyi sanfordi [381b]

Similar to the Whitney's Elf Owl, but with the upper parts much grayer and somewhat darker; the wings, shorter; and the tail, slightly longer.

DISTRIBUTION—Found in the southern portion of Lower California. (Family *Strigidae*)

Saw-whet Owl
Cryptoglaux acadica acadica [372]

ADULT MALE AND FEMALE—Upper parts, dark brown, sparsely sprinkled with white. Under parts, white, with heavy rich brown stripes. Tail crossed by three or four narrow white bars. Facial discs, grayish. Iris of eye, yellow; bill, black. Female usually slightly larger than the male.

LENGTH—About 8.00 inches.

DISTRIBUTION — From southern Alaska, British Columbia, and Nova Scotia southward to the Sierra Nevada Mountains, Arizona, New Mexico, Oklahoma, and south into Mexico. Also from Nebraska across into the Allegheny Mountains of Pennsylvania, and into Maryland. It spreads southward in winter to southern California, the Gulf, and sometimes as far as Georgia and North Carolina.

This little midget of an Owl, sometimes also called the Acadian Owl, is one of the smallest of our birds of prey—only the Elf Owl being smaller. During the daylight hours it remains concealed amid thick branches, in so dull and torpid a state that it may sometimes be taken in the hand. As dusk approaches (that time of twilight called by the English "owl-light"), it becomes the veritable embodiment of animated ferocity and energy, and in its rapacious vigor is the very antithesis of its daytime self. With surprising courage this little fury in feathers does not hesitate to attack such relatively large mammals as rats, small rabbits, or squirrels, though its favorite fare is the white-footed or

deer mice. The common note of the bird, from which it derives its name, is a penetrating, rasping call, given in triads, and resembling the sound made by the filing of a large saw: *scree-kaw, scree-kaw, scree-kaw*. Other notes include liquid cooing sounds, together with clucks, gurgles, and faint screams. (Family *Strigidae*)

Short-eared Owl

Asio flammeus flammeus [367]

ADULT MALE AND FEMALE—Upper parts, light yellowish-brown heavily streaked with black. Under parts, light straw color; the throat and upper breast, widely streaked, and the lower breast and abdomen, finely and narrowly streaked with dark brown. Tail, light cinnamon-brown barred with dark brown. Facial discs, not prominent; and ear tufts, short and inconspicuous. Iris of eye, yellow; bill, black. Female usually larger than the male.

LENGTH—About 15.50 inches.

DISTRIBUTION—Found all over the world. In North America south as far as Virginia, the northern part of the

Mississippi Valley, and the Dakotas, spreading south into South America in the winter.

With a light, bouncing, and apparently effortless flight, and irregular wing-strokes, the Short-eared Owl may often be seen, even on a sunny day, passing over marsh and meadow, flitting sometimes close to the ground after the manner of the Marsh Hawk, and sometimes high in the air. It is a bird primarily of the open country, and haunts fields, meadows, bushy pasture lands, salt marshes, sand dunes, and shores. Not infrequently it is seen flying to a considerable distance out over the open water. Its predilection for fenlands is reflected in the names Marsh Owl or Bog Owl, by which it is known in some sections of the country. This Owl is not very vocal, but in the spring utters a series of *hoots* or *toots,* repeated from ten to twenty times, and often given while the male birds are flying about after the females. The notes are reminiscent of

those of the Great Horned Owl, but are recognizably higher in pitch. Both sexes give voice to a startling high, squealing cry, similar to the yowl of a large cat, or emit snarling or growling notes like the syllables *mahyeeoouu* or *kayeeoouuww*. The bird is of great value to the farmer because of its enormous destruction of meadow mice. (Family *Strigidae*)

Siberian Gray Owl
Scotiaptex nebulosa barbata [370a]

Somewhat similar to the Great Gray Owl, but with facial discs and gular region, darker. Bill, yellow.

DISTRIBUTION—This northern European Gray Owl occurs casually in the Yukon Delta, Alaska.

The Siberian Gray Owl is also called the Mountain Owl, since its common range is among the mountains of western Siberia. In the winter it descends into central Europe as far as eastern Prussia. Like the corresponding North American form the body is very thickly and completely clothed with feathers. (Family *Strigidae*)

Siberian Hawk Owl
Surnia ulula pallasi [377]

ADULT MALE AND FEMALE—Upper parts, light brown, slightly darker on the hind neck. Crown spotted with white. Back irregularly marked with white; scapulars, white. Wings spotted with white. Tail barred with white. Facial discs, grayish-white. Chin, light brown. A darkish band from behind the ear coverts extends down along the sides of the neck. Bill and iris of eye, bright yellow. Under parts, white barred with light grayish-brown.

LENGTH—15.00 inches.

DISTRIBUTION — This European Hawk Owl (found in Scandinavia, Lapland, Finland, and Russia, and in winter southward into Europe) occurs on our continent as a casual visitant in Alaska. (Family *Strigidae*)

Snowy Owl
Nyctea nyctea [376]

ADULT MALE — White, barred (slightly more on the head, back,

wings, and tail) with grayish-brown. Facial discs, white. Ear tufts lacking. Iris of eye, yellow; bill, black.

ADULT FEMALE—Similar to the male but more heavily barred. Face, throat, middle of breast, and abdomen, pure unmarked white.

LENGTH—About 24.00 inches.

DISTRIBUTION — Throughout the northern portion of the Northern Hemisphere; in North America from southern Quebec, Manitoba, and British Columbia northward. In winter it descends irregularly into the northern United States, and in severe seasons may occur in great numbers throughout the country.

These great birds, adding so much of beauty and wildness to our winter landscape, do not breed south of the

Canadian border. In severe winters great numbers of them are forced southward, and straggle irregularly throughout the United States. Great flights of them have occurred in the winters of 1876–77, 1882–83, 1889–90, 1892–93, 1896–97, 1901–02, 1905–06, 1917–18, 1930–31, and 1934–35. The birds hunt by day, and during the hours of morning and evening twilight, watch for their prey from a low stub, large stone, tuft of grass, or small hillock, being creatures not of forests, but of open country. While with us, they are silent birds, for the most part, seldom uttering their shrill, whining, tremulous note. (Family *Strigidae*)

Southern Screech Owl

Otus asio asio [373]

Similar to the Eastern Screech Owl, but smaller.

DISTRIBUTION—From Virginia, Georgia, and the Gulf States westward to Louisiana; and northward up the valley of the Mississippi to western Tennessee, southern Illinois, southeastern Kansas, and into Oklahoma and Arkansas. (Family *Strigidae*)

Spotted Screech Owl

Otus trichopsis [373.1]

Somewhat similar to the Eastern Screech Owl, with the upper parts darker, mixed with black, gray, and tan, and darker on the head. Forehead spotted with white.

DISTRIBUTION—From southern Arizona southward into northern Mexico. (Family *Strigidae*)

Tengmalm's Owl

Cryptoglaux funerea magna [371a]

ADULT MALE AND FEMALE—Upper parts, umber brown barred with white; white-spotted on the crown. Wings with rows of white spots. Facial discs, dull white, partly surrounded by pure white and brown feathers. A black patch appears before the eye. Under parts, white mottled with reddish-brown. Abdomen similarly but very faintly marked. Legs and feet feathered. Bill, pale yellow. Iris of eye, bright yellow.

LENGTH—About 10.00 inches.

DISTRIBUTION—This northern European and Siberian form occurs as a rare visitant in the British Isles, and is casual on St. Paul Island, Alaska. Its range is in the Kamchatka and Kolyman districts of the eastern portion of Siberia. (Family *Strigidae*)

Texas Barred Owl

Strix varia helveola [368b]

Similar to the Northern Barred Owl, but with the toes unfeathered.

DISTRIBUTION—Restricted to the southern portion of Texas. (Family *Strigidae*)

Texas Elf Owl

Micropallas whitneyi idoneus [381a]

Similar to the Sanford's Elf Owl, but with the plumage appreciably browner, and showing no trace of gray admixture. "Eyebrows" and lores, light brown; patch beneath the ear, buffy, and with no posterior black border. Tail with broader, light-colored bands.

DISTRIBUTION—From the lower portion of the Rio Grande Valley in Texas, southward as far as Guanajuato and Puebla, Mexico, and to the Valley of Mexico. (Family *Strigidae*)

Texas Screech Owl

Otus asio mccalli [373b]

Similar to the Eastern Screech Owl, but slightly smaller, and with the under parts more heavily marked.

DISTRIBUTION—From the western and southern portions of Texas, southward into Mexico. (Family *Strigidae*)

Vancouver Pygmy Owl

Glaucidium gnoma swarthi [379d]

Similar in general to the California Pygmy Owl, but much darker throughout. It differs from the Rocky Mountain Pygmy Owl (which it also closely resembles) in smaller size, and in much darker and browner coloration.

DISTRIBUTION — Found on Vancouver Island, British Columbia. (Family *Strigidae*)

Western Burrowing Owl

Speotyto cunicularia hypugaea [378]

ADULT MALE AND FEMALE—Upper parts, dark dullish brown, barred and spotted with white and yellowish-white. Under parts, very light buffy brown, barred with darker brown. Tail, short; tarsus rather long, giving the bird a long-legged appearance. Toes with bristles.

LENGTH—About 10.00 inches.

DISTRIBUTION—In the plains region from the Pacific Coast east to the Dakotas and Texas. Also from British Columbia, and the eastern sides of the Rocky Mountains south into Guatemala.

In the rather dreary plains country, where prairie dogs abound, one comes frequently upon the amusing little

Burrowing Owls. Sometimes several will be seen gathered around one burrow, for their habit is to make their nests at the end of a hole deserted by a prairie dog, ground squirrel, or badger. They perform their hunting chiefly in the morning or evening twilight, but on dull days, and sometimes on fairly bright ones, may be seen catching large insects, chiefly grasshoppers. They also feed upon young mammals of several sorts—mostly their near neighbors—as well as upon lizards, frogs, horned toads, and sometimes even fish. (Family *Strigidae*)

Western Horned Owl

Bubo virginianus pallescens [375a]

Similar to the Great Horned Owl, but paler throughout, and slightly smaller.

DISTRIBUTION — From the Great Plains westward almost to the Pacific Coastal zone, straggling into Wisconsin, Illinois, British Columbia, and Manitoba, and extending southward into Mexico. (Family *Strigidae*)

Whitney's Elf Owl

Micropallas whitneyi whitneyi [381]

ADULT MALE AND FEMALE—Upper parts, grayish or grayish-brown, finely mottled and speckled with darker blackish-brown and reddish-brown. Tail, brown or grayish-brown, crossed by five or six narrow, irregular, pale brown bars. Head, smooth, without ear tufts. White eye-brow feathers; lores and throat, white encircled with a brownish ring. Under parts, white or whitish, marked with fine mottlings of grayish-brown, and streaked with vertical blotches of dark brown and reddish-brown.

LENGTH—About 5.90 inches.

DISTRIBUTION—From southern California east to southern Texas, and southward into Lower California, and through the tablelands of northern Mexico.

This tiny little Owl, the smallest in North America, is actually smaller—or at least shorter—than the common English Sparrow, although its fluffy feathers make it appear a somewhat larger bird. Unlike the Pygmy Owls, the Whitney's Elf Owls are strictly nocturnal, secreting themselves by day in the dusky retreat of some dense thicket, or a deserted woodpecker hole in a giant cactus or tree. In these latter situations the birds nest. During the day they are quite "tame"; that is, they will allow the close approach of an observer, probably being blinded by the light. This Owl seldom molests other birds, its chief food being large insects. Bailey writes that, "Major Bendire says they become active soon

after sundown. He has had them come to his camp, attracted probably by the insects which gathered about the guard fire through the night." (Family *Strigidae*)

Xantus's Screech Owl

Otus asio xantusi [373.2]

Somewhat similar to the Eastern Screech Owl, but with the upper parts grayish-brown, faintly flushed with pinkish-brown, and with fine barrings of reddish-brown. Breast, grayish-white washed with pinkish. Abdomen, whitish. The entire under parts are finely barred with reddish-brown, and streaked with dark brown. DISTRIBUTION—Restricted to the southern portion of Lower California. (Family *Strigidae*)

OYSTER-CATCHER FAMILY

Haematopodidae

Oyster-catchers are sandpiper-like birds, with strong legs and feet (the latter lacking the hind toe), and long stout chisel-shaped bills. Their colors are mainly black and white; their bills are bright red. They are birds of the sea beaches and flats, and are confined to the subtropical and tropical parts of the world. Only about twelve are known, of which four are found in

North America, relegated to the genus *Haematopus.*

NESTING. Our common eastern Oyster-catcher makes no nest, but deposits its eggs in any adequate (frequently shallow) depression in the sand. The eggs number usually three, and are white or creamy, blotched and spotted with rich brown, blackish, or lavender. The Black Oyster-catcher of the West lays from one to three eggs, either in the sand, or in gravel, or sometimes on bare rock. They are light buff or olive in color, spotted with dark brown, blackish, and purplish-gray. The incubation is

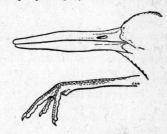

said to be performed only by the female. At night or on cloudy cool days she covers the eggs, but on bright days they are uncovered and allowed to be heated by the sun and the surrounding hot sands.

OYSTER-CATCHER

American Oyster-catcher

Haematopus palliatus palliatus [286]

ADULT MALE AND FEMALE—Back, and wing coverts, olive-brown; secondaries, white; primaries, dusky brown; upper tail coverts and base of the tail, white. End of tail, dusky brown. Head, neck, and upper breast, glossy black. Lower breast and abdomen, pure white. Bill and iris of eye, bright red. Legs and feet, grayish-pink.

LENGTH—19.00 inches.

DISTRIBUTION—Along the Gulf

Coast as far as Texas, and down to Brazil, and the West Indies (except the Bahama Islands). On the Atlantic Coast from Virginia to Florida. Occasionally it extends northward from Virginia as far as Massachusetts, and northward to New Brunswick. On the Pacific Coast it is found from Tehauntepec, Mexico, southward to Colombia. In winter it is not found north of Virginia.

Oyster-catchers are striking and beautiful beach birds, with their bold black and white pattern, and their laterally flattened, long, bright red bills. They are shy and wary birds, frequenting the outer bars and beaches, and never permitting a very close approach. Their long, stout, flattened bills form a most useful "oyster-knife" for forcing open the shells, not only of oysters, but of any bivalve molluscs washed up on the beachy shallows by the waves. The nest of these curious birds is merely a depression in the soft sand, made by the birds' bodies as they turn about several times to provide a shallow basin for the reception

of the two (rarely three) eggs. The voices of Oyster-catchers are recognizably sandpiper-like—but are louder, more flute-like, and with a melodious, wild ring. After the breeding is over, the birds gather in small flocks—a group of a dozen or more forming a very striking and attractive sight. (Family *Haematopodidae*)

Black Oyster-catcher
Haematopus bachmani [287]

ADULT MALE AND FEMALE—Brownish-black, or almost black; the head and neck with dull bluish-black reflections. Bill and legs, red.

LENGTH—17.25 inches.

DISTRIBUTION—From the Aleutian Islands southward along the Pacific

Coast of North America, as far as La Paz, Lower California, and the Kurile Islands.

"Mr. Loomis has taken Black Oyster-catchers on the Seal Rocks at Monterey, California, in July. They are said to be strictly littoral in their habits, always flying over the sea when moving from point to point." (Bailey). (Family *Haematopodidae*)

European Oyster-catcher
Haematopus ostralegus ostralegus [285]

Similar to the American Oyster-catcher, but with legs and feet a purplish-pink.

LENGTH—16.00 inches.

DISTRIBUTION—An occasional visitant in Greenland. (Family *Haematopodidae*)

Frazar's Oyster-catcher
Haematopus palliatus frazari [286.1]

Similar to the American Oyster-catcher, but with the upper parts darker; the upper tail coverts marked with brown; and a mottled black and white zone separating the black breast from the pure white abdomen.

DISTRIBUTION—From the Los Coronados Islands of Lower California southward along both coasts of that peninsula. (Family *Haematopodidae*)

PAROQUET
Carolina Paroquet
Conuropsis carolinensis carolinensis [382]

ADULT MALE AND FEMALE—Plumage, bright green except for head and neck, which is bright yellow; and the forehead, cheeks, shoulders, and flanks, which are orange; and the inner vanes of the wing feathers, which are brown. Under side of tail, yellowish.

LENGTH—12.50 inches.

DISTRIBUTION—Formerly found from the Great Lakes, Iowa, and Maryland west almost to the Rocky Mountains; southward into Texas and Florida; along the Atlantic coastal zone from Virginia southward.

The Carolina Paroquet is apparently an extinct species, though formerly it was exceedingly common, its "sharp rolling call" being one of the common notes of our more temperate states. The extermination of the bird is due

to its slaughter for bright-colored feathers, its capture by those who sold it for a cage bird, and to its destruction because of its depredations in fruit orchards. (Family *Psittacidae*)

Louisiana Paroquet
Conuropsis carolinensis ludovicianus [382a]

Similar to the Carolina Paroquet, but with the upper parts a light bluish-green.

DISTRIBUTION—From Colorado and Nebraska eastward through Ohio to western New York, and south through Kentucky to Louisiana and Oklahoma.

This is the Mississippi Valley or western form of the Paroquet, but it is now extinct. (Family *Psittacidae*)

PARROT FAMILY
Parrots, Paroquets and Macaws
Psittacidae

This very large family of about 275 members eats fruits and seeds. The birds are found in forests, where, as excellent fliers and equally successful

climbers, they fill the aisles with their loud raucous clamor. Almost all the members of the family possess the ability to utter words of human speech, if taught to do so. The bill is peculiar; the upper mandible is hooked and strongly decurved; the lower mandible, shorter, often deeper at its base, and scoop-shaped. The tongue is flexible, and often horny at the tip. There are four toes, arranged as in the Woodpeckers (Family *Picidae*); two in front and two in back. These double pincers, together with the strong beaks, make excellent climbing adaptations. The approximately 275 species and subspecies, tropical and subtropical for the most part, are found in the Western Hemisphere.

Of these, three are recorded from North America: one species of Parrot (genus *Rhynchopsitta*), and two sub-species of Paroquets (genus *Conuropsis*).

NESTING. The Parrots are believed to remain mated for life. As a group, they make their nests in the holes of trees, and their eggs are white. The Carolina Paroquet is reported to nest in a hollow tree, in low swampy regions, and to lay from three to five white, unmarked eggs. Pearson says of the Carolina Paroquet, "Many years have now passed since the Carolina Paroquet was seen in the Carolinas. Florida is, or was, its last stand. Dr. Frank M. Chapman found fifty or more individuals in the southern part of that State in 1889." The Thick-billed Parrot, a species which inhabits the mountains bordering the Mexican tableland, and which ranges up into the United States in the canyons of the Chiricahua Mountains of Arizona, probably has similar nesting habits.

PARROT
Thick-billed Parrot

Rhynchopsitta pachyrhyncha [382.1]

Somewhat similar to the Carolina Paroquet, but much larger; without

the yellow on the head and neck, and with the forehead, lores, broad stripe

over the eye, shoulders, and thighs, red. Rest of plumage, green.

LENGTH—16.50 inches.

DISTRIBUTION—From southern Arizona (very rarely) south into central Mexico. (Family *Psittacidae*)

PARTRIDGE FAMILY
Partridges and Quails
Perdicidae

These birds possess short dumpy bodies, short stout bills, strong scratching feet, and are, in general, more or less "hen-like." About two hundred forms are known, about one

hundred and forty of them being confined to the Old World. Nineteen members of the family have been recorded in North America. One of these is the European Partridge (*Perdix perdix perdix*), the rest are American species. In all, six genera are represented in our continent.

NESTING. These birds deposit their eggs on the ground, either in a slight depression among grasses, or at the base of some bush or small tree, usually in a nest made of grasses, weed stems, etc., (sometimes with the addition of leaves). The Mearns's Quail of our Southwest fashions an arched nest with a side opening, but this is unusual. The eggs of the *Perdicid* birds are many; from six to twelve; sometimes from fourteen to sixteen; and infrequently as many as eighteen to twenty. They are either unmarked white, buffy, or creamy-white;

speckled, blotched, or clouded with tints and shades of brown and lavender, etc.

PARTRIDGE
European Partridge
Perdix perdix perdix [288.1]

ADULT MALE—Upper parts, delicately marked with black, gray, and brown. Throat and sides of the head, rich brownish-buff. Junction of the lower breast and abdomen, with a rich

brown patch. Scapulars and tertials, streaked with buff. Primaries, barred with buff. Breast, light gray, delicately pencilled with black.

ADULT FEMALE—Similar to the male, but with the abdominal patch smaller, and the scapulars and tertials with black markings.

LENGTH—12.50 inches.

DISTRIBUTION—Small colonies of these introduced birds are found in northeastern New York, near the Ontario border; in Lehigh County, Pennsylvania, and in Kansas, Wisconsin, Iowa, and Minnesota. In the neighboring parts of Canada, as well as in the border states just mentioned, this European importation has been very successful. This desirable species of Partridge is becoming more abundant, and is rapidly extending its range eastward. This is not surprising, for in England it is a very hardy and adap-

table bird. It is the only indigenous, gallinaceous species in Britain which is not adversely affected by man's encroachment upon its wild domains; in fact, the bird flourishes best where agriculture is most advanced. It is a bird dear to the homestead, as well as to the sportsman, and seems able to maintain itself in spite of the demands made upon its numbers by hunters. Its call is loud, harsh, and powerful, but full of delightful tranquil rural associations for all those who love the placid English countryside. (Family *Perdicidae*)

PASSERIFORMES
(Order *Passeriformes,* or Perching Birds)

The Passeriformes, or Passerine birds, are the so-called Perching Birds. They are divided into two sub-orders; the Sub-order *Tyranni,* and the Sub-order *Passeres.* The former contains the Cotingas and the Flycatchers; and the latter, the familiar Larks, Warblers, Sparrows, Orioles, and the like. In North America, this order is represented by twenty-five families, and 672 species and subspecies, making it by far the largest order of birds on our continent. It is probable that there are twenty-one orders of living birds, containing about 28,000 species and subspecies, and of these about 14,000 are included in the single order Passeriformes. Passeriform birds emerge from the shell in an almost naked state, with only a trace of "natal down" on the upper parts of the body.

PAURAQUE
Merrill's Pauraque
Nyctidromus albicollis merrilli [419]

ADULT MALE—Upper parts, gray with a brownish cast. Crown patch, blackish. Wings, mottled with lighter and darker tones, and crossed by a white bar. Tail, finely barred with dusky, and marked with white. Chin, black barred with buffy. Throat, white. Under parts, light buff barred with black, and lightening on the abdomen. Flanks and breast, heavily barred with black; the latter washed with grayish-white.

ADULT FEMALE—Darker than the male, and with a smaller throat patch. Less white in the tail and wings.

LENGTH—About 14.50 inches.

DISTRIBUTION—In the Rio Grande Valley, Texas, and along the southern Gulf Coast of the state, southward into Tamaulipas, Mexico. In winter it passes farther south in Mexico to Puebla and Vera Cruz.

A bird similar in general appearance and habits to the rest of the Nighthawks. (Family *Caprimulgidae*)

PELICAN FAMILY
Pelecanidae

Pelicans are huge birds, with bodies measuring from slightly over four feet to nearly six feet. On land the Pelican

is grotesque and extremely awkward; and in the air it sails and flaps with an easy, but somewhat heavy grace. Pelicans are gregarious, and breed in huge colonies, building their large clumsy nests on the ground. The bill of the Pelican is extremely long,

heavy, flattened; with the upper mandible hooked, and with the lower one provided with a deep expansible pouch, some six inches or more in depth, in which fish are stored, later to be used as food for the young. Although there are some twelve known species and subspecies of these birds, only three are recorded from North America, contained in the single genus *Pelecanus*.

NESTING. Pelicans breed in large, often enormous colonies or rookeries, on shores or marshy islands. The large, bulky nest of sticks and twigs is built usually on the ground, but sometimes in low scraggly bushes. When the nest is on the ground, the soil is scraped together to form a mound about six or eight inches high. On this elevation the loosely-constructed nest is placed. The eggs, two or three in number, are a chalky white, sometimes with a similar chalky incrustation. Pelican Island, in the Indian River of Florida, supports a large and celebrated rookery. This was the first of such rookeries to be made a Government reservation. Here thousands of the birds may be seen nesting. Another reservation is located on East Timbalier Island in western Louisiana. Young Pelicans feed themselves by thrusting their heads and bills far into the huge pouch of their parents, extracting therefrom and gorging themselves with the semi-liquid, highly malodorous mass of fish stored therein by the older birds.

PELICAN
California Brown Pelican
Pelecanus occidentalis ealifornicus
[127]

Similar to the Eastern Brown Pelican, which is described in detail on the next page. The California Brown Pelican is larger, however, and has a red pouch.

DISTRIBUTION—From British Columbia along the Pacific Coast south-

ward as far as the Galapagos Islands. (Family *Pelecanidae*)

Eastern Brown Pelican

Pelecanus occidentalis occidentalis [126]

ADULT MALE AND FEMALE—Upper parts, dusky brown; wing coverts, pale gray; primaries, black; tail, gray. Head, white, washed with yellowish on the top. Narrow band down side of pouch, white. Rest of neck, rich chestnut-brown. Under parts, dark grayish-brown, the sides and flanks striped with white. Bill, mottled and tinged with red. A bare space around the eye, blue. Gular pouch and feet, blackish. LENGTH—50.00 inches.

DISTRIBUTION—From South Carolina southward along the coasts of the Atlantic and the Gulf of Mexico to subtropical and tropical America. In winter it is distributed from the Gulf States southward.

The Brown Pelican is unlike its relative, the White Pelican, in that it is strictly an ocean bird, and captures its fishy prey by diving. The fishing regions may be fifty miles or more distant from the breeding grounds. It plunges into the water from a height of about

twenty-five or thirty feet with a tremendous splash which throws the spray high in the air, and which may be heard on a quiet day for more than half a mile. The young feed by thrusting their heads down into the gular pouch of the parents, and gorge them-

selves on the stored malodorous mass of fish. (Family *Pelecanidae*)

White Pelican

Pelecanus erythrorhynchos [125]

ADULT MALE AND FEMALE—Plumage, white, washed with straw-yellowish on the breast and shoulders. Wing quills, largely black. A white, or straw-colored crest, and a horny prominence

on the upper edge of the bill. Bill, very long, with naked gular sac. Tail, very short; feet, webbed. LENGTH—60.00 inches.

DISTRIBUTION—From central British Columbia, southern Mackenzie, and central Manitoba south to eastern California, Utah, and Yellowstone Park. In winter it is found from southern California and the Gulf States, south to Central America.

One of America's most picturesque birds is the great White Pelican, with its five feet of length, nearly nine feet of wing-spread, and its weight of about sixteen pounds. (Family *Pelecanidae*)

PETREL
Ashy Petrel
Oceanodroma homochroa [108]

ADULT MALE AND FEMALE—Entire bird, ashy or leaden gray; the quills,

darker. Tail, dusky. Shoulders with a brownish cast, and under tail coverts showing a lighter patch.
LENGTH—8.5 inches.
DISTRIBUTION—Along the coast of California. (Family *Hydrobatidae*)

Beal's Petrel
Oceanodroma leucorhoa beali [106a]

Similar to the Leach's Petrel, but somewhat smaller.
DISTRIBUTION—Southeastern Alaska along the Pacific Coast southward to southern California. (Family *Hydrobatidae*)

Bermuda Petrel
Pterodroma cahow [98.1]

Similar to the Black-capped Petrel, but with a brownish crown and nape. The upper tail coverts, brown-spotted, and the inner vane of the outer tail feathers, white.
DISTRIBUTION—Formerly found on Castle Island, Bermuda, but now probably extinct. (Family *Procellariidae*)

Black Petrel
Oceanodroma melania [107]

Similar to the Ashy Petrel but with upper parts, sooty-black; and the

under parts, brownish-black. Wing coverts, grayish-brown.
DISTRIBUTION—Along the Pacific Coast from southern California southward along the western coast of Mexico. (Family *Hydrobatidae*)

Black-capped Petrel
Pterodroma hasitata [98]

ADULT MALE AND FEMALE—Upper parts, sooty brownish; region around the base of the bill, white. Cap, blackish extending to below the eye. The center of the forehead is fuscous, margined with white or whitish. Nape, white. Upper tail coverts, white. Outer pair of tail feathers, about three-quarters white basally. Under parts, white.
LENGTH—16.00 inches.

DISTRIBUTION — In the tropical North Atlantic, straggling up the coast accidentally, to Florida and northward. (Family *Procellariidae*)

Bulwer's Petrel
Bulweria bulweri [101]

ADULT MALE AND FEMALE—Upper parts, sooty; wings, grayer; under parts, sooty-brown.

LENGTH—10.50 inches.

DISTRIBUTION — Eastern Atlantic and western Pacific, a straggler in Greenland and Labrador. (Family *Procellariidae*)

Forked-tailed Petrel
Oceanodroma furcata [105]

ADULT MALE AND FEMALE—Light bluish-gray, except on chin, throat, and under tail coverts, which are

white. Shoulder and area about the eye, dark gray.

LENGTH—8.60 inches.

DISTRIBUTION — From the Arctic Circle south along the Atlantic Coast to the middle of California. (Family *Hydrobatidae*)

Guadalupe Petrel
Oceanodroma macrodactyla [106.1]

Similar to the Leach's Petrel, but with the feathers of the upper tail coverts showing broad dark tips; with larger feet, shorter bill, and much longer, more deeply forked tail.

DISTRIBUTION—In the Pacific Ocean about Guadalupe Island, California. (Family *Hydrobatidae*)

Kaeding's Petrel
Oceanodroma leucorhoa kaedingi [105.2]

Similar to the Leach's Petrel, but much smaller, and with the tail less deeply forked.

DISTRIBUTION — Off the Socorro Islands, Lower California. (Family *Hydrobatidae*)

Leach's Petrel
Oceanodroma leucorhoa leucorhoa [106]

Similar to the Wilson's Petrel, but with the tail forked.

DISTRIBUTION—Northern Atlantic and Pacific, from Greenland to Maine, and from southern Alaska to Japan. In winter as far south as Virginia and California. (Family *Hydrobatidae*)

Least Petrel
Halocyptena microsoma [103]

ADULT MALE AND FEMALE—Upper parts, shining brownish-black, shading to black on the wings and tail. Upper portion of wing, somewhat grayer. Under parts, slightly lighter than the upper.

LENGTH—6.00 inches.

DISTRIBUTION—Along the Pacific Coast of Lower California southward

as far as Panama. (Family *Hydrobatidae*)

Madeira Petrel

Oceanodroma castro castro [106.2]

ADULT MALE AND FEMALE—Plumage, unfirm sooty-brown; middle of the wing, grayer. Upper tail coverts, white, the feathers tipped with black. Tail, only slightly forked.

LENGTH—7.75 inches.

DISTRIBUTION—This eastern Atlantic bird is an accidental straggler in Indiana, Pennsylvania, and the District of Columbia. (Family *Hydrobatidae*)

Pintado Petrel

Daption capense [102]

ADULT MALE AND FEMALE—Head, back, and sides of neck, upper back, and lesser wing coverts and primaries, dark sooty-brown. Wing coverts, lower back, and upper tail coverts, white; the feathers tipped with sooty-brown. Base of tail, white; tip of tail, sooty-brown. Under parts, white; the under tail coverts, marked with sooty-brown. Bill and feet, dark brown.

LENGTH—14.00 inches.

DISTRIBUTION—The oceans of the Southern Hemisphere; accidental at Harpswell, in Casco Bay, Maine; and on the Pacific Coast at Monterey, California.

I have seen this lovely little Petrel only once, between the Azores and the north coast of Africa. It is one of the most delicate and beautiful of the sea-birds, with its white under parts, its delicately spotted or checkered mantle, and its large white wing-patches. The wings in flight are held straight out, in rigid fashion, as the bird veers about apparently without the slightest effort, and the tail is frequently spread out widely fanwise. This bird is known as the Cape Pigeon or Cape Petrel among sailors. It is one of the smaller Petrels, and perhaps the one most easily recognized. It is very common in the southern oceans, sometimes straggling northward in irregular fashion. In feeding, the bird frequently plunges into the water to seize bits of food which may be disappearing from view, but its headlong dives never take it to a greater depth than just beneath the surface of the waves. Flocks of these graceful fliers often crowd about the stern of a ship to regale themselves upon the petrellian tidbits of refuse thrown overboard from the galley. (Family *Procellariidae*)

Scaled Petrel

Pterodroma inexpectata [99]

ADULT MALE AND FEMALE—Upper parts, blackish-brown; under parts, pure white. Bill and feet, black.

LENGTH—13.00 inches.

DISTRIBUTION—"Accidental in Livingston County, New York, on Kiska and Kodiak Islands, the Aleutians (regularly?), and near Frosty Peak, and Sitka, Alaska." (A.O.U. Check List.) (Family *Procellariidae*)

Socorro Petrel

Oceanodroma socorroensis [108.1]

Similar to the Ashy Petrel, but somewhat larger and darker, and with the rump showing a whitish patch on the side.

DISTRIBUTION—Along the Pacific Coast from San Diego, California, southward along the western coast of Mexico. (Family *Hydrobatidae*)

Storm Petrel
Hydrobates pelagicus [104]

ADULT MALE AND FEMALE—Upper parts, sooty-black. Upper tail coverts, white; the longer feathers, tipped with black. Under tail coverts, mottled with whitish. Bill and feet, black.
LENGTH—5.50 inches.
DISTRIBUTION—The coasts of the North Atlantic generally, in summer, but does not breed in American waters.

This is the common Petrel of the eastern Atlantic Ocean, and the one

of the species called Mother Carey's Chicken or Stormy Petrel by sailors. It is common about the Hebrides, in summer, and frequently seen by tourists there. The birds are extremely graceful and swallow-like in flight, and often follow ships for the sake of the refuse thrown overboard. (Family *Hydrobatidae*)

White-bellied Petrel
Fregatta tropica tropica [110]

ADULT MALE AND FEMALE—Plumage, sooty-black, except for upper tail

coverts, flanks, and lower abdomen, which are white. Feathers of the under

tail coverts and throat, white at their bases.
LENGTH—8.00 inches.
DISTRIBUTION—An accidental visitant at St. Mark's, Florida. (Family *Hydrobatidae*)

White-faced Petrel
Pelagodroma marina hypoleuca [111]

ADULT MALE AND FEMALE—Upper parts, medium gray; crown, darker gray; upper tail coverts, light gray. Forehead, line over the eye, and under parts, white.
LENGTH—8.00 inches.
DISTRIBUTION—In the North Atlantic Ocean generally, breeding on the Salvage and Cape Verde islands. "The only North American record is

four hundred miles off the coast of New Jersey. . ." (A.O.U. Check List.) (Family *Hydrobatidae*)

Wilson's Petrel
Oceanites oceanicus [109]

ADULT MALE AND FEMALE—Entire bird, sooty-blackish (under parts, a trifle lighter), except for a broad patch of white at the base of the tail. Legs, long.

LENGTH—7.00 inches.

DISTRIBUTION—Atlantic Ocean, migrating as far north as Newfoundland, and found in summer commonly off the eastern coast of the United States.

These common, graceful, little Petrels are much given to sweeping about ships with an easy, flexible, swallow-like flight, following in their wakes

for long distances, and feeding on any soft refuse which may be thrown overboard. As they skim over the waves, their feet are let down to aid in their motion, and thus they seem to be walking on the water. Their white rumps are quite visible; also their squarely-cut tails, when near at hand. Their common food consists of small surface-swimming sea animals, or any floating organic matter which they can swallow. (Family *Hydrobatidae*)

PEWEE
Eastern Wood Pewee
Myiochanes virens [461]

ADULT MALE AND FEMALE—Upper parts, dark slaty-grayish-brown. Wings with two whitish bars. Under parts, white, faintly grayish; sides, and center of breast, slightly darker. Upper

mandible, black; lower mandible, yellowish.

LENGTH—6.53 inches.

DISTRIBUTION—From New Brunswick and Manitoba west to about the longitude of central South Dakota, and southward into Texas and Florida. It winters in Central America.

This species, *il penseroso* of our eastern birds, haunts tall majestic trees in somber groves, from out whose umbrageous depths it gives forth, as if constrained by a sense of duty, its sweet, plaintive, melancholy "song." The notes are of a clear quality, whistled and slurred: *pee ah weeee;* the first syllable with a slightly falling inflection, the last with a rising one. The utterance often consists of two sets of alternating phrases, thus: *pee ah weeee, pee aah.* The last part of the song falls off at its close in the most mournful note imaginable. This is one of the first bird songs of the early morning hours, and carries to

a surprising distance in the quiet summer woods. The Peewee is not an active bird, but sits without motion upon a high limb among the leaves, uttering its doleful lay, and ever and anon dashing out after passing insects. The Peewee resembles the Eastern Phoebe, but from it may be distinguished by its two whitish wing bars, and by its rigidly held, motionless tail. (Family *Tyrannidae*)

Large-billed Wood Pewee

Myiochanes richardsoni peninsulae [462a]

Similar to the Western Wood Pewee, but smaller; the upper parts, grayer; and the bill, larger.

DISTRIBUTION — Lower California. (Family *Tyrannidae*)

Western Wood Pewee

Myiochanes richardsoni richardsoni [462]

Similar to the Eastern Wood Pewee, but with no olive-greenish cast to the upper parts, and with no yellowish in the under mandible.

DISTRIBUTION—From British Columbia, Alberta, and Manitoba southward to western Texas and Lower California, and east to about the longitude of central South Dakota. It winters in Mexico and Central America. (Family *Tyrannidae*)

PHAINOPEPLA

Phainopepla

Phainopepla nitens lepida [620]

ADULT MALE—Plumage, entirely glossy bluish-black; a broad white patch in the wing shows prominently when the bird is in flight. Top of head, crested with long feathers, which can be raised vertically when the bird is alarmed. Iris of eye, red.

ADULT FEMALE—Upper parts, brownish-gray. Coverts, secondaries of wings, and lower tail coverts with whitish edgings to the feathers. White patch in the wing less extensive than that of the male. Under parts, brownish-gray and lighter than back.

LENGTH—7.37 inches.

DISTRIBUTION — From western Texas, across through southern Utah and southern California, and southward into Mexico. In winter it is not found north of the Mexican border.

The curious Phainopepla is the only member of the small family of Silky Flycatchers (*Ptilogonatidae*) to cross the borders of the United States. It is an elegant, trim, aristocratic bird, as it sits on an exposed perch watching

for passing insects. When alarmed the crest is raised almost vertically, its separate feathers being then easily seen. Again and again the bird launches itself out into the air after its flying insect prey, returning usually to the same perch, after the capture has been made. In flight the bird loses none of the grace which it displays when perched. The slow, but rather jerky wing strokes carry it easily and buoyantly through the air, the white patches in the wings forming a pleasing contrast with the glossy black body. The tail is long, slender, and notched, and frequently, just after the bird has alighted, is jerked upward with a saucy flirt. In song, the Phainopepla is a surprise. Sometimes it pours forth a medley of weak, squeaky, buzzy notes, with clear strong ones interspersed; and again with great vigor gives voice to a series of clear whistles, and phrases which suggest the notes of the Meadowlark and Red-winged Blackbird. (Family *Ptilogonatidae*)

PHALAROPE FAMILY
Phalaropodidae

The Phalaropes may be described as "swimming Sandpipers." They range in size from seven to nine inches, possess long bills, necks which are neither long nor short, webbed feet, and thick, heavy, compact, duck-like plumage for

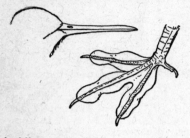

shedding water. The peculiar distinction which attaches to this family, is that the females perform, except for the basic necessities of procreation, all of the duties of the male; viz., courting, determination of the nesting site, taking the active and dominating leadership generally. The males assume the passive role, even to the maternal task of incubating the eggs. They are the undoubted "hen-pecked" members of the bird world. Not only are the activities of the sexes here reversed, but the size and coloration as well, for the females are larger and more brightly colored than their physiologically, anatomically, and sociologically chastened consorts. Two of the species spend the winter at sea. There are but three species, all residents of North America. One species, however, the Wilson's Phalarope, is a permanent resident.

NESTING. Phalaropes breed on the ground, in shallow depressions sparsely lined with grasses. Three or four eggs are laid. They are creamy, buff, greenish, gray, and marked with various blotchings, spottings, specklings, or scratchings of different tints and shades of brown.

PHALAROPE
Northern Phalarope
Lobipes lobatus [223]

ADULT FEMALE (A reversal of the usual condition occurs in the Phalaropes, the *female* being the brighter colored)—Upper part of back, crown, and sides of the head, bluish-gray. Wings, darker with a white bar. Sides of the neck, reddish-brown. Throat, white; breast, bluish-gray washed with reddish-brown. Abdomen, white.

ADULT MALE—Similar to the brighter female in pattern, but with the colors duller; the upper parts being a dark sooty-brown, streaked with light brown.

LENGTH—7.75 inches.

DISTRIBUTION — From Greenland across to Alaska, and southward to Labrador and northern British Columbia. In winter it is found in the interior of Canada and the United States, and south through the interior of the Americas to Patagonia, and also off the coasts of North and South America.

Ocean travelers often pass through large or small flocks of these birds, some fifty to a hundred miles off the

coast of New England and southward. Scattered flocks may be seen spread over a distance of fifty miles or more. As they swim about, turning rapidly this way and that, they resemble small Ducks, Snipe (at closer range), or small Sandpipers. The names Sea Snipe and Sea Sandpiper, call attention to these similarities. They have also been called "little swimming Sandpipers." The Phalaropes are unique in the bird world, in that the more brightly colored female is the active member of the pair, and the duller colored male, the inactive. It is the female which carries on the courting, selects the nesting site, and even relegates the duties of incubation to the male. (Family *Phalaropodidae*)

Red Phalarope
Phalaropus fulicarius [222]

ADULT FEMALE (A reversal of the usual condition occurs in the Phalaropes, the *female* being the brighter colored)—Upper parts, streaked with blackish- and yellowish-brown; wings, marked with black and white. Top of head, black; eye, surrounded by a white patch. Throat, bluish-slate-gray. The rest of the under parts, deep pinkish-brown. Rump, deep pinkish-brown.

ADULT MALE—Similar to the female in pattern, but duller throughout; the top of the head, black marked with yellowish-brown.

LENGTH—8.12 inches.

DISTRIBUTION—Found throughout the northern parts of the Northern Hemisphere, where it breeds in the Arctic regions. In winter it migrates southward, and in the United States is found in the interior southward to the Middle States and the Ohio Valley; but chiefly in winter it occurs at considerable distance off the coast at sea. Since it is frequently blown about by storms, it has been reported in California, Florida, Vermont, New York, Pennsylvania, Maryland, Massachusetts.

Phalaropes are often called Sea Geese, though they more nearly resemble Snipe or Sandpipers (see Northern Phalarope). The Red Phalarope is similar, in general, to the Northern when in its winter plumage, and difficult to identify, even though it is slightly larger. In its breeding plumage, the reddish under parts serve to

distinguish it, as also do the heavier bill and yellowish legs. The Northern Phalarope's bill is slender, and its legs are black. The Red Phalarope's notes are a sharp *kik kik* or *tit tit*. In its peculiar domestically reversed family life, it resembles the Northern species. (Family *Phalaropodidae*)

Wilson's Phalarope
Steganopus tricolor [224]

ADULT FEMALE (A reversal of the usual condition occurs in the Phalaropes, the *female* being the brighter colored)—Top of head, and back, bluish-gray. Line over the eye, white. A wide black stripe along the sides of the head and neck shades into a rich chestnut-brown, and continues along the lower neck and to the shoulders. Lower part of the throat and breast, delicate creamy pinkish-brown. Upper part of throat, and the abdomen, white.

ADULT MALE—Upper parts and crown, dusky washed slightly with brown. Sides of the neck bear a rich brown stripe. Line over the eye, white. Chin, white. Throat and breast, light creamy-brown. Abdomen, white.

LENGTH—8.75 inches; female slightly larger, 9.50 inches.

DISTRIBUTION—"Breeds from southern British Columbia, central Washington, central Alberta, southern Saskatchewan, southern Manitoba, southward to central California, Nevada, Utah, Colorado, Nebraska, southern Kansas (formerly), central Iowa, Missouri (formerly), northern Illinois, and northwestern Indiana. Winters from central Chile and central Argentina south to the Falkland Islands; occurs in migration on the Atlantic and Gulf coasts, from Maine to Florida and Alabama, and on the Pacific Coast from southern British Columbia to Lower California." (Chapman).

The Wilson's Phalarope is the most beautiful of this family; and indeed of all the water-birds. Its partially webbed toes enable it to swim easily and gracefully, or to run daintily without sinking over the mud and sand. Like tiny Ducks, and Sandpipers, it is

seen in small flocks. Its notes are low, soft, and sound like the subdued croaking of frogs. In their domestic relations, the sexes exchange roles, as is the case with our two other species of Phalaropes (see Northern Phalarope). (Family *Phalaropodidae*)

PHEASANT FAMILY
Phasianidae

The Pheasants, large, hen-like birds, many with extremely lustrous, brilliantly colored plumage, the colors often disposed in striking patterns, number about one hundred species,

and are distributed from the eastern shores of the Mediterranean Sea through central and southern Asia, and eastward through the whole of the Malayan Region. Two members of this group, the Ring-necked Pheasant

(*Phasianus colchicus torquatus*) of China, and the English Ring-necked Pheasant (*Phasianus colchicus colchicus*), have been imported into and interbred in the United States, and have spread widely over our country. Being bred largely in game farms, they are liberated, and now form one of our most valuable game birds. Thus they receive many a charge of shot which otherwise would have slain our own native species.

NESTING. Our American representative of this large family, the Ring-necked Pheasant, breeds in bushy pastures, old overgrown fields, grassy meadows, and sometimes in moderate woodlands. The nest is placed on the ground, or infrequently in a tree on the large deserted nest of some other bird. It is composed of the leaves of deciduous or evergreen trees, weed stems, dried grasses, and the like. The eggs are pale blue, pale bluish-green, varying to cream, light brown and olive-brown. In number they range from six to twelve; rarely from fourteen to sixteen.

PHEASANT
Ring-necked Pheasant
Phasianus colchicus torquatus [309.1]

ADULT MALE—Head and neck, greenish with purplish iridescence;

ring around neck, white. Breast, bronzy-reddish; the feathers narrowly margined with purplish-black. Rump, grayish-yellow. Flanks, light brownish; the feathers tipped with glossy bluish-black. Side of head, red. Tail feathers, long; the middle ones, very long and slender; and the whole structure, as long as or longer than the body itself. Bill, short and hen-like.

ADULT FEMALE — Brownish, speckled with black; lighter below. Tail, shorter.

LENGTH—About 35.00 inches.

DISTRIBUTION—From southwestern Maine westward to Minnesota, and

southward to Pennsylvania and Kansas. It is one of the commonest game birds in the East where most of them are a mixture of the English Pheasant (*Phasianus colchicus colchicus*) and the Ring-necked Pheasant. The latter is not native, but is an inhabitant of China. During the hunting season the perspicacious male pheasants' become very shy. (Family *Phasianidae*)

PHOEBE

Black Phoebe

Sayornis nigricans nigricans [458]

ADULT MALE AND FEMALE—Abdomen, under tail coverts, and outer vanes of the outer tail feathers, white; the under tail coverts, often marked with dark streaks.

LENGTH—6.62 inches.

DISTRIBUTION—From southeastern

Arizona, New Mexico, and Texas, southward into Mexico, except the

Pacific Coast region north of about longitude 19°. (Family *Tyrannidae*)

Eastern Phoebe

Sayornis phoebe [456]

ADULT MALE AND FEMALE—Upper parts, brownish-gray; the head, much darker, sometimes almost black. The two wing bars are faint grayish and almost invisible. Throat and breast, grayish-white; abdomen, very pale yellowish, washed on the sides with gray.

LENGTH—7.00 inches.

DISTRIBUTION — From Newfoundland and Manitoba south to South Carolina and western Texas, and westward to the Rocky Mountains. In winter it is found from North Carolina and northern Texas southward into Cuba and Mexico.

This most domestic of Flycatchers is

commonly found about farm buildings, particularly where streams or ponds are near at hand. It is almost sure to be found along the borders of any wooded stream, making its nest under bridges. Frequently also its nests may be found in outhouses, or on beams under porches. The "song" of the bird is *not* a clear whistled *Fee bee* (this note, so often heard in the spring, is the spring call of the Chickadee), but is a wheezy sort of performance, with some slight musical quality, and sounds like the whispered syllables *Fee ah bee; fee ah béwit.* These two phrases alternate. In the first phrase, there is a drop in pitch at the *ah* syllable; and in the second phrase, the final *bewit* note is quickly given, with a decided accent on the *be.* The favorite perch of the bird is on a limb overhanging a stream or pond, from which it makes frequent sallies out into the air after its winged insect prey. Upon each return to its perch it pumps its tail flexibly three or four times. This tail-pumping is also indulged in when the bird is alarmed. Phoebes come back year after year to the same nesting site, and may be induced to nest under porches, on little shelves. (Family *Tyrannidae*)

San José Phoebe
Sayornis saya quiescens [457a]

Similar to Say's Phoebe, but a paler gray.

DISTRIBUTION—In Lower California, from the United States boundary southward to about latitude 30°. (Family *Tyrannidae*)

San Lucas Phoebe
Sayornis nigricans brunnescens [458b]

Similar to the Black Phoebe, but with a browner cast.

DISTRIBUTION—The southern portion of Lower California. (Family *Tyrannidae*)

San Quintín Phoebe
Sayornis nigricans salictaria [458a]

Similar to the Black Phoebe, but darker; the darkest of the *nigricans* group.

DISTRIBUTION—In Lower California, from the United States border south to about latitude 30°. Also occurs sparingly in southern Arizona. (Family *Tyrannidae*)

Say's Phoebe
Sayornis saya saya [457]

ADULT MALE AND FEMALE—Upper parts, dark gray; wing quills and tail, black. Breast, gray; abdomen, brown. LENGTH—7.77 inches.

DISTRIBUTION — From about the longitude of middle Nebraska westward; and from the Yukon River, Alaska, southward to southwestern Texas and southern California. Rarely found as far east as Wisconsin, Illinois, and even Massachusetts. In winter it passes into Mexico.

This is the commonest Flycatcher of the West, and universally distributed. Its common note is a soft, rather plaintive *pèe-urr*, slurred downward. It is a true Flycatcher in its habits, notes, and food, adding to the smaller winged insects the much larger forms, such as large grasshoppers. (Family *Tyrannidae*)

PIGEON FAMILY
Pigeons and Doves
Columbidae

The members of this family possess small heads, bills with a soft swelling about the base of the nostrils, short necks, short legs, small feet, pointed wings (not long), and tails, sometimes long, or moderately so, but never short. The plumage is compact, sleek, and well "tailored." To this family belongs our famous but now extinct Passenger Pigeon (which see). Over six hundred species and subspecies make up this very large family, distributed nearly all over the world, but principally in temperate and tropical regions. They are birds either of trees and forests, or of cleared lands. Their food consists of fruits, seeds, and a few insects and smaller invertebrates. Twenty-one members of the *Columbidae* are found in North America, and are sufficiently different to be placed in eleven genera.

NESTING. The nests of these birds are of the platform type; fragile, loosely put together, and sometimes so shallow that it is remarkable that the eggs do not oftener roll out upon the ground. They are composed of twigs, strips of bark, weed stems, straws, etc., and are located in the crotch of a tree (usually near the trunk), among the thick branches, on rocks or stumps, in old walls, in the crevices of cliffs, in old buildings, or upon the ground. The now extinct Passenger Pigeon

used to nest in enormous colonies in trees. Sometimes a single tree would contain fifty or more nests, which were nothing more than the most fragile of platforms. *Columbid* birds lay one or two eggs, which are white, creamy-white, or pale buff, and unmarked.

PIGEON
Band-tailed Pigeon
Columba fasciata fasciata [312]

ADULT MALE—Upper part of back, brownish; lower part, bluish-gray. Back of neck with white collar, and back of this a bronzy wash extending down back over the other colors. Head

and under parts, purplish-pink. Abdomen, whitish. End of tail with broad pale gray band, bordered above by black.

ADULT FEMALE—Similar to the male but much duller and grayer; the white neck band often absent.

LENGTH—15.50 inches.

DISTRIBUTION—From British Columbia southward through Mexico to Guatemala, and east to Colorado and western Texas. (Family *Columbidae*)

Passenger Pigeon
Ectopistes migratorius [315]

ADULT MALE—Upper parts, bluish-slate color; the back and sides of the neck with pinkish, greenish, and purplish metallic iridescence. Middle of back and scapulars, washed with olive-brown. Tail with a broad white tip. Under parts, deep, rich, sheeny vinaceous, fading to white on the abdomen.

ADULT FEMALE—Similar to the male, but upper parts with less sheen and masked by a wash of olive-brown. Breast, pale grayish-brown, grading to whitish on the abdomen.

LENGTH—16.30 inches.

DISTRIBUTION—Now entirely extinct. Formerly ranged in immense numbers all over eastern North America, as far north as Hudson Bay.

Vast hordes of these lovely Pigeons formerly swept over eastern North America, darkening the sky in huge clouds in their flight. Now not a single bird remains. There is no authenticated record of its wild existence since August, 1906, when a solitary bird was shot in Fairfield County, Connecticut. The last captive Passenger Pigeon died in the Cincinnati Zoological Park in

1914. As late as 1813 Audubon, observing a flock over the banks of the Ohio near Louisville, carefully estimated the number of birds to be "one billion, one hundred and fifteen million, one hundred and thirty six thousand!" The birds were shot, trapped, stupefied by smoke, netted, clubbed, and stoned. They were used as food; and also often as fertilizer for fields. (Family *Columbidae*)

Red-billed Pigeon

Columba flavirostris flavirostris [313]

ADULT MALE—Back, bluish-gray; wings with blackish quills; tail with its end blackish. Neck, brownish. Wing coverts with reddish patch. Chin, tawny-brown. Head, neck, and breast, dull pinkish-purple. Abdomen and under tail coverts, slate color. Bill, red.

ADULT FEMALE—Similar to the male, but slightly smaller and duller.

LENGTH—14.17 inches.

DISTRIBUTION—From the southern parts of Lower California and Texas southward through Mexico to Central America.

The Red-billed Pigeon is found in the timbered country of the lower part of the Rio Grande of Texas. It is a shy bird. Its cooing notes are short, clear, and rather high-pitched. (Family *Columbidae*)

Scaled Pigeon

Columba squamosa [314.1]

ADULT MALE AND FEMALE—Plumage, dark grayish-brown; wings and tail, somewhat darker. Head, neck, throat, and breast with rich vinaceous reflections. Feathers of the sides of the neck, stiff and scaly, projecting over the hind neck as a sort of "cape," and with metallic violet reflections.

LENGTH—16.00 inches.

DISTRIBUTION—An accidental visitant to Key West, Florida.

This beautiful species, abundant in the islands of the Greater and Lesser Antilles, is one of the finest game birds of the region; its flesh being esteemed a great delicacy. It is strictly a dweller in tall trees, and is found among the high mountains, except during the spring, when it resorts to the seacoast and islets for the purpose of building its nest and rearing its young. (Family *Columbidae*)

Viosca's Pigeon

Columba fasciata vioscae [312a]

Similar to the Band-tailed Pigeon, but paler; with the upper parts, a light bluish-slate-gray; and with the crown and breast washed with delicate grayish.

DISTRIBUTION—Restricted to the Cape Region of Lower California. (Family *Columbidae*)

White-crowned Pigeon
Columba leucocephala [314]

ADULT MALE—Plumage, in general, a rich slaty-bluish. Crown, white; back of head, purplish-chestnut-brown; back of neck, iridescent greenish, each feather margined with black.

ADULT FEMALE—Similar to the male, but paler. The crown, ashy instead of white; and the back of the

head and neck, brownish with a metallic iridescence, and black margins to the feathers as in the male.

LENGTH—13.50 inches.

DISTRIBUTION—"South Florida Keys, the Bahamas, Greater Antilles, some of the Lesser Antilles, Swan Island, Cozumel Island, and the islands off the coast of Central America, from British Honduras to western Panama. Casual in winter in Monroe and Dade Counties, Florida. (About twelve Florida records.) (Family *Columbidae*)

PINTAIL
American Pintail
Dafila acuta tzitzihoa [143]

ADULT MALE—Back, gray, finely marked with wavy black lines. Speculum, bronze, with greenish iridescence, and bordered in front with a bar of cinnamon-brown. Extending down the wing are long black feathers edged with white. Head, throat, and fore-

neck, brown. Hind-neck, black, separated from the fore-neck by a white stripe. Lower fore-neck, breast, and abdomen, white. Middle tail feathers, much elongated and black. Bill and feet, slate.

ADULT FEMALE—Back, brown, its feathers with white edges. Crown and hind-neck, brown. Under parts, white or whitish, spotted with dusky-brown, especially on the neck. Bill and feet as in the male. No long tail feathers.

LENGTH—28.00 inches; female about 22.00 inches.

DISTRIBUTION—In North America from the extreme north southward to New Brunswick, Iowa, Illinois, up to British Columbia. In winter it is found from Virginia, Illinois, and British Columbia southward to Central America and the West Indies.

The graceful Pintail may be easily identified by its slender neck, pure white under parts, and long slender central tail feathers. It is an especially

neat, trim Duck. The notes of the Drake are mellow whistles; those of the Duck are muffled, mellow quacks. The Duck is a very somber colored bird, and lacks the long central tail feathers of the Drake, although in flight her body and neck are slender and graceful, like the male. Herbert K. Job aptly characterizes the Pintail as "the greyhound among the waterfowl." Pintails are shy birds in the wild state, though they are easy to domesticate and become quite tame. They are very hardy and robust in spite of their delicate and aristocratic appearance, and often appear in the spring migration before the ice has gone from the ponds and lakes. (Family *Anatidae*)

Bahama Pintail
Dafila bahamensis bahamensis [143.1]

The Pintail Ducks, in general, may be recognized by their rather long, graceful, slender backs; the narrow, graceful bill; and by the slender, elongated middle pair of tail feathers of the male birds. The Bahama Pintail's general coloration is tawny brown, mottled and streaked with darker brown. Wings have lustrous iridescent green, black, and tawny brown bands. Top of head and nape, brown, finely mottled with darker brown. Rest of the head and throat, white. Each side of the upper mandible bears a triangular reddish patch. Tail, tawny brown, shading at its tip to a much paler brown. Legs, black.

LENGTH—19.00 inches.

DISTRIBUTION—"The Bahamas, Porto Rico, some of the Lesser Antilles, the Guianas, and northern Brazil. Casual in Florida, Wisconsin, and Cuba." (Family *Anatidae*)

PIPIT
American Pipit

Anthus spinoletta rubescens [697]

ADULT MALE AND FEMALE—Upper parts, brownish-gray; the outer tail feathers, prominently tipped with white; the next pair, less deeply tipped. Line over the eye, whitish. Throat, white; breast, white streaked with black; abdomen, pure white.

LENGTH—6.38 inches.

DISTRIBUTION—In the Arctic regions of North America, southward into the higher Rocky Mountains. In winter it is found in the Gulf States, and westward through Nevada and southern California, and extending southward through Mexico into Central America.

As the Pipits migrate through the United States, they may be found near the Atlantic Coast, running about in the short grass of broad tidal marshes, often forming large flocks with Horned Larks and Snow Buntings. Inland they are found wherever there are

meadows and fields, grassy shores of lakes and ponds, ploughed land, or grassy hillsides. As the Pipit walks it wags its tail constantly, and when it flies, displays the white markings of the outer tail feathers. Like the Skylark of Europe, the Pipit sings as it mounts into the air, and also as it descends. Its song is not as rich and varied as the Lark's, but is a series of *te-dée, te-dée, te-dée, te-dée* notes, sounding like the muffled ringing of a little bell. Its call notes, given as it rises and flies away, sound like the hushed syllables *se-seep, se-seep, se-seep.* (Family *Motacillidae*)

Japanese Pipit
Anthus spinoletta japonicus [697.1]

Similar to the American Pipit, the upper parts being grayish-olive-brown, with faint darker streakings. Legs and feet, a pale pinkish-brown.

DISTRIBUTION—This subspecies is reported as a casual visitant on Nunivak Island, Alaska. (Family *Motacillidae*)

Meadow Pipit
Anthus pratensis [698]

ADULT MALE AND FEMALE—Upper parts, ashy-gray tinged with olive, the center of each feather marked with dark sooty-brown. Under parts, buffy-white, marked with many elongated brown spots.

LENGTH—5.75 inches.

DISTRIBUTION—A European species, occurring as an accidental straggler in Greenland. (Family *Motacillidae*)

Red-throated Pipit
Anthus cervinus [699]

ADULT MALE—Upper parts, dark ashy-gray; the rump and upper tail coverts, streaked. Face, throat, breast, and upper abdomen, pale vinaceous chestnut. Lower abdomen, buffy-white.

ADULT FEMALE—Similar to the male, but with the throat buffy, and the breast paler.

LENGTH—7.00 inches.

DISTRIBUTION—An accidental straggler in western Alaska, the Aleutian Islands, and also in Lower California. (Family *Motacillidae*)

Sprague's Pipit
Anthus spraguei [700]

Similar to the American Pipit, but the upper parts flecked with light

brown and ashy-white. Tail, brown, the two outer feathers largely white. Wings, a decided brown, with two

faint bars. The buff-tinted under parts are marked across the breast with a band of dark streaks.

DISTRIBUTION—In the interior plains of North America from Saskatchewan to the Yellowstone; migrating in winter into Mexico. (Family *Motacillidae*)

PLOVER FAMILY
Plovers, Turnstones, and Surf-birds
Charadriidae

Plovers somewhat resemble Sandpipers and Snipes. Their legs are relatively long; their wings, long and pointed; their necks and tails, short. Their

bodies are plump. The bill is peculiar in that it is relatively short and pigeon-like, and somewhat enlarged at the tip. Plovers run about rapidly over the ground, their legs "twinkling" as they run, making them look like little mechanical toys. Of the seventy-five or so species, twenty-one are found in North America, relegated to ten genera.

NESTING. Plovers deposit their eggs on the ground, either in a shallow depression of the bare soil; in a suitably protected spot among pebbles, seaweeds, and shells; in a hollow in a spread of moss; or in a depression which the birds line with leaves, grasses, and the like. Our common Killdeer lays its sharply pointed eggs sometimes among stones, sometimes in a depression in a plowed field, or in a slight hollow in an old upland pasture. The eggs of Plovers are much larger at one end than at the other (so that if the wind blows them they will roll around in a small circle and not roll away), and are a creamy-white, light brown, or olive, marked with specks, spots, and blotches of dark brown, black, lavender, etc.

PLOVER
American Golden Plover
Pluvialis dominica dominica [272]

ADULT MALE AND FEMALE—Upper parts, and top of head, black, spotted with white and bright yellow. Tail, dark brownish-gray, barred with white and somewhat tinged with yellow. Forehead, white, and from this area a broad white bar passes over the eye, broadening to a white patch on the side of the breast. Sides of the head, throat, neck, and under parts, jet black. Bill, black; legs and feet, dark gray.

LENGTH—10.50 inches.

DISTRIBUTION—Breeds in the Arctic regions of the Western Hemisphere, and spends its winters from Florida to the southern tip of South America, being rare in migration on the Pacific Coast.

On migration, Golden Plovers may be seen, but not at all commonly, on the sand above the high-tide mark on beaches, among the dunes, or more frequently running about in the short grass of hillsides or meadows where the ground has been burned over, and where stubble grass occurs. Often, too, they may be seen running about over ploughed fields. They run and fly rapidly, and all their motions are quick and energetic. Their notes are clear and musical, and in keeping with the birds' energetic actions. They have been represented by the syllables *queep, quee-lee-leep.* Another note sounds like *curdle* or *coodle,* or *queedle.* In their remarkable migrations, these birds are celebrated, passing south

from Nova Scotia to the northeastern coast of South America, a distance of 2,400 miles, and a flight over the open ocean unparalleled by any other species. In spring it returns to its northern nesting grounds by way of the northwestern coast of South America

and the Mississippi Valley. In its "round trip" each year, the bird covers a distance of about 8,000 miles. The birds are sometimes driven on to the New England coast by gales. (Family *Charadriidae*)

Belding's Plover
Pagolla wilsonia beldingi [280a]

Similar in general to the Wilson's Plover, but the upper parts, darker; the dark loral stripe or band, much broader; and the white frontal band, narrower.

DISTRIBUTION—Along the Pacific coastal zone of the Americas, from the middle portion of Lower California southward to Peru. The bird has twice been recorded near San Diego, California. (Family *Charadriidae*)

Black-bellied Plover
Squatarola squatarola [270]

ADULT MALE AND FEMALE—Back and hinder part of head, black barred and spotted with white. Wings showing white mark in flight. Tail, white barred with brownish-black. Sides of the head and neck, the throat, breast, and upper abdomen, black bordered with white on each side, the white meeting over the forehead. Sides of body under wings, black. Bill, legs, and feet, dark gray.

LENGTH—11.00 inches.

DISTRIBUTION—Over the Northern Hemisphere, breeding in the Arctic regions, and spending its winters in the Americas from Florida to Brazil.

The Black-bellied Plovers are fairly common migrants along our eastern coast in the fall and spring. The young, different in color from the

adults (their upper parts, lighter, with a golden wash on each feather; the under parts, white), are known to hunters as Beetle Heads. They are more numerous than the old birds, and far less shy. Black-bellies frequent the sand bars and flats exposed by the falling tide, where they feed often in company with Turnstones, Semipalmated Sandpipers, and Ringed Plovers. They do not bob up and down as do other Plovers. The pleasing musical whistle of this species is not unlike the *chér weet* of the Bluebird, but is lower in pitch, more drawn out, and possesses a plaintive, or mournful cadence. Black-bellied Plovers in either adult, immature, or winter plumage may be recognized by their white rumps and tails, and by the

black axillary feathers (under the wing). (Family *Charadriidae*)

Cuban Snowy Plover
Charadrius nivosus tenuirostris [278a]

ADULT MALE—Back, pale ashy-gray; the hinder part of the head, sometimes washed with light brown. Forehead, white. Crown band, ear coverts, and a patch on the side of the breast, black. Middle tail feathers, dull brown; outer tail feathers, white. Under parts, white.

ADULT FEMALE—Similar to the male, but with the black markings duller and grayer.

LENGTH—6.00 inches.

DISTRIBUTION — From Florida to Texas along the coast of the Gulf of Mexico; on the salt plains of Oklahoma and Kansas; and also apparently in Haiti and Porto Rico. Casually occurs near Toronto, Ontario. In winter it is found in the Bahamas, Haiti, Cuba, Yucatan, and Venezuela (on Margarita Island).

This bird is the southeastern representative of the Snowy Plover of the west. Its note is described as a low-pitched musical whistle, which may be represented by the syllables *pee-wée-ah* or *o-wée-ah*, the first and third syllables faint, the second one louder and stressed. In flight its call is a purring whistle. (Family *Charadriidae*)

European Golden Plover
Pluvialis apricaria apricaria [271]

Similar to our American Golden Plover, but with the under wing coverts pure white instead of dull gray.

DISTRIBUTION—Eastern Greenland.

This bird has for many centuries been an esteemed morsel for the table in the British Isles. Its call note is a clear, loud, high, musical, wild, free, and joyous whistle. (Family *Charadriidae*)

Killdeer Plover

Oxyechus vociferus vociferus [273]

ADULT MALE AND FEMALE—Upper parts, grayish-brown; under parts, white *with two black upper-breast bands. A rich cinnamon-brown patch at the base of the tail* shows in flight.

LENGTH—10.5 inches.

DISTRIBUTION—Whole of North America; rarer along the north Atlantic Coast; winters from Virginia and California southward to South America.

The Killdeer derives its name from its high, piercing, clear, though sweet notes, which sound like the syllables

kill-dee, kill-dee. In regions where the birds are common, they sometimes become annoying, for they continue their shrill notes throughout the day, and often far into the night when the moon is full. The Killdeer is found in open country, such as salt marshes, along the borders of lakes and streams; but especially in ploughed fields, old pastures, and cultivated land in general. It also breeds in such situations, depositing its four sharply pointed eggs in a shallow depression in the ground. The unusual shape of the eggs prevents them from being rolled out of their insecure saucer by the wind. The young birds are able to run about adroitly as soon as they emerge from the shell; an ability which they develop to high perfection as adults, for Killdeers are notably rapid runners. The country saying "to run like a Killdeer" is evidence of its reputation in

this respect. The wings of Killdeers are long, crescentic, and pointed, and bear their owners through the air in a vigorous, buoyant, graceful flight, reminding one of the flight of the Sparrow Hawk. (Family *Charadriidae*)

Little Ringed Plover

Charadrius dubius curonicus [276]

ADULT MALE AND FEMALE—Plumage, grayish-brown. Forehead, white. Fore-crown, face, upper breast, and upper back, black. Throat, collar, breast, and abdomen, pure white. Bill, black; orange at its tip. Legs and feet, orange.

LENGTH—7.00 inches.

DISTRIBUTION—A northern European and Asiatic bird, found accidentally on Kodiak Island, Alaska, and in San Francisco, California. (Family *Charadriidae*)

Mongolian Plover

Charadrius mongolus mongolus [279]

ADULT MALE AND FEMALE—Upper parts, soft mousy-gray; the primaries, darker and duskier. Region about the base of the bill, white. An irregular patch extends from the eye across the forehead, above which lies a corresponding area of mottled brown. Back of the neck, rich chestnut-brown. Chin and throat, to upper breast, also the sides of the body, rich chestnut-brown. This color also extends as a wide band up over the back of the neck and upper back. Lower breast, abdomen, and under tail coverts, whitish.

LENGTH—17.50 inches.

DISTRIBUTION—This Plover, of northwestern Siberia, is found as a casual visitant on Cape Prince of Wales, Nunivak Island, Alaska.

The Mongolian Plover, sometimes also referred to as the Lesser Sand Plover, is a bird of tidal flats, extensive beaches, and the wide muddy borders of tidal estuaries. It also occurs in cultivated fields, in its natural range, sometimes at considerable distances from the sea. (Family *Charadriidae*)

Mountain Plover
Eupoda montana [281]

ADULT MALE AND FEMALE—Upper parts, plain grayish-brown. Forehead and a line over the eye, white. Front border of the crown, and a stripe from the base of the bill backward to the eye, black. Under parts, white, grayish-white, or slightly tinged with light brownish. Tail, short. Bill, slenler.

LENGTH—8.55 inches.

DISTRIBUTION—In the western portion of the United States from the Dakotas and Montana southward to Texas. In winter it is found as far west as California, and south as far as Lower California; also to San Luis Potosi in Mexico. It occurs as an accidental straggler into Florida.

The Mountain Plover belies its name, for it is found breeding in the high arid plains of the west. Bailey says

that it breeds "in considerable abundance from the Staked Plains of Texas to Montana, and in Colorado up to 8,000 feet. It is a quiet bird, lacking the sharp markings and vociferousness of the Killdeer. Instead of haunting the ponds and meadows, it spends its time picking up grasshoppers and other small insects from the short prairie grass." It is a common winter

resident in southern California, especially in Los Angeles County. The name Mountain Plover was bestowed on the bird because the first specimen to be described was taken on the high central tableland of the Rocky Mountains, in the vicinity of Sweetwater, Wyoming. The local name of Prairie Plover is more descriptive of its habitat, and more appropriate. (Family *Charadriidae*)

Pacific Golden Plover
Pluvialis dominica fulva [272a]

Similar to the American Golden Plover, but with the yellow color richer, and the wings somewhat shorter.

DISTRIBUTION—This northern Asiatic bird is found also on the Pribilof Islands, and on the coast of Alaska. In winter it passes to China, and southward. (Family *Charadriidae*)

Piping Plover
Charadrius melodus [277]

ADULT MALE AND FEMALE—Upper parts, whitish-ash; forehead and ring around the neck, white. A band on each side of the breast, sometimes uniting into a continuous zone, black. Front part of the crown, black. Inner tail feathers, brownish; outer ones, white, with a blackish band near their tips. Under parts, white. Base of bill, yellowish or orange. Legs and feet, orange.

LENGTH—17.00 inches.

DISTRIBUTION — From Newfoundland southward to Virginia, and over all eastern North America. In winter it is found in Florida, and southward.

The sweet, melancholy, almost mournful notes of the little Piping Plover form a pleasing association in the minds of many a boy brought up on the lovely coast of New England. *Pip-pe'ee, pip-e'ee·* it calls, as it flits and runs about the beaches, tidal flats, or occasionally over a field near the tidewater. The first syllable is short, and a little higher in pitch than the second. The second syllable is prolonged, and with a slightly falling, plaintive, sometimes petulant cadence. As the bird runs about in the dry, whitish

sand above the upper tide line, it frequently stops and remains for sometime motionless and "frozen." At such times it harmonizes perfectly with its surrounding colors, and is impossible to locate until it begins running again. It relies so implicitly on its obliterative coloration and disruptive pattern, that it often squats quietly until the walker is almost upon it, when it springs up like a jack-in-the-box, and with a sharp startling *pip-p'ee,* hurtles away. Like its close relative, the Semipalmated Plover, it bobs and "teeters," resembling this cousin also in its pattern and color, but distinguishable from it by its much paler color, and by the fact that its black collar is usually broken, and does not completely cross the breast. (Family *Charadriidae*)

Ringed Plover
Charadrius hiaticula hiaticula [275]

ADULT MALE—Nape and upper parts, subdued brown. Forehead, lores, and gorget extending around the neck, black. A broad collar of white, and also a white forehead and white stripe over each eye. Outer tail feathers, white. Under parts, white. Bill, legs, and feet, orange.

ADULT FEMALE—Similar to the male, but with the black gorget or collar, less well defined.

LENGTH—7.75 inches.

DISTRIBUTION—In the Old World, and also in the eastern portion of Arctic America. In North America it is found breeding in Greenland, eastern Baffin Land, and probably in Ellesmere Land. It migrates southward along the European coasts.

A bird similar in general to our Semipalmated Plover. It is a very common bird in the British Isles. (Family *Charadriidae*)

Semipalmated Plover
Charadrius semipalmatus [274]

ADULT MALE AND FEMALE—Upper parts, grayish-brown; crown, similar. Fore-part of the crown, and feathers at the base of the upper mandible, black. A broad stripe under the eye, and a line connecting this to the base of the upper mandible, black. Forehead, white. Throat, sides of neck, and a collar about the neck, white. Inner tail feathers, brownish-gray; the outer ones, becoming progressively white. Band across the upper breast, black. Under parts, white. Base of the bill, orange; its tip, black. Legs and feet, yellow. Toes, webbed at the base (i.e., foot semipalmated, hence the bird's name).

LENGTH—6.75 inches.

DISTRIBUTION—From the extreme northern parts of the continent southward to the latitude of Labrador. In winter it is found from the Gulf States southward into Brazil.

The little Semipalmated Plover, or Ring Neck as it is often called, is an inhabitant, while with us, of beaches and low-tide mud flats, and is a common bird in all such situations. As they run about feeding, they utter a simple, sweet, twittering cry, which is a familiar and cheerful sound in the ears of all lovers of the seashore. *Tsee-w'ee, tsee-w'ee* they call, the first syllable lower, the second higher. It is easily imitated by every whistling boy and girl. Flocks of these attractive little Plovers are often associated with the Semipalmated Sandpipers (called Peeps), and with the Least Sandpipers. From the Peeps, which they much resemble at a distance, they may be distinguished by their habit of

bobbing. From the Piping Plover they may be separated by the black breast-encircling band. Their large, limpid eyes give them the name of Oxeye. (Family *Charadriidae*)

Upland Plover
Bartramia longicauda [261]

ADULT MALE AND FEMALE—Upper parts, mixed black and buffy-brown. Outer tail feathers, barred with black, white, and reddish-brown. Tail, long, reaching beyond the tips of the wings. Breast, buffy streaked with black. Abdomen, white. Sides of breast, buffy streaked with blackish.

LENGTH—11.50 inches.

DISTRIBUTION—In North America, largely in the interior. It breeds from Nova Scotia and Alaska southward to Virginia and Kansas, and winters south of the United States, and into South America.

The Upland Plover, also often called the Bartramian Sandpiper, is a bird of grassy hillsides (as its name "up-

land" indicates), grassy plains, fields, and pastures. It is a shy bird, flying off from an observer on foot, though it may be approached quite closely

on horseback, in a wagon, or a car. As it springs into the air in flight, it emits a wild, high, rolling whistle. Upon alighting it stretches its wings to their full extent over the back, before folding them. It often utters its rather mournful call on moonlight nights. It is the only large Sandpiper-like bird that one is likely to encounter in grassy fields and on hillsides. (Family *Scolopacidae*)

Western Snowy Plover
Charadrius nivosus nivosus [278]

ADULT MALE AND FEMALE—Back, pale buffy-gray; crown, same, bordered in front by a short black band. Face, white. Auricular patch and elongated spot at the side of the breast, black. Under parts, white. Down the length of the extended wing, a row of white blotches. Middle tail feathers, a dark sooty-brown toward the tips; the outer tail feathers, white. Bill, black. Legs, rather stout and gray; feet, gray.

LENGTH—6.50 inches.

DISTRIBUTION—Over the western portion of the United States, and eastward as far as western Nebraska, Kansas, and Texas. In winter it migrates south into South America as far as Chile.

The Snowy Plover is a rapid runner; its feet fairly twinkle as the little body is whisked swiftly along in an even gliding motion. It is a bird of the outer beaches, between the last high tide line and the sand dunes. Like many of its kind, its voice is shrill, piping, and rather plaintive; its notes

sounding like the whistled syllables *peet-te'et, peet-te'et,* as though it were calling attention to its being petite. Bailey says, delightfully of this bird, "On the shores of the Salt Lake while the great white gulls disport themselves in the air and on the water, the plump little Snowy Plover is trotting along the beach, gathering his food as he goes. If frightened, he drops into the deep footprint of a horse, and is lost to view, so well does his back match the dull gray surface. Though so small, he is one of the most attractive bits of life in his big landscapes." The Snowy Plover may be distinguished from the similar Semipalmated Plover by its lighter upper parts, and by the absence of a complete black band across the upper breast. (Family *Charadriidae*)

Wilson's Plover

Pagolla wilsonia wilsonia [280]

ADULT MALE—Back, cheeks, and crown, brownish-gray. Lores, front part of crown, and a wide band across the breast, black. Forehead and a slight ring around the neck, white. Line over eye, white. Throat, white. The sides of the head and the nape,

sometimes show brownish markings. Inner tail feathers, brown; the outer ones, white. Under parts, pure white. ADULT FEMALE—Similar to the male in pattern, but with the black markings replaced by deep brownish-gray. Breast band, lighter brown. LENGTH—7.50 inches. DISTRIBUTION — From Virginia, across to Lower California and southward to the Gulf States. In winter it migrates southward to Brazil. It is reported as a casual wanderer as far north as Nova Scotia.

The Wilson's Plover is a rather quiet, retiring bird, and a denizen of sandy beaches and mud flats exposed by the falling tide. Although it is predominantly a maritime species, it may sometimes be found inland along the muddy and sandy shores of estuaries where the tidal effects are pronounced. Here it runs about—not in flocks, but singly or by twos and threes—industriously picking up small crustaceans, and insects. Only later in the fall do

the birds gather in small loose flocks. Its notes are quite unlike those of other Plovers, and consist of double-notes, sweet, mellow, flute-like, which may be represented by the repeated syllables *queep-peeip.* They have been described as half whistle and half chirp. Sometimes it calls *pip-pip-peep,pip-pip-peep,* the first two notes decidedly chirping in quality. The Wilson's Plover is larger than either of its close relatives, the Semipalmated and the Piping Plovers. From these it may be most easily distinguished in the field by its bill, which is longer and heavier. (Family *Charadriidae*)

POCHARD

Pochard
Nyroca ferina [146.1]

ADULT MALE—Upper parts, vermiculated gray and brown; the head and neck, chestnut-brown. Secondaries of wing, gray; no metallic speculum. Throat, whitish; under neck and breast, black. Abdomen, grayish speckled brown. Bill, longer than the head, and black encircled by a blue band.

ADULT FEMALE—Somewhat similar to the male, but with the upper parts browner. Under parts, whitish; freckled with dusky on the throat, and darker on the abdomen. Bill, duller than in the male.

LENGTH—19.50 inches.

DISTRIBUTION—This Old World Duck occurs as a casual straggler on the Commander and Pribilof islands, Alaska. (Family *Anatidae*)

POOR-WILL

Desert Poor-will
Phalaenoptilus nuttalli hueyi [418c]

Similar to Nuttall's Poor-will, but much lighter; upper parts, a light pinkish-tan; the darker black markings greatly reduced and sometimes absent altogether.

DISTRIBUTION — From the lower reaches of the Colorado River valley of southeastern California, through southwestern Arizona, and the extreme northeastern corner of Lower California. (Family *Caprimulgidae*)

Dusky Poor-will
Phalaenoptilus nuttalli californicus [418b]

Similar to the Nuttall's Poor-will, but decidedly darker throughout.

DISTRIBUTION—"California west of the Sierra Nevada, and the Mohave and Colorado deserts, from the head of the Sacramento Valley south to northwestern Lower California, to latitude about 30°30'." (A.O.U. Check List.) (Family *Caprimulgidae*)

Nuttall's Poor-will
Phalaenoptilus nuttalli nuttalli [418]

Somewhat similar to the Eastern Whip-poor-will, but smaller, and much lighter, with a large white throat-patch, and three outer tail feathers evenly tipped with white.

DISTRIBUTION—From Montana and British Columbia south and west to Kansas, Nebraska, Dakota, and the eastern slopes of the Sierra Nevada Mountains. In winter it passes into Mexico, and southward. (Family *Caprimulgidae*)

San Ignacio Poor-will
Phalaenoptilus nuttalli dickeyi [418d]

Similar to the Dusky Poor-will, but differing chiefly in being decidedly smaller; with less black on the head, shoulders, and upper breast; and with more white at the end of the outer tail feathers.

DISTRIBUTION—The southern three-fourths of Lower California. (Family *Caprimulgidae*)

PTARMIGAN

Alaska Ptarmigan
Lagopus lagopus alascensis [301d]

Similar to the Willow Ptarmigan, but slightly larger, and, in the summer plumage, generally exhibiting more of a reddish cast.

DISTRIBUTION—Alaska generally, except along the southeastern coast, and extending eastward for an undetermined distance. (Family *Tetraonidae*)

Alexander's Ptarmigan
Lagopus lagopus alexandrae [301b]

Similar to the Willow Ptarmigan, but with the plumage darker throughout, especially that of the upper parts. The bill is smaller and narrower.

DISTRIBUTION — From Shumagin Island, off the Alaskan Peninsula, east to Baranof and neighboring islands. (Family *Tetraonidae*)

Allen's Ptarmigan
Lagopus lagopus alleni [301a]

Similar to the Willow Ptarmigan, but with the primaries of the wing more or less mottled with dark brown. Shafts of the secondary feathers sometimes black.

DISTRIBUTION— Restricted to Newfoundland. (Family *Tetraonidae*)

Chamberlain's Ptarmigan
Lagopus rupestris chamberlaini [302e]

Similar to the Townsend's Ptarmigan, but with the upper parts grayer, and more finely and densely vermiculated. Neck and upper back, brown, finely and narrowly barred or vermiculated with black.

DISTRIBUTION—On the Adak Island of the Aleutian Archipelago.

Chamberlain's Ptarmigan, also known as the Adak Ptarmigan, is the grayest of all the Ptarmigans found on the Aleutian chain. (Family *Tetraonidae*)

Dixon's Ptarmigan
Lagopus rupestris dixoni [302f]

Similar to the Nelson's Ptarmigan, but much darker, the plumage almost black, and in this respect more like the Evermann's Ptarmigan, but differing from that subspecies in that the feathers of the upper breast and back are more or less finely vermiculated with a light yellowish-brown.

DISTRIBUTION—On the islands near Sitka, Alaska. (Family *Tetraonidae*)

Evermann's Ptarmigan
Lagopus rupestris evermanni [302.1]

ADULT MALE—Upper parts, black or blackish slightly tinged with rusty-brown. Breast, same; abdomen, white or whitish.

ADULT FEMALE—Upper parts, brown, blotched and barred with black, and with the feathers tipped with white or grayish-light-brown. Under parts, similar, but showing no white, and with the black barrings broader.

LENGTH—15.00 inches.

DISTRIBUTION—On Attu Island of the Aleutian Archipelago. (Family *Tetraonidae*)

Kellogg's Ptarmigan
Lagopus rupestris kelloggae [302h]

Similar to the Rock Ptarmigan, but darker, with the black markings more extensive. The crown, nearly solid black.

DISTRIBUTION — Northwestern Greenland, Arctic America generally, and the interior of Alaska. (Family *Tetraonidae*)

Kenai White-tailed Ptarmigan
Lagopus leucurus peninsularis [304a]

Similar to the White-tailed Ptarmigan, but the summer or breeding plumage, much paler; and the fall coloration (while passing into the white winter plumage), much grayer.

DISTRIBUTION—Restricted to the Kenai Peninsula of Alaska. (Family *Tetraonidae*)

Nelson's Ptarmigan
Lagopus rupestris nelsoni [302b]

ADULT MALE—Upper parts, deep brown with very fine compact vermiculations. Upper breast, barred with bright tawny-brown and black. Abdomen, white.

ADULT FEMALE—Upper parts, black barred with rusty-brown; the feathers margined with whitish. Under parts, brown barred with black and tipped with whitish.

LENGTH—14.00 inches.

DISTRIBUTION — On Unalaska Island, Aleutian chain. (Family *Tetraonidae*)

Northern White-tailed Ptarmigan
Lagopus leucurus leucurus [304]

ADULT MALE AND FEMALE—Plumage, finely marked with black, white, and grayish-brown; the wing, tail, and

under parts (except breast), white. In winter the birds are entirely snowy white. Bill, black.

LENGTH—13.00 inches.

DISTRIBUTION—From northern British Columbia and Alberta southward along the Rocky Mountain zone to northwestern Montana, Colorado, and northern New Mexico, and westward to Washington and Vancouver Island.

A mountain species, pure white in winter, almost entirely concealing the birds among the snow and ice of the upper heights. The birds are fairly common in Glacier National Park in Montana. (Family *Tetraonidae*)

Rainier White-tailed Ptarmigan
Lagopus leucurus rainierensis [304b]

Resembles the Northern White-tailed Ptarmigan, but with the dark areas of the plumage more blackish, and with the light buffy areas appreciably paler in tone.

DISTRIBUTION—Found in the Cascade Mountains of Washington. (Family *Tetraonidae*)

Reinhardt's Ptarmigan
Lagopus rupestris reinhardi [302a]

Similar to the Rock Ptarmigan, but not so regularly nor so coarsely barred on the upper parts.

DISTRIBUTION — From Greenland across into northern Labrador. (Family *Tetraonidae*)

Rock Ptarmigan
Lagopus rupestris rupestris [302]

ADULT MALE—Upper parts, black; narrowly, irregularly, and thickly barred with shades of light brown and white. Middle of back, largely black. Tail, dark brown tipped with white. Primaries and secondaries, white. Crown barred with rusty and creamy brown. Breast and sides, light brown, closely and narrowly barred with

black, and more or less mottled with white. Abdomen, pure white.

ADULT FEMALE—Similar to the male, but with less brown on the head and neck. Throat, breast, and sides, pale light brown barred with darker. Under parts, pale, and lightly barred.

In winter both sexes are largely white.

LENGTH—15.00 inches.

DISTRIBUTION—From the Arctic regions of North America (except Arctic Labrador) south to the Gulf of St. Lawrence and the high mountains of British Columbia. It extends westward through Alaska and out on to the Aleutian Islands.

Rock Ptarmigans are fairly common in Alaska. During the winter they are more likely to be found in open country than are the Willow Ptarmigans, which frequent the woods. (Family *Tetraonidae*)

Sanford's Ptarmigan

Lagopus rupestris sanfordi [302g]

Similar to Turner's Ptarmigan, but much lighter, notably on the throat and breast, and less heavily barred with black on those parts. Head also less heavily barred with black, and with the black loral patch less prominent. Feathers of the back bear fewer black markings.

DISTRIBUTION—Found on the island of Tanaga, in the Aleutian Archipelago. (Family *Tetraonidae*)

Southern White-tailed Ptarmigan

Lagopus leucurus altipetens [304c]

Similar to the White-tailed Ptarmigan, but slightly larger; and in the fall transitional plumage, a more pronounced brown. The upper parts are a pale cinnamon-brown.

DISTRIBUTION—Restricted to Colorado and New Mexico. (Family *Tetraonidae*)

Townsend's Ptarmigan

Lagopus rupestris townsendi [302d]

ADULT MALE—Upper parts, brown; the back, finely vermiculated with black. Upper portion of back, shoulder region of wings, as well as head and neck, blotched with black. Reddish patch over the eye. Breast, mottled; abdomen, white.

ADULT FEMALE—Similar to the male, but lighter.

LENGTH—15.00 inches.

DISTRIBUTION—Found on Kiska and Adak islands of the Aleutian Archipelago. (Family *Tetraonidae*)

Turner's Ptarmigan

Lagopus rupestris atkhensis [302c]

Similar in general to the Townsend's Ptarmigan, and with the upper parts lacking the black mottlings.

DISTRIBUTION—As the subspecific name of the bird suggests, this Ptarmigan is found on Atka Island of the Aleutian Archipelago. (Family *Tetraonidae*)

Ungava Ptarmigan

Lagopus lagopus ungavus [301c]

Similar to the Willow Ptarmigan, but with a heavier bill.

DISTRIBUTION—From the eastern shores of Hudson Bay eastward through northern Quebec. (Family *Tetraonidae*)

Welch's Ptarmigan

Lagopus rupestris welchi [303]

Similar to the Rock Ptarmigan, but decidedly grayer.

DISTRIBUTION—Confined to Newfoundland. (Family *Tetraonidae*)

Willow Ptarmigan

Lagopus lagopus albus [301]

ADULT MALE—Upper parts, black, irregularly and thickly barred with rusty and lighter brown. Tail, dark brown, narrowly tipped with white. Throat, upper breast, and sides, rich reddish-brown; the two latter more or less barred with black. Primaries and secondaries, white. Lower abdomen, mostly white.

ADULT FEMALE—Similar to the male, but with less brown, or none, on the head and neck. Throat, breast, and sides, light brown widely barred

(In summer plumage)

(In winter plumage)

with black. Middle of abdomen, paler and crossed by broken black bars.

In winter both sexes are entirely pure white, with dark brown tails tipped with white.

LENGTH—15.00 inches.

DISTRIBUTION—From the Arctic regions to about central Canada, passing south in winter to the northern border of the United States, or just north of it. Not found in New York or the New England States, ordinarily, but recorded once each from Maine and Massachusetts.

The concealing coloration of the Ptarmigans is interesting; mottled in summer to correspond to the various shades of grays, browns, and whites of the environments of the birds; and pure white in winter to harmonize with snow and ice, and simulate the lumps of same. The nest is made on the ground, and the eggs vary in number from seven to eleven. "Come seven, come eleven" murmurs Mother Ptarmigan, as she crouches expectantly in her chilly nest. The voice of the Ptarmigan during the mating season is hoarse and loud. Its food consists of insects and vegetation, and in winter it finds a scanty subsistence in berries, and on buds and terminal twigs of willows and dwarf alders. The Eskimos and others of the far north depend for a considerable portion of their food on the Ptarmigans. (Family *Tetraonidae*)

PUFFIN

Atlantic Puffin

Fratercula arctica arctica [13]

ADULT MALE AND FEMALE—Upper parts, wings, and tail, blackish. Head and foreneck, washed with brownish; a grayish white collar on the nape. Sides of head and throat, white, washed with light gray. Breast and abdomen, white. Bill, very deep, ridged, and marked with grayish-blue, yellow, and vermilion. Its base almost as deep as the head. A horny spine over the eye. Feet, orange.

LENGTH—13.00 inches.

DISTRIBUTION—From Quebec and southern Greenland southward to Nova Scotia, Bay of Fundy, and Maine. In winter it is found uncommonly south as far as Massachusetts, and casually to Long Island and New Jersey.

Puffins are found in the north inhabiting rocky ledges, where soil for their subterranean nest burrows is deep enough, and also on islands where they make their excavations under the coarse grass. As they fly off to sea, their short dumpy bodies, short tails, short rounded wings, and awkwardly held bright-colored legs give them a most grotesque appearance. As they sail in from the sea and maneuver

about to alight on a ledge, they are positively mirth-provoking. The name Sea Parrot is well bestowed. Their commonest note is a short, hoarse grunt or groan, often with an aspirate quality. While about the nest they give voice to a low, hen-like, purring note, or to a series of mellow clucks, and a low, soft whine. Puffins capture their fishy food by diving. Under water they are expert and extremely rapid swimmers. Their prey is gripped in powerful beaks. Several dives may be made, and finally with several fish held together in their beaks, the birds swing in toward the cliffs with a stiff, rapid beating of their ridiculous little wings. (Family *Alcidae*)

Horned Puffin
Fratercula corniculata [14]

Similar to the Atlantic Puffin, but with a blackish throat.

DISTRIBUTION—"Breeds on the Siberian coast, the Commander Islands, both sides of the Bering Strait, Kotzebue Sound, and St. Michael to Forrester Island, Alaska. Winters from the Aleutian and Commander islands south to the Kurile Islands, and from the Queen Charlotte Islands to California (Pacific Grove)." (A.O.U. Check List.)

This species, a more northern form of Puffin than its Atlantic congener, is similar in its habits. Its utterance has been described by Nelson as a "hoarse, snuffling, rattling note." (Family *Alcidae*)

Large-billed Puffin
Fratercula arctica naumanni [13a]

Similar to the Atlantic Puffin, but larger.

DISTRIBUTION—Coasts and islands of the Arctic Ocean, from central western Greenland to Nova Zemlya and Spitzbergen; mainly resident. (Family *Alcidae*)

Tufted Puffin
Lunda cirrhata [12]

ADULT MALE AND FEMALE—Upper parts, sooty-black. Sides of the head about the eyes with a wide band of white, and with a long crest of soft yellowish feathers springing from over each eye. Bill, compressed, almost as deep as long, and much decorated with grayish-blue, yellow, and red. Base of bill, pale greenish. Eye ring and feet, vermilion. Under parts, dark gray.

LENGTH—15.00 inches.

DISTRIBUTION—From Bering Strait to Japan, and to the coasts and islands of Alaska to southern California.

Tufted Puffins are similar in general appearance, flight, and habits to the Atlantic Puffin. Bailey says of them, "The bright and oddly-shaped bill, white eyes, and yellow nuptial tufts, which flutter in the wind, give the bird a most distinguished appearance. Its bill is not only an ornament but a most effective weapon. When caught in its burrow the Puffin inflicts painful wounds with it, sometimes actually cutting to the bone, its jaws remaining set until pried apart, or until the bird is killed." The natives of the Puffins' nesting regions catch the birds in nets, after which they use the flesh for

food and the skins for making coats or "parkas"—the feather-side turned inward for greater warmth. (Family *Alcidae*)

PYRRHULOXIA
Arizona Pyrrhuloxia

Pyrrhuloxia sinuata sinuata [594]

ADULT MALE—Upper parts, light gray washed with brownish; wings and tail, dark gray. Area about the base of the bill, as well as the throat, patch on the lower breast, thighs, and under surface of the wings, light rosy-red. Sides of breast and abdomen, light gray. Head, prominently crested with tip of the crest darker red. Bill, conical, heavy, and short.

ADULT FEMALE—Red about the bill and on the under parts, absent or nearly so. Under parts, brownish.

LENGTH—9.00 inches.

DISTRIBUTION—From western Texas, southwestern New Mexico, and Arizona, southwest to northwestern Mexico.

The Pyrrhuloxia may be described as a Cardinal in gray and red; in fact,

one of its common names is Gray Cardinal. Another, bestowed on account of its prominent beak, is Parrot-bill. In general habits and song, it resembles its close relative, the Eastern Cardinal. (Family *Fringillidae*)

San Lucas Pyrrhuloxia

Pyrrhuloxia sinuata peninsulae [594b]

Similar to the Arizona Pyrrhuloxia, but slightly smaller, and with a decidedly larger bill.

DISTRIBUTION — Lower California. (Family *Fringillidae*)

Texas Pyrrhuloxia

Pyrrhuloxia sinuata texana [594a]

ADULT MALE—Similar in general to the Arizona Pyrrhuloxia, but darker. The upper parts are dark gray; the bill stouter, and prominently marked about its base with black.

ADULT FEMALE—Similar to the female Arizona Pyrrhuloxia, but with a grayish wash on the breast and sides.

DISTRIBUTION — Restricted in its range to the northeastern portion of Mexico, and northward into southern Texas. (Family *Fringillidae*)

QUAIL
Arizona Scaled Quail
Callipepla squamata pallida [293]

ADULT MALE AND FEMALE—General plumage, pale bluish-gray and

dull brownish. Head and short crest, fawn-brown tipped with white. Most of the under parts, and the fore parts appear as if scaled. Lower abdomen, buffy. Sides, dark gray streaked with white. Lower back, with stripes of white on each side.

LENGTH—10.70 inches.

DISTRIBUTION—From Arizona to western Texas, and southward into the Valley of Mexico.

A bird of dry washes and gulches, scrub oaks, chaparral, mesquite, and cactus, but never very far from water. (Family *Perdicidae*)

California Quail
Lophortyx californica californica [294]

ADULT MALE—Upper parts, dark smoky- or dusky-brown; deep reddish-brown stripes along the sides of the back. Crest, black. Back of the head, with an olive-brown patch, bordered on the front and sides by black and white lines. Throat, black with a white border. Breast, bluish-gray. Abdomen, scaled, except for a dark chestnut-brown, median patch. Flanks, dark olive-brown streaked with white.

ADULT FEMALE—General color of the plumage, dark smoky- or grayish-brown. Head, without black or white markings. Abdomen, scaled, but lacking the central chestnut patch or the brownish on the sides. Sides of the body, streaked with white.

LENGTH—9.50 inches.

DISTRIBUTION—Along the Pacific Coast from Monterey County, commonly to southern Oregon, and less

commonly northward. Introduced and naturalized in British Columbia and Washington.

This bird is similar in its habits to the Valley Quail. (Family *Perdicidae*)

Catalina Quail
Lophortyx californica catalinensis [294b]

Similar to the Valley Quail, but larger and somewhat darker. Similar also to the California Quail, but larger, and with the upper parts a less deep brown.

DISTRIBUTION—Found on Catalina Island off the coast of California. (Family *Perdicidae*)

Chestnut-bellied Scaled Quail
Callipepla squamata castanogastris [293a]

The male of this form is similar to the Arizona Scaled Quail, but bears a large chestnut-brown patch on the abdomen. The females of the two birds are much alike, but the female Chestnut-bellied form bears a much rustier brown abdomen.

DISTRIBUTION—From the northwestern portion of Texas southward to

the Lower Rio Grande Valley, and southward into northeastern Mexico. (Family *Perdicidae*)

Gambel's Quail

Lophortyx gambeli gambeli [295]

ADULT MALE—Upper parts, unmarked bluish-gray. Crown, reddish-brown; crest, black. Forehead and throat, black with a white border. Tertials, margined with white. Breast, gray. Abdomen, with buffy and black patches. Flanks, reddish-brown streaked with white.

ADULT FEMALE—Similar to the male, but without the conspicuous markings. Head, unmarked brownish-gray. Throat, buffy streaked with dark brown. Abdomen, unmarked lightish brown; flanks, chestnut brown.

LENGTH—9.75 inches.

DISTRIBUTION—From southeastern California to western Texas; and from southern Utah and Nevada southward through the central portion of Sonora, Mexico.

In the valleys of the Lower Colorado and Gila rivers, one finds this attractive little Quail in abundance, running about among the creosotes, mesquites, and cactus. The call of the cock bird is a loud, shrill *chu-chaaa, chu-chaaa,* the clarion call of the defiant young

feathered Lochinvar. In the fall large flocks of sometimes a hundred or more birds assemble, feeding dispersedly during the daytime but coming together at dusk to roost communally among the dense bushes of some sheltered bottom. They are excellent game birds, and even though levied upon severely by the hunter, are able to maintain themselves by virtue of their rapid reproduction (from ten to twelve eggs is the normal clutch). The food of the Gambel's Quail is very varied, consisting of: grains of all sorts, berries, the beans of the mesquite, insects —especially beetles, and other large forms, with an abundance of grasshoppers. The birds are not easy to

flush, and prefer running and hiding, to taking wing—a habit which aids in their preservation. Their flesh is dainty and delicious. (Family *Perdicidae*)

Mearns's Quail

Cyrtonyx montezumae mearnsi [296]

ADULT MALE—Back, pale brown, with vermiculations, barrings, and streakings of black and white. Head markings, black and white, with the end of the crest, fawn-brown. Median line of under parts, dark brown; the sides, slaty-gray spotted with white.

Head, with a full crest of soft depressed feathers. Tarsus and feet, very heavy and stout. Bill, stout.

ADULT FEMALE—Upper parts, coarsely mottled, but finely barred with brown, lavender, and black; the feathers, with coarse white shaft streaks. Head, without stripes. Chin, whitish. On the neck, a lavender cape, speckled and bordered with black. Rest of under parts, light lavender or cinnamon-brown; the breast and sides, with black specks and shaft streaks.

LENGTH—9.00 inches.

DISTRIBUTION—In northern Mexico, western Texas, southern portion of New Mexico, and southern Arizona.

In the grassy and bushy regions of the mountains of western Texas, the Mearns's Quail finds country exactly suited to its liking, where running and hiding is made easy. The note of the

bird is a characteristic soft, mellow *cher-r-r-r-r*, given with a rapid wavering tremolo. (Family *Perdicidae*)

Mountain Quail

Oreortyx picta palmeri [292]

ADULT MALE—Upper parts, deep olive-brown. Crest black. Top of head, bluish-gray. Throat and flanks, rich chestnut-brown; the latter, broadly banded with black and white. Sides of the back, with yellowish-brown

stripes. Breast, plain unmarked bluish-slaty-gray.

ADULT FEMALE—Similar to the male, but with a slightly shorter crest.

LENGTH—11.00 inches.

DISTRIBUTION—Along the Pacific Coast region, in humid zone, from

Washington southward as far as Santa Barbara, California.

In winter, when the mountains are covered with deep snows, these Quails, together with the Plumed Quails, descend into the foothills. Their habits are said to be practically identical. (Family *Perdicidae*)

Olathe Quail

Lophortyx gambeli sanus [295a]

ADULT MALE—Upper parts, dull neutral gray; crown, a rich chestnut-brown. The breast bears a light buffy patch, and the abdomen is a solid buff or dull, light brownish-white.

ADULT FEMALE—Similar to the male, but with a somewhat darker crown, and darker chin and throat. The under parts are pale buffy, with an olive or whitish cast.

LENGTH—10.45 inches.

DISTRIBUTION—Found locally in southwestern Colorado.

This beautiful Quail is said to be derived from the Gambel's Quail, and was introduced into its present locality many years ago. Its habits are similar to those of the Gambel's Quail. While it is a desirable game bird, its rapidity of breeding probably prevents its extermination. (Family *Perdicidae*)

Plumed Quail

Oreortyx picta picta [292a]

Similar to the Mountain Quail, but with the upper parts decidedly olive in tone. The hind neck is usually partly or entirely bluish-slate-gray like the breast. Forehead, usually paler in color, frequently whitish. Inner border of the tertials are a lighter buffy-brown, sometimes almost creamy-whitish. Plume on the head, long and prominent.

LENGTH—11.00 inches.

DISTRIBUTION—From the western slopes of the Cascade Mountains of northern Oregon (except close to the coast), southward along both sides of the Sierra Nevada. Also in the southern coast ranges as far as the northern part of Lower California.

The Plumed Quail, like the Mountain Quail, is a denizen of high mountain glens, where foamy streams plunge downward. As winter draws near, they gradually descend into the lower foothills. Their notes are similar to the last loud whistle of the Eastern Bob-white. They also frequently give voice to a subdued, but defiant crow, somewhat like that of a young bantam rooster. (Family *Perdicidae*)

San Lucas Quail

Lophortyx californica achrustera [294d]

Similar to the Valley Quail, but with the upper parts and the flanks, paler; the band across the breast, grayer; the buffy patch on the lower breast, much paler; and the dark feather edgings of the lower breast and abdomen, narrower.

DISTRIBUTION—From Rosario, Lower California (about latitude 30°), south to the Cape district. (Family *Perdicidae*)

San Pedro Quail

Oreortyx picta confinis [292b]

Similar to the Plumed Quail, but with the upper parts distinctly grayer. The back, rump, and upper tail coverts, olive-gray.

LENGTH—11.00 inches.

DISTRIBUTION—Found in the San Pedro Martir Mountains of Lower California. (Family *Perdicidae*)

San Quintín Quail

Lophortyx californica plumbea [294c]

Similar to the Valley Quail, but with the plumage less brownish and more plumbeous (darker gray) in tone.

DISTRIBUTION—From the Pacific Coast of Lower California, eastward to the foothills of the Sierra San Pedro Martir, between latitudes 30° and 32°; sometimes rarely to San Felipe on the Gulf of California coast. (Family *Perdicidae*)

Valley Quail

Lophortyx californica vallicola [294a]

Similar to the California Quail, but generaly lighter in color. The upper parts are grayish-brown, with the edges of the tertials creamy or white; and the flanks, olive-grayish or grayish-brown.

DISTRIBUTION—In the more arid zones from Oregon southward through California and western Nevada, as far south as Cape St. Lucas in Lower California. (Family *Perdicidae*)

QUAIL-DOVE
Key West Quail-dove
Oreopeleia chrysia [322]

ADULT MALE AND FEMALE—Upper parts, reddish-brown, with brilliant metallic iridescence. Wings, reddish-brown, without sheen. A white line below the eye. Breast, vinaceous; abdomen, white.

LENGTH—11.00 inches.

DISTRIBUTION—Formerly found on Key West; now in the Bahama Islands, Cuba, Haiti, and on the Isle of Pines.

"The Quail-doves inhabit wooded districts where they live on the ground. Their flight is low and noiseless, and

they are difficult birds to observe unless one can find some tree, on the fallen fruits of which they are feeding." (Chapman). (Family *Columbidae*)

Ruddy Quail-dove
Oreopeleia montana [322.1]

Similar in general to the Key West Quail-dove, but with the back a more reddish brown. The abdomen is a deep creamy buff.

LENGTH—11.00 inches.

DISTRIBUTION—This tropical American species has been twice reported from Key West, Florida. (Family *Columbidae*)

RAIL FAMILY
Rails, Gallinules, and Coots
Rallidae

This large family includes the peculiar Gallinules, and Coots, as well as the Rails themselves. They are birds with small heads, fairly long necks, short bodies, short rounded wings, short tails, long legs, and very large strong

feet. The Rails possess long bills, but the bills of Gallinules and Coots are short, stout, and more or less hen-like. The voices of all the members of the family are also hen-like. These birds inhabit dense marshes where they skulk and run about among the reeds; or towards night, come timidly out along the muddy edges of ponds and streams, or on mud flats beyond the margin of the rushes. They are often called mud hens. *Rallidae* are distributed over most of the globe, and number about two hundred and twenty-five different forms. Of these, eighteen are found in North America; twelve in the genus *Rallus;* two in the genus *Porzana;* one in the genus *Coturnicops;* two in the genus *Creciscus;* and one in the genus *Crex.*

NESTING. The members of this large family make their nests of reeds, rushes, grasses, etc., placing them among the rushes in marshy spots, or on the ground in damp meadows. Sometimes the nest is placed on a floating platform of reeds (e.g., the Coot and the Purple Gallinule). The eggs, ranging in number from six to sixteen, are dull white, creamy, buffy, or drab; spotted with browns and lavenders.

RAIL
Belding's Rail
Rallus obsoletus beldingi [209]

Similar to the King Rail, but with the bars on the flanks much narrower, and the general tone of the plumage paler. DISTRIBUTION—Found in Lower California. (Family *Rallidae*)

Black Rail
Creciscus jamaicensis stoddardi [216]

ADULT MALE AND FEMALE—Crown, gray. Hind neck and upper back, supporting a large deep-chestnut patch. Back and rest of upper parts, dark brownish-black, finely but prominently barred with white. Head, neck, and breast, dark slate-gray. Abdomen and under tail coverts, dark brownish-black, crossed by narrow but prominent, slightly wavy, white bars. Bill and tail, very short.

LENGTH—5.50 inches.

DISTRIBUTION—From central New England, Minnesota, Iowa, and Kansas, southward through New Jersey and into Florida. In winter some individuals are found in the southern part of Georgia, Florida, and in southern Louisiana, but the bird winters chiefly south of the United States.

This and the Farallon Rail, are the two smallest Rails on our continent. The Black Rail is an inhabitant of grassy meadows, where it runs about inconspicuously like a little feathered mouse, and is, therefore, very difficult of observation. It seldom flies when disturbed, but secretes itself in a tuft of grass. The calls of the bird have been described as a low *croo-croo-croo-o*, like the beginning of the Yellow-billed Cuckoo's song, and a *kik, kik, kik, kik* or *kuk, kuk, kuk, kuk*. These latter notes are uttered by the

male; the former by the female. Apparently central New England is about

the northernmost limit of the bird's breeding range, though it may occur farther north. (Family *Rallidae*)

California Clapper Rail
Rallus obsoletus obsoletus [210]

ADULT MALE AND FEMALE—Upper parts, olive-gray; the wings and back, striped with dusky-brown. Chin, white; throat and breast, unmarked cinnamon-brown. Flanks, dusky, narrowly barred with white. Tail, very short.

LENGTH—17.50 inches.

DISTRIBUTION — From Washington southward into Lower California, and the salt marshes of the Pacific Coast.

The notes of Clapper Rails are loud, harsh, and cackling. The California Clapper Rails are fairly common in the salt marshes of Los Angeles County, California. (Family *Rallidae*)

Farallon Rail
Creciscus jamaicensis coturniculus [216.1]

ADULT MALE AND FEMALE—Upper parts, black or blackish, the feathers finely barred and speckled with white. Nape patch, chestnut-brown; this color extending to the top of the head. Forehead, slate color. Under parts, rich leaden-gray; the lower abdomen, flanks, and under tail coverts, barred with white.

LENGTH—5.50 inches.

DISTRIBUTION—Along the Pacific Coast of the United States, this Rail is found breeding in the coastal marshes of California. The bird occurs as a casual visitor in Lower California, as well as in Oregon and Washington.

The Farallon Rail, often known as the Black Rail, is an interesting bird because of its apparent rarity. Actually the bird is probably common enough, but has been able hitherto to escape scrutiny. Hoffman says of it, "Few people have deliberately set out to see a Black Rail, and still fewer have succeeded. There is probably no bird in the United States that eludes observation better than this mouse-like inhabitant of the tangled salicornia. A meeting is usually entirely accidental; there is a brief view of a small black bird with short fluttering wings and dangling legs that drops hurriedly into the nearest shelter. There is a well-known breeding ground for the bird near San Diego where a few zealous collectors, by indefatigable kicking and turning over of masses of salicornia, have found a number of nests; but even they have rarely seen the sitting bird, which slips out on the other side and apparently never returns to a nest that has once been uncovered." The notes of the Farallon or Black Rail have been described as clear and plaintive, and sounding somewhat like the syllables *clee-cle, clée-cle.* (Family *Rallidae*)

Florida Clapper Rail
Rallus longirostris scotti [211b]

Somewhat similar to the King Rail, but with reddish-brown wing coverts, and a clear, unmarked cinnamon-brown neck and breast.

LENGTH—14.50 inches.

DISTRIBUTION—"Salt marshes of the Gulf Coast of Florida and the Atlantic Coast at Jupiter Inlet and

Palm Beach." (Chapman). (Family *Rallidae*)

King Rail
Rallus elegans elegans [208]

Somewhat similar to the Virginia Rail, but much larger, and lacking the gray cheeks.

LENGTH—15.00 inches.

DISTRIBUTION—From Connecticut and South Dakota (sometimes straggling north into Maine), southward to

Florida. In winter it is found from Virginia and the lower portion of the Mississippi Valley, southward into the Gulf States. (Family *Rallidae*)

Light-footed Rail
Rallus obsoletus levipes [210.1]

Similar to the California Clapper Rail, but smaller, the feet lighter, the bill slenderer, and the whole coloration much darker.

DISTRIBUTION—Found only in southern California. (Family *Rallidae*)

Louisiana Clapper Rail
Rallus longirostris saturatus [211a]

Similar to the Northern Clapper Rail, but with the general tone of the plumage much darker.

LENGTH—14.50 inches.

DISTRIBUTION—Found most commonly in the salt marshes of Louisiana, but also in similar situations on the coasts of Mississippi, Alabama, and Texas. (Family *Rallidae*)

Mangrove Clapper Rail
Rallus longirostris insularum [211d]

Similar to the King Rail, but with reddish-brown wing coverts, and with the neck and breast much paler and of a clear, unmarked brown. The brown centers of the back feathers are lighter, more olive in tone, and narrower. The slate-colored edges of the feathers are more extensive and bluer in tone, giving the back a lighter, more bluish cast.

LENGTH—14.50 inches.

DISTRIBUTION—Found in the salt marshes of the Florida Keys. (Family *Rallidae*)

Northern Clapper Rail
Rallus longirostris crepitans [211]

ADULT MALE AND FEMALE—Upper parts, pale greenish-olive; the edges

of the feathers, grayish-white. Wings, grayish-brown; the wing coverts, pale cinnamon-brown washed with grayish. Tail, brown. Throat, white. Breast, pale light brown washed with grayish, and flecked. Abdomen and sides of body, brownish-gray, finely barred with white.

LENGTH—14.50 inches.

DISTRIBUTION—From Connecticut south in the salt marshes of the Atlantic Coast, to North Carolina. In winter it is found from Long Island (rarely), southward along the coast. It sometimes wanders north as far as Massachusetts, or along the Gulf Coast as far as Louisiana. (Family *Rallidae*)

Virginia Rail
Rallus limicola limicola [212]

ADULT MALE AND FEMALE—Upper parts, dark sooty-brownish, or blackish; the feathers margined with pale

grayish-brown. Wings and tail, darker; the wing coverts, reddish-brown. Lores, whitish; cheeks, gray. Throat, white; the rest of the under parts, reddish-brown. Flanks and under tail coverts, barred or mottled with blackish and white.

LENGTH—9.50 inches.

DISTRIBUTION—From British Columbia, Manitoba, Labrador, Long Island, Pennsylvania, westward to northern Illinois and central California. In winter it is found from about the latitudes of Pennsylvania and central California southward to Cuba and Guatemala.

Fresh water, or brackish marshes, choked with cattails, rushes, and briers, are the favorite haunts of the Virginia Rail. From such impenetrable situations, one hears the grunting notes of the birds, which sound like those of little pigs. Rails step daintily about in their marshy and miry habitat, cocking up their absurd little tails at each mincing step. They are difficult birds to flush, and when disturbed prefer to slip into some tangle of reeds and briers to taking flight. Their flight is weak, and they soon drop back among the friendly intricacies of the morass. (Family *Rallidae*)

Water Rail

Rallus aquaticus aquaticus [212.1]

ADULT MALE—Crown, hind neck, and upper parts, olive-brown; the center of each feather displaying a black streak. Cheeks, neck, and breast, gray. Flanks, blackish barred with white. Bill, red; legs and feet, brownish-flesh color.

ADULT FEMALE—Similar to the male, in general, but duller in tone; the wing coverts sometimes barred with white.

LENGTH—11.50 inches.

DISTRIBUTION—An Old World species, occurring accidentally in Greenland.

The very shy, retiring habits of this Rail cause it to be regarded in England as a very rare bird. It inhabits fens, marshes, and watercourses, generally, and makes its way rapidly about among the tangle of floating vegetation. It is an easy and graceful swimmer and diver. (Family *Rallidae*)

Wayne's Clapper Rail

Rallus longirostris waynei [211c]

Similar to the Northern Clapper Rail, but in general much darker; the under parts with more ashy markings, and the under tail coverts with fewer.

DISTRIBUTION—Along the southern Atlantic Coast, in the salt marshes, from southeastern North Carolina to central Florida. (Family *Rallidae*)

Yellow Rail

Coturnicops noveboracensis [215]

ADULT MALE AND FEMALE—Upper parts, dark creamy-brown, mottled with brown and black. The feathers of the back are marked with white

wavy crosslines. Wings, dusky brown, bearing large white patches in the secondaries. Throat and breast, light brownish. Middle of abdomen, white.

LENGTH—6.37 inches.

DISTRIBUTION—North America, in general, from Nova Scotia and Hudson Bay south to Cuba, and westward into Nevada and California. (Family *Rallidae*)

Yuma Clapper Rail

Rallus obsoletus yumanensis [210a]

Similar to the California Clapper Rail, but with the feet smaller; the tarsi and the bill slenderer; and the foreneck brighter, with a more pinkish cast.

DISTRIBUTION—From the Laguna Dam on the Colorado River, southward through the valley, at least as far as Yuma. (Family *Rallidae*)

RAVEN

American Raven

Corvus corax sinuatus [486]

Similar to the Northern Raven, but slightly smaller; the bill also slightly smaller; the feathers of the under parts glossier.

DISTRIBUTION—In western North America from British Columbia south through Mexico to Guatemala, in the zone bounded by the Rocky Mountains and the Pacific. (Family *Corvidae*)

Northern Raven

Corvus corax principalis [486a]

ADULT MALE AND FEMALE—Black; the feathers in good light showing a metallic bluish sheen. Feathers of the throat, longer; bill, very heavy and stout. Feet, large and stout.

LENGTH—24.25 inches.

DISTRIBUTION — From Greenland, across to northern Maine, and west to the Rocky Mountains, south as far as the mountains of northern Georgia.

This great black bird, the giant of the family, once was more common in the Eastern States than at present. It occurs southward along the range of

the Allegheny Mountains, where it is often observed. Its voice, in keeping with its size, is more or less crow-like but hoarser, harsher, and deeper. The common note may be represented by the syllable *kr-r-r-rkrukk*, with a rolling, vibrant quality. At a distance, the Raven resembles a large crow. Its wing

strokes are more leisurely than the rather labored flapping strokes of the Crow, and the bird is more given to sailing without flapping. (Family *Corvidae*)

White-necked Raven

Corvus cryptoleucus [487]

Similar to the Northern Raven, but smaller; and with the feathers of the neck, completely round and pure white on their basal halves, this color being more or less concealed by the overlying feathers.

DISTRIBUTION—From Colorado and western Kansas south to northern Mexico, southwest to southern California, and east to western Texas.

The White-necked Raven, often called "crow" in the West, is a denizen of hot deserts, sterile valleys, and cactus and yucca country, generally. It frequents towns and villages, as well as stockyards and corrals, and in winter becomes quite tame. Its common call is a *crannkk, crannkk* that is hoarser than the Crow's call, more nasal, and somewhat resembling the deep throaty call of the Northern Raven. (Family *Corvidae*)

REDHEAD

Redhead

Nyroca americana [146]

ADULT MALE—Back, gray, with narrow wavy black lines; speculum, gray. Upper back, black. Head and neck, rich deep reddish-brown. Breast, black; abdomen, white. Under tail feathers, black. Bill, slate-colored, crossed by a black bar at its tip; its form, broad and flat, rising at its base in an abrupt curve to the forehead. Legs and feet, gray.

ADULT FEMALE—Back, brownish-gray; crown and neck, pale brown. Chin, white; the throat, neck, breast, and sides, brown. Middle of abdomen, white; the lower abdomen, brown. Bill and feet, slate-color.

LENGTH—19.00 inches.

DISTRIBUTION—From Labrador and British Columbia, to Maine, Minnesota, and California. In winter it is found from Maryland and southern British Columbia southward to the West Indies and Lower California.

The Redhead and Canvas-back are much alike, in appearance as well as in flavor. Both are accounted superior

game birds. The Redhead is only very slightly smaller, but the bill is differently shaped (see the illustrations of these two species), and there is less reddish-brown on its head and neck. The Redhead is the eastern, and the Canvas-back is the central and western bird. The Redhead is both a sea and inland-water duck. (Family *Anatidae*)

REDPOLL
Common Redpoll
Acanthis linaria linaria [528]

ADULT MALE—Upper parts, streaked with grayish and brownish hues; crown patch, bright crimson; two wing bars, grayish-white; rump, pink. Middle of throat, blackish; breast and upper part of abdomen,

faintly rose-pink; their sides streaked with brown.

ADULT FEMALE—Similar to the male, but lacking the rosy tinge on the rump and under parts.

LENGTH—5.32 inches.

DISTRIBUTION—Northern portion of the Northern Hemisphere, descending in winter into the northern part of the United States. It also occurs irregularly during the winter in Virginia, Kansas, Alabama, Colorado, and northern California.

Common Redpolls travel in flocks, often in company with Goldfinches, and in winter frequent groves of birches and clumps of willows and alders in swamps and along stream courses. Often, also, they may be discovered in old weed fields, in the weedy margins of little-used country roads, and in overgrown pastures. When alarmed the whole flock rises together and swirls off, usually only for a short distance. As they go, the birds utter a soft, throaty *chut, chut*, and the whole effect may be likened to the muffled rattling of a handful

of small pebbles. Another call, sweet and plaintive in character, is almost identical with that given by the Eastern Goldfinch and the Pine Siskin.

The bright crimson crown and the black chin patch are the field recognition marks of this dainty little Finch, and serve to identify both sexes. The rosy suffusion of the breast of the male bird shows to good advantage in strong light, and is one of the most delicate and pleasing colors to be found in the plumage of any of our native birds. (Family *Fringillidae*)

Greater Redpoll

Acanthis linaria rostrata [528b]

Similar to the Common Redpoll, but larger; with darker upper parts, and a heavier, blunter bill.
LENGTH—5.50 inches.
DISTRIBUTION—The Greater Redpoll is an inhabitant of Greenland, but with the approach of winter moves southward through Labrador, and into Massachusetts, New York, northern Illinois, Michigan, and Indiana. (Family *Fringillidae*)

Hoary Redpoll

Acanthis hornemanni exilipes [527a]

Similar to the Common Redpoll, but much whiter, and much less streaked. Rump, lower breast, and abdomen, white. Sides of body, with few dark streaks. Pinkish breast patch is more restricted than in the Common Redpoll.
LENGTH—5.00 inches.
DISTRIBUTION—The Arctic regions, descending in winter southward, infrequently as far as central Ontario, northern Illinois, and Michigan, and sometimes into central New England. (Family *Fringillidae*)

Holboell's Redpoll

Acanthis linaria holboelli [528a]

Similar to the Common Redpoll, but appreciably larger, and with a longer bill.
DISTRIBUTION—This rare Redpoll inhabits the bleak northern regions of the Northern Hemisphere; and in winter ranges southward in North America, sometimes as far as the United States, where it is infrequently found in northern New England. It is not uncommon in winter in the provinces of Ontario and Quebec.

In habits and notes, the Holboell's Redpoll is similar to its other Redpoll relatives found in North America. (Family *Fringillidae*)

Hornemann's Redpoll

Acanthis hornemanni hornemanni [527]

Similar to the Hoary Redpoll, but larger. The bill is heavier and not so sharply pointed.
LENGTH—6.00 inches.
DISTRIBUTION—In Greenland, from about 70° north, and in Iceland. In winter it is found in the Province of Quebec, and occasionally in the region of Hudson Bay, and in Ontario. (Family *Fringillidae*)

REDSHANK

Iceland Redshank

Totanus totanus robustus [253.1]

ADULT MALE AND FEMALE—Upper parts, brown, sparsely barred and more heavily spotted with darker. Lower back and rump, white. Secondaries, white. Tail, white with brown bars. Under parts, white, spotted and streaked with brown.
LENGTH—11.50 inches.
DISTRIBUTION—A bird of Iceland and the British Isles, found as a rare straggler in Greenland. (Family *Scolopacidae*)

REDSTART

American Redstart

Setophaga ruticilla [687]

ADULT MALE—Upper parts, shining black; a broad patch in the wing; a broad band across the middle of several of the outer tail-feathers; and the sides of the breast and abdomen, brilliant orange-red. Throat and upper breast, black; abdomen, white.

ADULT FEMALE—In general, grayish or brownish-olive where the male is black; and yellow or pale salmon-

yellow where the male is orange-red; except that the breast is a light slaty-gray.

LENGTH—5.41 inches.

DISTRIBUTION—From Labrador and Alaska southward over almost all of North America, except on the Pacific Coast where it is rare or absent. It winters in the West Indies, Central and South America.

The Redstart is a woodland bird, delighting in open woods, and sapling growths, but rare or absent in bushy or vine-tangled terrain. While a true Warbler, it partakes also of the habits of Flycatchers, and secures at least a third of its food on the wing. This habit displays to the best advantage its brilliantly contrasting colors of orange and black. The female is, to my mind, one of the most harmoniously colored of our native birds, with her inimitable combination of sedate grayish-brown and yellow, and is, by many observers preferred to the male. Among the Cubans the bird is known as the *candelita* or little torch. The songs of the Redstart are short, hurried, sweetly sibilant strains, resembling the notes of the Yellow Warbler, though usually much quicker, as the bird snatches a bit of song "between

bites." In this agitated activity of song and snap-and-swallow style of feeding, the bird passes its day—a sort of skip-and-dash fluster, not unknown to busy business men and women in the bustle of a large city! The songs may be reproduced by whispering between set teeth the syllables *wee se si* or *wee se wéet, se wít*. (Family *Compsothlypidae*)

Painted Redstart
Setophaga picta picta [688]

ADULT MALE AND FEMALE—Entire bird, black, except for bright red lower breast and abdomen, white eyelid, wing patch, under tail coverts, and outer tail feathers.

LENGTH—5.20 inches.

DISTRIBUTION—Southwestern North America from the mountains of Arizona and New Mexico southward through Mexico to Guatemala.

In habits this Redstart is much like its eastern representative. It is found in the mountains, among the evergreen oaks, pines, and alders, and

seems to prefer the neighborhood of springs, streams, and waterfalls. (Family *Compsothlypidae*)

ROAD-RUNNER
Road-runner
Geococcyx californianus [385]

ADULT MALE AND FEMALE—Upper parts, brownish and white streaked, darkest on the wings. Crest and upper back, washed with bluish-black, merging into a metallic greenish beyond. Tail, long and bluish-green-bronze; its tips with broad white patches, except on the middle pair of feathers. Throat, white; breast, brownish-white streaked with black. Abdomen, white. Bill and feet, large and heavy. The bare skin about the eye is orange and blue, and the head-feathers are bristle-tipped and erectile into a ragged crest. The entire plumage of the bird is coarse and harsh.

LENGTH—22.00 inches.

DISTRIBUTION—From southwestern Kansas, southern Colorado, and central California and Nevada (rarely north as far as southern Oregon), south through northern and into central Mexico.

The comical Road-runner is one of the most picturesque and astonishing birds of the dry cactus-covered ranges of the cattle country of the West. With

tail held straight out behind it, it runs with astounding speed ahead of a horse and wagon, on long stretches of roadway, easily keeping its distance; though, of course, it is no match in speed with a modern automobile. When flushed, it flies or glides a short distance, showing large white patches on the ends of the tail feathers, and prominent white crescents in the

wings. It is found in the cactus country and brushy mesas of southern California, and chaparral generally, and is not unknown among the hens about farms. Its notes remind one of the Black-billed Cuckoo's call—a series of soft cooing tones, each one a little more drawn out and lower in pitch than its predecessor. Its food consists of large insects, and other small invertebrates, and it does not at all disdain snakes. Its alarm note is a rattling, clacking *bur-r-r-r-rrrrrrr*. (Family *Cuculidae*)

ROBIN

Eastern Robin

Turdus migratorius migratorius [761]

ADULT MALE—Top of head, blackish; rest of head, darker than the back. Back, brownish-gray. A white spot above the eye, and white patches on the tips of the two outer tail feathers. Bill, yellow. Throat, white, narrowly streaked with black; the rest of the under parts (except the middle of the lower abdomen and vent region, which are white), brownish-orange.

ADULT FEMALE—Similar to the male but lighter throughout. Head, the same color as the upper parts.

LENGTH—10.00 inches.

DISTRIBUTION—The whole of eastern North America, west to Alaska and to the Rocky Mountains, and south to Virginia, and along the mountains into Georgia. In winter it is found distributed from the Northern States southward, progressively increasing in numbers. (Family *Turdidae*)

The familiar Robin was named by our English forefathers because of the general resemblance which they thought it bore to the much smaller (5.75 inches) English Robin Redbreast. The resemblance is not a very close one, and the bubbling, tinkling song of the English bird is quite different from our own. The Robin's habits and song need hardly be recorded here. Five robins of the genus *Turdus* are listed

for North America in the A.O.U. Check List of 1941. These are the:

1. Eastern Robin (above)

2. Northwestern Robin

Turdus migratorius caurinus [761c]

Similar to the Eastern Robin, but darker throughout, and with the small white tail patches very much restricted.

DISTRIBUTION—From Alaska (region of Glacier Bay) southward through the Pacific Coast region of British Columbia, into Washington. (Family *Turdidae*)

3. San Lucas Robin

Turdus confinis [762]

Similar to the Eastern Robin, but with the plumage everywhere paler.

DISTRIBUTION—Restricted to the Cape Region of Lower California. (Family *Turdidae*)

4. Southern Robin

Turdus migratorius achrusterus [761b]

Similar to the Eastern Robin, but smaller and paler.

DISTRIBUTION—In the lowlands of North and South Carolina, and Virginia. (Family *Turdidae*)

5. Western Robin

Turdus migratorius propinquus [761a]

Similar to the Eastern Robin, but with the outer tail feathers lacking the small white tips.

DISTRIBUTION—From British Columbia, south along the entire zone of the Rocky Mountains, as far as the southern part of the Mexican tableland, and west to the Pacific. In winter it is distributed from Oregon and Colorado southward, progressively increasing in abundance. (Family *Turdidae*)

ROOK

Rook

Corvus frugilegus frugilegus [490.1]

ADULT MALE AND FEMALE—Entire bird, black glossed with purple and violet; the bases of the feathers, gray. Region about the base of the bill ("face"), bare; the skin, very rough and covered with a whitish scurf. Bill and feet, black.

LENGTH—18.00 inches.

DISTRIBUTION—Europe and the British Isles; accidental in Greenland.

The Rook (to lovers of Dickens, always associated with Mr. Winkle's unhappy hunting adventure) is probably the commonest bird of the British

Isles, and one of the most popular, in general. Formerly it was regarded as a menace, and in the reign of Henry VIII, an act of Parliament was passed to provide for its extermination. Rook pie was anciently a great delicacy. (Family *Corvidae*)

RUFF

Ruff

Philomachus pugnax [260]

ADULT MALE—Plumage, black with purplish iridescence, or rusty-brown barred with purplish and other hues.

Very variable. The feathers of the breast are much elongated and form a shield of black, black and white, or rusty-brown. Two variously colored tufts of feathers arise from the hinder part of the neck.

ADULT FEMALE—Back, black marked with grayish-brown; inner wing feathers, barred with black and grayish-brown. Throat and breast, grayish. Under parts, whitish.

LENGTH—12.50 inches.

DISTRIBUTION—This European species has been recorded some twenty odd times with us. The bird strays occasionally to the Bering and Pribilof Islands, and to Greenland, Ontario, Nova Scotia, Long Island (New York), Indiana, the District of Columbia, North Carolina, Barbados, and northern South America. The male of this bird is known as the Ruff; the female as the Reeve. (Family *Scolopacidae*)

SANDERLING

Sanderling

Crocethia alba [248]

ADULT MALE AND FEMALE—Upper parts, grayish-white, with small markings of black and chestnut-brown. Rump, dark brown. Tail, grayish-brown. Sides of head, throat, neck, and breast, tinged with rusty-brown and spotted with black. Rest of under parts, white. In flight, the spread wings show a long conspicuous line of white.

LENGTH—8.00 inches.

DISTRIBUTION—This is a nearly cosmopolitan species, breeding in the Arctic and Subarctic regions, and in North America migrating through the United States to spend the winter from central California, Texas, Virginia, and Bermuda southward to Chile and Patagonia.

Sanderlings are birds of the outer beaches. They form long lines along the edge of the surf. When a wave recedes, they rush forward, following the receding line of water, probing the sand with feverish haste, and then, with the return of the next wave, retreat rapidly up the beach again. It is a very amusing and interesting habit to watch. In this way it secures much

(In winter plumage)

of its food: small crustaceans that burrow in the wet sand. Sanderlings, when in flight, display a very prominent white stripe in the wing, a more conspicuous field mark of this sort than any other bird of its kind shows. In fall plumage, the Sanderlings are the palest, or whitest of all the Sandpipers. In New England, gunners call them Whiteys. Along the beaches of New Jersey, Long Island, Connecticut, and Massachusetts they are very common migrants. Some very few may be found spending the winter on Cape Cod, and on Muskegat Island. As the birds run about the beach, their little legs "twinkling" and carrying the body along in a sort of rapid mechanical-toy fashion, they utter a sharp, high *chit* or *kit*. (Family *Scolopacidae*)

SANDPIPER FAMILY
Woodcock, Snipe, and Sandpipers
Scolopacidae

The members of this large family are mostly birds of the temperate and northern portions of the Northern

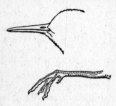

Hemisphere during their nesting seasons. They are birds of the seacoasts chiefly, though some are found inland on the shores of lakes, ponds, and wide rivers. During the nesting season they are solitary, but at migration and during the winter they are gregarious, and may be seen in large flocks on the beaches, or in flight. *Scolopacidae* are characterized by their relatively small size, generally less than twelve inches; demurely colored plumage, browns and grays, with light-colored underparts predominating; relatively long legs; short tails; rather long, flat, pointed wings; and quite long bills. The bills are peculiar in that the upper mandible is—in some species—slightly moveable at the tip. Many of the *Scolopacids* indulge in surprising courtship demonstrations, strutting, puffing, dancing, etc., and often give voice to elaborate and intricate musical performances which occasionally equal those of some of our finest song birds. About one hundred species make up this large family, of which there are fifty-six species and subspecies recorded for North America, distributed among twenty-six genera.

NESTING. The members of this great family nest on the ground, in a scantily lined depression, laying about three or four eggs, varying greatly in color, but chiefly speckled, spotted, and blotched with black, various browns, and lavenders.

SANDPIPER
Aleutian Sandpiper
Arquatella ptilocnemis couesi [235a]

ADULT MALE AND FEMALE—Upper parts, blackish, prominently marked with light yellowish-brown; wings, gray. Greater coverts edged with white, and some of the secondaries, entirely white. Upper tail coverts, sooty-brown. Outer tail feathers, ashy-gray; the inner ones sooty-brown. Throat and breast, brownish-gray, streaked with black. Abdomen, white.

Sides of the body, and the under tail coverts, streaked with brownish-gray.

LENGTH—9.00 inches.

DISTRIBUTION—On the coast of Alaska, and the adjacent Aleutian Islands. North as far as the Kowak River, and westward to the Commander Islands, Kamchatka. (Family *Scolopacidae*)

Baird's Sandpiper
Pisobia bairdi [241]

ADULT MALE AND FEMALE—Upper parts streaked and spotted with grayish, black, and buffy. Line over the eye, and the chin, white. Breast, buffy streaked with gray. Abdomen, white.
LENGTH—7.30 inches.
DISTRIBUTION—In Alaska and westward in the Arctic regions, migrating in winter through the interior of the United States into South America, and rarely seen on the Atlantic and Pacific coasts.

"During migrations Baird's Sandpipers are common, usually in small flocks, along the shores of lakes and ponds over the western prairie country." (Bailey.) (Family *Scolopacidae*)

Buff-breasted Sandpiper
Tryngites subruficollis [262]

ADULT MALE AND FEMALE—Upper parts, dull brownish-buff, marked with black or blackish. Under parts, unmarked rich light creamy-brown. The under surface of the wings are beautifully mottled and marbled with black, on a creamy white background. The bill is relatively short, less than an inch in length.
LENGTH—8.00 inches.
DISTRIBUTION—In the interior of Canada and the district of the Yukon, northward to the Arctic coast. In migration they pass through Texas and Louisiana most abundantly, on their way to Uruguay and Peru.

The Buff-breasted Sandpipers in the spring are killed in large numbers in Texas and Louisiana by pot-hunters, since they travel in closely compacted flocks, and may be brought down in showers by a single discharge. They are found in migration on sandy prai-

ries, and open places, where they feed upon grasshoppers, crickets, and other insects, and especially upon ants and their eggs. Often too, they are found

searching along the shores and shallow pools for minute molluscs, crustaceans, and aquatic insects and their larvae and nymphs. (Family *Scolopacidae*)

Commander Sandpiper
Arquatella ptilocnemis quarta [235c]

Similar in general to the Aleutian Sandpiper, but with the foreneck a somewhat darker slate color, and with less white admixture. The upper parts are more prominently marked with a brighter brown, giving to the back a quite rusty-reddish hue.

DISTRIBUTION — A Commander Island form of Sandpiper, occurring also as a casual visitant on Attu Island, of the Aleutian Archipelago. (Family *Scolopacidae*)

Curlew Sandpiper
Erolia testacea [244]

ADULT MALE AND FEMALE—Upper parts, a mixture of black, blackish, and rusty-brown. Under parts, reddish-brown. Bill, slightly decurved.
LENGTH—8.00 inches.
DISTRIBUTION — A Siberian and oriental species, occurring occasionally in Alaska, Ontario, Nova Scotia, Maine, Massachusetts, New York, and New Jersey. On Long Island it occurs as a transient visitant in the spring and fall. (Family *Scolopacidae*)

Eastern Solitary Sandpiper
Tringa solitaria solitaria [256]

ADULT MALE AND FEMALE—Upper parts, olive-brown; the head slightly streaked with black; and the back sparsely speckled with white. A dusky wash on the front of the neck. Five

pairs of outer tail feathers, white barred with black. Wing, plain, not showing a stripe of white when extended. Abdomen, white; sides of the body sometimes barred with black.

LENGTH—8.40 inches.

DISTRIBUTION — From northern Quebec to central Alberta, and south from Nebraska across to northern Pennsylvania. Winters in Florida, and southward into South America.

The Solitary Sandpiper is the only one (except the Spotted Sandpiper) which is regularly found away from the seacoast, along the borders of streams and inland bodies of water. It delights in muddy shoals and shores, where it steps daintily around, nodding its head and neck (but not teetering its tail) as it goes. When it flies it shows a great expanse of white in the spread tail, but no line of white in the spread wing. Both of these features serve to distinguish it from the Spotted Sandpiper, which it resembles. It rises higher in its flight than does the Spotted Sandpiper, and its process is irregular. One sees the bird more often along wooded ponds than elsewhere; the Spotted Sandpiper is more

a bird of bodies of water and streams in open places. The notes of the Solitary Sandpiper are a faint sweet *tweet tweet,* clear and musical, but distinctly and incisively uttered. They resemble the notes of the Spotted Sandpiper, but are given only seldom, and then usually as the bird takes off in flight. (Family *Scolopacidae*)

Least Sandpiper
Pisobia minutilla [242]

ADULT MALE AND FEMALE—Similar to the Semipalmated Sandpiper, but with more chestnut-brown color in the upper parts; greenish-yellow legs; and a slenderer, somewhat longer bill. The breast also is often slightly more heavily streaked.

LENGTH—6.00 inches.

DISTRIBUTION—From Sable Island and Newfoundland to northwestern Alaska. In winter it migrates through the southern parts of Canada and through the United States to North Carolina, Texas, southern California, and southward.

In habits and appearance this Sandpiper is similar to the Semipalmated species, which see. It is slightly less common in New England and along the Atlantic Coast, and also a little smaller than the Semipalmated. In fact, as its name implies, it is the smallest of our Sandpipers. It is more often found inland than the Semi-

palmated species, and usually occurs in grassy, low, wet meadows, and along the borders of inland ponds and rivers. Because of this the bird is frequently called Meadow Oxeye. Its common call note is more peeping than that of its Semipalmated cousin, sometimes having an almost petulant quality. (Family *Scolopacidae*)

Pectoral Sandpiper
Pisobia melanotos [239]

ADULT MALE AND FEMALE—Upper parts, grayish washed with rusty brown, and speckled with brownish-black. Rump and the base of the tail, dark sooty-brown, tipped with light reddish-brown. The outer tail feathers

are somewhat lighter than the central ones. Sides of the neck, and the breast, pale buffy streaked with gray. Abdomen, white.

LENGTH—9.00 inches; female smaller than the male.

DISTRIBUTION—In North America breeding in the Arctic regions, and in winter migrating to South America, rarely passing along the Pacific Coast.

The Pectoral Sandpiper, Krieker, or Grass Bird, is an inhabitant of grassy marshes, and is rarely seen on sandy beaches, bars, or mud flats. When disturbed the birds squat flat, and are difficult to flush. When they do arise, they spring into the air, making off with a harsh, sharp *kriek-kriek*. Both male and female birds may be fairly well described as larger replicas of the

Least Sandpiper. (Family *Scolopacidae*)

Pribilof Sandpiper
Arquatella ptilocnemis ptilocnemis [235b]

Somewhat similar to the Aleutian Sandpiper, but with a much lighter crown, and with the lower breast bearing an irregular black patch.

LENGTH—10.00 inches.

DISTRIBUTION—Breeds in the Pribilof Islands, and migrates to the adjacent coast, spreading southward south of Norton Sound, Alaska. (Family *Scolopacidae*)

Purple Sandpiper
Arquatella maritima [235]

Similar to the Aleutian Sandpiper, but darker, grayer, and with less light yellowish-brown markings in the upper parts.

LENGTH—9.00 inches.

DISTRIBUTION—Through the northern portions of the Northern Hemisphere, and in North America chiefly in the northeastern region, from far north, migrating in winter into the Eastern and Middle States, the Great Lakes region, and the Upper Mississippi Valley. It occurs casually in Florida.

The Purple Sandpiper, often called the Winter Snipe by gunners, is found

in small flocks, feeding on the rocks of shores, or outlying rocky islets. Its figure is short and squat, and its note a whistling twitter. (Family *Scolopacidae*)

Red-backed Sandpiper

Pelidna alpina sakhalina [243a]

ADULT MALE AND FEMALE—Upper parts, grayish; the feathers broadly edged with reddish-brown and marked with black. Wings, brownish-gray. Breast, whitish and faintly streaked

with blackish. Middle of abdomen bears a large black patch. Lower abdomen, white.

LENGTH—8.00 inches.

DISTRIBUTION—Arctic regions in North America. In winter it is found from California and the Gulf States southward to South America.

This American bird (also called by the Old World name of Dunlin) occurs on mud flats, and outer sandy beaches; often in company with the Sanderlings. Infrequently it may be seen in grassy marshes. In breeding plumage the birds are known as Redbacks; in winter plumage as Leadbacks. Their notes are soft, and may be written *peurr, peurr*. When disturbed they fly off with a sharp *chittit, chitit* (Family *Scolopacidae*)

Rufous-necked Sandpiper

Pisobia ruficollis [242.2]

ADULT MALE AND FEMALE—Upper parts, brownish and streaked; the head, darker and streaked with black.

Collar, brown and black-streaked. Under parts, dark brown. Feet, black.

DISTRIBUTION—Found in northeastern Siberia and northwestern Alaska. (Family *Scolopacidae*)

Semipalmated Sandpiper

Ereunetes pusillus [246]

ADULT MALE AND FEMALE—Upper parts, brownish-gray mixed with black and blackish. Rump, grayish-brown. Upper tail coverts, blackish. Central tail feathers, darker than the others. Breast, faintly streaked or finely spotted with blackish. Abdomen, white. Legs, black or blackish.

LENGTH—6.30 inches.

DISTRIBUTION—Confined to eastern North America, breeding in the Arctic regions, and wintering from the Gulf States southward into South America.

These delicate little Sandpipers occur in large numbers along the seacoast, as well as on the shores of inland lakes, where they are often associated with other members of their family, particularly with the very similar Least Sandpipers. Least and Semipalmated Sandpipers are often indiscriminately called Peeps, from their common note. They run about in agitated fashion, feeding with nervous haste, probing

their bills rapidly into the sand, and keeping well together in compact companies. From their closely similar relatives, the Least Sandpipers, the Semipalmated species may be distinguished by their slightly grayer upper parts, and especially by their black or blackish, instead of greenish-yellow, legs. Also the bill is shorter and somewhat thicker, though this is a less usable character in the field than the leg color. This is the commonest of the smaller Sandpipers on our eastern coast. Even though this little bird becomes very plump and fat when food is abundant, it is not often killed for its flesh, except by those in keen need of food. The name Semipalmated refers to the toes, which are only partially webbed. (Family *Scolopacidae*)

Sharp-tailed Sandpiper
Pisobia acuminata [238]

ADULT MALE AND FEMALE—Upper parts, mixed brown and black; wings, darker. Line over the eye, white. Breast, buffy streaked with blackish. Abdomen, white. Tail feathers, pointed.
LENGTH—8.70 inches.
DISTRIBUTION—This eastern Asiatic form (migrating to Java and Australia) is found on the coast·of Alaska. (Family *Scolopacidae*)

Spoon-bill Sandpiper
Eurynorhynchus pygmeus [245]

ADULT MALE AND FEMALE—Upper parts, brown; under parts, white. Bill, spoon-shaped near the tip.
DISTRIBUTION—This oriental species occurs as a rare straggler on Choris Peninsula and Wainwright Island, Alaska. (Family *Scolopacidae*)

Spotted Sandpiper
Actitis macularia [263]

ADULT MALE AND FEMALE—Upper parts, light brown; head, slightly streaked and back slightly spotted with black. Under parts, white, everywhere bearing round black or blackish spots. When the wing is spread in flight it shows a fairly conspicuous whitish

stripe. Outer tail feathers, barred with white.
LENGTH—7.50 inches.
DISTRIBUTION—North America generally, as far north as the latitude of Hudson Bay. In winter it is found from southern British Columbia, diagonally down to Louisiana and South Carolina; and to South America and sparingly into Argentina.

The little Spotted Sandpiper, Peep, or Teeter-tail, as it is called, is a very common bird in the summer along the

coast, and also along the borders of streams, ponds, and lakes. This is the species usually seen teetering along the edges of ponds and rivers in summer, starting up with a shrill *peet-weet, peet-weet, peet-weet;* curving gracefully along the windings of streams until it suddenly turns and comes to rest on some little sand bar just hidden by a bend in the bank. It runs along very rapidly, just at the water line, and when it pauses, suddenly disappears from sight because of its very effective obliterative coloration. From its habit of balancing or teetering as it stands still (which it seldom does), it derives its name of Teeter-tail. The young birds are difficult of identification, since their under parts are pure white, without markings. The very round, prominent spo´ on the under parts of the adult birds are plainly visible. The Spotted and the Solitary Sandpipers are closely alike, but the Solitary shows much more white in the tail, and the Spotted shows a fairly prominent white line in the extended wing. (Family *Scolopacidae*)

Stilt Sandpiper
Micropalama himantopus [233]

ADULT MALE AND FEMALE—Upper parts, mixed gray, black, blackish, brown, and white. Head, lighter with light reddish-brown markings. Under parts, whitish. Breast, streaked; and

abdomen brokenly cross-barred with black. Legs, greenish-yellow or dull olive-green.

LENGTH—8.25 inches.

DISTRIBUTION—Breeds within the Arctic circle, and migrates through eastern North America to spend the winter from Florida into South America.

The Stilt Sandpiper is a bird both of the beaches and the marshes, and in the latter situation is often seen in company with the Yellow Legs, which it resembles both in behavior and appearance. Its legs, however, are a duller, more olive color, and the bird itself is appreciably smaller. (Family *Scolopacidae*)

Western Sandpiper
Ereunetes mauri [247]

ADULT MALE AND FEMALE—Upper parts, bright chestnut-brown mottled with black and gray; sides of head, grayish, with the ear coverts bright chestnut. Breast, thickly spotted with dusky. Abdomen, white.

LENGTH—6.50 inches.

DISTRIBUTION—In British America and Alaska. In the fall it passes through western North America to Central and South America. Infrequently it is seen in migration on the Atlantic Coast. (Family *Scolopacidae*)

Western Solitary Sandpiper
Tringa solitaria cinnamomea [256a]

Similar in general to the Eastern Solitary Sandpiper, but with the spottings of the back cinnamon brown instead of creamy or white, and with the sides of the face lighter. Slightly larger than the eastern form.

DISTRIBUTION—In western North America. In migration moving southward through the Great Basin and the Pacific Coast region, and wintering from Lower California southward.

In its habits, as well as in its general appearance, this western subspecies of the Solitary Sandpiper is virtually the counterpart of its eastern relative. (Family *Scolopacidae*)

White-rumped Sandpiper
Pisobia fuscicollis [240]

ADULT MALE AND FEMALE—Upper parts, brownish-gray spotted with black. Base of tail, pure white. Sides

of the head, neck, and breast, streaked with gray. Under parts, white.

LENGTH—7.50 inches.

DISTRIBUTION—Found breeding in the interior of North America north of Hudson Bay, and migrating, chiefly through the east, to southern South America.

This delicate little Sandpiper is to be encountered on sandy beaches, mud flats, and pools bordered with marsh, where it often consorts with other small Sandpipers. (Family *Scolopacidae*)

Wood Sandpiper
Rhyacophilus glareola [257.1]

ADULT MALE AND FEMALE—Upper parts, brownish tinged with olive-green. Head and upper part of neck, streaked with white. Back and wings, spotted with white. Upper tail coverts, white marked with brown; rump, narrowly white. Tail, white with narrow brown bars. Under parts, white; throat and breast streaked with dusky-brown. LENGTH—9.00 inches.
DISTRIBUTION—A European species, straggling to eastern North America. (Family *Scolopacidae*)

SAPSUCKER
Natalie's Sapsucker
Sphyrapicus thyroideus nataliae [404a]

Similar to the Williamson's Sapsucker, but with the under parts more like those of the Yellow-bellied Sapsucker, and with the upper parts more definitely barred with black and white.
DISTRIBUTION—In the forests of the higher Rocky Mountains, from Montana to central Arizona, and New Mexico. In winter it is found from the southern portion of New Mexico and western Texas south into Mexico. (Family *Picidae*)

Northern Red-breasted Sapsucker
Sphyrapicus varius ruber [403a]

Similar to the Southern Red-breasted Sapsucker, but with all the colors deeper and more brilliant.

DISTRIBUTION—From southern Alaska southward along the Pacific

Coast region into the Santa Cruz Mountains of California. (Family *Picidae*)

Red-naped Sapsucker
Sphyrapicus varius nuchalis [402a]

Similar to the Yellow-bellied Sapsucker, but slightly larger, and with the nape-band brilliant red. The red of the throat reaches around toward the side of the neck. Female similar, but with white throat.
DISTRIBUTION—From British Columbia southward into Colorado and northeastern California, keeping to the Rocky Mountain region. In winter it is found from southern California to northwestern Mexico. (Family *Picidae*)

Southern Red-breasted Sapsucker
Sphyrapicus varius daggetti [403]

Somewhat similar to the Yellow-bellied Sapsucker, but with the crown, entire throat, and the breast, dull red.
DISTRIBUTION—In the mountainous regions from southern Oregon south into northern Lower California. (Family *Picidae*)

Williamson's Sapsucker

Sphyrapicus thyroideus thyroideus
[404]

ADULT MALE—Upper parts, jet black. Rump, large patch on wing coverts, fine spots on wing quills, and

two stripes on the side of the head, white. Throat and breast, black with a median stripe of bright red; abdomen, bright yellow.

ADULT FEMALE—Entire bird barred with brown, or with black and white. Head, brown; rump, white. Throat, sometimes with a red median stripe; and the upper breast, sometimes with a black patch. Middle of the abdomen, yellow.

LENGTH—9.37 inches.

DISTRIBUTION—In the higher mountain regions of western North America from southern British Columbia and Wyoming south as far as northern New Mexico and southeastern California. In winter from southern California and western Texas into Mexico. (Family *Picidae*)

Yellow-bellied Sapsucker

Sphyrapicus varius varius [402]

ADULT MALE — Back irregularly barred with black and yellowish-white. Wing feathers spotted with white, their coverts largely white. Crown and

throat, deep red; a white line from the base of the bill passes below the eye; another from above the eye passes backward to the side of the crown, and then downward toward the shoulder. Middle tail feathers with broken black bars, the outer ones margined with white. Upper breast, black; sides of breast and abdomen, white barred with black. Rest of under parts, pale yellow.

ADULT FEMALE—Similar, but with a white throat, and broken white bars on the outer tail feathers.

LENGTH—8.56 inches.

DISTRIBUTION—From about the latitude of the Great Slave Lake south into central New England and northern Illinois, and along the Allegheny Mountains into northwestern Georgia. In winter it is found from southern Illinois and southern Virginia southward into northwestern Mexico.

In the spring, Sapsuckers are noisy, jovial birds, uttering their screaming notes many times in succession. During the fall, however, they are quiet

and reserved, giving vent, only infrequently, to an insignificant mewing call, not likely to attract attention. Sapsuckers do not live chiefly upon sap, as some suppose, but feed to a large extent upon ants and, strangely enough, upon wild fruits. The birds girdle tree trunks with rings of small holes and from them drink the exuding sap, as well as eat some of the cambium of the trees. Old apple trees are the ones most frequently ringed by the Sapsuckers, but other trees are tapped as well, some of the favorites being pear, birch, white ash, maple, and even hickory. (Family *Picidae*)

SCOTER

American Scoter
Oidemia americana [163]

ADULT MALE—Entire bird, black; with the base of the upper mandible, orange or orange-yellow.

ADULT FEMALE—Upper parts, grayish-brown; cheeks, broadly grayish, white, or whitish. Upper breast and sides of the body, grayish-brown. Lower breast and abdomen, white or whitish, faintly barred with grayish-brown.

LENGTH—19.00 inches.

DISTRIBUTION—From Labrador to Alaska along the Bering Sea coast, and northward. In winter it spreads south to Colorado, California, and eastward to the Great Lakes, and along the Atlantic Coast from Maine southward to South Carolina and Florida.

The American Scoter is the smallest of our species, and resembles, at a

distance, the Black Duck, in whose company it is often found. The Black Duck, however, does not dive, and

when in flight shows a whitish under surface to the wings. (Family *Anatidae*)

Surf Scoter
Melanitta perspicillata [166]

Similar to the American Scoter, but differing chiefly in possessing a large white patch on the nape, and a white crown-spot. Bill, orange, yellow, and

white. Female is similar to the female of the White-winged Scoter, but with less whitish on the head, and with no speculum. Feet of both sexes, orange.

DISTRIBUTION — From Newfoundland northward. In winter it extends along the coast as far as Florida, and inland to Illinois. Westward it reaches Lower California. (Family *Anatidae*)

Velvet Scoter
Melanitta fusca [164]

ADULT MALE—Entire bird, velvet-black, except for a white seculum in the wing, and a small white patch behind the eye. Bill, orange-yellow and swollen and black at its base. Legs and toes, orange; webs, black.

ADULT FEMALE—Dusky brown, with a grayish white patch before the eye, and a similar but smaller one behind it. Speculum duller than in the male.

LENGTH—22.00 inches.

DISTRIBUTION—This northern European species of Scoter has been reported from Greenland. It is similar in habits and in general appearance to the American Scoter. Its plumage, however, shows a rich velvety sheen. (Family *Anatidae*)

White-winged Scoter
Melanitta deglandi [165]

ADULT MALE—Plumage, black, except for a prominent white speculum in the wing, a white spot below the eye, and a grayish-brown zone on the sides of the body. Bill, orange; its base, black. Feet and legs, orange.

ADULT FEMALE — Grayish-brown; speculum, white; spot on the auricular region and at base of bill, whitish. Under parts, light grayish-brown. Bill, dark.

LENGTH—22.00 inches.

DISTRIBUTION—From Labrador and North Dakota northward. In winter it is found from Virginia across to Illinois and into Lower California.

This is the most abundant species of Scoter off the coast of southern New England and southward during the

winter months. It is associated with the other Scoters, and with the Black Duck at this season. In the autumn the White-wing also is found in the valley of the Connecticut and Hudson rivers, and on inland lakes and large ponds. Scoters feed in shallow water, and dine continually. (Family *Anatidae*)

SEEDEATER
Sharpe's Seedeater

Sporophila morelleti sharpei [602]

ADULT MALE—Upper parts, and a band across the breast, black. Patches in the wing, the sides of the neck, the rump, and the under parts, white.

ADULT FEMALE—Upper parts, grayish-brown; the wings slightly darker, and bearing two light yellowish-brown bars. Under parts, light yellowish-brown or buffy.

LENGTH—4.60 inches.

DISTRIBUTION — From the southeastern portion of Texas southward into eastern Mexico.

This diminutive, camouflage-patterned little *Fringillid* is to be found inhabiting bushy and weedy regions throughout its range. (Family *Fringillidae*)

SHEARWATER FAMILY
Shearwaters, Fulmars, and Petrels
Procellariidae

This large family, numbering about eighty species and subspecies, is, in general, a group of light-plumaged, gull-like birds, dwellers on all the seas, and possessed of extraordinary powers of flight. They are not found inland unless driven far out of their natural habitat by severe storms. The Shearwaters are usually mistaken for Gulls. They breed on the islands of the southern oceans, and come northward off our coasts in summer. The Petrels (not to be confused with the Storm Petrels of the Family *Hydrobatidae*) are similar to Shearwaters; they possess longer wings and tail, and hence are more graceful birds in flight. The Fulmars exhibit in their flight something almost of the ease and grace of Albatrosses, and in this respect differ markedly from the Shearwaters and Petrels. The Family *Procellariidae*, as a whole, is characterized by the large bill, slightly hooked at its tip; by nostrils opening to the exterior through tubes; by a short tail; by long pointed wings; and by three webbed toes. The fourth toe is either small or absent. So much fat is stored in the bodies of these birds that sailors have often burned them as torches. Fifteen species and subspecies of Shearwaters are found in the waters off the North American coasts, grouped into three genera, *Puffinus, Thyellodroma,* and *Adamastor.* Five species of Petrels are similarly found, allocated to three genera, *Pterodroma, Bulweria,* and *Daption.* Only one species of Fulmar occurs, represented by two subspecies in the genus *Fulmarus.*

NESTING. These birds carry out their nesting on cliffs, on the bare ground, or in the turf; sometimes under a projection, sometimes on the bare rock in open view, or sometimes in a slight depression in the soil. Occasionally the nest is scantily lined with a few grasses. Infrequently the nest is in a

burrow in the ground, in a small rocky cave, or in a crevice in a cliff. The single egg is chalky white in color, though sometimes a smooth vitreous white, and often stained by its contact with the soil.

SHEARWATER
Allied Shearwater
Puffinus assimilis baroli [92.1]

Similar to the Manx Shearwater, but smaller.

DISTRIBUTION — Eastern Atlantic; occurs as an accidental straggler on Sable Island, Nova Scotia, and on Sullivan's Island, South Carolina. (Family *Procellariidae*)

Audubon's Shearwater
Puffinus lherminieri lherminieri [92]

ADULT MALE AND FEMALE—Upper parts, sooty-black; under parts, white

washed on the sides of the breast with grayish. Under tail coverts and a patch on the flanks, sooty-brown.

LENGTH—12.00 inches.

DISTRIBUTION—Long Island, along

coast southward to the West Indies and Bahamas. (Family *Procellariidae*)

Black-tailed Shearwater
Adamastor cinereus [97]

In general similar to the Cory's Shearwater. Upper parts, ashy-gray; tail, black. Under parts, white. Bill, yellowish. Feet, bluish-slate.

DISTRIBUTION—This species occurs only as an accidental straggler off the coast of California in the region of Monterey. (Family *Procellariidae*)

Black-vented Shearwater
Puffinus opisthomelas [93]

ADULT MALE AND FEMALE—Upper parts, sooty-gray, fading slightly on neck and head. Under parts, white; under tail coverts, sooty-gray.

LENGTH—13.62 inches.

DISTRIBUTION—In the Pacific Ocean along the coast of Lower California and Mexico, and migrating northward to California and Vancouver Island, British Columbia.

Flocks of many thousands of these Shearwaters are often seen off the California coast, resting on the surface in calm weather, or flying in large circles or swirls when the wind is strong. It is only occasionally that they straggle as far north as the southern part of the British Columbia coast. (Family *Procellariidae*)

Cory's Shearwater
Puffinus diomedea borealis [88]

ADULT MALE AND FEMALE—Upper parts, ashy-brown; wings and tail somewhat darker. Sides of head and neck, light ashy-brown. Under parts, white, faintly tinged on the breast with gray. The under tail coverts mottled with gray. Bill, yellow or yellowish.
LENGTH—21.00 inches.
DISTRIBUTION—In the North Atlantic off the coast of Massachusetts and Long Island, New York, south to about the latitude of Virginia, and west to the coast of Brazil. (Family *Procellariidae*)

Greater Shearwater
Puffinus gravis [89]

ADULT MALE AND FEMALE—Upper parts, dark sooty-brown; a white band

across the middle of the tail. Bill, blackish. Under parts, white.
LENGTH—20.00 inches.
DISTRIBUTION—All along the Atlantic Coast of the Americas, from the Arctic Circle south to Cape Horn.

From May to September the Greater Shearwater is a common summer visit-
ant to our Atlantic Coast. Travellers across the Atlantic in summer see countless thousands of these birds, skimming gracefully over the tops of the waves, or floating upon the water. They congregate in large flocks about fishing boats, but do not follow passenger steamers as do the Gulls. (Family *Procellariidae*)

Manx Shearwater
Puffinus puffinus puffinus [90]

Similar to the Audubon's Shearwater, but larger, and with a shorter tail.
DISTRIBUTION — Eastern Atlantic. Occurs as an accidental straggler in Greenland and on Long Island, New York. (Family *Procellariidae*)

Mediterranean Shearwater
Puffinus diomedea diomedea [88a]

This is the Old World representative of Cory's Shearwater, which it resembles.
DISTRIBUTION—Occurs as an accidental straggler on Long Island, New York. (Family *Procellariidae*)

New Zealand Shearwater
Thyellodroma bulleri [96.2]

ADULT MALE AND FEMALE—Head, lesser wing coverts, and tail, black. Mantle, gray. Greater wing coverts, gray tipped with white. Outer primaries, black; two thirds of their inner webs, white. Cheeks mottled with grayish-white. Under parts, white.
LENGTH—16.50 inches.
DISTRIBUTION—"New Zealand seas east and north over the Pacific to the coast of Chile, and in small numbers in autumn, off the coast of California (Pt. Pinos) and British Columbia. Breeds on Mokohinu Island, New Zealand." (A.O.U. Check List.)

This is our only Shearwater with a gray mantle in striking contrast to the black head and tail. Bailey says of this unusual Shearwater, "Mr. Loomis secured a specimen of" this Shearwater "about six miles west of Point Pinos [California] on November 6, 1896. As this was the fourth of the species known to science, and the others had come from New Zealand seas, the record is of great interest, and . . . suggests that persistent observations along the Pacific Coast may add largely to the list of pelagic wanderers from the southern seas." (Family *Procellariidae*)

Pale-footed Shearwater
Puffinus carneipes [95.1]

ADULT MALE AND FEMALE—Entire plumage, a rich chocolate-black. Bill, fleshy-white; its culmen and the tips of the mandibles, brown. Legs and feet, a yellowish-flesh color.

DISTRIBUTION—This species is a rare straggler to the coast of California. (Family *Procellariidae*)

Pink-footed Shearwater
Puffinus creatopus [91]

ADULT MALE AND FEMALE—Upper parts, brownish-gray. Under parts, white; sides of body and lower abdomen, grayish. Bill, yellowish; feet and legs, flesh color.

LENGTH—19.00 inches.

DISTRIBUTION — Along the Pacific Coast from the latitude of Monterey, California, south to the coast of Chile, South America. (Family *Procellariidae*)

Slender-billed Shearwater
Puffinus tenuirostris [96]

ADULT MALE AND FEMALE—Plumage, entirely sooty-brown or blackish, paling on the throat. Under wing coverts, white. Bill, relatively small, slender, and sharp.

LENGTH—13.00 inches.

DISTRIBUTION — From the Bering Sea eastward to the coast of North America from Sitka, Alaska, to southern California. (Family *Procellariidae*)

Sooty Shearwater
Puffinus griseus [95]

ADULT MALE AND FEMALE—Upper parts, dark sooty; bill, blackish. Under

parts, light sooty. At a distance it looks uniformly black.

LENGTH—17.00 inches.

DISTRIBUTION — In summer along the north Atlantic coast, from South Carolina northward. In winter it retreats to the Southern Hemisphere. (Family *Procellariidae*)

Townsend's Shearwater
Puffinus auricularis [93.1]

Similar to the Black-vented Shearwater, but much darker (nearly black) on the upper parts, and with smaller feet and bill.

DISTRIBUTION — Pacific Coast of southernmost Lower California, and southward. (Family *Procellariidae*)

Wedge-tailed Shearwater
Thyellodroma cuneata [96.1]

ADULT MALE AND FEMALE—Upper parts, dusky-brown; sides of the neck, mottled gray and white. Middle tail feathers, elongated. Under parts, white.

LENGTH—17.00 inches.

DISTRIBUTION—"North Pacific Ocean, from the Hawaiian Islands north to the Bonin Group and Lower California." (A.O.U. Check List.) (Family *Procellariidae*)

SHELD-DUCK

Sheld-duck

Tadorna tadorna [141.2]

ADULT MALE—Back, wing coverts, upper breast and under parts, white. Head, neck, and speculum, green. Scapulars, black. Breast, chestnut brown. Bill with a red knob at its base.

ADULT FEMALE—Similar to the male, but duller, and without the red knob on the bill. Legs and feet, flesh-color.

LENGTH—26.00 inches.

DISTRIBUTION—This British and European species is accidental in Ipswich Bay, Massachusetts.

These curious birds seem to form a connecting link between the Ducks and the Geese. The name Sheld means

parti-colored. The males and females are much alike in color and in pattern. The male does not change color. Both sexes assist in the rearing of the young. (Family *Anatidae*)

SHELDRAKE

Ruddy Sheldrake

Casarca ferruginea [141.1]

ADULT MALE — Plumage, orange-brownish; neck ring, black. Wing cov-

erts, white; speculum, coppery-green. Rump, upper tail coverts, and tail, black. Bill, legs, and feet, black.

ADULT FEMALE—Similar to the male, but paler, without the neck ring, and much whiter on the head.

LENGTH—26.00 inches.

DISTRIBUTION—This central European and Asiatic species is a rare

wanderer to the British Isles, and is an accidental straggler to Greenland, and, on our continent, to New Jersey and North Carolina. (Family *Anatidae*)

SHOVELLER

Shoveller

Spatula clypeata [142]

ADULT MALE—Back, dark brown. Head and neck, dark bluish-green, iridescent. Lower neck and breast, pure white. Scapulars and wings, largely white; their tips, black. Speculum, green. Lower breast and abdomen, bronzy chestnut-brown. Tail with white outer feathers. Bill, broad near the tip, and like a shovel. Legs, orange or brownish.

ADULT FEMALE—Upper parts, light brown marked with darker; under parts, lighter. Speculum somewhat similar to the male's.

LENGTH—20.00 inches.

DISTRIBUTION—Over the Northern Hemisphere, but in North America from Alaska and northwestern Canada, through British Columbia and Minnesota south to Texas, chiefly in the interior. In winter it is found from British Columbia, Illinois, eastward to Maryland, and southward into northern South America.

Shoveller Ducks paddle and sail about in the shallow waters of ponds, swamps, and the like, scooping up mud and vegetation in their flattened spoon-like bills, straining the mud and water out at the sides, and swallowing the soft vegetable material thus separated out. The edges of the bill are provided with a fringe of closely set bristles, which act as a very effective strainer. It often skims the surface of the water for floating food, or tips up and stands on its head in the shallows, while it guzzles in the delectable mud below. It is a rather quiet bird, its low quack sounding more like the syllables, *coook, coook*. They are

usually seen in small flocks, or in pairs, paddling about in friendly fashion, with deliberate movements. Reports as to their desirability for the table vary. Some say that the birds are lean and scrawny, making a poor stringy dish; others state that they are fairly good; but all agree that they

are never very fat, except in winter. (Family *Anatidae*)

SHRIKE FAMILY
Laniidae

The Shrikes, often called the Butcher Birds because of their habit of impaling their prey on thorns, barbs of a fence, sharp splinters, and the like, are true song birds. Their bills are

hooked at the tip, like the bills of miniature hawks, and well adapted for seizing and tearing their prey which consists of small mammals (such as various species of mice and shrews); small birds (such as chickadees, kinglets, the smaller sparrows and warblers, etc.); small frogs and reptiles; and large insects such as grasshoppers, crickets, and large beetles. The plumage is predominantly gray, black, and white, and the birds are sometimes confused with the Mockingbird. The tail is relatively long and rounded at its tip; the wings are short and not pointed. The Shrikes are a large family, well represented in the Old World. In North America eight species and subspecies are found, contained in the single genus *Lanius*.

NESTING. The nests of Shrikes are to be found in thickly branched trees, often among impenetrable tangles of thorny twigs, or in a mass of interlacing vines. They are rather bulky structures composed of twigs, leaf- and weed-stems, grasses and leaves, and lined with soft dry grasses, mosses, and feathers. The eggs number from four to six or seven, and are grayish, greenish, or bluish-green, sometimes deeper, sometimes paler, and spotted or blotched with browns, lavenders, grays, and purples.

SHRIKE

California Shrike
Lanius ludovicianus gambeli [622b]

Similar to the Northern Shrike, but with upper tail coverts light gray, and under parts more brownish.

DISTRIBUTION — From British Columbia down along the Pacific Coast as far as Lower California.

"Mr. Grinnell says that the California Shrike is such a persistent destroyer of the Jerusalem Cricket, and other injurious insects, that it is undoubtedly one of our most beneficial birds from the agriculturalist's standpoint, and should be protected." (Bailey.) (Family *Laniidae*)

Island Shrike
Lanius ludovicianus anthonyi [622c]

Similar to the California Shrike, but smaller and generally darker; the under parts, gray, fading to white on the throat and vent, and the white patches in the wings and tail much reduced.

LENGTH—8.77 inches.

DISTRIBUTION—Restricted to the Santa Barbara Islands of California. (Family *Laniidae*)

Loggerhead Shrike
Lanius ludovicianus ludovicianus [622]

Similar to the Northern Shrike, but with the under parts without bars.

DISTRIBUTION—The Eastern States generally, and Canada from British Columbia to Maine, and southward through Massachusetts and western Pennsylvania into the Mississippi Valley, Virginia and Florida. It spends its winters in the Southern States. (Family *Laniidae*)

Migrant Shrike
Lanius ludovicianus migrans [622e]

Similar to the Northern Shrike, but not lighter on the forehead, and with

the black eye bands meeting over the top of the base of the bill. Bill, entirely black.

LENGTH—9.00 inches.

DISTRIBUTION—From southeastern Manitoba through Wisconsin and

Michigan to Maine, Quebec, and New Brunswick. South to Texas, and east to Virginia. It spends its winters in the Mississippi Valley and Texas. (Family *Laniidae*)

Nelson's Shrike
Lanius ludovicianus nelsoni [622f]

Resembles the California Shrike, but with slightly darker upper parts; the upper tail coverts, more whitish (paler); and the under parts, grayer, particularly on the lower abdomen and under tail coverts.

DISTRIBUTION—The lower half of the peninsula of Lower California to the Cape district; also on Santa Margarita Island. (Family *Laniidae*)

Northern Shrike
Lanius borealis borealis [621]

ADULT MALE AND FEMALE—Upper parts, gray; lighter on the forehead and over the eye. A broad black band from the base of the bill extends behind the eye. Wings and tail marked with black and white, which show prominently during flight. Upper tail coverts, grayish. Under parts, grayish-white, thickly crossed by fine wavy brownish lines. The bill, heavy with its upper mandible hooked at the tip, and black in color, except for the basal portion of the lower mandible, which is horn or flesh color.

LENGTH—10.32 inches.

DISTRIBUTION—Canada, south to southern Ontario and Quebec, spreading southward in winter to Virginia, Kansas, Arizona, and California.

The Shrike, or Butcher Bird, is an extremely swift and acrobatic flyer. Dashing after some small bird, it finally overtakes its prey, bears it to the

ground, and kills it by repeated blows. Its favorite perch is the topmost twig of a tree, whence it scans the country round about. The Shrike is a most accomplished songster—giving voice to a sweet, varied, warbled strain, interspersed with Catbird-like notes. Its white, black, and gray plumage makes it easy of identification in the field. A peculiar habit of Shrikes is the impaling of prey on thorns, on sharp twigs, or on the barbs of a wire fence. (Family *Laniidae*)

Northwestern Shrike
Lanius borealis invictus [621a]

Similar to the Northern Shrike, but larger; the upper parts paler, and the white wing markings more expanded.

DISTRIBUTION—From Northwestern Alaska and Mackenzie southward to the extreme northern part of British Columbia, Alberta, and Saskatchewan. In winter it straggles irregularly south

as far as northern California, Arizona, New Mexico, and Texas, and eastward into Minnesota. (Family *Laniidae*)

White-rumped Shrike
Lanius ludovicianus excubitorides [622a]

Similar to the Northern Shrike, but with plain white under parts. Rump, paler.

DISTRIBUTION—From Manitoba and Saskatchewan southward to the tablelands of Mexico, along the zone from the eastern edge of the Great Plains to (but not including) the Pacific coastal region. (Family *Laniidae*)

SILKY FLYCATCHER FAMILY
Ptilogonatidae

These birds are similar to the Waxwings (Family *Bombycillidae*) in their general habits, but possess rounded wings, bristles at the base of the bill, and naked nostrils. There are but four known species of these birds, confined to Central America and Mexico. One of these, the curious Phainopepla

(*Phainopepla nitens lepida*) occurs within the borders of the United States.

NESTING. Silky Flycatchers' nests are rather loosely constructed affairs composed of twigs, and sometimes of weed stems and mosses. They are lined with fine plant materials, and may be found among the branches of a large tree or bush, ordinarily from about ten to twenty feet from the ground. The birds prefer a country abounding in thickets, or often open woodlands, generally not far removed from water. The two or three eggs are a dull whitish or light gray, spotted with black.

SISKIN
Mexican Pine Siskin
Spinus pinus macropterus [533a]

Somewhat similar to the Northern Pine Siskin, but with the under parts paler, and less heavily streaked.

LENGTH—5.00 inches.

DISTRIBUTION—In the higher mountains of southern Mexico, and also in the Sierra San Pedro Martir, and in the Sierra Juarez of Lower California. (Family *Fringillidae*)

Northern Pine Siskin
Spinus pinus pinus [533]

ADULT MALE AND FEMALE—Upper parts, grayish; the feathers margined with brown and streaked with black. Wings, brownish; the feathers edged with yellow, and with bright yellow bases. Tail, brown; all but the middle feathers bright yellow at their basal halves, and prominent when the tail is spread. Under parts, grayish-white heavily streaked with black.

LENGTH—5.00 inches.

DISTRIBUTION—North America, from Alaska southward to our northern states, and along the Rocky and Sierra mountains southward to Mexico; and along the Allegheny Mountains southward into North Carolina. It spends the winter in the United States southward to the Gulf of Mexico, and into Lower California.

Pine Siskins are erratic and variable in their migratory movements, and rove about the country in small flocks, often in company with troops of their congeners, the Goldfinches, which they somewhat resemble in appearance, notes, habits, and undulatory flight.

They are to be found most commonly in spruces, pines, and birches, where they feed avidly on the seeds. Although they are constitutionally restless little midgets, they exhibit small concern for the near presence of an observer, but continue to feed and to frisk among the tips of the branches, uttering a plaintive, husky *chée-ee, chée-ee.* In the winter they may be

distinguished from Goldfinches by the heavy dark streakings of their under parts, or by the emission, from time to time, of a curious wheezy *zheeee,* unlike the call of any other northern bird.

When flushed, they rise in a body, and whisk off, showing, to the quick and acute observer, distinct yellow patches in the tail and wings. Their appearance in the northeastern part of our country, at least, is irregular; during some winters they appear in large flocks; in other years not one may be seen. (Family *Fringillidae*)

SKIMMER FAMILY
Rynchopidae

Skimmers are, as their name implies, birds which skim above the surface of the quiet waters offshore, or above bays, tidal inlets, and the like, with their mouths open, and with their peculiar, long, blade-like lower mandible cutting just beneath the surface of the water, where it gathers up and swallows small aquatic animals. How such a thin, knife-like edge can so successfully function in this way seems incomprehensible. Skimmers nest in close colonies on sandy beaches. Their wings are long, and their flight grace-

ful and gull-like. Of the five species, distributed over the warmer parts of the globe, but one, the Black Skimmer (*Rynchops nigra nigra*), is found breeding in North America, or occurring here at all.

NESTING. Our Black Skimmer, the only representative of the Family *Rynchopidae* in North America, builds no nest, but deposits its eggs in a slight hollow in the sand, or among the shells on a beach. The eggs, from three to five in number, are white, dull-whitish, or light brownish-white, heavily blotched with rich chocolate-brown.

SKIMMER

Black Skimmer

Rynchops nigra nigra [80]

ADULT MALE AND FEMALE—Upper parts and wings, black. Outer tail feathers, white; inner ones, black washed with brownish. Sides of head, forehead, under parts, and the tips of the secondaries, pure white. Bill, bright red; its tip, black; and in form, thin and blade-like with the under-mandible longer.

LENGTH—18.00 inches.

DISTRIBUTION—From southern New Jersey southward in eastern United States, but wanders irregularly as far north as Nova Scotia. In winter it is found from the Gulf States southward as far as northern South America.

The Black Skimmer feeds by flying just above the water, with its long blade-like under-mandible cutting be-

low the surface like a can-opener. The birds are never found far out at sea, nor very far inland, but may commonly be seen along the shore, and in shallow bays. Their strongly contrasted black and white; the peculiarly

shaped, red bill; and their long pointed wings and graceful flight, make them very attractive birds. (Family *Rynchopidae*)

SKUA

Chilean Skua

Catharacta chilensis [35.1]

Similar to the Northern Skua, but with the axillars and under-wing coverts a deep cinnamon-brown, sometimes darker, sometimes lighter. The under parts are a uniform dull rusty or cinnamon-brown.

DISTRIBUTION—A South American species, straggling northward in summer to the coasts of California, Washington, and British Columbia. (Family *Stercorariidae*)

Northern Skua

Catharacta skua [35]

ADULT MALE AND FEMALE—Upper parts, wings, and tail, dark sooty-brown; the shafts of the wing and tail-feathers, white or whitish, except at their tips. Inner vanes of outer wing feathers, white at their bases. Neck, dark dirty brown, somewhat lighter than the back, and more or less irregularly streaked with whitish. Under parts similar to the upper parts, but somewhat lighter.

LENGTH—22.00 inches.

DISTRIBUTION—Mainly in the eastern portion of the North Atlantic, from the Shetland Islands northward. In winter it spreads south to Gibraltar, and rarely to the coast of Long Island, New York. There is one record from the coast of California.

Like the Jaegers, the Northern Skua may be said to be a hawk-like, gull-like, high-seas robber! It is a bird of

the North Atlantic, and of the tundra wastes of the northlands. (Family *Stercorariidae*)

SKYLARK

Skylark

Alauda arvensis arvensis [473]

ADULT MALE AND FEMALE—Upper parts, brown streaked with black; the tail somewhat darker, its outer feathers more or less white. Breast, buffy streaked with black; abdomen, lighter. The nail of the hind toe is as long, or longer than the toe itself.

LENGTH—7.50 inches.

DISTRIBUTION — Europe generally, except in southern Spain and southern Italy; the British Isles; sometimes in Greenland and Bermuda.

The Skylark has been introduced on Vancouver Island, British Columbia, and several times birds have been

brought to this country and liberated, with the hope that the species would establish itself here. In 1887 a small colony of the birds became established near Flatbush, Long Island. Here a nest containing young was found. Again in July 1865 a singing bird was recorded and another nest found. The species was still present in this same locality as late as 1907, but since that time no further observations have been recorded. It is probable that the bird is now extinct in the United States. This seems strange, since, in some parts of the country, it would appear that the same ecological conditions prevail as in the bird's European and British haunts. (Family *Alaudidae*)

SNIPE

European Snipe

Capella gallinago gallinago [229]

Closely similar to the Wilson's Snipe, but possesses more white on the wing coverts; shows usually fourteen instead of sixteen tail feathers, the outer ones being broader than those of the Wilson's.

DISTRIBUTION—This north European Snipe occurs casually in Greenland, and accidentally in Labrador and Bermuda. (Family *Scolopacidae*)

European Jack Snipe
Lymnocryptes minimus [230.2]

ADULT MALE AND FEMALE—Upper parts, mottled black, reddish-brown, and buff; the black showing greenish and purplish iridescence. Under parts, white; the neck and breast, spotted; the abdomen, unmarked.

LENGTH—8.00 inches.

DISTRIBUTION — This Old World species has been reported from Labrador. (Family *Scolopacidae.*)

Wilson's Snipe
Capella delicata [230]

ADULT MALE AND FEMALE—Back and wings, mixed reddish-brown, black, and white. Center of crown, black bisected by a buffy line, and

separated by two buffy lines from two other brown lines from the base of the bill to the eyes. Tail, reddish-brown barred with black. Throat, gray; breast, brown streaked with black. Abdomen, white. Sides of body, gray barred with black.

LENGTH—11.25 inches.

DISTRIBUTION—From Labrador to Alaska south to northern New Eng-

land (rarely to Connecticut), across to northern Illinois and northern California. In winter it is found from California, southern Illinois, and South Carolina, southward to northern South America.

A bird of the fresh-water marshes, and low wet meadowlands. When flushed, it makes off with a curious twisting flight, uttering a harsh *skaaaap* or *scaipe*. (Family *Scolopacidae*)

SOLITAIRE
Townsend's Solitaire
Myadestes townsendi [754]

ADULT MALE AND FEMALE—Upper parts, brownish-gray; the wings with two whitish bars. The bases of the primaries and secondaries are a light yellowish-brown. Tail feathers, tapering, and with the outer webs grayish-white. Tips of the inner webs also grayish-white. Under parts, pale grayish-brown. Bill, short and flattened; wider at the base.

LENGTH—8.65 inches.

DISTRIBUTION — From British Columbia southward into central Mexico, and from the Black Hills of Dakota westward to the Pacific, chiefly in the mountains. In winter it is found south to southern Arizona, and the northern part of Lower California.

The Solitaire during its breeding season, is a bird of lonely mountain heights, where, among the dwarf evergreens, bare rocks, and little stream valleys filled with stunted vegetation, it gives voice to its clear, ringing song. It is a common songster, and is often heard or seen on the mountain trails in Glacier National Park or Yellowstone National Park. In flight, and in its habit of running rapidly and then suddenly halting and sitting bolt upright, it resembles the Robin. Its coloration and contour suggest the Mockingbird. The Solitaire breeds at higher altitudes than any other American thrush. In the Sierra

Nevada they have been found nesting at a height of very nearly 8,000 feet. (Family *Turdidae*)

SORA

Sora

Porzana carolina [214]

Somewhat similar to the Virginia Rail, but smaller, and with no brown in the wings; the region about the base of the bill and throat, black; short yellow bill and greenish legs.

LENGTH—8.50 inches.

DISTRIBUTION — From Newfoundland across to British Columbia, and

southward to Long Island, and across to southern California. Winters from South Carolina, across to California, and south into South America. (Family *Rallidae*)

SPARROW

Abreojos Sparrow

Passerculus rostratus halophilus [544b]

Similar to the San Lucas Sparrow, but larger and much darker; the upper parts, more olivaceous in tone, without the grayish cast.

DISTRIBUTION—The southwest coast of Lower California. (Family *Fringillidae*)

Acadian Sparrow

Ammospiza caudacuta subvirgata [549.1a]

Similar to the Sharp-tailed Sparrow, but paler, and with the under parts inconspicuously streaked with pale greenish-gray.

DISTRIBUTION—From southeastern Quebec, Prince Edward Island, and Cape Breton Island, south to the shores of Penobscot Bay, Maine, and in the salt marshes along its range. In winter it is found on the shores of South Carolina, Georgia, and northwestern Florida. (Family *Fringillidae*)

Alameda Song Sparrow

Melospiza melodia pusillula [581l]

Similar to the Samuels's Song Sparrow, but smaller, with shorter wings and tail, and with the plumage more of an olive-brown. Under parts and line over the eye, more or less yellowish.

DISTRIBUTION—In the region of the southern arm of San Francisco Bay, in the salt marshes, from Islais Marsh, San Francisco County, to Richmond in Contra Costa County. (Family *Fringillidae*)

Alberta Fox Sparrow

Passerella iliaca altivagans [585h]

Similar to the Slate-colored Fox Sparrow, but browner, and with the wings and tail showing a redder tone of brown.

DISTRIBUTION — In summer it is found in the interior of British Columbia and in the extreme western portion of Alberta. In winter it occurs in California, chiefly west of the deserts, and southward into the northwestern portion of Lower California, about as far as Rosario—the northern quarter of the peninsula. (Family *Fringillidae*)

Aleutian Savannah Sparrow
Passerculus sandwichensis sandwichensis [542]

Similar to the Eastern Savannah Sparrow, but a darker brown, and with the under parts paler and marked with darker brown. Region over and about the eye, yellowish.

DISTRIBUTION—Found on the Island of Unalaska, and contiguous islands, Alaska. In winter it is found eastward and southward along the coast of British Columbia and to middle California. (Family *Fringillidae*)

Aleutian Song Sparrow
Melospiza melodia sanaka [581r]

In general similar to the Eastern Song Sparrow, but larger, darker, and grayer. This subspecies is the largest

of all the American Song Sparrows. DISTRIBUTION — "The Shumagin

Islands and adjacent parts of the Alaskan Peninsula and the Aleutian Islands." (A.O.U. Check List.) (Family *Fringillidae*)

Ashy Sparrow
Aimophila ruficeps canescens [580d]

This subspecies resembles the Rufous-crowned Sparrow, but the under parts are grayer, and it possesses longer wings and tail.

DISTRIBUTION—The extreme southern part of California, in the San Diego region, and the extreme northwestern part of Lower California. (Family *Fringillidae*)

Atlantic Song Sparrow
Melospiza melodia atlantica [581t]

Similar to the common Eastern Song Sparrow, but with the upper parts decidedly grayer; with very narrow, inconspicuous reddish-brown edges to the feathers; and with the blackish streakings more distinct. It also closely resembles the Dakota Song Sparrow, but with the upper parts more grayish.

DISTRIBUTION—Found along a narrow coastal strip of the Atlantic seaboard, and on the coastal islands, from Long Island, New York, south as far as North Carolina. (Family *Fringillidae*)

Bachman's Sparrow
Aimophila aestivalis bachmani [575a]

Similar to the Eastern Lark Sparrow, but with the upper parts reddish-brown, streaked with black only on the back, or not at all. The line over the eye is a light creamy-brown, or light yellowish-brown. Under parts, white; the breast and sides of the body washed with light brownish, and unmarked.

DISTRIBUTION — From central Illinois, southern Indiana, southern Ohio, central Virginia, southward into north-western Florida and central Texas. In winter it is found from southern North Carolina southward into Florida, and casually in the District of Columbia.

The Bachman's Sparrow is a bird of open oak woods, old fields, overgrown pastures, and scrub-lands generally. Its

song is reminiscent of that of the Field Sparrow, but louder, sweeter, and more "silvery" in tone. (Family *Fringillidae*)

Baird's Sparrow
Ammodramus bairdi [545]

ADULT MALE AND FEMALE—Back, light brown spotted with black; the feathers with lighter edgings. Head, yellowish-brown or buff; the sides of the crown streaked with black. Under parts, white. Black stripes on the sides of the throat. Upper breast, sides, and flanks streaked with black. Tail, deeply forked; the feathers all narrow and sharply pointed.

LENGTH—5.10 inches.

DISTRIBUTION—From the plains country of Saskatchewan southward to Nebraska and Colorado. In winter it passes to northwestern Mexico. It is sometimes found in the State of Washington. (Family *Fringillidae*)

Bangs's Sparrow
Amphispiza bilineata bangsi [573b]

Similar to the Desert Sparrow, but with shorter wings and tail; a slightly larger bill; and with the general tone of the upper parts slightly paler.

DISTRIBUTION—In the peninsula of Lower California, from about latitude 26°, to the Cape district. (Family *Fringillidae*)

Belding's Sparrow
Passerculus beldingi [543]

Similar to the Bryant's Sparrow, but somewhat smaller; the upper parts, darker and with an olive cast; the under parts more heavily streaked with blackish and brownish.

LENGTH—5.02 inches.

DISTRIBUTION—"The salt marshes along the coast of southern and of Lower California, from Santa Barbara to San Quentin Bay, and Todos Santos Island." (Bailey.)

The Belding's Sparrow, or Belding Marsh Sparrow as it is sometimes called, is reported by Bailey to be an abundant resident of the salt marshes along the coast of southern California, and has been found nesting in the marsh grass just above the reach of the tide. (Family *Fringillidae*)

Bell's Sparrow
Amphispiza belli belli [574]

ADULT MALE AND FEMALE—Upper parts, brownish-gray, graying on the head, and usually without appreciable streaking. Coverts and tertials of the wing edged with light creamy-brown. Edge of wing, yellowish. Tail, black, inconspicuously marked with dusky. Throat bordered by black and white stripes. Ring around the eye, and spot on the sides of the head, white. Under parts, white; the breast bearing a black blotch.

LENGTH—5.30 inches.

DISTRIBUTION — From the central part of California in the valleys and foothills of the mountains west of the Sierra Nevada and the San Bernardino ranges, southward into northern Lower California.

The Bell's Sparrow delights in hot, sandy, dreary yucca, cactus, and sage-

brush-covered alkali plains, and mesas. In summer it climbs the mountains up to an altitude of 5,000 feet. (Family *Fringillidae*)

Bischoff's Song Sparrow
Melospiza melodia insignis [581q]

Similar to the Eastern Song Sparrow, but much larger and darker; with a larger bill, and the spots of the under parts fused into continuous patches of color.

DISTRIBUTION—Found on the Kodiak Island and on the neighboring coast of the Alaskan Peninsula. (Family *Fringillidae*)

Black-throated Sparrow
Amphispiza bilineata bilineata [573]

ADULT MALE AND FEMALE—Upper parts, unmarked, uniform grayish-brown. Tail, except the middle feathers, marked with white. Lores and large throat patch, black. Sides of head, dark gray, bearing two white stripes. Under parts, white.

LENGTH—5.03 inches.

DISTRIBUTION — From the western part of Kansas southward into central and eastern Texas, and northeastern Mexico.

In the southwestern deserts the Black-throated Sparrow is a common and welcome singer. *Tsa weee, ah wee, ah weeee*, it trills in endless variation on this theme, the song being given while the performer sits in the top of some elevated bush—much after the manner of our own common Song Sparrow. Its striking gray, black, and white costume renders this agreeable little

species as pleasant to the eye as its cheerful little strain is to the ear. (Family *Fringillidae*)

Botteri's Sparrow
Aimophila botterii botterii [576]

ADULT MALE AND FEMALE—Upper parts, gray streaked with brown and spotted with black. Edge of the wing, yellow or yellowish. Under parts, unmarked dull buffy.

LENGTH—5.75 inches.

DISTRIBUTION—From the region of southern Arizona and about the lower Rio Grande Valley in southwestern Texas, southward through Mexico as far as Chiapas (southernmost Mexico).

The upper parts of this Sparrow remind one of the Eastern Field Sparrow, but the bill is darker. The song is somewhat similar to the Field Sparrow's and consists of a sweet trill, followed by several separate notes. (Family *Fringillidae*)

Brewer's Sparrow
Spizella breweri breweri [562]

ADULT MALE AND FEMALE—Underlying color of upper parts, grayish-brown streaked with black. Under parts, dusky white. Cheek region has indistinct darker patch. Bill, sharp.

LENGTH—4.94 inches.

DISTRIBUTION — From British Columbia southward to southern Arizona, and from western Nebraska and western Texas westward to the Pacific Coast. In winter it passes into Mexico and is found along the western edge of the table-land country.

Brewer's Sparrow is found in sage-brush regions throughout its range, and is often called the Sagebrush Chippie, so faithfully does it follow the occupation of that vegetable. Bailey once found it singing ". . . at 8,400 feet on the snowy crest of the Sierra, but on the sunny slope below was the inevitable sage." Like many of the smaller sparrows, it flies only short distances when disturbed, running along under the grasses and bushes like a small gray mouse. Only when it mounts into the top of a bush to sing is it profitably observable. Its song is a bright, cheerful, energetic little lay, rather metallic, tinkling, and insect-like, and somewhat resembling that of the Marsh Wrens. (Family *Fringillidae*)

Brown's Song Sparrow
Melospiza melodia rivularis [581g]

Similar to the Desert Song Sparrow, but larger and duller; the colors more reddish-brown, and the pattern of markings less distinct. The bill is more compressed, longer, and slenderer.

DISTRIBUTION—Found in the southern portions of Lower California among the mountain districts. (Family *Fringillidae*)

Bryant's Sparrow
Passerculus sandwichensis bryanti [542c]

Similar to the Western Savannah Sparrow, but smaller, and uniformly darker, with the yellow over the eye more prominent. The under parts are more heavily streaked.

LENGTH—4.75 inches.

DISTRIBUTION—Found about San Francisco and Monterey bays, in the salt marshes. In winter it passes south along the coast to southern California; sometimes into the Valley of Mexico. (Family *Fringillidae*)

California Black-chinned Sparrow
Spizella atrogularis cana [565a]

Similar to the Mexican Black-chinned Sparrow, but lacking the black face and chin; with the shoulders a lighter brown, and with a longer tail.

DISTRIBUTION—From Mariposa, Alameda, and Inyo counties, California, southward through the northern quarter of Lower California. In winter it descends farther south in Lower California to the Cape San Lucas region. (Family *Fringillidae*)

California Sage Sparrow
Amphispiza nevadensis canescens [574.1b]

Similar to the Bell's Sparrow, but somewhat larger and uniformly very much paler.

DISTRIBUTION—". . . in Owens Valley and adjacent areas in eastern California and extreme western Nevada." (A.O.U. Check List.) (Family *Fringillidae*)

Cape Colnett Sparrow
Aimophila ruficeps lambi [580e]

Similar to the Ashy Sparrow, but a much darker, more slaty-brown.

DISTRIBUTION — Western Lower California, from just below the United States south to the region of Blanco Bay. (Family *Fringillidae*)

Cape Sable Seaside Sparrow
Ammospiza mirabilis [551.1]

ADULT MALE AND FEMALE—Upper parts, ashy-greenish with a grayish tinge, but with a more greenish cast than in any of the other seaside Sparrows. Crown, ashy-greenish-gray; its sides broadly striped with black. The center of the back, and the "shoulders" with broad black stripes and wide greenish-whitish-ashy margins. Under parts, white without any buffy wash. Breast and sides, streaked with brownish. Bend of the wing, and a line from the base of the bill to the eye, yellow.
LENGTH—6.00 inches.
DISTRIBUTION—In Florida, in the salt marshes of the coast, and in the vicinity of Cape Sable.

This species, discovered and described by Arthur H. Howell, in February, 1918, may prove to be the last new species of bird to be found in the eastern portion of North America, unless the 1942 proposed new species, Sutton's Warbler (*Dendroica potomac*), which see, is admitted as a species. (Family *Fringillidae*)

Cassin's Sparrow
Aimophila cassini [578]

ADULT MALE AND FEMALE—Upper parts, light ashy-gray streaked with light sandy-brown, and marked with small black tips to the feathers. Upper tail coverts with transverse dark streaks. Edge of wing and shoulder, yellow or yellowish. Under parts, gray-

ish-white, washed with brown on the upper breast and sides of the body.
LENGTH—5.47 inches.
DISTRIBUTION—From Kansas southward into Arizona and northern Mexico, and from Texas northwest as far as Nevada.

The Cassin's Sparrow is a bird of low mesquite plains, hiding in the dense bushes, but rising upward to deliver its flight song. The gray upper parts with sandy-brown streakings are diagnostic. (Family *Fringillidae*)

Clay-colored Sparrow
Spizella pallida [561]

ADULT MALE AND FEMALE—Back and scapulars, brown broadly streaked with black; two buffy wing bars. Crown, light brown, with pale central

stripe, and black-streaked sides. Line over the eye, whitish or buffy. Sides of the head, buffy-brown, bordered above and below by narrow black streaks. Cheeks, whitish, bordered below by a dusky streak running along the side of the throat. Hinder part of neck, gray and finely streaked. Under parts, white or whitish, washed on the upper breast and sides with brown.
LENGTH—5.08 inches.

DISTRIBUTION—From the plains country of Saskatchewan, southward into Iowa and Nebraska, and from Illinois westward into Montana. In winter it is found in Lower California, and central Mexico.

The Clay-colored Sparrow is a bird of low bushes, valleys, and stream courses. It is almost entirely a terrestrial bird, although during the nesting season the male sings from the top of some low bush. (Family *Fringillidae*)

Coronados Song Sparrow
Melospiza melodia coronatorum [581x]

Similar to the San Clemente Song Sparrow, but with the tarsus (lower part of leg) decidedly shorter, and the bill smaller.

DISTRIBUTION—On the Los Coronados Islands of Lower California. (Family *Fringillidae*)

Dakota Song Sparrow
Melospiza melodia juddi [581j]

Similar to the Eastern Song Sparrow, but with the upper parts paler, especially on the sides of the neck. Line over the eye, white. Feathers near the shoulders, darker. Under parts, white, with the dark streakings on the breast narrower, sharper, and clearer.

DISTRIBUTION—From southwestern Saskatchewan and eastern Montana southeastward to the Turtle Mountains of North Dakota. In winter it is found in Texas and New Mexico. (Family *Fringillidae*)

Desert Sparrow
Amphispiza bilineata deserticola [573a]

Similar to the Black-throated Sparrow, but somewhat larger, and with the grayish-brown of the upper parts paler, and washed with a browner hue. The white spot at the end of the

outer tail feathers is much smaller. Under parts, pure white.

LENGTH—5.18 inches.

DISTRIBUTION—On the arid plains of the United States from western Texas and New Mexico westward to the coast of the southern part of California, and from the northern parts of Utah and Nevada south into Lower California and northern Mexico.

As in color, so in habits and song is the Desert Sparrow similar to the Black-throated Sparrow. (Family *Fringillidae*)

Desert Song Sparrow
Melospiza melodia saltonis [581a]

ADULT MALE AND FEMALE—The general tone of the bird is a light reddish-brown. Upper parts, light grayish; the back streaked with rusty

brown, and usually lacking any blackish streakings on the feather shafts. Upper breast streaked with reddishbrown; rest of under parts, gray.

LENGTH—5.74 inches.

DISTRIBUTION — From southeastern California and southern Nevada down into the peninsula of Lower California, and into Mexico as far as Sonora.

The Desert Song Sparrow is the palest of all the Song Sparrows; its pale hue blending well with the desert colors of its habitat. (Family *Fringillidae*)

Dusky Seaside Sparrow
Ammospiza nigrescens [551]

Similar to the Northern Seaside Sparrow, but with the upper parts very dark, almost black, the feathers nar-

rowly margined with grayish and grayish-olive-green. Under parts, very sharply streaked with black and white.

LENGTH—6.00 inches.

DISTRIBUTION—On the eastern coast of Florida, in the marshes at the northern end of the Indian River.

An interesting species, since it is restricted to an area of only a few square miles in extent. (Family *Fringillidae*)

Eastern Chipping Sparrow
Spizella passerina passerina [560]

ADULT MALE AND FEMALE—Upper parts, brownish streaked with black; crown, bright reddish-brown, set off by a white line over the eye and a black line through it. Sides of head, gray. Bill, small, black, and conical. Under parts, white or grayish-white; tail, slender and distinctly notched.

LENGTH—5.37 inches.

DISTRIBUTION — Eastern North America, from Newfoundland and the Great Slave Lake region southward to the Gulf States, and westward to the Great Plains. It winters in the Gulf States, and southward into Mexico.

One of the most useful and delightful inhabitants of our gardens, lawns, public parks, and farms, is the diminutive and sociable little Chippy or Hair Bird. Its sweet, subdued, ingenuous song is to be heard at all hours of the day during the nesting period. This, in its commonest form, is a series of rapidly delivered, soft, sweet *chip* notes, which may be deliberately uttered, or run off into a little musical trill. Like the House Wren, the Chippy has taken kindly to man's occupation of the land, and finds a congenial harborage in the vines of porches, in grape arbors, and in ornamental garden bushes. It has an especial liking for small cedars and other evergreens. One of the bird's common names, Hair Bird, refers to its habit of lining its grass-and-root-built nest with black, coarse hair, usually horse-hair. I have seen the birds pulling this material from the stuffing of old discarded automobile cushions on a country dump. Chippies are most often seen

hopping about on a closely-cut lawn, where their bright chestnut caps at once proclaim their identity. When seen perched against the sky, the little notch in the tip of the tail is quite apparent. (Family *Fringillidae*)

Eastern Field Sparrow
Spizella pusilla pusilla [563]

ADULT MALE AND FEMALE—Upper parts, pale tawny-brown, with two whitish wing bars. Sides of head, grayish, with a light, ill-defined, whitish stripe over the eye. Bill, light pinkish-brown. Under parts, whitish, and unmarked except for a tinge of pale pinkish-brown on the breast.

LENGTH—5.68 inches.

DISTRIBUTION—The eastern section of North America, from Quebec and Manitoba southward to South Caro-

lina, Alabama, and central Texas; rare in the extreme northern portion of its range. It winters from Virginia and Illinois into the Gulf States.

Demure in color, retiring in disposition, modest, sweet and clear of song, the Field Sparrow appeals strongly to those whose affections are attuned to the artless things of the wild, and who, with Izaak Walton, like "to be quiet and go a-fishing." It is in such a mood that one should seek out the haunts of the Field Sparrow, and listen to its song. *Whee, whee, whee, whee-whee-whee-e-e-e-eeeeeeeeee*, it trills, the strain consisting of several clear, sweet, subdued, whistled notes all on virtually the same pitch; the first few given slowly and deliberately, the rest increasing progressively in rapidity, until the final ones are trilled off in a sort of anti-climactical fashion. Sometimes the order of the notes is reversed. The Field Sparrow inhabits dry grassy fields, scrubby pastures, or forest clear-

ings where weeds abound. (Family *Fringillidae*)

Eastern Fox Sparrow
Passerella iliaca iliaca [585]

ADULT MALE AND FEMALE—Tail, rich reddish-brown. Upper parts, similar, but washed with slaty bluish-gray. Sides of throat and breast bearing prominent rich reddish-brown spots, which sometimes coalesce, forming a central breast blotch. The abdomen and sides of the body bear large, sharply defined, rich, dark brown arrow-head-shaped spots.

LENGTH—7.26 inches.

DISTRIBUTION—From central Canada, Quebec, and Newfoundland, westward into Alaska, passing south for the winter into Virginia, and from this state spreading southward to the Gulf States.

Fox Sparrows nest chiefly in Canada and into Alaska, where they sing with persistence. The song, one of the most

beautiful uttered in the Sparrow tribe, is a loud, rich, energetic lay, composed of full clear tones somewhat suggesting the performance of the Purple Finch, but shorter and clearer. It is often given in two grades of tone: one, clear and loud; the other, much subdued, and uttered chiefly in the evening twilight (more rarely in the morning), and heard in the very early spring. The rendition of the song during the fall migration lacks the sprightliness of the spring version, and is far less frequent. During the spring and fall migrations Fox Sparrows create a tremendous rustling among the dead leaves on bushy hillsides, in sheltered ravines, and along the edges of woods, as they scratch vigorously for their food, dashing the leaves backwards with surprising energy. They are gregarious birds at this season, and when flushed fly up into the middle of some near-by bush or small tree—never far from the ground—to investigate the cause of their disturbance. Their large size and rich brown coloring causes them to be mistaken by some for thrushes. Their call note is a thin, fine, wiry, short *ssit*. (Family *Fringillidae*)

Eastern Grasshopper Sparrow

Ammodramus savannarum australis [546]

ADULT MALE AND FEMALE—Upper parts, pale grayish streaked with darker gray, black, and brown. A buffy line divides the darker crown. Under parts, uniform buffy-grayish-white, unmarked. Bill, stout and heavy for so small a bird.

LENGTH—5.38 inches.

DISTRIBUTION—The eastern portion of the United States, from Vermont, Massachusetts, and Minnesota, westward to the Great Plains, and southward to the Gulf of Mexico. It spends its winters from North Carolina southward into Mexico, and Cuba.

Dry fields and meadows, old pastures overgrown with grass and scrub, and old hillsides in the vicinity of abandoned farms are the favorite haunts of this secretive midget of a Sparrow, which is seldom seen, except by those who become acquainted with its furtive habits and unusual song. It seldom flies far when flushed, but rises just ahead of the walker, and flitting low,

with a nervous jerky flight just above the tops of the tall grasses, soon drops from sight again into its friendly cover. Here it squats down, or runs, mouselike, along the ground. The shortness of the tail, and large bill, both give to

the bird a chunky, over-balanced appearance. The song is unique—a thin, buzzy, insectoid utterance, like the syllables *tsick, tsick, tserrrrrrrr*, which almost exactly resemble the stridulations of the Meadow Grasshopper (*Orchelimum vulgare*). (Family *Fringillidae*)

Eastern Henslow's Sparrow

Passerherbulus henslowi susurrans [547]

ADULT MALE AND FEMALE—Top of head, nape, and its sides, a grayish-olive; rest of upper parts, brown streaked with blackish. Under parts, white; the breast, and sides of the body, narrowly streaked with black. Bill, short and stout; tail, short and narrow; the characteristics of the bill and tail give the bird a dumpy, top-heavy, unbalanced appearance.

LENGTH—5.00 inches.

DISTRIBUTION—From New Hampshire, southern Ontario and Minnesota, southward to Missouri and Virginia; rare or absent in some parts of its range. It spends the winter in our southern states, from its breeding grounds to the Gulf of Mexico.

Henslow's Sparrow is a small, shy bird of grassy fields and damp meadows. In such situations it may best be identi-

fied by its notes—a simple two-syllabled song, *fee-sic,* and a slightly longer performance, less frequently uttered, *sis, r-r-rit, srit, srit.* The first song is probably the shortest song of any of our native birds. The second song is excessively thin, fine, and insectoid. The bird keeps well to the ground and out of sight among the tangle of grasses. When seen, in one of the rare moments when it is perched on a stone, or fence-post, its heavy head, and thin tail, together with its diminutive size, aid in its identification. (Family *Fringillidae*)

Eastern Lark Sparrow

Chondestes grammacus grammacus [552]

ADULT MALE AND FEMALE—Upper parts, brownish-gray streaked with blackish; tail, almost black, its outermost feathers tipped with white. Crown and ear coverts, chestnut-brown. A white line passes through the center of the crown and over each eye. Sides of throat bear an irregular black streak. Under parts, white; the center of the breast bearing a small dark spot.

LENGTH—6.25 inches.

DISTRIBUTION—From Manitoba south into Texas throughout the extent of the Great Plains as far east as Illinois, spreading south in winter into Mexico.

The Lark Sparrow is one of the finest singers of all the great Finch family, and may be heard commonly in the central part of our country, where the bird inhabits grassy fields, scrubby pastures, and hillsides. The song reminds one of that of the Indigo Bunting, Goldfinch, and Purple Finch combined, with a touch of the notes of the Yellow-breasted Chat. Beginning as a series of sweet, not loud notes, it passes into a series of loud, clear, rollicking

tones, interspersed with soft, melodious notes, and semi-trills, until the singer seems to pause for breath before once again bursting with full vigor into the song. (Family *Fringillidae*)

Eastern Savannah Sparrow

Passerculus sandwichensis savanna [542a]

ADULT MALE AND FEMALE—Upper parts, brown with blackish streaks. A yellowish line passes from the base of the bill over each eye, and a narrow yellowish line divides the crown. Sides of the body and under parts, whitish finely streaked with dark brown, more heavily on the sides. The streaks *in-*

frequently form a darker patch in the center of the breast. Tail, short. Legs and feet, flesh color or distinctly pinkish.

LENGTH—5.68 inches.

DISTRIBUTION—From Labrador and the western Hudson Bay region south as far as northern New Jersey, eastern Long Island, and Missouri, and westward as far as the Great Plains. It spends the winter from Virginia and southern Illinois southward into Mexico and Cuba.

Dry grassy fields are the usual haunts of this tiny species, which often bursts out of the grass almost from under foot

as one walks along, flits a short distance and then drops back into the grass again. As the bird flies the shortness of the tail is apparent to the observer who remembers the rule to regard only the wings, back, and tail of a flying bird. The characteristic song of the Savannah Sparrow, which, however, must be listened for with attention, is an insignificant, grasshopper-like, musical double trill, introduced by three fine, high, insectoid notes, thus: *tsip, tsip, tsip, tsreeeee, tsreeeee.* The three introductory notes are so thin, fine, short, and high-pitched as to be perceptible only to acute ears. The second of the long terminal trills is slightly lower in pitch than the first. The yellowish line over the eye and the short tail are the diagnostic field marks for this attrac-

tive little species. In its flight the bird is nervous and jerky. Often it will mount a large stone, or the top of a fence post, to deliver its ingenuous little song. (Family *Fringillidae*)

Eastern Song Sparrow

Melospiza melodia melodia [581]

ADULT MALE AND FEMALE—Upper parts, brown with darker streakings; the crown, a richer brown, divided by a narrow grayish line, and bordered over each eye by a similar line. Rather prominent black lines extend, slightly broadening as they go, backward and downward from the base of the bill. Cheeks, rich brown. Under parts, grayish-white, prominently streaked with rich brown; the streaks apparently fusing together in the center of the breast, forming a "breast-pin" patch. Tail, rather long and slender.

LENGTH—6.30 inches.

DISTRIBUTION — Over the whole eastern section of North America from Quebec and Manitoba southward to Virginia and northern Illinois, and westward to the Great Plains. In winter it is found in the southern half of the United States from Massachusetts and southern Illinois to the Gulf of Mexico.

The favorite haunts of this common and much-loved little songster are among alders along stream courses, old bushy pastures, along country roadsides, among vine tangles, and in the edges of woodlands. It runs in and out of the tangles near the ground, mouse-fashion, and when flushed flits nervously away, its flexible tail switching in flight. The bird sings, from an elevated perch, a loud, cheerful, energetic lay, one of the most exuberant songs of spring, and the earliest song to be heard in the north. It begins with three (sometimes two) clear notes, followed by a simple whistled and trilled medley, the whole performance being readily rendered into the words

Maids, maids, maids; put on your tea kettle-ettle-ettle-ettle. There are many variations, sometimes given by the same bird at different times. The chief

field marks of the bird are the broad markings on the sides of the throat, and the central "breast-pin" in the middle of the heavily-streaked breast. (Family *Fringillidae*)

Eastern Tree Sparrow
Spizella arborea arborea [559]

ADULT MALE AND FEMALE—Upper parts, brownish with black streaks; the wings, with two white bars. Crown, tawny-brown. Sides of body, faintly pinkish-brown. Under parts, grayish-white, unmarked, save for a small dark spot in the center of the breast, which is sometimes faint, sometimes absent.
LENGTH—6.36 inches.
DISTRIBUTION—Northeastern North America, from Labrador and the region west of Hudson Bay, west to the Great Plains. In winter it ranges southward through the northern states as far as the latitude of South Carolina and Tennessee.

These far-north nesting birds delight, while with us in winter, in old weed fields, weedy fence rows, and the scraggy borders of country roads, where, when the snow lies deep on the ground, they gather in large flocks to feed on the seeds of such weeds as amaranth, crab grass, ragweed, or any seed-bearing weed which lifts its head above the snow. While feeding they

are constantly active, and keep up a continuous conversation, consisting of low, musical double notes, sounding like the syllables *tweet-wit*, so rapidly uttered as to sound almost like one note. Energetic, nervous, and untiringly on the move, Tree Sparrows offer the observer but few opportunities to study them at leisure. The song, uttered occasionally on migration, is

somewhat similar to a Canary's song, but is thin, subdued, sweet, rather plaintive, and "conversational." (Family *Fringillidae*)

Eastern Vesper Sparrow
Pooecetes gramineus gramineus [540]

ADULT MALE AND FEMALE—Upper parts, pale grayish-brown with darker streakings; the sides of the body, grayish-white. Under parts, whitish narrowly streaked with grayish-brown. Shoulder (wrist) patch, light reddish-brown or "bay." Outermost pair of tail feathers, white; the next pair, partly so and showing when the bird flies.
LENGTH—6.12 inches.
DISTRIBUTION—In the eastern portion of North America from New Brunswick and Manitoba south to Virginia, Illinois, and Missouri. It winters from Virginia across to southern Illinois, and southward into the Gulf States.

The Vesper Sparrow is an inhabitant of fields and dry meadows, scrubby pasture lands, cleared hillsides, weedy fence-rows, and similar situations.

From a fence post, stone, or from the top of a low bush or tree, it gives forth its ingenuous, sweet, somewhat plaintive song, beginning in unmistakable fashion with two low, soft notes, followed by two more some four

or five tones higher. The remainder of the song quickly follows—a succession of softly sweet trills, somewhat similar to those which close the Song Sparrow's song, but less vigorous. A suitable rendition in words is *Oh, oh, see, see, what-a-pretty-little-bird-I-be.* The song is most frequently delivered in the early morning, or evening, from which latter time of singing the bird derives its name. (Family *Fringillidae*)

English Sparrow
Passer domesticus domesticus [688.2]

ADULT MALE—Back, brown streaked with black; top of head, grayish, with a chestnut patch flanking each side. Two white bars and a stripe of chestnut on each wing. A large jet black bib occupies the throat and upper breast in the breeding season. Rest of under parts, grayish-white or grayish. Bill, short and stout, similar to the bills of some of the true Sparrows, and black in color.

ADULT FEMALE—Back, lighter brown than the male, lightly streaked with blackish and buff. Head, grayish-brown, unmarked. Breast washed with light grayish-brown; rest of under parts, soiled white.

LENGTH—6.33 inches.

DISTRIBUTION—This European Weaver Finch was first brought over to the United States and liberated in some numbers at Brooklyn, New York, in 1850 and 1852. During subsequent years others were brought over and released in various places, including Quebec and Halifax. Since these years it has multiplied amazingly, and now is thoroughly naturalized and spread abroad over nearly all of the United States and Canada.

English Sparrows, or House Sparrows as they are called, superficially resemble our true Sparrows of the family *Fringillidae*. Formerly they were present in hordes in our cities and towns, but with the diminution in the number of horses has come also a diminution of the Sparrow's chief urban food supply, i.e., the oats in the droppings of their equine purveyors. Hence the Sparrows have withdrawn to farms, where scraps and seeds of all kinds

(especially grains fed to chickens) furnish them with an ample table. House Sparrows are undesirable, since they are pugnacious, aggressive, and far too numerous, and oust several species of our own native birds from their nesting cavities in trees, or from nesting boxes. They have no song, but only a harsh *churp.* (Family *Ploceidae*)

European Tree Sparrow
Passer montanus montanus [688.3]

Resembles somewhat the common English Sparrow, but with crown and back

of the head chestnut-brown; lores, ear coverts, and throat, black; and neck, almost surrounded by a white collar. Wing with two white bars. Unlike the English Sparrow in that the sexes are alike.

DISTRIBUTION—Introduced into the United States in 1870 at St. Louis, Missouri, and occurring in the region.

This bird might easily be mistaken for an English or House Sparrow except for the chestnut colored head, and the two white wing bars. It is a more active and lively bird than its near relative, and is more at home in trees. (Family *Ploceidae*)

Florida Grasshopper Sparrow

Ammodramus savannarum floridanus [546b]

Similar, in general, to the Eastern Grasshopper Sparrow, but smaller, with the upper parts much darker, and the under parts much paler. The chestnut-brown of the upper parts is reduced, and replaced by black. The sides of the crown are blackish, and the region between the shoulders, much blacker. The bill is somewhat larger.

DISTRIBUTION—Found in the Kissimmee Prairie Region of central Florida. (Family *Fringillidae*)

Forbush's Sparrow

Melospiza lincolni gracilis [583a]

Similar to Lincoln's Sparrow, but with the upper parts browner, and with the line over the eye brown rather than gray.

DISTRIBUTION — From British Columbia to California along the Pacific Coast. (Family *Fringillidae*)

Gambel's Sparrow

Zonotrichia leucophrys gambeli [554a]

Similar to the White-crowned Sparrow, but with the white line over the

eye reaching forward to the base of the bill. The lores are not black.

LENGTH—6.16 inches.

DISTRIBUTION—From Alaska and eastern Oregon, east to Montana. In its migrations through western United States to Lower California and to the central part of Mexico, it straggles irregularly eastward as far as Iowa. (Family *Fringillidae*)

Golden-crowned Sparrow

Zonotrichia coronata [557]

Somewhat similar to the White-throated and White-crowned Sparrows, but with the crown plain yellow; its sides bordered with black. Under

parts, grayish, their sides tinged with brown.

LENGTH—7.2 inches.

DISTRIBUTION—Alaska, passing southward along the Pacific Coast, where it spends the winter from Oregon southward to the northern portion of Lower California. (Family *Fringillidae*)

Gray Sage Sparrow

Amphispiza belli cinerea [574.1a]

Similar to the Bell's Sparrow, but with the upper parts, paler; the throat stripes, more broken and narrower; the breast spot, somewhat smaller; both the throat stripes and the breast spot are a dull gray instead of blackish.

DISTRIBUTION—Restricted to the peninsula of Lower California. (Family *Fringillidae*)

Harris's Sparrow
Zonotrichia querula [553]

ADULT MALE AND FEMALE—Upper parts, brown; the back and scapulars, streaked with blackish, and the wings bearing two white bars. Top of head, back of same, and throat (reaching down on to the upper breast), solid jet-black. Black streaks extend down through the middle of the breast. Rest of under parts, white. Sides of body and flanks, light brownish streaked with darker.

LENGTH—7.00 inches.

DISTRIBUTION — From the region west of Hudson Bay to Illinois and the Dakotas. Occurs as an accidental visitant in British Columbia, Oregon, and California. In winter it migrates into Texas, and probably Mexico.

The general habits of Harris's Sparrow are similar to those of the White-throated Sparrow. Its notes, too, are in

quality like those of the White-throat —pure, loud, clear, whistled tones. The birds are found commonly in thickets bordering the edges of woodlands, and along stream courses. Like the White-throated Sparrows, they seldom mount high in trees, but confine themselves to bushes, when perching, and when feeding make a great to-do in scratching among the dry leaves. (Family *Fringillidae*)

Heermann's Song Sparrow
Melospiza melodia heermanni [581c]

ADULT MALE AND FEMALE—General tone of the plumage, brownish or olive. Upper parts, streaked with blackish. Under parts, similarly streaked, but with the markings on the breast distinct, and not run together into a blotch, as in the Eastern Song Sparrow. The bird is similar to the Eastern Song Sparrow, but smaller, and browner or more olive; the streaks on the upper parts are generally broader, and those on the breast darker.

LENGTH—5.70 inches.

DISTRIBUTION—In the central valleys of California, migrating southward. Occurs casually in Nevada. (Family *Fringillidae*)

Howell's Seaside Sparrow
Ammospiza maritima howelli [550f]

Similar to the Northern Seaside Sparrow, but with the upper parts slightly more olive, less grayish and with broad, indistinct markings. Crown, streaked; nape, plain. Under parts, darker than in the Northern Seaside Sparrow, and more extensively washed with gray. Breast, dark brownish-buff.

DISTRIBUTION — Along the Gulf coasts of Alabama and Mississippi, spreading in winter along the northern coasts of Florida and Texas. (Family *Fringillidae*)

Inyo Fox Sparrow
Passerella iliaca canescens [585m]

Similar to the Slate-colored Fox Sparrow, but with a more grayish cast.

DISTRIBUTION—Found in the White Mountains of Inyo and Mono counties, of eastern California. In winter it occurs in southern California, and in northern Lower California. (Family *Fringillidae*)

Ipswich Sparrow
Passerculus princeps [541]

ADULT MALE AND FEMALE—Upper parts, pale brownish-gray; the back, head, and upper tail coverts, with black and rich brown. Nape and rump bear few or no streaks. White line over the eye. Wings, grayish-brown marked with pale light-brown. A spot of light yellow before the eye, and a wash of the same over the bend of the wing. Under parts, white; the breast and sides lightly streaked with blackish and light brown.

LENGTH—6.25 inches.

DISTRIBUTION — Found on Sable Island off the coast of Nova Scotia, and in winter distributed along the Atlantic coastal strip, especially among the sand dunes, from Sable Island south as far as Georgia.

The Ipswich Sparrow during its migrations may be found along the northeastern Atlantic Coast, among the sand dunes, and in the broad reaches of coarse beach grass that occur on our coast; often in company with Horned Larks and Snow Buntings. It runs like a little brownish-gray mouse here and there among the stems of grass; or, when flushed, flies with a short flippy motion for only a short distance. It is similar in appearance to the Savannah Sparrow, which is also often abundant among the dunes and in the beach grass, but from that bird may be distinguished by its larger size and uniformly paler coloration. It is also somewhat like the Vesper Sparrow, but without the white outer tail feathers. If one is close to the Ipswich Sparrow, it will be seen that a white stripe divides the center of the crown.

Its song is similar to that of the Savannah Sparrow. When on its migra-

tions through New England, its only note is a faint *tsip*. (Family *Fringillidae*)

Kenai Song Sparrow
Melospiza melodia kenaiensis [581o]

Similar to the Yakutat Song Sparrow, but larger, and with the upper parts of a more uniform and less streaked coloration.

DISTRIBUTION—"Coast of the Kenai Peninsula, Alaska, from the eastern side of the Cook Inlet to Prince William Sound." (A.O.U. Check List.) (Family *Fringillidae*)

Kodiak Fox Sparrow
Passerella iliaca insularis [585f]

Similar to the Eastern Fox Sparrow, but with the back not so distinctly

streaked; the tail nearly the same color as the back; and the breast spots, a grayer brown and larger.

DISTRIBUTION—In summer found on Kodiak Island at the base of the Aleutian Peninsula, Alaska. In winter it occurs south along the coast, as far as southern California. (Family *Fringillidae*)

Labrador Savannah Sparrow
Passerculus sandwichensis labradorius [542d]

Similar to the Eastern Savannah Sparrow, but with the legs and wings longer, and the bill shorter and thicker.

DISTRIBUTION—This subspecies of the Savannah Sparrow is found breeding in Labrador, and wintering to the southward along the Atlantic Coast. (Family *Fringillidae*)

Laguna Sparrow
Aimophila ruficeps sororia [580c]

Similar to the Rufous-crowned Sparrow, but with a somewhat larger, heavier bill; with the upper parts appreciably brighter reddish-brown; with the under parts, paler; the breast, more grayish; and the throat and middle of the abdomen, white or whitish.

DISTRIBUTION—Restricted to the southern part of Lower California. (Family *Fringillidae*)

Large-billed Sparrow
Passerculus rostratus rostratus [544]

ADULT MALE AND FEMALE—Upper parts, a light grayish-brown, with faint streakings of blackish. Under parts, whitish or grayish-white, extensively and heavily streaked with sandy-brown. Bill, long; rather heavy and swollen, and its culmen curved.

LENGTH—5.30 inches.

DISTRIBUTION—From Santa Barbara, California, southward along the Pacific Coast. In winter it is found from Santa Cruz, California, to Cape St. Lucas and Guaymas, Mexico.

A peculiar Sparrow with a peculiar range. Bailey writes that Mr. Stephens reports the bird as a common winter resident of the seacoast of southern California, where it is seldom found more than half a mile from the water's edge; however, that it prefers streets and the neighborhood of buildings, to the marshes. It is reported at San Pedro Harbor as common on the wharves and breakwaters, and also "even hops fearlessly about the decks of vessels, feeding on crumbs and flies." (Family *Fringillidae*)

Leconte's Sparrow
Passerherbulus caudacutus [548]

Somewhat similar to the Grasshopper Sparrow and to the Henslow's Sparrow, but with the under parts, a light yellowish-brown. Also similar to the Sharp-tailed Sparrow, but with a light yellowish-brown throat, and a white stripe dividing the center of the crown.

LENGTH—5.00 inches.

DISTRIBUTION — From Manitoba, south into the Great Plains and western prairie country, Minnesota, the Dakotas region. In winter it migrates through Illinois, Kansas, Iowa and neighboring states to South Carolina, Georgia, Florida, Alabama, Mississippi, Louisiana, and Texas.

This rare and shy Sparrow breeds in willow runs and grassy fields in Manitoba. Ernest Thompson Seton describes its song as "so thin a sound, and so creaky, that I believe it is usually attributed to a grasshopper." He says that the song is delivered from some low perch, a little above the tops of the grasses, and is a tiny, husky, double note, sounding like the syllables *reese, reese.* During the winter, in the Gulf States, Leconte's Sparrow is a bird of thickets and tangles, often in low marshy spots. (Family *Fringillidae*)

Lincoln's Sparrow
Melospiza lincolni lincolni [583]

ADULT MALE AND FEMALE—Upper parts, brownish, finely streaked with black, gray, and dark brown. Tail feathers, narrow. Side of the throat with a buffy stripe. Under parts, white, finely streaked with black. Breast, crossed by a buffy band.

LENGTH—5.75 inches.

DISTRIBUTION—From Nova Scotia west to Alaska, and south to northern New York, northern New England, northern Illinois, the higher Rocky Mountains, and the Sierra Nevada. In winter it ranges from southern Illinois and southern California southward into Mexico. It is rarely found east of the Allegheny Mountains at this season.

The Lincoln's Sparrow is an extremely shy and retiring bird. On its migrations it keeps itself well hidden in brush tangles, along old fences and

stone walls, in masses of poison ivy or bittersweet, or slips in and out of catbrier, or among fallen logs covered with dried weeds. It very closely resembles the Song Sparrow, but shows a buffy band across the breast. The tail is also somewhat shorter. It breeds among the northern evergreens, and sings a song similar to the bubbling strain of the House Wren. (Family *Fringillidae*)

Louisiana Seaside Sparrow

Ammospiza maritima fisheri [550c]

Somewhat similar to the Northern Seaside Sparrow, but with the upper parts darker, and with the breast and sides of the body heavily washed with a rusty cream-brown, and streaked with dark gray or blackish.

DISTRIBUTION—"Breeds in the salt marshes on the Gulf Coast, from Grand Isle, Louisiana, to High Island, Texas; winters south to Corpus Christi, Texas." (Chapman.) (Family *Fringillidae*)

MacGillivray's Seaside Sparrow

Ammospiza maritima macgillivraii [550d]

Similar to the Louisiana Seaside Sparrow, but with the upper parts, grayer and less blackish. The breast and flanks are very faintly suffused with light cream-brown and streaked with gray.

DISTRIBUTION—Found along the coastal zone, in the salt marshes, from North Carolina southward into northern Florida. (Family *Fringillidae*)

Mendocino Song Sparrow

Melospiza melodia cleonensis [581p]

Similar to the Samuel's Song Sparrow in size, and with the whole bird lighter in general tone, and more brownish or rusty. The black streaks of the upper parts are more restricted; the spottings of the breast are edged with light or rusty-brown; and in place of the black on the sides of the head and neck, is a reddish or rusty-brown color.

DISTRIBUTION — Coastal strip of southern Oregon, and southward along the coast of northern California, from Yaquina Bay, Oregon, to Tomales Bay, northern California. (Family *Fringillidae*)

Merrill's Song Sparrow

Melospiza melodia merrilli [581k]

Similar to the Eastern Song Sparrow, but with the upper parts grayer, darker, and more uniform in coloration; the edges of the feathers grayer. The bird is slightly smaller, and has a relatively smaller bill.

LENGTH—6.02 inches.

DISTRIBUTION—From the mountains of northern California, through Oregon and Washington (east of the Cascade Range), as far as northwestern Idaho. In winter it is found as far south as Mexico. (Family *Fringillidae*)

Mexican Black-chinned Sparrow

Spizella atrogularis atrogularis [565]

A small sparrow, a trifle larger than the common Eastern Chipping Sparrow, or Chippy, but with the bill and

wings shorter and the tail somewhat longer. Upper parts similar to those of the Chippy. Head, neck, and the entire under parts, gray; the latter somewhat lighter in tone than the head. Region about the base of the bill, and the upper part of the throat, black. Bill, reddish or flesh color.

DISTRIBUTION—From Arizona and the southern part of New Mexico southward over the Mexican tableland to Puebla and Michoacan. In winter it migrates south of the Mexican border. (Family *Fringillidae*)

Mississippi Song Sparrow

Melospiza melodia beata [58ɹu]

Similar to the common Eastern Song Sparrow, but generally with a darker and grayer tone, and the upper parts showing little or no admixture of red-

dish-brown. The black streakings of the back itself are heavy and pronounced, and the stripes on the side of the crown are blackish-brown. The bill is much larger, with its upper mandible swollen at its base.

DISTRIBUTION—Restricted to the Mississippi Valley region, wandering casually in winter, and during migration, as far east as Florida. (Family *Fringillidae*)

Modesto Song Sparrow

Melospiza melodia maillardi [58ɪy]

Similar in general to the Heermann's Song Sparrow, but darker, and with a larger bill.

DISTRIBUTION—Found in the Sacramento and lower San Joaquin River valleys, in California, southward from Tehama County to Stanislaus County. (Family *Fringillidae*)

Modoc Song Sparrow

Melospiza melodia fisherella [58ɪv]

Similar to the Heermann's Song Sparrow, but larger, with the upper parts paler and less brown, and with the streaks of the under parts browner and less blackish in tone.

DISTRIBUTION—From the southeastern portion of Oregon, northwestern Utah, and southwestern Idaho, southward through the eastern part of California as far as Owens Valley, and northward as far as the Shasta Valley. In winter it is widely distributed throughout western and southern California. (Family *Fringillidae*)

Mono Fox Sparrow

Passerella iliaca monoensis [585n]

Similar to the Thick-billed Fox Sparrow, but with the upper parts slightly paler and more ashy in tone, and with a smaller bill.

DISTRIBUTION—In the region of Mono Lake, on the eastern slopes of the Sierra Nevada in extreme east central California. In winter it is found in the western foothills of the Sierra Nevada in southern California, and also in the northern part of Lower California west of the deserts. (Family *Fringillidae*)

Mountain Song Sparrow

Melospiza melodia fallax [581b]

Similar to the Eastern Song Sparrow, but with the brownish color duller and grayer; with the tail and wings longer; the bill slightly smaller and slenderer.

LENGTH—6.03 inches.

DISTRIBUTION—From eastern Oregon, southern Idaho, and southern Montana, south through the Rocky Mountains and the Sierra Nevada of California. In winter it passes into western Texas and northern Mexico. (Family *Fringillidae*)

Nelson's Sparrow

Ammospiza caudacuta nelsoni [549.1]

Similar to the Sharp-tailed Sparrow, but smaller, with the upper parts darker, the back being more of an olive-brown, and the feathers bearing broad whitish margins. Throat, breast, and sides of the body, deep brownish-buff, only very lightly, if at all, streaked with blackish.

LENGTH—5.50 inches.

DISTRIBUTION — From the Great Slave Lake, Canada, and western central Alberta, to southwestern Manitoba, Minnesota, and the northeastern portion of South Dakota. In winter it is found on the Atlantic and Gulf coasts from North Carolina southward to Florida and westward to Texas. During migration it reaches as far north on the Atlantic Coast as Maine, and occurs accidentally in California.

During migration, and in winter, this interior North American Sharp-tailed Sparrow may be found in flocks together with the Acadian Sharp-tailed

Sparrow and the Sharp-tailed Sparrow. From the Sharp-tailed Sparrow it may be distinguished by its rather bright brownish breast, which, at a distance, appears to be entirely plain and unstreaked. The Acadian Sharp-tailed Sparrow presents a breast bearing definite, but indistinct, streakings. (Family *Fringillidae*)

Nevada Savannah Sparrow

Passerculus sandwichensis nevadensis [542e]

Similar to the Western Savannah Sparrow, but in general tone, much paler, with more white, and the black streakings much less defined.

DISTRIBUTION — Probably through the Great Basin, and in Nevada in Humboldt and Washoe counties. In winter it is found south to the Colorado Desert, and Los Angeles County, California. (Family *Fringillidae*)

Northern Sage Sparrow

Amphispiza nevadensis nevadensis [574.1]

ADULT MALE AND FEMALE—Upper parts, light grayish-brown; back, narrowly and sharply streaked with blackish. Tail, black; the outer web of outer tail feathers, white. Sides of throat with series of narrow blackish streaks, forming a discontinuous stripe. A blackish spot in the center of the upper breast. Under parts, whitish; sides of the body and flanks faintly washed with light brown.

LENGTH—5.85 inches.

DISTRIBUTION—From Oregon and Idaho southward into California and New Mexico. In winter it is found in western Texas, Arizona, New Mexico, and the southern portion of California.

The Northern Sage Sparrow is a bird of the sage-brush plains, in the desert portions of its range, where its coloration harmonizes well with its grayish-greenish-brownish surroundings. From the somewhat similar Bell's Sparrow, it may be distinguished by its broken, instead of continuous, stripe on the side of the throat, and its long blackish tail. (Family *Fringillidae*)

Northern Seaside Sparrow
Ammospiza maritima maritima [550]

ADULT MALE AND FEMALE—Upper parts, grayish-olive-greenish. Line from the base of the under mandible down the side of the throat, blackish. Line from the base of the upper mandible to eye, yellow. Bend of the wing (wrist), yellow. Tail, grayish-brown; the outer webs of its feathers margined with olive-greenish. Breast, white washed with creamy-brown in winter; plain white or whitish in summer. In both seasons, faintly streaked with gray. Throat and middle of abdomen, whitish, darkening to grayish on the sides.

LENGTH—6.00 inches.

DISTRIBUTION—Along the Atlantic Coast, in the wide salt marshes from the southern portion of Massachusetts southward into Virginia. In winter a few individuals may be found in the salt marshes along the Rhode Island and Connecticut coast (rarely in southern Massachusetts), but the majority spend the winter from Virginia to northern Florida.

Seaside Sparrows are almost never found beyond the sight or sound of the sea waves in salt marshes, where it may be found in company with such close relatives as the Song Sparrow, Swamp Sparrow, Savannah Sparrow, and Sharp-tailed Sparrow. Its short, insectoid, buzzing song, consisting of but four or five notes, is sometimes given from the top of a small bush, the tip of a tall reed, or may be uttered while the bird flies a short distance up into the air. They are mostly birds of the ground, however, and pass most of their time threading their way among the bases of marsh grasses, in

a mouse-like fashion, and secure from prying eyes. When flushed they rise only a short distance above the grasses,

and flit a few feet away before dropping down again out of sight. (Family *Fringillidae*)

Nuttall's Sparrow
Zonotrichia leucophrys nuttalli [554b]

Similar to the White-crowned Sparrow, but with the upper parts brownish instead of grayish, and the streakings dark brown or black. The under parts are a brownish-gray. The line over the eye extends to the base of the bill, and the lores are not black.

LENGTH—6.26 inches.

DISTRIBUTION—From British Columbia southward to Monterey, California; passing in winter into Lower California. (Family *Fringillidae*)

Oregon Vesper Sparrow
Pooecetes gramineus affinis [540b]

Similar to the Western Vesper Sparrow, but smaller, with the underlying color of the upper parts a light buffy-brown, rather than a grayish-brown; and all the lighter colored areas of the plumage, washed with a pinkish-buffy hue. The general effect is to render the bird browner in tone than the Western Vesper. The bill is slenderer than in that species.

LENGTH—5.36 inches.
DISTRIBUTION—Found in western Oregon and California. (Family *Fringillidae*)

Pine-woods Sparrow

Aimophila aestivalis aestivalis [575]

ADULT MALE AND FEMALE—Upper parts, light chestnut-brown streaked with black, and the feathers margined by light gray. Line over the eye, grayish or whitish. Shoulders tinged with yellowish. Tail, grayish-brown; the feathers all narrow, and the outer ones much shorter than the others. Breast and sides of the body washed with pale ashy-brown; the breast sometimes showing a few scattered blackish spots. Center of abdomen, white.
LENGTH—5.80 inches.
DISTRIBUTION—From the southeastern part of Georgia southward into central Florida. In winter it is found only in central and southern Florida.

The Pine-woods Sparrow is found only in pine woods where there is an undergrowth of the scrub palmetto, and is considered by many one of our very sweetest and purest-toned singers. There is an artlessness and tenderness in its song that goes straight to the heart. Chapman has given a description of this song which should be known by every bird lover. He says, "In my opinion, its song is more beautiful than that of any other American sparrow. It is very simple—I write it *che-e-e-e—de, de, de; che-e—chee-o, chee-o, chee-o, chee-o*—but it possesses all the exquisite tenderness and pathos of the melody of the Hermit Thrush; indeed in purity of tone and in execution I should consider this Sparrow the superior songster. It sings most freely very early in the morning and late in the afternoon, when the world is hushed, and the pine trees breathe a soft accompaniment to its divine music." This tiny songster is an exceedingly diffident, retiring mite, keeping itself well concealed amid the undergrowth, except during the utterance of its ingenuous little lay. (Family *Fringillidae*)

Puget Sound Sparrow

Zonotrichia leucophrys pugetensis [554]

Similar to Nuttall's Sparrow, but differing from it chiefly in possessing slightly less brownish, and more grayish upper parts; grayer under parts, especially on the upper breast; a slightly smaller bill; and longer wings and tail.

DISTRIBUTION—"Pacific Coast belt, from Vancouver Island and the mouth of the Fraser River, British Columbia, south to Mendocino County, California. Winters south to San Diego County, California." (A.O.U. Check List). (Family *Fringillidae*)

Rock Sparrow

Aimophila ruficeps eremoeca [580b]

Similar to the Rufous-crowned Sparrow, but with the prevailing color of the upper parts ashy, instead of grayish-brown. The feathers of the back show dull brownish central streaks and black shafts.
LENGTH—5.70 inches.
DISTRIBUTION—From the central portion of Texas, through the southwestern portion of the state, as far as Orizaba (Vera Cruz, southeastern Mexico). (Family *Fringillidae*)

Rufous-crowned Sparrow

Aimophila ruficeps ruficeps [580]

ADULT MALE AND FEMALE—Upper parts, grayish or grayish-brown, widely streaked with a pronounced darker reddish-brown. Throat bordered by a narrow black stripe. Sides of head and neck, pale buffy. Under parts, the same color or slightly more brownish. Crown, a decided reddish-brown.

LENGTH—5.27 inches.

DISTRIBUTION—From the northern part of California, southward along the coast into the northern part of Lower California. (Family *Fringillidae*)

Rufous-winged Sparrow
Aimophila carpalis [579]

ADULT MALE AND FEMALE—Upper parts, buffy-brown, sharply streaked with black. Crown, grayish, heavily streaked with reddish-brown, and divided in the middle by a narrow grayish-white line. A brownish streak extends behind the eye, and two black stripes extend from the base of the bill down along the sides of the throat. The lesser wing coverts show a bright rufous patch. Under parts, white or grayish-white.

LENGTH—5.18 inches.

DISTRIBUTION — In southern Arizona, and southward into northwestern Mexico, through Sonora and into northern Sinaloa.

The Rufous-winged Sparrow is short-winged, and is found in the foothills of the Santa Catalina Mountains of Arizona. Here they ascend to an altitude of from 3,000 to 4,500 feet, feeding on the ground in small flocks, and acting very much like the little Chipping Sparrow, which they closely resemble in habits and appearance. The conspicuous reddish-brown patch in the wing at once identifies the bird in the field. (Family *Fringillidae*)

Rusty Song Sparrow
Melospiza melodia morphna [581e]

ADULT MALE AND FEMALE—Upper parts, olive-brownish, with a decided rusty tinge, and obscurely streaked with brown and black. Breast, broadly streaked with heavy dark reddish-brown; abdomen, less so. Flanks, olive-brownish.

LENGTH—6.07 inches.

DISTRIBUTION — From the southern portion of Alaska to Oregon, in the Pacific coastal zone. In winter it is found in southern California.

The general appearance of this Sparrow is dark brown. Bailey observes that the bird is said to be an especially water-loving species, and that it is found in swamps, brush patches along streams and coastal waters. (Family *Fringillidae*)

Samuels's Song Sparrow
Melospiza melodia samuelis [581d]

Similar to Heermann's Song Sparow, but much smaller, and with a slenderer bill.

LENGTH—5.40 inches.

DISTRIBUTION—Found in the coastal region of California, from Humboldt County southward to Santa Cruz County. (Family *Fringillidae*)

San Clemente Song Sparrow
Melospiza melodia clementae [581i]

Similar to the Heermann's Song Sparrow, but with the upper parts a light olive-gray, with narrow black streaks. The streakings on the under parts are narrow and sharp.

LENGTH—Nearly 6.00 inches.

DISTRIBUTION—Off the coast of southernmost California on the San Clemente, San Miguel, and Santa Rosa islands; and on the Coronados Islands of Lower California.

The San Clemente Song Sparrow resembles the San Diego Song Sparrow, but is larger and grayer. (Family *Fringillidae*)

San Diego Song Sparrow
Melospiza melodia cooperi [581m]

Similar to the Heermann's Song Sparrow, but slightly smaller, and much lighter and grayer in general tone.

DISTRIBUTION—"Southern coast

district of California north to Monterey Bay, east to Fort Tejon, San Bernardino, etc., and the north Pacific Coast district of Lower California, south to San Quentin Bay." (Ridgway.) (Family *Fringillidae*)

San Lucas Sparrow
Passerculus rostratus guttatus [544a]

Similar to the Large-billed Sparrow, but with the upper parts very much darker, showing no brownish tinge, and with the under parts more closely and completely spotted.

DISTRIBUTION—Found on the San Benito Islands off the coast of Lower California. "In winter it spreads along the coast to San Jose de Cabo and to San Jose and Carmen islands in the Gulf; north to San Pedro and Monterey County, California." (Family *Fringillidae*)

San Miguel Song Sparrow
Melospiza melodia micronyx [581w]

This subspecies (*Melospiza melodia*) is the grayest of all the Song Sparrows. The plumage lacks almost completely any brown tone. Otherwise the bird is similar to the Eastern Song Sparrow.

DISTRIBUTION — Restricted to San Miguel Island, California. (Family *Fringillidae*)

Santa Barbara Song Sparrow
Melospiza melodia graminea [581h]

Similar to the Heermann's Song Sparrow, but smaller, with the upper parts decidedly more grayish, and with the streakings of the under parts narrower. The bill is slenderer.

LENGTH—5.32 inches.

DISTRIBUTION—The bird breeds on the Santa Barbara Islands, and in winter migrates to the adjacent mainland of California, south of Santa Barbara.

This Song Sparrow also resembles the Samuels's Song Sparrow, but is grayer above. Its tail is shorter, and its feet are larger than this subspecies. (Family *Fringillidae*)

Santa Cruz Sparrow
Aimophila ruficeps obscura [580f]

Similar to the Rufous-crowned Sparrow, but darker and less brownish; with a heavier bill, and slightly longer and heavier legs and feet.

DISTRIBUTION—"Santa Cruz Island, and probably Santa Catalina and Santa Rosa islands, California." (A. O.U. Check List.) (Family *Fringillidae*)

Scott's Sparrow
Aimophila ruficeps scotti [580a]

Similar to the Rufous-crowned Sparrow, but with the upper parts a brighter reddish-brown, and the margins on the feathers a lighter gray. The breast is a much lighter gray color. Throat and middle of the abdomen, white or whitish. In spite of the brighter colors of the upper parts, the generally paler color of the bird makes it appear the less brightly colored of the two.

LENGTH—5.70 inches.

DISTRIBUTION — From the western part of Texas west into southern Arizona, and south as far as the northern quarter of Mexico.

The Scott's Sparrow is a resident of the upper levels, occurring at altitudes of 2,000 to 4,000 feet in winter; and reaching nearly up to 10,000 feet in summer, in the Santa Catalina Mountains of Arizona. Its song is described as "short and rather mechanical." (Bailey.) (Family *Fringillidae*)

Scott's Seaside Sparrow
Ammospiza maritima peninsulae [550a]

Similar to MacGillivray's Seaside Sparrow, but much darker; the sides and under parts more heavily streaked.

DISTRIBUTION—In the salt marshes along the western coast of Florida from Tampa Bay to Lafayette County. (Family *Fringillidae*)

Sharp-tailed Sparrow

Ammospiza caudacuta caudacuta [549]

ADULT MALE AND FEMALE—Upper parts, brownish-olive-green, marked with gray and white; the crown, olive-brownish, divided by a grayish line. Ear coverts, gray, bordered by brownish borders—one over the eye, and the other down along the side of the throat. Bend of the wing, yellow. Tail feathers, narrow and sharply pointed, the outer ones shorter than the others. Throat and abdomen, white. Breast and sides washed with light creamy-brown, the former with fine streaks.

LENGTH—5.85 inches.

DISTRIBUTION—From Massachusetts to Virginia, in the salt marshes along the Atlantic Coast. In winter its range is from New Jersey to Florida, along the coast in the salt marshes. Occasionally at this season some individuals are found along the Massachusetts coast.

Sharp-tailed Sparrows are found among the marsh grasses, running

about like little mice, and seldom taking wing. The tail tapers to a point, instead of spreading, and this feature, together with the light brown lines of the side of the head, and the sharp breast markings, serve to identify the bird. Its song is short, weak, and husky. (Family *Fringillidae*)

Shumagin Fox Sparrow

Passerella iliaca unalaschcensis [585a]

A very pale "edition" of the Eastern Fox Sparrow.

DISTRIBUTION—Alaska and the Shumagin Islands. (Family *Fringillidae*)

Slate-colored Fox Sparrow

Passerella iliaca schistacea [585c]

Similar to the Thick-billed Fox Sparrow, but smaller, both in length of body and in dimensions of bill.

LENGTH—6.70 inches.

DISTRIBUTION—In the Rocky Mountains of British Columbia and the United States, from Colorado westward to California, Washington, and Oregon. In winter it wanders into Kansas, and southward into southern California, Arizona, and Nevada. (Family *Fringillidae*)

Sooty Fox Sparrow

Passerella iliaca fuliginosa [585e]

ADULT MALE AND FEMALE—Upper parts, uniform dull brown (wings and tail the same), and without streakings, as in the Eastern Fox Sparrow. Under parts, white or whitish heavily spotted with dull brown.

LENGTH—7.10 inches.

DISTRIBUTION—In the coastal region of southwestern British Columbia, southward into northwestern Washington. In winter it passes south and is found along the coast of northern California down to San Francisco.

The Sooty Fox Sparrow, as the name suggests, is a much duller bird than our Eastern Fox Sparrow. The spots on the under parts are more confluent than in other forms of Fox Sparrows. (Family *Fringillidae*)

Sooty Song Sparrow
Melospiza melodia rufina [581f]

Similar to the Eastern Song Sparrow, but sootier, i.e., darker—the darkest of the *Melospiza melodia* group.

DISTRIBUTION—On the outer islands of southeastern Alaska, from Chicha-

gof to Forrester and Duke islands. Also on the Queen Charlotte Islands, British Columbia. (Family *Fringillidae*)

Stephen's Fox Sparrow
Passerella iliaca stephensi [585d]

Similar to the Thick-billed Fox Sparrow, but somewhat larger, and with a much larger bill.

LENGTH—Over 7.00 inches.

DISTRIBUTION—Found in the higher San Bernardino and San Jacinto mountains of southern California. (Family *Fringillidae*)

Suisun Song Sparrow
Melospiza melodia maxillaris [581s]

Similar to the Heermann's Song Sparrow, but with the general coloration of the bird much darker, and with the blackish streaks on the body everywhere much deeper and broader. It also somewhat resembles the Samuels's Song Sparrow, but is slightly larger, and the brown coloration is more extended and darker in tone. The base of each side of the bill bears bulbous enlargements.

DISTRIBUTION—Found in the salt marshes bordering the Suisun Bay, in Solano County, California. (Family *Fringillidae*)

Swamp Sparrow
Melospiza georgiana [584]

ADULT MALE AND FEMALE—Upper parts, brown streaked with black; the wings, darker. Crown, rich reddish-brown. Throat, whitish with gray sides; the rest of the under parts, grayish-white. Flanks, tinged with light brown.

LENGTH—5.89 inches.

DISTRIBUTION — Eastern North America, from Labrador and Manitoba, southward to New Jersey, Pennsylvania, and northern Illinois, and west to the Great Plains. In winter it is found from the latitudes of Kansas, southern Illinois, and central Massachusetts, southward to the Gulf of Mexico.

During its migration the Swamp Sparrow may be found in dry bushy pastures, hillsides, and similar situations, far from water; but on its breeding

grounds the bird is a denizen of fresh or salt-water marshes, wet grassy meadows, or the borders of swampy streams. Its song, easily learned, and quite distinctive, is a simple succession of sweet *tweet* or *tweelt* notes, rapidly delivered, sometimes so rapidly as to run into a little trill, reminiscent of the song of the Chipping Sparrow. It is, however, sweeter than the Chippy's song, with more body, and the notes possess a liquid, globular character, as though they partook of the lush and watery nature of the bird's habitat. Because of the retiring disposition of the bird and the inaccessibility of its environs, it is more frequently heard than seen. It delights in threading the lower tangles of grass and reeds just at the water line, or creeping mouse-like among the tussocks of peat bogs. (Family *Fringillidae*)

Texas Sparrow
Arremonops rufivirgatus rufivirgatus [586]

ADULT MALE AND FEMALE—Upper parts, olive-green; wings and tail, more decided greenish. Shoulder (wrist) of the wing edged with bright or straw yellow. Crown, with a broad central grayish-olive stripe bordered on each side by a wide line of deep brown. Line over the eye, whitish. Under parts, white or dull ashy-white, usually washed on the upper breast and sides of the body with buff.

LENGTH—6.50 inches.

DISTRIBUTION—Southern North America, from southeastern Texas (infrequently Louisiana) southward into the eastern part of Mexico.

The Texas Sparrow, a dull-colored and unobtrusive little bird, inhabits thickets, and bushy and weedy country generally. Its ingenuous little song is uttered from the top of a weed or small bush, and resembles somewhat the song of the Eastern Chipping Sparrow—a series of rapidly-pronounced *chips,* sometimes running into an irregular trill, but with a sweeter, clearer tone than the Chippy's —a performance which has in it a suggestion of the Eastern Yellow Warbler's strain. When disturbed, the singer does not fly far, but, diving into the intricacies of the nearest coppice, is flushed only with the greatest difficulty. (Family *Fringillidae*)

Texas Seaside Sparrow
Ammospiza maritima sennetti [550b]

Similar to the Eastern Seaside Sparrow, but upper parts showing a more decided greenish tinge, and marked on the nape, and usually on the head and back with black.

DISTRIBUTION—This species is restricted to the coast of Texas. (Family *Fringillidae*)

Thick-billed Fox Sparrow
Passerella iliaca megarhyncha [585b]

ADULT MALE AND FEMALE—Upper parts, plain, unmarked slaty-gray; or, in some cases, with a wash of brownish. The wings, rump, upper tail coverts, and tail, distinctly washed with rusty-brown. Under parts, white, spotted with brown; the spots of the upper breast smaller, and more scattered. Bill, thick and heavy.

LENGTH—About 7.00 inches.

DISTRIBUTION—In the Sierra Nevada, both on the eastern and on the western slopes. In winter it descends into the southern coastal portion (Los Angeles County) of California.

The gray upper parts and thick heavy bill serve to distinguish this Sparrow from the Townsend's Fox Sparrow. Its larger size and thicker bill set it apart from the somewhat similar Slate-colored Fox Sparrow; and its slightly smaller size distinguishes it from the Stephen's Fox Sparrow. (Family *Fringillidae*)

Timberline Sparrow
Spizella breweri taverneri [562a]

Similar to Brewer's Sparrow, but slightly larger, with a longer tail, and uniformly darker in general tone.

DISTRIBUTION—In the high mountains in northwestern British Columbia, and in Madison County, Montana. (Family *Fringillidae*)

Townsend's Fox Sparrow

Passerella iliaca townsendi [585g]

Similar to the Sooty Fox Sparrow, but browner; and the rump, a brighter brown than the back.

DISTRIBUTION—The southern portion of Alaska, passing southward in winter into northern California. (Family *Fringillidae*)

Trinity Fox Sparrow

Passerella iliaca brevicauda [585j]

Similar to Stephen's Fox Sparrow, but with head, neck, back, and spots on the breast decidedly brownish. Tail, slightly shorter.

DISTRIBUTION—"In inner north coast ranges of California, from north Yolla Bolly Mountain, Trinity County, south to Mt. Sanhedrin, Mendocino County, and Snow Mountain, Colusa County. Winters in the coast district from Marin and Napa counties, south to Los Angeles County." (A.O.U. Check List.) (Family *Fringillidae*)

Valdez Fox Sparrow

Passerella iliaca sinuosa [585k]

Similar to the Shumagin Fox Sparrow, but with the plumage much more slaty-gray. The under parts, more heavily spotted, and the bill, noticeably shorter and slenderer.

DISTRIBUTION—Found in Alaska in the Prince William Sound territory, on Middleton Island, and on the Kenai Peninsula. In winter it passes into California and central Oregon, and southward into the northern portion of Lower California. (Family *Fringillidae*)

Wakulla Seaside Sparrow

Ammospiza maritima juncicola [550e]

This subspecies (*Ammospiza maritima*) is the darkest and blackest of all the Seaside Sparrows.

DISTRIBUTION—Along the Gulf Coast of Florida from St. Andrews Bay southward as far as Taylor County, and probably farther. (Family *Fringillidae*)

Warner Mountains Fox Sparrow

Passerella iliaca fulva [585i]

Similar to the Yosemite Fox Sparrow, but browner.

DISTRIBUTION—Found in the mountains of the extreme northeastern part of California, north into Oregon, and east of the Cascade Mountains as far as Crook County. In winter it occurs in Los Angeles County, California, and in northern Lower California. (Family *Fringillidae*)

Western Chipping Sparrow

Spizella passerina arizonae [560a]

Similar to the Eastern Chipping Sparrow, but with grayer upper parts.

DISTRIBUTION—Alaska to Mexico. It winters from California to southern Mexico. (Family *Fringillidae*)

Western Field Sparrow

Spizella pusilla arenacea [563a]

In general similar to the Eastern Field Sparrow, but with the upper parts grayer and paler above, and with little or no brownish on the breast.

DISTRIBUTION—In the Great Plains, from eastern Montana to Nebraska and South Dakota. It spends the winter as far south as northeastern Mexico, and sometimes is found in Louisiana. (Family *Fringillidae*)

Western Grasshopper Sparrow

Ammodramus savannarum bimaculatus [546a]

Similar to the Eastern Grasshopper Sparrow, but with a more pronounced brownish color on the upper parts, and paler on the under parts.

DISTRIBUTION—From Montana and British Columbia southward to Mexico, from the Great Plains to the Pacific; and south into Mexico for the winter. (Family *Fringillidae*)

Western Henslow's Sparrow

Passerherbulus henslowi henslowi [547a]

Similar to the Eastern Henslow's Sparrow, but paler.

DISTRIBUTION—An inhabitant of the central western states, passing southward in winter to Texas. (Family *Fringillidae*)

Western Lark Sparrow

Chondestes grammacus strigatus [552a]

Very similar to the Eastern Lark Sparrow, but with a more finely streaked back.

DISTRIBUTION—The Pacific Coast of North America, from British Columbia and Manitoba to Mexico, wintering as far south as Central America. (Family *Fringillidae*)

Western Savannah Sparrow

Passerculus sandwichensis alaudinus [542b]

Similar to the Eastern Savannah Sparrow, but paler and with a more slender bill.

DISTRIBUTION — From Alaska into Mexico, and from the Great Plains west to the Sierra Nevada Mountains; wintering from southern California southward. (Family *Fringillidae*)

Western Tree Sparrow

Spizella arborea ochracea [559a]

Similar to the Eastern Tree Sparrow, but with darker, blacker, and more streaked upper parts.

DISTRIBUTION — Alaska, south to Mexico, and west of the Great Plains. (Family *Fringillidae*)

Western Vesper Sparrow

Pooecetes gramineus confinis [540a]

Similar to the Eastern Vesper Sparrow, but with a slenderer bill and slightly paler plumage.

DISTRIBUTION — From the Great Plains to the Sierra Nevada Mountains, and from Saskatchewan to Arizona and New Mexico; wintering in Mexico. (Family *Fringillidae*)

White-crowned Sparrow

Zonotrichia leucophrys leucophrys [554]

ADULT MALE AND FEMALE—Upper parts, brown; the wings with two white bars. Crown, black, divided by a prominent broad white stripe. A broad white stripe extends backward from each eye. Sides of head and back of neck, pale grayish-brown. Under parts, grayish-white and unmarked.

LENGTH—6.88 inches.

DISTRIBUTION—From the Hudson Bay region and Labrador southward into northern New England, New Mexico, Arizona, and California (on the higher elevations of the Rocky and Sierra Nevada mountains). It passes its winters in the southern states, and from there southward into Mexico.

This large handsome Sparrow is found, during migration, in bushy tangles, thickets, tall weeds in old fields, and often in small woods and coppices. It is an infrequent singer while migrating through our northern states, but on its breeding grounds in the far north, or on high mountains, it utters its rather plaintive song—a series of restrained, soft, whistled notes, of

which the terminal ones are rich, sweet, and somewhat buzzy in character, like the notes of the Black-throated Green Warbler. (Family *Fringillidae*)

White-throated Sparrow
Zonotrichia albicollis [558]

ADULT MALE AND FEMALE—Upper parts, rich brown; the wings with two white bars. Crown, black divided by a narrow white line; a yellow line extends before, and a white line over each eye. Breast and throat, grayish, except for a prominent, pure white throat patch, sharply set off by the gray around it. Abdomen, white.

LENGTH—6.74 inches.

DISTRIBUTION—From Labrador and the western part of the Hudson Bay region, southward into Massachusetts (on the mountains), northern New York, northern Michigan, and eastern Montana, sometimes straggling to the Pacific Coast. It spends its winters in the southern part of the United States, from about the latitude of southern Massachusetts.

The White-throated Sparrow during its migrations is found among bushes and weed patches, particularly on hillsides, where it makes a great rustling among the leaves as it searches for food. In the northern forests and

among the mountains of New England, its pure, clear, whistled song is one of the delights of the mountain climber and forest tramper. Although there are several variations of the song, its principal form may be rendered in the syllables *Oooh teee whey, whey, whey, whey.* The first note is low; the second high; and the four or five *whey* notes are about midway. These last notes are pure, crystal, whistled tones, sometimes with a slight tremolo. When the bird sings this tremolo variation, to some ears it seems to say *Oooh, poor Sam Peabody, Peabody, Peabody.* In Vermont the bird is often called Whistling Jack. White-throats are gregarious birds during migration, and whirl up from a clump of bushes, if disturbed, with sharp alarm notes, sounding like the syllables *tseet, tseet.*

The crown stripe of this species is *narrow*, whereas that of the White-crowned Sparrow is *broad*. (Family *Fringillidae*)

Worthen's Sparrow
Spizella wortheni [564]

Similar to the Western Field Sparrow, but with the sides of the head a plain, unmarked gray; and with no brownish streak behind the eye. The tail is somewhat shorter than in the Western Field Sparrow.

DISTRIBUTION—From the extreme southwestern corner (central Grant County) of New Mexico, southward along the plateau of northeastern Mexico to southern Puebla. (Family *Fringillidae*)

Yakutat Fox Sparrow
Passerella iliaca annectens [585l]

Similar to the Eastern Fox Sparrow, but smaller; with the back not quite so distinctly streaked, and smaller bill.

DISTRIBUTION—Along the southern coast of Alaska as far north as Prince William Sound, and perhaps to Cook Inlet (at the base of the Aleutian peninsula). In winter it ranges southward into California.

The Yakutat Fox Sparrow closely resembles the Sooty Fox Sparrow, but is not quite so brown in tone. It also resembles the Townsend's Fox Sparrow. (Family *Fringillidae*)

Yakutat Song Sparrow
Melospiza melodia caurina [581n]

Similar to the Sooty Song Sparrow, but with the plumage grayer, not so brownish, and with the bill longer.

DISTRIBUTION—Along the southern part of the Alaskan coast from Yakutat Bay to Lituya Bay. In winter it is found along the coast of British Columbia, and ranges south as far as San Francisco Bay. (Family *Fringillidae*)

Yosemite Fox Sparrow
Passerella iliaca mariposae [585o]

Similar to the Thick-billed Fox Sparrow, but generally more uniformly gray in tone, and with the bill slenderer and sharper.

DISTRIBUTION—Found in the central portion of the Sierra Nevada of California, from the region about Mt. Shasta southward to Kearsage Pass, Inyo County. In winter it occurs in southern California and in Lower California. (Family *Fringillidae*)

SPOONBILL
Roseate Spoonbill
Ajaia ajaja [183]

ADULT MALE AND FEMALE—Plumage, pink; neck and upper back, white, sometimes faintly flushed with pink. Head and throat, bare. Sides of upper breast, light brownish; basal half of the tail, same. Feathers at the base of the neck, slightly lengthened, and slightly darker than the surrounding ones. Lesser wing coverts, and upper and under tail coverts, deep carmine. Bill, long and widely spatulate at its tip, forming a large flat spoon.

LENGTH—32.00 inches; bill 6.25 inches.

DISTRIBUTION — From the Gulf States southward through subtropical into tropical America.

In flight, the Roseate Spoonbill is a striking sight, with its long extended neck, large bill, and brilliant colora-

tion which is apparent at a considerable distance. After it has alighted in a shallow pool it becomes even more noteworthy. No wading bird in our continent is so brightly colored. It is only by vigorous protection that the bird is kept from being exterminated. The Spoonbill secures its food by advancing slowly through the shallow water, swinging its large spoon-shaped, open bill from side to side. (Family *Threskiornithidae*)

STARLING FAMILY
Sturnidae

Starlings are chunky birds, with short tails, broad feet, and long prominent bills. The plumage is black or black- ish, and the birds resemble, at first glance, some "blackbird," and are

often confused with members of this family by those who pay only casual attention to matters of bill and tail. About seventy species and subspecies of Starlings are known and widely dis- tributed in the Old World. In 1890 the common Starling (*Sturnus vul- garis vulgaris*) was imported into the United States, and has thriven too well here. The Crested Mynah (*Aethi- opsar cristatellus cristatellus*) of south China, introduced into British Colum- bia, has not done so well.

NESTING. Starlings are the most adaptable birds when it comes to nest- ing. Almost any cavity or crevice which affords shelter and room for the nest will be made use of, pro- viding it is at a favorable distance from the ground. This means from three to four feet upward. Thus the nests may be found in holes in trees (often deserted woodpecker holes); in natural cavities in trees and stumps (as in old apple orchards); in cavities in rocks and cliffs; in the cornices of buildings; in church towers; under porches; behind window blinds; some- times in barns; in haystacks; and, alas,

too often in bird houses put up for our native birds. The nest itself is a bulky structure composed of grasses, straw, bits of bark or paper, string, twigs, sometimes fragments of seaweed (near the coasts), a few leaves, and is lined with soft grasses, cotton, a few feath- ers, and the like. The eggs, from five to seven or eight, are a somewhat glossy white, whitish, or a pale blue. Three broods are sometimes raised.

STARLING
Starling
Sturnus vulgaris vulgaris [493]

ADULT MALE AND FEMALE—Upper parts, iridescent greenish and purplish; the feathers tipped with light brown- ish creamy spots. Under parts similar, but the spots appearing only on the sides of the body. Wings, tail, lower abdomen, and under-tail coverts, dark brownish-gray; the feathers edged with light creamy brown. Bill, long and yel- low. Feet, large. In winter both the adults and the young are lighter, more heavily spotted, and possess dark gray- ish-brown (sometimes almost black) bills. In this plumage the birds appear larger.

LENGTH—8.50 inches.

DISTRIBUTION—In North America from New Brunswick, southern Que- bec, and Ontario, westward to the Rocky Mountains, and south into Texas and Florida.

The Starling, a European species, was introduced into the United States (in Central Park, New York City) in 1890 and 1891. From the one hundred birds brought in during these years, have descended the countless thou- sands now scattered all over the east- ern portion of our continent. They drive away from nesting holes several species of our own native birds, and are noisy, dirty, and far too numerous. Nevertheless they render good service in their destruction of enormous numbers of the larvae of the pestiferous Japanese beetle, and other injurious insects. In their food habits the birds are entirely beneficial. Starlings nest in holes and cavities, and usually oust species that we would rather have about our homes, such as Bluebirds, Flickers, Crested Flycatchers, Downy Woodpeckers. Even Wrens and Chickadees are driven away, and their nest holes enlarged to receive a family of noisy unpleasant Starlings. The Star-

ling is the only "blackbird-like" bird with a yellow bill in spring and summer. (Family *Sturnidae*)

STILT
Black-necked Stilt

Himantopus mexicanus [226]

ADULT MALE—Top and back of head, back of neck, back, and wings, greenish-black. Tail, gray. The remainder of the plumage is pure white, except that there is a faint flush of cinnamon-pinkish on the breast. Legs and feet, red; bill, black, long, and very slender.

LENGTH—15.00 inches.

DISTRIBUTION — From Oregon, Utah, Colorado, and Nebraska, southward to the northern part of Lower California, and east to the coast of Louisiana, central Florida, and the Bahamas, and southward into northern South America. Formerly the bird extended its range as far north as into New Jersey.

Stilts are unusually graceful, alert, elegant birds, as they pick their way daintily—even fastidiously — among

the aquatic plants in the shallow waters of a pond or marsh, in their search for any minute life that they may chance upon. Upon alighting, they often raise their black pointed wings high up vertically over the body before folding them deliberately over their immaculately white plumage—a striking and graceful gesture. This motion of the wings may also be seen among a flock of feeding birds. (Family *Recurvirostridae*)

STINT
Long-toed Stint

Pisobia subminuta [242.1]

ADULT MALE AND FEMALE—Upper parts, a dull light rusty-brown, more or less spotted and streaked with black and blackish. Breast, white or grayish-white, streaked with dark gray and lighter tones of dusky. The abdomen bears a large blackish patch.

LENGTH—17.50 inches.

DISTRIBUTION—An Asiatic species, this bird has been found on Otter Island of the Pribilof Group, Alaska.

The Long-toed Stint is similar to the common Least Sandpiper, but with longer toes, long wings, and darker general plumage. (Family *Scolopacidae*)

STORK FAMILY
Storks and Wood Ibises
Ciconiidae

The members of the Stork family are mainly birds of the Eastern Hemisphere. The most famous is, of course, the Common Stork (*Ciconia ciconia*), the fabled purveyor of babies. Characteristics of the family will be readily remembered in connection with the

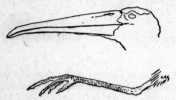

Stork; viz., long, heavy bill; long neck; long legs; long, broad, rounded wings; and relatively short tail. The neck and bill are held straight out while the bird is in flight. About twenty species are known. Three of them occur in the New World, but only one reaches North America, the Wood Ibis (*Mycteria americana*).

NESTING. These birds construct huge bulky nests, in reality great hollow platforms of sticks and twigs. The most famous member of the family, the White Stork of the Old World, breeds occasionally in dead trees or on cliffs, but prefers the structures of man, and may be found nesting commonly on the tops of old chimneys, towers, roofs, or on large boxes and platforms erected for the purpose. A pair of these birds, returning to the same nest year after year, soon builds up the structure to several feet of thickness. The eggs, from three to five in number, are pure white. To have a pair of Storks nesting about one's dwelling is regarded as an indication of the favor of Providence, particularly in the matter of an increase of one's offspring. Our North American representative of the *Ciconiidae* family, the Wood Ibis, breeds chiefly in Florida, in colonies which number hundreds and even thousands of pairs of birds. The nest is placed far up in the tallest tree which the birds can find, at a height of fifty to a hundred feet or more, and consists at first merely of a shallow platform of sticks and the like. Since this structure may be revisited and utilized year after year, it finally becomes quite thick and bulky. The two or three eggs of this species are unmarked white.

STORM PETREL FAMILY
Hydrobatidae

Stormy or Storm Petrels are the so-called Mother Carey's Chickens, and are found on oceans the world over. The name Petrel is a contraction of *Petrellus*, or little Peter, and refers to the birds' habit of seemingly walking on the water, as St. Peter is recorded

to have done. The name Mother Carey is probably derived from the Latin *Mater Cara* (tender mother) and refers to the Virgin, under whose especial protection, so the sailors aver, the birds are enabled to weather the fierce ocean storms. The feet of Petrels are relatively large and webbed; the wings are long and slender, and possess great power; and the tail is more or less forked or notched. In North America there occur fourteen species and subspecies of Storm Petrels, allocated to six genera: *Oceanodroma, Hydrobates, Halocyptena, Oceanites, Fregetta,* and *Pelagodroma.*

NESTING. The Storm Petrels nest on outlying islands of the sea, in a rocky crevice, or cleft, or beneath a slight overhang of rock on a ledge or shelf, or sometimes in a burrow in the soil. The nest itself is a slight affair, depending for its structure on its situation, but sometimes with a ring of pebbles about the margin, and within this some grasses, weeds, rootlets, with perhaps a few feathers—a coarse and ill-assembled structure. The single egg is often white, or white with a ring or scattered band of specks or spots around or near the larger end.

SURF-BIRD
Surf-bird
Aphriza virgata [282]

ADULT MALE AND FEMALE—Upper parts, the head, neck, and upper breast, slate-gray streaked and speckled with white and whitish. Scapulars spotted with brown. Wing with a broad white bar. Base of tail and upper tail coverts, white. Lower breast and abdomen, white speckled with dusky.

LENGTH—10.00 inches.

DISTRIBUTION — From Alaska to Chile, along the Pacific Coast, and to the Straits of Magellan.

The Surf-bird is a rather rare inhabitant of the Pacific Coast of the Americas. It probably breeds in the Alaskan mountains, in the south central portion of that territory, for example in Mt. McKinley Park and the Forty-mile River System, though its nest and eggs have not yet been found. In winter it is found more or less regularly on the Queen Charlotte Islands, Vancouver Island, and the coast of southern Alaska, and thence to the tip of South America, as noted above. It occurs on the Hawaiian and other islands in the Pacific Ocean, and its presence on our coasts is rare. Its name is derived from its habit of run-

ning about just at the edge of the breaking waves, often being deluged by their far-flung spray. It seems to

be a sort of "cross" between a Turnstone and a Plover; in fact one of its vernacular names is Plover-billed Turnstone. (Family *Charadriidae*)

SWALLOW FAMILY
Hirundinidae

Swallows are gracefully-flying birds, with long, narrow, crescentic wings; short legs; small, weak feet; and short, vertically flattened bills; but with deep, wide, gaping mouths; and tails either deeply forked, or only moderately notched, and containing twelve feathers. In the common Barn Swallow the outer pair are by far the longest. Swallows spend most of their waking hours swooping and sailing about in the air, deftly spanning up flying insects of all sorts. Over one hundred of these graceful birds are now known, spread over the whole globe. The eighteen Swallows recorded in North America are allocated to nine genera.

NESTING. While Swallows are often seen during their migrations among the branches of trees, and in the reeds and bushes of marshy regions, where they chiefly roost during their north and south journeyings, yet they do not nest in such situations, except that the Tree Swallows often use the hole of a tree, no matter where it may be found. Some species of Swallows nest in crevices of cliffs, in holes in trees, and often in nesting boxes. (Tree Swallow and Purple Martin). Some nest under the overhanging ledge of a cliff, or under the projecting eaves of a barn (Cliff or Eave Swallow, and

the Violet-green Swallow); or within a barn close to the roof on a rafter or beam (Barn Swallow); or in a horizontal tunnel in a sand bank (Bank Swallow, and Rough-winged Swallow). Swallows are social or gregarious birds in their domestic relations, often nesting in close colonies. The Cliff or Eave Swallow constructs a jug-like or retort-like nest within whose bulbous base the grass and feather lining receives the eggs. Closely compacted rows of these little jugs with their rough mud or clay pelleted surfaces are often seen by the hundreds lined up under the projecting eaves of barns, locally in the northern New England States, more particularly in Maine. The nests themselves of hole-building Swallows, at the end of their tunnels, or bottoms of their holes or jugs, are composed of a rather sparse collection of grasses, straws, and feathers. The nests of other species, which build more or less in the open, are of the same general materials, often with the addition of bits of paper, cloth, string, fragments of cotton, etc. These are held together with a foundation of mud or clay. Swallows lay about four or five eggs. The colors are either white, grayish-white, pinkish-white, or creamy; sometimes unmarked or else

more or less profusely spotted with various tones of brown.

SWALLOW

Bahama Swallow

Callichelidon cyaneoviridis [615.1]

ADULT MALE AND FEMALE—Upper parts, dull greenish; the wings and tail with a bluish cast. Under parts, white. Tail, deeply forked.

DISTRIBUTION—Recorded from the Dry Tortugas, and Tarpon Springs, in Florida, and is thought to occur also in the keys off the Florida coast. (Family *Hirundinidae*)

Bank Swallow

Riparia riparia riparia [616]

ADULT MALE AND FEMALE—Upper parts, grayish earthy-brown. Under parts, white; the upper breast crossed by a grayish-brown band. Tail very slightly forked, and when fully spread appearing almost square across.

LENGTH—5.20 inches.

DISTRIBUTION—From Alaska and Labrador south to northern New Jersey, Kansas, and southern California. In winter it passes south as far as Brazil.

The Bank Swallow, in its migration and final dispersal in spring, is associated with stream valleys, since its

natural nesting sites are in vertical sand and clay banks common along stream courses. Sometimes the birds excavate nesting holes in sand banks where highway workers have been digging. While feeding, Bank Swallows may be seen coursing over the surfaces of lakes and large streams. At such times they may be identified by their white under parts crossed by a brown band at the upper breast. Remember the phrase *Bank bears brown band.* They are, in the main, silent birds, but when they do speak, they say *trit, trit, trit* in a gritty sort of voice; or prolong the utterance into *treet* or *treckt;* and in the spring, repeat these notes with an almost musical iteration, achieving something which might be termed a song. (Family *Hirundinidae*)

Barn Swallow
Hirundo erythrogaster [613]

ADULT MALE—Upper parts, glossy purplish-blue. Forehead, throat, and upper breast, rich chestnut. Lower breast and abdomen, salmon. Tail, deeply forked, with all but its middle feathers bearing white spots near their tips.

ADULT FEMALE—Similar, but with the under parts flesh color, or very pale yellowish, or almost white. Tail not quite so deeply forked.

LENGTH—6.95 inches.

DISTRIBUTION—All of the North American Continent, from Alaska eastward, and into Greenland. In winter it passes south, as far as the southern part of Brazil.

No species of bird, among our smaller kind, has entered more extensively into our national art and literature than this extremely domestic little Swallow, which is, fortunately, a species very valuable economically from the standpoint of American agriculture. Barn Swallows formerly nested in caves and in the cavities of trees, but do so now only where barns and similar structures are absent. The Barn Swallow is not to be confused with the Cliff, or Eave Swallow. The former

nests only *within* barns; the latter plasters its vase of mud *without,* usually under the eaves. The call notes of the Barn Swallow are a series of low musical twitterings, which occasionally, during the mating season, become sufficiently varied and prolonged

to be considered almost a true song. This mating performance is given while the birds are flying high in the air, or while at rest and warming themselves in the spring sun, perched most often on a telephone wire, or along the ridge pole of a barn. All sorts of flying insects, captured awing, form the dietary of the Barn Swallow. Flies make up about 38 per cent; beetles about 20 per cent; bugs about 20 per cent; wasps and some few bees about 18 per cent; and flying ants, moths, and miscellaneous insects about 20 per cent. (Family *Hirundinidae*)

Coahuila Cliff Swallow
Petrochelidon fulva pallida [612.1a]

Similar to the Cuban Cliff Swallow, but slightly larger, and with all the colors uniformly paler.

DISTRIBUTION—From about Kerr County, Texas, southward into Mexico as far as Coahuila and Tamaulipas. (Family *Hirundinidae*)

Cuban Cliff Swallow
Petrochelidon fulva cavicola [612.1]

Similar to the Northern Cliff Swallow, but with forehead and rump, chestnut.

DISTRIBUTION—Reported once from Dry Tortugas, Florida. (Family *Hirundinidae*)

European Swallow

Hirundo rustica rustica [613.1]

ADULT MALE—Upper parts, sides of the neck, and a band across the breast, black with violet and bluish reflections. Forehead and throat, rich chestnut-brown. Under parts, pinkish. Tail, deeply forked.

ADULT FEMALE—Similar to the male, but paler, with somewhat shorter outer tail feathers.

LENGTH—7.50 inches.

DISTRIBUTION — This commonest Swallow of England occurs as an accidental straggler in Greenland. A close relative of our common Barn Swallow.

No bird more engaged the attention and affections of Gilbert White of Selborne than the gentle common Swallow. And while the great naturalist was not convinced that the birds actually did hibernate under the water, or in cliffs or ruined towers, yet he was also not convinced that they did not! A quaint observation of his is worth quoting: "By means of a straight cottage chimney I had an opportunity this summer of remarking at my leisure how Swallows ascend and descend through the shaft; but my pleasure in contemplating the address with which this feat was performed to a considerable depth in the chimney, was somewhat interrupted by apprehensions lest my eyes might undergo the same fate with those of Tobit." This whimsical allusion is to the uncanonical book of Tobit, 2:10, "And I knew not that there were sparrows in the wall, and mine eyes being open, the sparrows muted warm dung into mine eyes, and a whiteness came into mine eyes; and I went to the physicians, but they helped me not." (Family *Hirundinidae*)

Lesser Cliff Swallow

Petrochelidon albifrons tachina [612a]

Similar to the Northern Cliff Swallow, but smaller, and the forehead darker.

DISTRIBUTION—Western Texas, the Rio Grande Valley, and eastern Mexico as far as Vera Cruz. (Family *Hirundinidae*)

Mexican Cliff Swallow

Petrochelidon albifrons melanogaster [612b]

Similar to the Northern Cliff Swallow, but smaller, with chestnut forehead.

DISTRIBUTION—From Southern Arizona south into Mexico. (Family *Hirundinidae*)

Northern Cliff Swallow

Petrochelidon albifrons albifrons [612]

ADULT MALE AND FEMALE—Back, dark slaty-blue, slightly streaked with whitish; forehead, creamy-white. Sides of head, and throat, chestnut; ring around the neck, brownish-gray. Upper tail coverts, pale brick-red. Breast, brownish-gray, darker in the center; abdomen, whitish. Tail, dark slaty-blue, not forked, but square across the tip, and fan-shaped when spread widely in flight.

LENGTH—6.01 inches.

DISTRIBUTION—From the tree-limit in far northern North America, south to about northern New Jersey, Kentucky, and southern Texas, across to southern California. In winter it migrates into Central and South America.

The characteristic nests of the Cliff Swallow (or Eave Swallow as it is frequently called) never fail to attract admiring interest wherever they appear. Shaped like retorts, or ancient tear-bottles, and composed of pellets of mud or clay, they are placed commonly under the projecting eaves of a barn or similar building, or in a sheltered spot on a cliff, or high firm embankment, often fifty or more in a colony. Within the jug-like structure is placed the nest of wool, feathers, dry grass, and bits of soft moss. The notes of the bird are of the twittering, or

chippering sort, so common among Swallows. There is no true song. The Cliff Swallow is the decided friend of the southern cotton-grower, since it feeds voraciously upon the destructive cotton boll weevil. Other pests destroyed by the bird include the wheat billbug, clover root curculio (and other species of snout beetles), and the very pestiferous chinch bug. (Family *Hirundinidae*)

Rough-winged Swallow

Stelgidopteryx ruficollis serripennis [617]

Somewhat similar to the Bank Swallow, but with the entire throat, and

breast, grayish-brown. The barbs on the outer vanes of the outer primary feathers protrude, and are recurved.

LENGTH—5.75 inches.

DISTRIBUTION — From British Columbia, Manitoba, and northern Mass-

achusetts, southwest to Mexico. It passes the winter in Central America. (Family *Hirundinidae*)

San Lucas Swallow

Tachycineta thalassina brachyptera [615a]

Similar to the northern Violet-green Swallow, but with a shorter wing.

DISTRIBUTION—Restricted to Lower California. (Family *Hirundinidae*)

Tree Swallow

Iridoprocne bicolor [614]

ADULT MALE—Upper parts, iridescent greenish-blue. Under parts, pure white. Tail only very slightly concave across its end, appearing square-cut in flight.

ADULT FEMALE—Upper parts usually somewhat duller, with the iridescent sheen often masked.

LENGTH—5.90 inches.

DISTRIBUTION—From Labrador and Alaska southward on the Pacific Coast to about central California, and on the Atlantic Coast to about northern New Jersey. In winter it is found from South Carolina and southern California into the tropics.

The Tree Swallow is the first of these birds to arrive in the New England States in the spring, and the first to

leave in the fall. In the latter season they begin to congregate by thousands, and to sit in long lines on telegraph wires, usually near swampy or low-lying land, particularly along coastal marshes. Some few individuals winter over, even in the northern states, and during this season subsist, not upon insects, but upon such berries as those of the red cedar, and bayberry. The notes of the Tree Swallow are a series of shrill, lively twitterings, typically hirundine in character, though higher pitched than those of most Swallows. Sometimes, during the breeding season, the notes rise to the level of a rather sweet, broken warbling song, uttered by the male. (Family *Hirundinidae*)

Violet-green Swallow
Tachycineta thalassina lepida [615]

Somewhat similar to the Tree Swallow, but with the cheeks also white,

and the upper parts with a violet-green tinge.

DISTRIBUTION—A western species, ranging from British Columbia to Mexico, and from the eastern border of the Rocky Mountains to the Pacific. (Family *Hirundinidae*)

SWAN
Mute Swan
Sthenelides olor [178.2]

Similar to the Whistling Swan, but larger, with the neck usually thrown into a graceful curve when the bird is swimming. The bill is orange col-

ored, with a tuberculate enlargement at its base. The whole body is submerged deeper in the water than is

that of the Whistling Swan, and hence its tail is less conspicuous.

LENGTH—58.00 inches.

DISTRIBUTION—This European and Asiatic species has been naturalized in North America, and is now found in the lower portion of the Hudson River Valley, New York, on Long Island, and straggling rarely southward along the New Jersey coast. Its note is loud and trumpet-like, but the bird is not much given to vocalization. (Family *Anatidae*)

Trumpeter Swan
Cygnus buccinator [181]

ADULT MALE AND FEMALE—Entire bird, white; its bill and feet, black. In the spring the cutting edge of the lower mandible is reddish.

LENGTH—65.00 inches.

DISTRIBUTION—In the wilder regions of the interior of our continent; rarely seen.

This magnificent Swan—the largest—may be on the road to extinction. Slaughtered both for food and for feathers, it is now one of the rarest of American birds. Formerly immense flocks of these great white birds darkened the heavens with their mingled V-shaped flocks, and formed what was probably the most impressive spectacle of bird life on our continent. Its voice is louder and has a more clarion quality than that of the Whistling Swan. It is more incisive and musical than the voice of the Whooper Swan. The bird formerly bred from

the Arctic Ocean south in Canada, and into the northwestern states, and wintered as far south as the Gulf of Mexico. A few individuals are still found in a wild state in British Columbia, and in the region of our Yellowstone National Park. A few also are preserved in captivity. (Family *Anatidae*)

Whistling Swan

Cygnus columbianus [180]

ADULT MALE AND FEMALE—Plumage, white. Lores with a small yellow spot. Bill and feet, black.

LENGTH—55.00 inches.

DISTRIBUTION—Breeding within the Arctic Circle of North America, this great bird winters from British Columbia eastward to the Chesapeake Bay, southward to the Gulf of Mexico, and in the lower part of the Mississippi Valley. It is rarely found on the New England or New Jersey coast.

The great Whistling Swan passes high overhead during its migrations to and from its arctic breeding grounds, uttering a high, loud, shrill note, which although not exactly a whistle, has probably given the bird its name. It

also utters other notes, especially a bass *honk,* and honking notes higher in the scale. This is the commonest wild Swan of the eastern states, though rare north of the Chesapeake Bay. It often is found in large parks, and has become quite tame because of its protection. In its migrations it chooses three separate routes: along the Atlantic Coast, through the Mississippi Valley, and along the Pacific Coast. They fly very high, and hence usually escape notice during their protracted migratory flights. Great numbers of Swans are killed each year during migration, when the birds may be forced down from their journeying heights by sleet or other storms. At such times the birds take refuge on any open bodies of water which they can reach. It is then that they are slaughtered in large numbers. Many die as the result of exposure to the elements when their plumage is covered with heavy sleet, or their wings rendered useless by coatings of ice. They are often used for food. Huge flocks of these magnificent

birds were formerly common as winter residents from the coast of Massachusetts southward to the Carolinas, but these flocks have passed into oblivion. The "death song" of the Swan has long been sung in poetry. Forbush says, "The song of the dying Swan has been regarded as a pleasing myth for many years, but Elliot asserts that he once heard it . . . when a Swan, mortally wounded in the air, set its wings, and sailing slowly down, began its death song, continuing until it reached the water 'nearly half a mile away.' The song was plaintive and musical, and sounded at times like the soft running of an octave. Inquiry among local gunners revealed the fact that some had heard similar sounds from Swans that had been fatally hurt." The Whistling Swan builds a huge nest, in the Arctic, and when leaving it for any length of time, carefully covers the eggs with a mass of soft moss pulled from out the sides of the bulky structure. (Family *Anatidae*)

Whooper Swan
Cygnus cygnus [179]

ADULT MALE AND FEMALE—Entire bird, white; the legs and feet, black. The anterior part of the bill is depressed, and black in color; the basal part is quadrangular, and of a lemon-yellow hue.

LENGTH—60.00 inches.

DISTRIBUTION—This northern European Swan formerly bred in Greenland, where it now is of only casual occurrence.

The Whooper Swan (also known as the Whooping Swan or Wild Swan) is closely related to the Mute Swan, but it ranges much farther north during its breeding season, its nesting grounds being north of the Arctic Circle. The notes of this great bird—it weighs some twenty-four pounds—are similar to the blasts of a bass trombone; they are short notes, uttered with great power, and given three or four at a time, keeping rhythm with the upward and downward strokes of the wings. (Family *Anatidae*)

SWIFT FAMILY
Micropodidae

Swifts superficially resemble Swallows (Family *Hirundinidae*). The mouth is unusually wide and gaping; the bill

very short; the wings long, slender, and crescentic; the tail short; the salivary glands well developed and secreting a sticky substance used in the construction of the nest. The oriental Swifts (genus *Callocalia*) make their nests entirely of this salivary material. Most Swifts fasten their nests to vertical surfaces in caves, hollow trees, chimneys, etc. As a rule they do

not perch on twigs, but cling to vertical surfaces. They are among the most rapid fliers known—hence the name. They eat insects captured awing. About one hundred and fifty Swifts are known, almost world-wide in distribution, though the majority are tropical. Five species and subspecies are found in North America, relegated to four genera.

NESTING. Our Swifts form their nests of small twigs, glued together with a heavy, viscid secretion from the salivary glands—a gluey or cement-like substance, which toughens and hardens, and with which the bracket-like nest is firmly affixed to the inside of a chimney, a rocky cave, or a hollow tree. Our common Chimney Swift has abandoned, natural cavities, however, in preference for chimneys. The White-throated Swift makes its nest of vegetable fibers, bark, and feathers; and the Black Swift tucks its nest cozily in the crevice of a rocky mountain cliff, the nest itself being a flimsy structure composed of grass and rootlets. The Esculent Swift of the orient (a species not found in North America, however) fashions its nest entirely of its own saliva-glue, attaching it to the wall of a rocky cave. It is this nest which forms the stock for the famous bird's nest soup of the oriental people. (To the writer's palate, this dish has the flavor of a weak and insipid chicken soup.) Our Swifts lay from one egg (Black Swift) to four or six, all pure white and unmarked.

SWIFT
Black Swift
Nephoecetes niger borealis [422]

Similar to the Chimney Swift, but nearly two inches longer; with sooty-

black upper parts; paler under parts; tail without spines, slightly notched.

DISTRIBUTION—From British Columbia southward through the mountains of the United States to Central America. More common in the states along the Pacific Coast. (Family *Micropodidae*)

Chimney Swift
Chaetura pelagica [423]

ADULT MALE AND FEMALE—Upper parts, dark sooty-brown. Under parts, somewhat lighter; the throat lighter still. Wings, long and narrow, and crescentic in flight. The shafts of the tail feathers project beyond the ends of the vanes in the form of sharp rigid spines.

LENGTH—5.43 inches.

DISTRIBUTION—The whole of eastern North America, from Labrador and Manitoba to Florida, and eastward to the Great Plains. In the fall the birds gather in the Gulf States and depart south of the United States for the winter. Their wintering region is as yet unknown.

One of the commonest of our aerially-feeding birds is this attractive little species, so often spoken of as the "bow and arrow of the sky" because of its characteristic flight contour. With nervous haste it dashes about through the air in an erratic, flittering, bat-like progress, occasionally sailing in graceful curves on rigid crescentic wings. Swifts are well-named, for probably no other birds are able to shoot with greater speed through the air, or to zig-zag from side to side with greater rapidity. Though Swifts fly by day, they are more active during the hours of morning and evening twilight, or during cloudy days before storms. In the spring especially, they utter, as they fly, a cheerful, though scarcely musical chittering or chippering note. The food of Swifts is composed of all sorts of flying insects captured in the widely-gaping mouth. They feed enormous numbers of minute insects to the young, returning to the nest with their

mouth-pouches distended with food. The nest is a shallow bracket of small dead twigs, stuck together with a deep yellowish, gluey saliva, and fastened to the inner wall of a chimney, dead tree, or hollow in a cliff, with the same adhesive. (Family *Micropodidae*)

Vaux's Swift

Chaetura vauxi [424]

Similar to the Chimney Swift, but somewhat smaller and browner.

DISTRIBUTION—From British Columbia southward along the Pacific Coast, locally, and eastward sometimes to Montana and Arizona. It winters in Mexico and Central America. (Family *Micropodidae*)

White-rumped Swift

Micropus pacificus pacificus [424.1]

Similar to the Chimney Swift, but with the rump white.

DISTRIBUTION—Sometimes found in Alaska. (Family *Micropodidae*)

White-throated Swift

Aëronautes saxatalis saxatalis [425]

Similar to but slightly larger than the Chimney Swift; with a spineless,

notched tail; and the breast, middle of the abdomen, and flanks, white.

DISTRIBUTION—In the Rocky Mountains from Montana, and western Nebraska, in the Black Hills, and on the Pacific Coast to middle California. In winter it is found in Mexico and Central America. (Family *Micropodidae*)

TANAGER FAMILY

Thraupidae

Tanagers are stout, rather heavily-built perching birds, with somewhat heavy bills, the upper edge (culmen) of which is slightly rounded, and the tip of the upper mandible slightly notched. The nostrils are naked and relatively large. The tail is somewhat shorter than the wings. Males show

conspicuous red in the plumage; the females are greenish-yellow or olive—very obliterative colors among the green leaves. The rather short, rich song of the tanager is sometimes hoarse. Five tanagers are found in North America, all contained in the single genus *Piranga*.

NESTING. Our tanagers construct a rather shallow, saucer-shaped nest of twigs, strips of bark, weed stems, and grasses, lining it with finer grasses and hair. The Scarlet Tanager, however, sometimes makes its nest almost entirely of rootlets. Tanagers' nests may be looked for on horizontal limbs of trees. The Scarlet Tanager generally prefers a smaller tree, placing the nest rather low; although in woodlands the nest may be placed as high as forty feet from the ground. The Summer Tanager occasionally builds as high as sixty feet. Its nest is sometimes so thinly woven that the eggs are visible from beneath. In the Central and Southern States, however, the nest may be much more compact, made so by the addition of soft plant down and moss. Tanagers' eggs are a lighter or darker greenish-blue or bluish-green; sometimes almost emerald green; and spotted, blotched and speckled with browns, lavenders, lilacs, etc.

TANAGER

Cooper's Tanager

Piranga rubra cooperi [610a]

Similar to the Summer Tanager, but larger, with the under parts a distinct rosy-pink rather than vermilion, and with a longer, heavier bill.

DISTRIBUTION — Extreme southern California through Arizona and New Mexico, southwest into northwestern Mexico, spreading south into western Mexico in winter. Occasionally found in southern Colorado.

Cooper's Tanager is most commonly found in cottonwood growth. (Family *Thraupidae*)

Hepatic Tanager

Piranga flava hepatica [609]

ADULT MALE—Upper parts, dull red; the breast and shoulders tinged with grayish-brown. Crown, bright red; ear coverts, brownish streaked with white. Under parts, bright red, washed on the sides with brownish. Lower mandible, bluish-gray.

ADULT FEMALE—Upper parts, dull olive-greenish; the middle of the back,

grayer. Under parts, yellowish-olive, shading to grayish-olive on the sides.

LENGTH—7.35 inches.

DISTRIBUTION—From Arizona, through the central part of New Mexico and southwestern Texas, southward through Mexico to Guatemala.

Similar to the Scarlet Tanager in habits and habitat, but with a clearer, rounder, less hoarse song. (Family *Thraupidae*)

Scarlet Tanager

Piranga erythromelas [608]

ADULT MALE — Plumage, bright scarlet; wings and tail, black.

ADULT FEMALE—Upper parts, dull greenish; wings and tail, washed with brownish. Under parts, greenish-yellow.

LENGTH—7.25 inches.

DISTRIBUTION—From New Brunswick and Manitoba westward to the Great Plains, and southward to Virginia and southern Illinois. In winter it is found in Central and South America.

No more brilliant bird visits our northern forests than this torch of glowing

flame—a veritable bit of the tropics. Even though, as a rule, the bird keeps well up toward the tops of tall trees, yet in the bright sunlight it can hardly be overlooked. The female, on the other hand, is most difficult to locate; her green and yellowish garb rendering her unusually well concealed among the leaves. The Tanager's song is quite amusing. *Zzzrrheet, zzzrreet; zzheeu, zzheeu, zzheeu,* it wheezes, as though afflicted with laryngitis, but still just able to attempt its song. In spite of its peculiar hoarse, forced quality, the song is quite loud, carries for a considerable distance, and is easy to identify. (Family *Thraupidae*)

Summer Tanager
Piranga rubra rubra [610]

ADULT MALE—Upper parts, rich, dull, dark red; with a brownish cast to the wings and tail. Under parts, vermilion.

ADULT FEMALE—Upper parts, unmarked yellowish-olive, sometimes with a faint grayish cast. Under parts, dull or olive-yellow.

LENGTH—6.80 inches.

DISTRIBUTION—Throughout the eastern central United States, and west as far as western Texas. In winter it is found in Cuba and in South America as far south as Peru.

The Summer Tanager is a familiar bird to those in the Southern States,

found commonly in growths of pines and oaks. Its call note is a distinctive *Tsicky, tucky tack!* (Family *Thraupidae*)

Western Tanager
Piranga ludoviciana [607]

ADULT MALE—Upper parts, black; wing patches and rump, bright yellow. Head and neck, brilliant orange-red; rest of under parts, bright yellow.

ADULT FEMALE—Upper parts, olive-green; the back and shoulders, grayish. Wing bars, yellowish; under parts,

pale yellowish; forehead, sometimes reddish.

LENGTH—6.50 inches.

DISTRIBUTION — British Columbia south to Arizona, and west to the

Pacific. In winter it is found in Mexico and Central America. (Family *Thraupidae*)

TATTLER
Polynesian Tattler
Heteroscelus brevipes [259.1]

ADULT MALE AND FEMALE—Upper parts, gray; the feathers of the foreneck, breast, and flanks, whitish, and terminated by small gray crescents. Rest of under parts, whitish. Side of head marked with black. Lores, brown. Tail, short. Feet and legs, greenish-gray.

DISTRIBUTION—A rare Sandpiper, and a straggler on St. Paul Island, in the Pribilof Group, Alaska. (Family *Scolopacidae*)

Wandering Tattler
Heteroscelus incanus [259]

ADULT MALE AND FEMALE—Upper parts, plain slaty-gray; tail coverts, similar. Under parts, white barred with slaty-gray.

LENGTH—11.00 inches.

DISTRIBUTION—On the Pacific Coast, from British Columbia northward. In winter it is found south as far as the Hawaiian Islands and the Galapagos.

The Wandering Tattler is a bird of rocky points and headlands, where it picks its way delicately about, tilting

its tail as it goes. It often associates with Surf-birds and Black Turnstones, but from them may be separated by its plain dark gray upper parts. When in flight its wings appear unusually long for a Sandpiper, and as it goes it utters a high, clear, sweet, whistle—*Wheee-wi-wi-wi*. Often when approaching a steep rocky slope, the Tattler runs daintily down, instead of flying. (Family *Scolopacidae*)

TEAL

Baikal Teal

Nettion formosum [139.1]

Similar in general to the Green-winged Teal, but with the bend of the wing streaked with reddish-brown, black, and white. Speculum, greenish-brown. Under tail coverts and sides spotted with brown. Bill, black. Feet and legs, dull reddish.

LENGTH—About 15.00 inches.

DISTRIBUTION—"Breeds in northern and eastern Siberia, mainly between latitude 48° and 72° north, and longitude 80° and 175° east. Winters in China and Japan. Casual in Alaska."

(A.O.U. Check List.) (Family *Anatidae*)

Blue-winged Teal

Querquedula discors [140]

Similar in general to the Green-winged Teal, but with the wing coverts blue, and with a large crescentic white cheek patch. The female Blue-wing resembles the female Green-wing, but has blue wing coverts, and a greenish-brown speculum indistinctly tipped with white or whitish. Slightly smaller than the Green-wing.

DISTRIBUTION—In North America largely east of the Rocky Mountains, from Alaska across to Ohio, Illinois, Kansas, and New Brunswick. In winter

it is found from Virginia and the lower part of the Mississippi Valley to California, Lower California, and northern South America. (Family *Anatidae*)

Cinnamon Teal

Querquedula cyanoptera [141]

ADULT MALE—Back, dusky-brown; the shoulders spotted with shades of brown. Lesser wing coverts, light blue; middle coverts, tipped with white. Speculum, green. Tertials, broadly tipped with blue, green, black, and rich light brown. Head, neck, breast, and sides of body, bright cinnamon-brown. Chin and crown, blackish. Abdomen, dull brown.

ADULT FEMALE—Upper parts, dusky-brown scalloped with light brown. Head and neck, buffy finely speckled with dusky-brown. Crown, darker. Under parts, brownish mottled with dusky.

LENGTH—15.75 inches.

DISTRIBUTION—From southern Canada southward through western United States to Chile and the Falkland Islands; sometimes wandering irregularly eastward into the Mississippi Valley.

The Cinnamon Teal is one of the commonest of our western Ducks, inhabiting shallow tule-bordered lakes, ponds, and marshes. Just after the young are

hatched, the parent birds molt, and then, in their helpless condition, fall prey by the thousands to hunters. Unless such practice is stopped, this splendid bird will be in danger of extermination. The females of this Duck and of the Blue-winged Teal are quite similar. In the Cinnamon Teal, however, the general coloration is darker, and the breast is a deeper brown, and more spotted. (Family *Anatidae*)

European Teal
Nettion crecca [138]

Similar to the Green-winged Teal, the two females being indistinguishable, but the male *crecca* lacks the white bar before the wing, and its inner scapulars are a creamy-brown with a sharp black mark on their outer webs.

DISTRIBUTION—This European species occurs very rarely and accidentally in Greenland, Labrador, Nova Scotia,

Maine, Massachusetts, Connecticut, New York, New Jersey, Virginia,

North Carolina, and Ohio. (Family *Anatidae*)

Falcated Teal
Eunetta falcata [137.1]

In appearance, somewhat similar to the European Teal. Back, gray; the upper portion marked with fine undulating lines; the lower portion, uniform. Wing feathers, crescentic and stiff. Speculum, shining green with a white border. Head, crested. Forehead and crown, dull brownish. Region about the eye, back of the head, and the crest, iridescent greenish. Line over the eye, dull brown. Sides of the head below the auriculars and down to the neck, lustrous reddish-bronze. Throat, white. Neck below throat with two narrow bands, the first green, the second white. Breast, dull brown marked with small narrow white and brownish crescents. Abdomen, gray marked with white. Under tail coverts, black. Sides, white with a black band.

LENGTH—About 15.00 inches.

DISTRIBUTION—This Asiatic species is recorded as casual on St. George Island, in the Pribilof Group, Alaska. (Family *Anatidae*)

Green-winged Teal
Nettion carolinense [139]

ADULT MALE — Back, gray; the shoulders crossed by a white bar. The shoulders and sides are finely cross-lined with black and white. Head, light chestnut-brown; forehead and chin, blackish. A wide crescent of green and black encloses the eye, and reaches to the base of the crest. Wing, with a green and black speculum bordered above by light brown, and below by white. Breast, light creamy-brown spotted with black. Under tail coverts, black bordered by rich light creamy-brown.

ADULT FEMALE—Back, sides, and breast, dusky-brown mottled and scaploped with light creamy-brown. Base of the wing, slaty-bluish; its speculum much as in the male. Throat and abdomen, whitish.

LENGTH—13.75 inches.

DISTRIBUTION—Over the whole of our continent. Breeds in Colorado, Oregon, and California, but chiefly in Canada. In winter it ranges south as far as Honduras and Cuba.

Green-winged Teals are birds of grass-fringed ponds, marshes, meadow creeks, the bays of marshy lakes, rather than of large clear lakes and rivers. They are often seen standing on their

heads, their tails uptilted, while they guzzle about on the bottom for submerged seeds, soft-water plants, and the succulent roots of various aquatics. In all this delectable activity they are often accompanied by flocks of Mallards. These little Teals become excessively fat and toothsome, and are accounted among the most savory tidbits of the epicure. It is not surprising, therefore, that they are becoming

scarce in the East, where hunting is more concentrated. From the Blue-winged Teal, the Green-winged may be distinguished by the white mark in front of the wing, and by the absence of any white mark on the head. The green of the speculum shows well only in good light. (Family *Anatidae*)

TERN

Aleutian Tern
Sterna aleutica [73]

ADULT MALE AND FEMALE—Upper parts, pearl-gray. Crown, black. Line from eye to base of bill, black. Throat, white; rest of under parts, pearl-gray with a distinct brownish tinge. Tail, deeply forked.

LENGTH—14.00 inches.

DISTRIBUTION—"Breeds on two small islands in Norton Sound, on Kodiak Island, and near Yakutat, Alaska; and occurs on the Bering Sea coast of Siberia. South in winter to Japan." (A.O.U. Check List.) (Family *Laridae*)

Arctic Tern
Sterna paradisaea [71]

Closely similar to the Common Tern, but with less gray on the shaft portion of the inner webs of the outer primaries; with a slightly longer tail, a slightly shorter bill, a slightly shorter tarsus, and usually lacking the black tip of the bill.

LENGTH—15.50 inches.

DISTRIBUTION — Along the Arctic coast, almost to the North Pole, and southward, breeding as far south, though not commonly, as Massachusetts, Alaska, Aleutian Islands, northern British Columbia, to northern Manitoba. In winter it is found in the Antarctic Ocean south as far as latitude 74°.

The Arctic Tern, closely similar to the Common Tern, is very rare along the

Atlantic Coast of North America during its long migration into the Antarctic regions. During this period it is a bird of the open ocean. As soon as the young of this hardy bird are strong enough to fly, the entire family leaves the region of the North Pole, and several months later appear in the Antarctic, having performed a journey over the ocean of some 11,000 miles. Arctic Terns arrive at the northern nesting grounds about the middle of June, and leave for the Antarctic shortly after the middle of August. After spending about four months or so in the Antarctic, they start north. Thus their round trip each year of 22,000 miles must be accomplished in about twenty weeks' time—more than a thousand miles per week of perilous winging over an uncharted route. As they nest, winter, or journey, they are constantly in the region of the longest day and shortest night—they see more daylight in their lives than any other living creature. Their notes are quite

similar to those of the Common Tern, but are higher, shriller, and have been aptly likened to the squeals of a small pig. (Family *Laridae*)

Black Tern

Chlidonias nigra surinamensis [77]

ADULT MALE AND FEMALE—Back, wings, and tail, slate-gray. Entire head, and under parts, except under-tail coverts, black. Bill and feet, black.

LENGTH—10.00 inches.

DISTRIBUTION—From Alaska southward in the interior to Illinois, Kansas, and California. In migration it

occurs irregularly on the Atlantic Coast from New Brunswick and Maine southward, spending the winter south of the United States as far as Chile.

Black Terns are birds of plains and prairies, where they feed chiefly upon insects during the nesting season. In

the fall migration, when they appear on our Atlantic Coast, they resemble in habits and food, the coastal members of the *Laridae*. It is our only Tern with almost entire blackish plumage. Its common note is a sharp, high, squealing *peeek*, like the magnified, prolonged call of the Hairy Woodpecker. (Family *Laridae*)

Bridled Tern

Sterna anaethetus melanoptera [76]

Similar to the Sooty Tern, but smaller, with a dark gray instead of a blackish back, and with the white area of the forehead extending on the sides to a point behind the eyes.

DISTRIBUTION—Breeds in the Bahamas and West Indies, and is accidental in its occurrence in South Carolina, Georgia, and Florida. (Family *Laridae*)

Brown's Tern

Sterna antillarum browni [74a]

Closest in appearance to the Least Tern, but differing chiefly in that the black crown extends backward in a crest reaching to the middle of the upper neck. The upper parts are a darker gray; the under parts, a less pure white (i.e., more marked with grayish) ; and the bill, more narrowly tipped with black (or black absent entirely).

DISTRIBUTION—From central California to southern Mexico, along the Pacific Coast. In winter it is found south along the Pacific Coast of Central America and South America as far as Peru. (Family *Laridae*)

Cabot's Tern

Thalasseus sandvicensis acuflavidus [67]

ADULT MALE AND FEMALE—Back and wings, delicate, light pearl-gray. Primaries, silvery-gray; shaft parts of the inner webs, white, except for black tips. Top of head, black and crested; rest of plumage, pure white. Feet, black. Bill, black with brilliant yellow tip.

LENGTH—16.00 inches.

DISTRIBUTION — Atlantic Coast of South Carolina south to Florida, and along the Gulf Coast to eastern Mexico; sometimes straggling north as far as the coast of Massachusetts. In winter it migrates south of the United States to the West Indies and Central America. (Family *Laridae*)

Caspian Tern

Hydroprogne caspia imperator [64]

Similar to the Royal Tern, but slightly larger; or about as large as the Herring Gull. It is the largest of all our Terns. From the Royal Tern it may be distinguished by its less deeply forked tail, and its slightly greater size (though this is not always apparent).

LENGTH—21.00 inches.

DISTRIBUTION—Interrupted and local, from Newfoundland and the Great Slave Lake to Texas. In winter it is found sparingly on the southern coasts of the United States, spending the colder months mostly south of the Gulf of Mexico.

This, the largest of our Terns, might be mistaken for a Gull, were it not for its pointed, red bill, and forked

tail. In its migrations it is much more a bird of inland waters than the Royal Tern, though it also occurs along the coasts. (Family *Laridae*)

Common Tern

Sterna hirundo hirundo [70]

ADULT MALE AND FEMALE—Back and wings, pearl-gray. Top of head, black. Tail, white, and deeply forked. Bill, red with a blackish tip. Feet, orange-red.

LENGTH—15.00 inches.

DISTRIBUTION — From Greenland and northern Canada, east of the Plains, and locally to the Gulf States. In winter it is found from Florida southward to the southern tip of South America, and during migration, on the Pacific Coast from British Columbia southward to the southern part of Lower California.

Common Terns, Sea-swallows, Mackerel Gulls—by whatever name these birds are known—are always welcomed by those who love beauty and grace in bird flight. The name Sea-swallow is a particularly happy one. Hundreds of them breed along the New England coast. Small islets are often seemingly enveloped in a snowstorm with the whirl of their glistening pinions, while the air vibrates with their shrill cries of alarm and defiance if the nesting grounds are invaded. Their common cry is a shrill, mildly harsh *ti-err, ti-*

err or *tee-arrr, tee-arrr.* Coursing back and forth over the water, especially where tidal ripples occur, and over shallows where small fish congregate, the bird pauses for a moment, hovers, and then with a splash, dives head foremost beneath the surface, emerging with a shake of the plumage, and with a shining fish gripped in its long red bill. It is, however, a matter of surprise to many, to observe the number of dives which do not result in captures. The reddish bill tipped with black serves to distinguish the Common Tern from its close con-

geners, the Roseate and the Arctic Terns. (Family *Laridae*)

Eastern Sooty Tern
Sterna fuscata fuscata [75]

ADULT MALE AND FEMALE—Back, wings, and tail, sooty-black. Outer tail feathers, white. Top of head, and line through the eyes to the base of the bill, black. Under parts, white. Bill and feet, blackish.

LENGTH—17.00 inches.

DISTRIBUTION — Widely dispersed over the tropical and subtropical coasts of the entire globe. In the Americas it is found from the Carolinas and western Mexico to Chile, wandering sometimes as far north as New England.

Of this rather distinctive Tern (it is our only Tern with black upper parts and white under parts), Chapman says, "So far as I am aware, the Sooty Tern

breeds in the Atlantic States only in the Dry Tortugas of Florida, where

about 19,000 nested when Watson made his important studies of their habits in 1907. The period of incubation is twenty-six days. The warning note is a shrill *e-e-e-e;* they also utter a squeaky *quack,* and a nasal *ker-wacky-wak,* as well as other calls, being very noisy birds." (Family *Laridae*)

Elegant Tern
Thalasseus elegans [66]

Similar to the Royal Tern, but smaller, with the bill longer and slenderer, and the under parts tinged with delicate pink.

LENGTH—16.50 inches.

DISTRIBUTION — Along the Pacific Coast of the Americas, from California southward to Chile. It occurs in the autumn at Monterey, California, together with the Royal Tern, but in fewer numbers. (Family *Laridae*)

Forster's Tern
Sterna forsteri [69]

Closely similar to the Common Tern, but with the tail almost the same color as the back and wings. The tips of the wings of Forster's Tern show a silvery reflection; those of the Common Tern are a dead, dull, darkish gray.

LENGTH—15.00 inches.

DISTRIBUTION—In the interior and on the coasts from California, Manitoba, and Virginia, south to Texas and Louisiana, sometimes wandering as far north as Massachusetts. In winter it is found from California and Texas southward into Brazil.

Unlike its close relative, the Common Tern, Forster's Tern breeds in marshes, not on sandy coastal beaches. Its notes are harsh, chattery, and protracted. (Family *Laridae*)

Gull-billed Tern
Gelochelidon nilotica aranea [63]

Similar to the Common Tern, but slightly larger, paler, with a black, heavy, almost gull-like bill, and black feet.

LENGTH—14.50 inches.

DISTRIBUTION — Widely dispersed, from Virginia to Florida and to Mexico, wandering rarely as far north as New Brunswick. In winter it is found from southern Texas southward.

The Gull-billed Tern used to be more common than now along the Atlantic Coast; its numbers are apparently decreasing. The bill, while not exactly similar to that of a Gull, is heavier, shorter, and less like that of other Terns. Its voice is described as a "chattering laugh," or more like that of a Katydid. Peterson gives it as a "rasping, three-syllabled *za-zi-zi* or *Katydid*." (Family *Laridae*)

Least Tern
Sterna antillarum antillarum [74]

ADULT MALE AND FEMALE—Back, wings, and tail, light pearl-gray. Forehead, pure white, enclosed by black lines from the eye to the base of the bill. Top of head, black. Under parts, white. Bill, bright yellow with a blackish tip. Feet, yellow.

LENGTH—9.00 inches.

DISTRIBUTION—From Massachusetts through South Dakota and southern California, locally distributed; southward to northern South America. In winter it is found from the coast of Louisiana southward to Argentina, and to the east coast of Africa.

The smallest of the Terns, as the name implies. Its small size, and yellow bill are diagnostic. (Family *Laridae*)

Noddy Tern
Anoüs stolidus stolidus [79]

ADULT MALE AND FEMALE—Dark sooty or grayish-brown; the lores, black; the crown, silvery-whitish. Tail, rounded; the middle feathers being longest.

LENGTH—15.00 inches.

DISTRIBUTION—"Breeds in the Florida Keys (Dry Tortugas), the Bahamas, and West Indies, and from British Honduras to Margarita Island, Venezuela; and on St. Helena, Tristan da Cunha and Ascension islands. Casual in Bermuda and eastern Florida." (Chapman.)

The Noddy Tern has been reported north of Florida on our coasts, where, like many other sea birds, it has been

forced northward in the paths of the frequent tropical hurricanes. However, it is known to nest, with us, only in the Dry Tortugas of Florida. It is our only Tern with a rounded tail. Chapman describes its notes as "a low reedy *cack,* at times increased to a rolling guttural *k-r-r-r-r.*" (Family *Laridae*)

Roseate Tern
Sterna dougalli dougalli [72]

ADULT MALE AND FEMALE—Back and wings, pearl-gray. Wings tipped with black; not conspicuous at a distance. Tail, pure white and deeply forked. Top of head, jet black. Under parts, white tinted with pinkish (roseate flushed); bill, black and reddish at its base; feet, red.
LENGTH—15.50 inches.

DISTRIBUTION—From Nova Scotia (though rarer north of Cape Hatteras) to Florida, along the Atlantic Coast. In winter it is found from the Bahamas to Brazil. It also occurs on the coast of Scotland, and on many of the coasts all over the Eastern Hemisphere.

This lovely Tern is an uncommon summer resident along the southern New England coast. Its migration periods coincide with those of its congener, the Common Tern. Its habits, too, are similar, but its voice is a harsher, more strident *caack, caack.* In general, the darker bill, the greater extent of the black of the crown, and the whiter appearance of the bird in flight, are characteristics which aid in separating the Roseate from the Common Tern. (Family *Laridae*)

Royal Tern
Thalasseus maximus maximus [65]

ADULT MALE AND FEMALE—Back and wings, pearl-gray. Inner web of primaries, except tips, white; the outer webs, and shaft parts of the inner webs, silvery slate-gray. Top and back of head, lustrous black; the feathers long, and forming an irregular crest. Back of neck and tail, white; the tail deeply forked. Under parts, pure white. Bill, orange-red.
LENGTH—19.00 inches.

DISTRIBUTION — From the Gulf States, California, and Virginia southward to Brazil and southern Peru; sometimes wandering north as far as the Great Lakes, and the northern coast of Massachusetts. In winter it is found from California and the Gulf States southward.

Royal Terns are birds of the seacoasts, seldom or never venturing into inland waters. They fly back and forth over the waves, now and then plunging beneath the surface from a height

of fifteen feet or so; the impetus of their dive carrying them completely under the water. When they emerge, they usually hold a living fish in their bills. Once threatened with extermination at the hands of feather hunters, the birds are now, thanks to legislation, safe from this fate, and are increasing in numbers. They are extremely picturesque, their large size, and red bills making them one of the splendid assets along our southern shores. One never tires of watching these graceful birds—or any species of Tern, for that matter—as they course about, resembling large white swallows in their general manner of flight, splashing head first into the water again and again. In the winter months the Royal Tern is the one usually seen along the coast of Florida. It often robs the huge slow-flying Pelicans of their fishy prey. Its common note is a screaming *kee-err, kee-err* or *kier, kier.* (Family *Laridae*)

Socorro Sooty Tern

Sterna fuscata crissalis [75a]

Similar to the Eastern Sooty Tern, but with the under tail coverts decidedly ashy instead of pure white.

DISTRIBUTION—Along the Pacific Coast of Mexico and Central America from Sinaloa to Panama, and southward as far as the Galapagos Islands. It has been rarely reported along the coast of Lower California. (Family *Laridae*)

Trudeau's Tern

Sterna trudeaui [68]

ADULT MALE AND FEMALE—Upper parts, light slate-gray, paling to white or whitish on the crown and forehead. Tips of wings, black. Tail, deeply forked. Side of the head and the neck, white. A wide band of black reaches from over the eye down to the side of the nape. Under parts, pure white. Bill, black. Legs and feet, pink or salmon.

DISTRIBUTION—Along the coasts of Uruguay and Argentina, and on St. Ambrose Island, off the coast of Chile. An accidental straggler to Great Egg Harbor, New Jersey. (Family *Laridae*)

White-winged Tern

Chlidonias leucoptera [78]

This Old World species of *Chlidonias*, with white in the wings, and also called the White-winged Black Tern, is an accidental straggler to our Hemisphere.

DISTRIBUTION—With us, "accidental at Lake Koshkonong, Wisconsin, (July 5, 1873), and on Barbadoes." (A.O.U. Check List.)

This accidental "American" bird is found in central and southern Europe (sometimes to central Asia; more often in Australia), and along the shores of the Mediterranean. Its appearance in Wisconsin is interesting. (Family *Laridae*)

THRASHER

Bendire's Thrasher

Toxostoma bendirei [708]

Similar to the Palmer's Thrasher, but smaller; with upper parts a pale gray-

ish-brown, and under parts brownish-white.

DISTRIBUTION — Southeastern California, Arizona, and rarely in Colorado. (Family *Mimidae*)

Brown Thrasher

Toxostoma rufum [705]

ADULT MALE AND FEMALE—Upper parts, rich reddish-brown; wing coverts tipped with white, forming two not very conspicuous bars. Bill, relatively long, slightly decurved, and yellowish. Tail, long. Under parts, white and heavily marked (except on the throat and middle of the abdomen) with large, prominent, wedge-shaped black spots.

LENGTH—11.42 inches.

DISTRIBUTION — From Maine and Manitoba over the eastern portion of the United States southward to the Gulf States. In winter it is found extending from Virginia and the lower portion of the Mississippi Valley southward.

The haunts of the Brown Thrasher are scrubby hillsides, bushy pastures, vine tangles, hedgerows, sandy barrens where pines and low scrubs

abound, and not infrequently the tangled portions of gardens and city parks. Though not strictly a bird of woodlands, yet it is often found where timber has been cut, and where new growth is forming a "sproutland." When singing, the Thrasher mounts into the top of a bush, or on an outer, prominent branch of a lone small tree, and there pours out a loud, emphatic, definitely-phrased strain, similar to that of the Catbird, but richer and sweeter. It is not so varied as the Mockingbird's glorious lay, but sometimes not very inferior to it. The song may be given in the words *Plant-a-seed; plant-a-seed; drop-it; drop-it; cover-it-up; cover-it-up; pull-it-up; pull-it-up; eat-it-it; eat-it-it,* sometimes for so long a period at a time that it becomes tiresome. The Thrasher is a much shyer bird than its cousins, the Catbird and the Mockingbird, and is more frequently seen dashing for cover, when its long tail and rich brown coloring look very attractive. Because of its large consumption of noxious insects,

the Thrasher deserves our whole-hearted protection. (Family *Mimidae*)

Brownsville Thrasher

Toxostoma curvirostre oberholseri [707b]

This is the smallest of the three *curvirostre* subspecies. The spots on the breast are very large and deltoid. The terminal spots on the three or four pairs of outer tail feathers are sharply defined, and white. Under parts, cream-buffy, deepening to brown toward the lower abdomen; flanks, brown.

DISTRIBUTION—From southeastern Texas into northeastern Mexico. (Family *Mimidae*)

California Thrasher

Toxostoma redivivum redivivum [710]

ADULT MALE AND FEMALE—Upper parts, rich dark brown, darkening on the sides of the head. Breast, grayish brown; upper abdomen, somewhat lighter; lower abdomen and under tail coverts, rusty-brown. Throat, whitish. Bill, long and much decurved.

LENGTH—12.27 inches.

DISTRIBUTION—West of the Sierra Nevada Mountains in California and southward into Lower California.

The California Thrasher is readily identifiable by its very long, decurved bill, and long tail which is held up

at an angle as the bird runs along the ground. This elevation of the tail brings into view the rusty-brown patch under its root. It is a bird of thickets along stream-courses, or in chaparral country on hill slopes, where it runs along under cover, or sings a typically phrased Thrasher song from some elevated perch. (Family *Mimidae*)

Crissal Thrasher

Toxostoma dorsale dorsale [712]

ADULT MALE AND FEMALE—Upper parts, dark grayish-brown; tail, indistinctly tipped with reddish-brown.

Throat and line along its side, white. Under parts, brownish; the under tail coverts, rich, dark reddish-brown. The bill, long and much decurved.

LENGTH—12.00 inches.

DISTRIBUTION — From Utah and Nevada south into Lower California, and from western Texas to California.

This bird, called also the Red-vented Thrasher, inhabits junipers and mesquite tangles on the rocky sides of canyons, or may be found around ranches and farms. (Family *Mimidae*)

Curve-billed Thrasher

Toxostoma curvirostre curvirostre [707]

ADULT MALE AND FEMALE—Upper parts, light brownish-gray, the wings bearing two narrow white bars. Tail,

blackish; its four pairs of outer feathers conspicuously tipped with white. Under parts, grayish-white; breast and sides, thickly spotted and smirched with darker. Throat, white; flanks, light brown.

LENGTH—10.95 inches.

DISTRIBUTION—From New Mexico and the western portion of Texas, southwestward into southern Mexico.

In the thorn brush country of southern Texas and northern Mexico, the large, dark grayish-brown figure of the Curve-billed Thrasher is a familiar sight. Its notes—loud, liquid, two-syllabled, and far-carrying—are characteristic sounds of such a region. (Family *Mimidae*)

Desert Thrasher

Toxostoma lecontei arenicola [711a]

Similar to the Leconte's Thrasher, but with the upper parts a darker gray; the tail, nearly black; and the breast, medium gray.

DISTRIBUTION — Restricted to the northern part of Lower California. (Family *Mimidae*)

Leconte's Thrasher

Toxostoma lecontei lecontei [711]

ADULT MALE AND FEMALE—Upper parts, pale grayish-brown; tail tipped

with light gray. Under parts, white, faintly washed with creamy, light brown; throat, white.

LENGTH—10.75 inches.

DISTRIBUTION—From southwestern Utah to southern California, in the desert region, and south into northwestern Mexico.

A sand-colored bird found inhabiting the hottest and most sterile deserts of the continent; also on the mesas, among thorns, Spanish bayonets, cactuses and the like; where temperatures of 130° Fahrenheit are not uncommon. Leconte's Thrasher, like the Roadrunner of the West, can easily outrun a man. (Family *Mimidae*)

Mearns's Thrasher

Toxostoma cinereum mearnsi [709a]

Similar to the San Lucas Thrasher but with the upper parts darker, sides of the body browner, the under parts with blacker markings, and the bill slightly less decurved.

DISTRIBUTION — Restricted to the northern quarter of the peninsula of Lower California. (Family *Mimidae*)

Palmer's Thrasher

Toxostoma curvirostre palmeri [707a]

Similar to the Curve-billed Thrasher, but with less conspicuous wing bars,

and without white tips on the outer tail feathers.

DISTRIBUTION—In southern Ari-

zona, south into Sonora, Mexico, being found chiefly on the cactus deserts, and on the mountains up to about 3000 feet. (Family *Mimidae*)

Sage Thrasher

Oreoscoptes montanus [702]

ADULT MALE AND FEMALE—Upper parts, dull grayish-brown, with small inconspicuous darker streakings. Two narrow wing bars, white. The inner webs of the two to four outer tail

feathers are tipped with white. Under parts, grayish-white; the breast and sides marked with long dark brown spots. Flanks and under tail coverts washed with light brownish.

LENGTH—8.50 inches.

DISTRIBUTION—From Montana to western South Dakota, and southwestward to western Nebraska and eastern Colorado; westward to the Sierra Nevada and Cascade mountains, and south into Lower California and northern Mexico.

Typical of the sagebrush country of the West, the Sage Thrasher may be seen commonly in summer, perched atop a tall sage bush, uttering its varied lay and continuing the performance after the sun is down, sometimes long after dark, and not infrequently well into a moonlit night. The song is similar to that of the Brown Thrasher of the East, but a trifle harsher. The nest, a typical Thrasher's, is placed in a sage bush. The eggs are beautiful—a rich greenish-blue, spotted with rich dark brown.. The Sage Thrasher may be identified at a distance by its habit of jerking its tail upwards now and then. (Family *Mimidae*)

San Lucas Thrasher

Toxostoma cinereum cinereum [709]

Similar to the Brown Thrasher, but with the upper parts grayer, and with white tips on the outer tail feathers.
DISTRIBUTION — Restricted to the southern portion of the peninsula of Lower California. (Family *Mimidae*)

Sennett's Thrasher

Toxostoma longirostre sennetti [706]

Similar to the Brown Thrasher, but with a longer bill and shorter wings. The upper parts are duller, and the wedge-shaped markings on the under parts are heavier.
DISTRIBUTION—From southeastern Texas into northeastern Mexico. (Family *Mimidae*)

Sonoma Thrasher

Toxostoma redivivum sonomae [710b]

Similar to the California Thrasher, but slightly larger, and with the back, breast, and sides of the body a somewhat grayer, less warm, brown.
DISTRIBUTION—Northern California, from the head of the Sacramento Valley, and the inner Coast Ranges, to Eldorado County, and through the San Francisco Bay region as far as Santa Cruz. (Family *Mimidae*)

Trinidad Thrasher

Toxostoma dorsale trinitatis [712a]

Similar to the Crissal Thrasher, but with the plumage a darker, more

slaty-gray; and the bill, longer and more distinctly decurved.
DISTRIBUTION — In the Trinidad Valley in the northern part of Lower California. (Family *Mimidae*)

THRUSH FAMILY
Thrushes, Robins, Bluebirds, Stonechats, and Solitaires

Turdidae

Thrushes are almost completely worldwide in their distribution, and include in their "family circle" such famous species as our own Robin, Bluebird, Solitaire, and Hermit Thrush, as well as the European Nightingale, Missel Thrush, and the so-called "Blackbird" of Europe. Thrushes are in general

about seven to ten inches in length, of modest colorings, often with spotted under parts, and are superlative songsters. Fruits are their chief food, but they also take many insects. Over seven hundred species and subspecies are known. About two hundred inhabit the Western Hemisphere, and of these, thirty-four are recorded from North America, contained in nine genera.
NESTING. Since our thrushes inhabit so many different localities—the ground, trees, rocks, etc.—their nesting sites and nests vary accordingly. Our northeastern spot-breasted Thrushes (e.g., the Wood Thrush, Hermit Thrush, Olive-backed Thrush, Gray-cheeked and Bicknell's Thrushes, and the Veery) make their rather bulky, cup-shaped nests of grasses, a few small twigs, bark, fibers, leaves; sometimes

interweaving bits of paper, cloth, or fine thin birch bark. The whole is often given form by a layer of leaf-mold or mud, concealed among the layers of the softer materials. The lining of the nests includes (varying somewhat with the species): fine rootlets, pine needles, hair, fine grasses, mosses, and the like. The nests are placed either on the ground sunken in a bed of moss, in a tuft of reindeer "moss" (lichen), or under a small blueberry bush, small spruce, hemlock, or fir. They may be found in cool damp woods, on a mountain side, or at the edge of a trail or old lumber road. The Hermit Thrush and Veery often build in such localities. Sometimes the nests are placed quite high up in a spruce or fir balsam (Olive-backed Thrush). The Wood Thrush also locates its nest in a tree, on a horizontal branch from three or four to fifteen feet high. This nest resembles that of the Robin with its grass, mud, and sometimes string, paper, etc. It may be found in all sorts of places, wherever there is a shelf for its support, and some sort of over-arching protection from the weather—as in the crotch of a tree, corner of a porch, under an old bridge, on the rafter of a dilapidated building, on a window ledge, in a cornice, under a disused wagon body, or on a "robin shelf" put up especially for the birds.

The Bluebird departs from the usual thrush procedure, and makes its nest of fine grasses, some hair, and a few feathers, in the bottom of a cavity in a tree trunk or limb—using either a natural cavity, a deserted Woodpecker hole, or a nesting box. Bluebirds are especially fond of old apple orchards, where natural cavities and abandoned woodpecker holes usually abound. The eggs of thrushes in general number from three to five (rarely six or seven), and are bluish-green, greenish-blue; sometimes deep in color (Robin or Wood Thrush), or very pale blue, almost white (Bluebird). They are usually plain and unmarked, but sometimes (as with the Gray-cheeked Thrush) are spotted and blotched with reddish-brown and lilac tones.

THRUSH
Alaskan Hermit Thrush
Hylocichla guttata guttata [759]

Similar to the Eastern Hermit Thrush, but with the tail a decidedly more reddish-brown, and a whiter eye-ring. The breast is more washed with buff.

DISTRIBUTION—In the Pacific coastal region from Alaska to British Columbia. In winter it migrates south into Mexico. (Family *Turdidae*)

Audubon's Hermit Thrush
Hylocichla guttata auduboni [759a]

Similar to the Eastern Hermit Thrush, but with the upper parts grayer, and the tail paler.

DISTRIBUTION — Restricted to the Rocky Mountains, and extending into Guatemala. (Family *Turdidae*)

Bicknell's Thrush
Hylocichla minima minima [757a]

Similar to the Gray-cheeked Thrush, but slightly smaller and browner above; more buff-colored below; and with a slenderer bill. These differences, however, are practically of no use in the field for distinguishing the two birds.

DISTRIBUTION—From Nova Scotia south into the higher mountains of New York and New England, migrating south through the Eastern States and wintering in Haiti and northern South America.

This attractive and rare Thrush is similar in all ways to its larger congener, the Gray-cheeked Thrush, except in its nesting range. It may be

found in New England on all the
mountains that rise above 3,500 feet.
It is a shy species, and even on its
nesting grounds is seldom seen, and
less often heard than most other
Thrushes. Its song is a thin, wiry,
tremulous, upward-spiralling strain.
The notes, though buzzing in charac-

ter, are sweet and decidedly plaintive.
The bird sings *tsee, tsee, treeee-ee-ee-
ee-e*, the final note ending in a delicate quavering trill. Bicknell's Thrush
is a denizen of the red and black
spruce zones. (Family *Turdidae*)

Dwarf Hermit Thrush

Hylocichla guttata nanus [759c]

Similar to the Eastern Hermit Thrush,
but smaller; with the breast tinged
with buff and heavily marked with
large wedge-shaped spots.
DISTRIBUTION — From Washington,
south along the Sierra Nevada Mountains. During its migration into Lower
California and northwestern Mexico
it spreads eastward into Nevada and
Arizona. (Family *Turdidae*)

Eastern Hermit Thrush

Hylocichla guttata faxoni [759b]

ADULT MALE AND FEMALE—Upper
parts, olive-brown; the upper tail coverts and tail, rich reddish-brown—
quite distinct from the back in good
light. Under parts, white; sides of
throat and breast, spotted with black;

abdomen, unmarked white. Eye-ring,
buffy-white.
LENGTH—7.17 inches.
DISTRIBUTION—From Labrador
south and westward to Michigan;
along the higher Allegheny Mountains
into Pennsylvania; in the higher Cats-
kill Mountains; into northern New
York; down through New England
along the mountains and into the
higher mountains of western Massachusetts; sometimes into the mountains
of northwestern Connecticut.

The Hermit Thrush may be distinguished from other native Thrushes,
and recognized almost as far as it
can be seen by its deliberate habit of
lowering and lifting its reddish-brown
tail, especially when alarmed. During
its migration, its only note is a deep
throaty *churck*. On its nesting grounds,
the bird gives voice to its justly-
famed song—a series of pure, clear,
flute-like notes, superior in beauty of

tone to the notes of any other American songster. Beginning low in the
scale, the song rises with the utterance of each phrase. To modify John
Burroughs' splendid interpretation, the
song runs thus: *Oh, holy holy—ah,
purity purity—ee, sweetly sweetly.* The
final phrase is thin, clear, and high-
pitched, and does not carry as far

as the lower-pitched phrases. In the woodlands the song has a ringing, almost ventriloquial character, and is pronounced with a sort of reverent deliberation, as though the bird were solemnly and sweetly chanting the praises of its Creator. (Family *Turdidae*)

Gray-cheeked Thrush
Hylocichla minima aliciae [757]

ADULT MALE AND FEMALE—Upper parts, olive-brown; the cheek (or auricular patch) marked off from the rest of the head by an irregular buffy line, finely streaked with black. In this species the eye is *not* set off by a buffy ring. Under parts, white; the sides of the throat and the entire· breast, spotted with black. Sides of abdomen, slightly washed with light grayish-brown.
LENGTH—7.58 inches.
DISTRIBUTION—From Alaska eastward to Labrador. Not known to nest south of the Canadian border. Its migrations take it through the Eastern States into Central America.

The Gray-cheeked Thrush is an unusually silent migrant through our Eastern States, frequenting the same situations as its close relatives the Bicknell's and

the Olive-backed Thrushes. In our continent its nesting regions are in a belt near the limit of tree-growth in Alaska and Canada, where it makes its nest in scrubby alders and willows

along the banks of streams and on the shores of swamps and sloughs. (Family *Turdidae*)

Mono Hermit Thrush
Hylocichla guttata polionota [759f]

Similar to the Sierra Hermit Thrush, but with the upper parts decidedly browner.
DISTRIBUTION—In the White Mountains of California, in Mono and Inyo counties. (Family *Turdidae*)

Monterey Hermit Thrush
Hylocichla guttata slevini [759d]

Similar to the Sierra Hermit Thrush, but extremely pale and ashy.
DISTRIBUTION — Along the coastal belt in California from the northern part of Trinity County to the southern part of Monterey County. In winter it is found in Lower California, Arizona, and Sonora, Mexico. (Family *Turdidae*)

Northern Varied Thrush
Ixoreus naevius meruloides [763a]

Similar to the Pacific Varied Thrush, but with a longer and more pointed wing. The female is paler and grayer in tone, and the white markings in the plumage are more extensive.
LENGTH—10.00 inches.
DISTRIBUTION—During the breeding season, in the interior of northern Alaska; in winter migrating down as far south as southern California.

The male of this subspecies of Varied Thrush is closely similar to the male Pacific Varied Thrush, but the females differ as noted above. The Northern Varied Thrush sometimes goes under the name of the Pale Varied Thrush. It inhabits dense spruce forests, and is seldom seen far from wooded solitudes, except in winter in the southern portions of California. In general habits and song it is similar to its Pacific relative. (Family *Turdidae*)

Olive-backed Thrush
Hylocichla ustulata swainsoni [758a]

ADULT MALE AND FEMALE—Upper parts, uniform brown with a decided olivaceous cast, especially in strong light. The eye shows a prominent en-

circling buffy ring, and the cheeks (or auricular patches) are slightly lighter than the rest of the head. Breast, white spotted with black; abdomen, white, its sides faintly spotted with olive-brown.

LENGTH—7.17 inches.

DISTRIBUTION—From Manitoba and New Brunswick southward as far as the Allegheny Mountains in Pennsylvania, and the Catskills in New York. In winter it migrates into Central and South America.

The Olive-backed, or Swainson's Thrush, during its migrations, slips through our woodlands and scrublands, almost without a sound. It keeps close to the ground, avoids observation by quietly flitting off through the tangles, and only rarely gives voice to a sharp, liquid *whit*. Seldom does it sing at such times, and then not in the full vigorous song which characterizes the bird on its northern breeding grounds. Here it is one of the most persistent singers of middle mountain slopes. Its typical song is sweet, upward-spiralling, and somewhat abrupt. It may be expressed by the words *Oh a curdle wheedle sweeter* or *Oh Aurelia will ya will ya*. The notes ascend upward in a rather sweet broken spiral, the final note being thin and high. The song is sometimes shorter, sometimes longer, but always the same form. It is most frequently heard on moderate elevations in the White Mountains, in the red spruce zones. Farther north the bird is also commonly found in the valleys. Where the Hermit Thrushes and the Olive-backed Thrushes are singing together, the rather crude, simple, broken strain of the Olive-back is easily distinguished from the pure, clear, finished, varied, phrased, more deliberate song of the incomparable Hermit. (Family *Turdidae*)

Pacific Varied Thrush
Ixoreus naevius naevius [763]

Similar to the Northern Varied Thrush, but with upper parts, ashy; and with head and breast band, black. Line from the eye to the back of the

head, rusty-brown. Under parts, varying rusty-brown.

DISTRIBUTION—From Yakutat Bay, Alaska, southward into Humboldt County, California. In winter it is found from the extreme southern part of Alaska southward into southern California. (Family *Turdidae*)

Red-winged Thrush
Arceuthornis musicus [760]

ADULT MALE AND FEMALE—Upper parts, olive-brown. Under parts, white with large brown spots and streaks. Upper breast (and sometimes the throat), tinged with faint reddish-brown. Flanks, washed with olive. The under wing coverts, a pale orange-yellow.

LENGTH—9.00 inches.

DISTRIBUTION—An accidental straggler in Greenland.

This bird is the justly famous Throstle, or Song Thrush (*Turdus musicus*) of Europe, and is one of the finest singers among the great Thrush family. Its song may be described as like that of a "glorified (American) robin." (Family *Turdidae*)

Russet-backed Thrush
Hylocichla ustulata ustulata [758]

Similar to the Olive-backed Thrush, but with the tail a slightly darker brown than that of the back; the

breast and sides of the head, buffy; the breast with large wedge-shaped spots.

DISTRIBUTION — From Alaska to Oregon along the coast; in winter

passing into Guatemala. (Family *Turdidae*)

Sierra Hermit Thrush
Hylocichla guttata seqoiensis [759e]

Similar to the Gray-cheeked Thrush, but decidedly paler, and with a light cinnamon-brown tail.

DISTRIBUTION—From southern British Columbia southward into southern California. In winter it is found in Texas and southward into northern Mexico. (Family *Turdidae*)

Willow Thrush
Hylocichla fuscescens salicicola [756a]

Similar to the Veery, but with the upper parts decidedly olivaceous.

DISTRIBUTION — From British Columbia southward along the Rocky Mountains, and east to the Dakotas. In the course of its migrations into South America (as far as southern Brazil) it wanders irregularly into Illinois and South Carolina. (Family *Turdidae*)

Wood Thrush
Hylocichla mustelina [755]

ADULT MALE AND FEMALE—Upper parts, rich brown; head, reddish-brown. Under parts, white; the breast and sides of abdomen, with large, prominent, round, blackish spots; middle of abdomen, clear white.

LENGTH—8.29 inches.

DISTRIBUTION—From Quebec, Vermont, and Minnesota (in the lowlands; not on the mountains), south to Virginia and Kansas. In winter it passes into Central America.

In the east the Wood Thrush is the largest of our "spot-breasted" Thrushes, and one of the commonest found in our woodlands. It is a true woodland bird; never found in orchards, scrub growths, nor very high up on mountain slopes in the north (where its place is taken by the Olive-backed Thrush). Its song, approaching in beauty (but not equalling it) the song of the famed Hermit Thrush, is noteworthy for its purity and sweetness of tone. It consists of a series of liquid-clear notes in groups of three, with a pause between each triad, and may be syllabified thus: *ah-oh-lee, oh-lee-lay, pee-dle-eee*. The first triad is low and full, the second slightly higher, and the third and last rises high, clear, and fine. The whole song is reiterated often, with some slight variations, and is given in a calm, serene, unhurried manner, with a decidedly

spiritual quality attending the notes. While singing, the bird is usually perched on a horizontal branch, in a leafy situation, about six to ten feet from the ground, where it sits and sings without motion for long periods at a time. It feeds upon the ground, and when seen there, the contrasting colors of its dull brownish back and rich reddish-brown head offer a convenient and unmistakable field recognition mark. Its food consists of wild fruits, insects, small salamanders, spiders, small snails, centipedes and their kin, and worms of various sorts. (Family *Turdidae*)

TITMOUSE FAMILY
Titmice, Chickadees, Verdins, and Bush Tits
Paridae

The Titmice are mainly birds of the more northern and higher parts of Eurasia, and are not very well represented with us. The bill is short, stout, somewhat rounded, and sharp. The

wings are short and rounded, the tail relatively long, and the feet stout and strong. Titmice are small birds, being roughly less than six and a half inches in length. Their small size is reflected in the family name, *Paridae*, from *parvus*, the Latin for small. They are active, bustling, inquisitive, nervous, and apparently cheerful and optimistic birds. They are also gregarious, except during the nesting season; and are found most commonly in wooded regions. The chickadees (of which there are twenty-one kinds in North America) are the most familiar members of the group with us. Approximately three hundred species and subspecies of titmice are known, and thirty-nine occur in North America, distributed among four genera.

NESTING. The nest of parid birds occupies the natural cavity of a tree or stump, or a deserted woodpecker hole. The Verdin, however, makes an external nest of stems, etc., globular in shape, and with a side opening, placed near the outside of a thorny bush or tree. The Bush Tit makes a similar, but longer and more gourd-shaped nest. All the nests are lined with soft grasses, hair, wool, feathers, soft moss, or a combination of these materials. The situation of the hole-nesting species varies from a few feet above the ground to twenty or twenty-five feet; sometimes more. The eggs of parids number from four to eight or nine; and are unmarked white or whitish, or very pale bluish or greenish finely speckled with browns or lilacs.

TITMOUSE
Ashy Titmouse
Baeolophus inornatus cineraceus [733b]

Similar to the Plain Titmouse, but with the upper parts not showing a brownish cast.

DISTRIBUTION — Restricted to the Cape Region of Lower California. (Family *Paridae*)

Black-crested Titmouse
Baeolophus atricristatus atricristatus [732]

ADULT MALE AND FEMALE—Upper parts, unmarked gray; crest of head,

black. Forehead, white or light brownish-white. Under parts, white.
LENGTH—5.50 inches.
DISTRIBUTION—"From southeastern Texas west to El Paso, south to eastern Mexico." (Bailey.) (Family *Paridae*)

Bridled Titmouse
Baeolophus wollweberi annexus [734]

ADULT MALE AND FEMALE—Upper parts, olive-gray; crown patch, gray;

crest feathers, black; sides of head marked ("bridled") with black. Throat, black; under parts, whitish.
LENGTH—4.75 inches.
DISTRIBUTION—From southern Arizona and western Texas southward

to Orizaba in south central Mexico. (Family *Paridae*)

Gray Titmouse
Baeolophus inornatus griseus [733a]

Similar to the Plain Titmouse, but lighter above and below, and without brownish in the plumage.

DISTRIBUTION — From Colorado westward to Nevada and southeastern California. (Family *Paridae*)

Oregon Titmouse
Baeolophus inornatus sequestratus [733c]

Similar to the Plain Titmouse, but the plumage a duller leaden-gray throughout, with scarcely any brownish tinge on the upper parts. Under parts, lightly washed with gray. Slightly smaller than the Plain Titmouse.

DISTRIBUTION—Between the Coast and Cascade ranges of California (in Siskiyou County), and in Jackson County, Oregon. (Family *Paridae*)

Plain Titmouse

Baeolophus inornatus inornatus [733]

ADULT MALE AND FEMALE—Upper parts, brownish-gray. Under parts, gray, fading to grayish-white on the abdomen. Head, crested.

LENGTH—5.30 inches.

DISTRIBUTION—Along the Pacific coastal zone, from Oregon southward through California.

A Quaker among birds is the quiet, reserved Plain Titmouse, inhabiting by preference the live oak groves of the

West Coast. Its notes are a leisurely, clear *too-wit, too-wit, too-wit*, similar to the *peter, peter, peter* (or the *ter-pee, terpee, terpee*) of the Tufted Titmouse of the East, but not so rapid. (Family *Paridae*)

San Diego Titmouse

Baeolophus inornatus transpositus [733d]

Similar to the Plain Titmouse, but slightly larger and grayer, and with a much heavier bill.

DISTRIBUTION — In southwestern California, from Santa Barbara County southeastward into San Diego County. (Family *Paridae*)

San Pedro Titmouse

Baeolophus inornatus murinus [733e]

Similar to the Plain Titmouse, but larger; with the upper parts distinctly grayer, and the under parts a much darker gray.

DISTRIBUTION—From about the region of northwestern Lower California from the United States boundary, south through about the northern third of the peninsula. (Family *Paridae*)

Sennett's Titmouse

Baeolophus atricristatus sennetti [732a]

Similar to the Black-crested Titmouse, but larger; with clearer gray upper parts, and the forehead usually tinged with brown.

DISTRIBUTION—It ranges in the central portion of Texas, "from Tom Green and Concho counties east to the Brazos River, and from Young County south to Nueces and Bee counties." (A.O.U. Check List.) (Family *Paridae*)

Tufted Titmouse

Baeolophus bicolor [731]

ADULT MALE AND FEMALE—Upper parts, gray; forehead, black; head, crested. Under parts, white or whitish, with a large patch of light reddish-brown or orange-brown on the sides of the abdomen.

LENGTH—6.00 inches.

DISTRIBUTION—The whole of eastern United States from northern New Jersey across to southern Iowa, and south to the Gulf of Mexico. Of uncommon occurrence in western Connecticut and New York.

One of the commonest of the spring woodland notes in the Eastern and Southern states is the clear *péter, péter, péter* call of the Titmouse, which is often varied to sound like *to-pée, to-pée, to-pée*. Its "Chickadee" call, though harsher, is much like the common Chickadee's note. Titmice are found in tall trees, and are easily identified by their active, acrobatic behavior, demure coloration, and crested head. They frequently come to

feeding stations at the window ledge. (Family *Paridae*)

TOWHEE
Abert's Towhee
Pipilo aberti [592]

ADULT MALE AND FEMALE—Upper parts, dull unmarked grayish-brown, darkening in hue on the head; the quills of the feathers edged with gray. Lores and chin, black or blackish. Under parts, light pinkish-brown, fading on the abdomen, but darkening to a tawny-brown on the under tail coverts.
LENGTH—8.68 inches.
DISTRIBUTION—From Colorado westward into southeastern California, Arizona, and New Mexico.

"The cinnamon-colored *aberti* is the largest of the plain towhees. It is said to be extremely shy. Major Bendire gives its alarm note as *huit, huit*. At Phoenix [Arizona] it is common among the mesquites and cottonwoods." (Bailey.) (Family *Fringillidae*)

Alabama Towhee
Pipilo erythrophthalmus canaster [587b]
Similar to the Red-eyed Towhee or Chewink, but with the sides of the body and the flanks somewhat paler;

the white markings of the tail feathers more restricted; the bill somewhat larger; and the tail slightly longer. The female is more grayish than the female Red-eye.
DISTRIBUTION—Found in central Georgia and Alabama. (Family *Fringillidae*)

Anthony's Towhee
Pipilo fuscus senicula [591.1a]

Similar to the California Towhee, but smaller; with the upper parts darker; and the under parts grayer, sometimes with an olive-grayish wash.
LENGTH—8.09 inches.
DISTRIBUTION—From southern California southward into Lower California. (Family *Fringillidae*)

Arctic Towhee
Pipilo maculatus arcticus [588]

ADULT MALE—Back, black mixed with olive-grayish. Head, neck, and upper breast, black. Wings and tail, much marked with white. The wing bars, and the white edgings to the primaries sometimes form an extensive white patch. Lower breast and abdomen, white. Flanks, reddish-brown.
ADULT FEMALE—Somewhat similar to the male, but with the black replaced by dull olive-brown. Upper parts, streaked with black. Throat and upper breast, grayish-brown. White markings not at all prominent.
LENGTH—7.62 inches.
DISTRIBUTION—On the Great Plains and the eastern foothills of the Rocky Mountains, from Saskatchewan southward into southern Colorado, and from the Missouri River westward into western Montana. In winter it is found spreading southward into Texas and westward into Washington. Casually present in Wisconsin and Iowa.

The song of the Arctic Towhee is described as shorter and more wooden, i.e., less musical than that of the Red-eyed Towhee or Chewink. In other respects this more northern form is similar to its eastern cousin. (Family *Fringillidae*)

California Towhee

Pipilo fuscus crissalis [591.1]

ADULT MALE AND FEMALE—Upper parts, unmarked dull grayish-brown; head slightly darker. Throat, light brown streaked with dusky-brown. Middle of abdomen, white or whitish; the sides washed with grayish-brown. Under tail coverts, reddish-brown. LENGTH—8.93 inches.
DISTRIBUTION — From Mendocino and Shasta counties, southward to Santa Barbara and Kern counties, California, and west of the Sierra Nevada range.

The California Towhee is a familiar, homelike, domestic bird, frequenting lawns, city parks, barnyards, and gardens. Because its call note is a thin, fine *chip,* it has been given the common name of Brown Chippy. Its squeaky song lacks the pleasing musical quality of the Red-eyed Towhee's invitation to *"drink your teeeeee."* (Family *Fringillidae*)

Canyon Towhee

Pipilo fuscus mesoleucus [591]

ADULT MALE AND FEMALE—Upper parts and sides of the body, dull unmarked grayish-brown. Top of head, light reddish-brown. Throat, buffy, with fine dark spots. Upper breast bears a large ill-defined patch made up of large coalesced spots. Abdomen, whitish. Lower abdomen, flanks, and under tail coverts, yellowish- or creamy-brown. LENGTH—8.21 inches.
DISTRIBUTION — From Arizona to western Texas, and from the eastern

part of Colorado southward into central Mexico.

In the mountains, these Towhees are found in canyons, among the rocks and ledges. (Family *Fringillidae*)

Cape Colnett Towhee

Pipilo maculatus umbraticola [588i]

Similar to the San Diego Towhee, but darker, and with a smaller bill. The color difference is more apparent in the female than in the male.
DISTRIBUTION — In northwestern Lower California. (Family *Fringillidae*)

Green-tailed Towhee

Oberholseria chlorura [592.1]

ADULT MALE—Upper parts, olive-gray, passing into bright olive-green on the wings and tail. Cheek (malar) stripe, white. The edge of the wing, and under tail coverts, bright yellow. Throat, white. Middle of abdomen, white. Bill, smallish and conical. Wing, longish and pointed.
ADULT FEMALE—Similar to the male, but with the colors somewhat duller.
LENGTH—6.63 inches.
DISTRIBUTION—Found in the interior plateau region of the United

States, from the western border of the Great Plains to the Coast Ranges in California, and northward into Mon-

tana. In winter it is found in the southern portion of Lower California and as far south as central Mexico. (Family *Fringillidae*)

Guadalupe Towhee
Pipilo consobrinus [589]

Similar to the Oregon Towhee, but a more sooty black; with much shorter wings and tail; and with much larger hind claws.

DISTRIBUTION—Found on Guadalupe Island off the coast of Lower California. (Family *Fringillidae*)

Large-billed Towhee
Pipilo maculatus magnirostris [588e]

Similar to the San Diego Towhee, but with a much larger bill; paler under parts; and the upper parts much more olive-brown in tone.

DISTRIBUTION—In the Cape district of Lower California. (Family *Fringillidae*)

Nevada Towhee
Pipilo maculatus curtatus [588f]

Similar to the Spurred Towhee, but with a shorter wing, a much shorter

tail, and with the coloration in general somewhat darker in tone.

DISTRIBUTION—From central southern British Columbia to eastern Oregon, Nevada, and into northeastern California. In winter it spreads south into the Colorado River valley, in southeastern California. (Family *Fringillidae*)

Oregon Towhee
Pipilo maculatus oregonus [588b]

ADULT MALE—Upper parts, black, inconspicuously marked with white. Wing bars reduced to disconnected round white spots. Ends of outer tail feathers sparingly marked with white. Sides of body, very dark brown.

ADULT FEMALE—Similar to the male, but with the black replaced by very dark sooty-brown, sometimes almost blackish, and indistinctly streaked with black.

LENGTH—7.63 inches.

DISTRIBUTION—British Columbia to central (San Francisco) California. Winters southward to southern California. (Family *Fringillidae*)

Oregon Brown Towhee
Pipilo fuscus bullatus [591b]

Similar to the Sacramento Brown Towhee, but with the sides of the body and flanks a more deeply brownish-slate-gray, and with a longer and heavier bill.

DISTRIBUTION—Found in the southwestern portion of Oregon, and in the upper parts of the valleys in Josephine and Jackson counties. (Family *Fringillidae*)

Red-eyed Towhee
Pipilo erythrophthalmus erythrophthalmus [587]

ADULT MALE—Entire head and throat, upper breast, back, wings, and tail, glossy black. Primaries, margined with white on their outer edges; and the outer tail feathers, tipped with white. Lower breast and abdomen, white; the sides flanked with a broad stripe of chestnut-brown. Bill, large and black. Iris of eye, bright red.

ADULT FEMALE — Light reddish-brown where the male is black. Sides of breast and abdomen, light chestnut-brown.

LENGTH—8.25 inches.

DISTRIBUTION—From Maine, Ontario, and Manitoba southward to Georgia and Louisiana, and west to the Great Plains. In winter it is found from Virginia and southern Illinois southward into Florida and the eastern portion of Texas.

The Towhee, or Chewink as it is often called, is to be looked for in areas of scrub oak, bushy pastures, clearings in the forest where sproutlings are beginning to assert themselves, the shrubby

margins of light woods, and shallow stream courses where copses abound. It is primarily, however, a bird of dry lands, and delights to scratch and rustle in the dry leaves. Chewinks do not fly very far when flushed, and bounce along on their short, rounded wings, with their long tails nervously sweeping from side to side. The call note at once gives a clue to the bird's identity. It is a sharp, nasal, abruptly-terminating *chewink;* the last syllable whisked out with an upward inflection, as though the bird had snapped a musical whip-lash. The song is short and musical: *Tick-you; tiddle-iddle-*

iddle; the last part, a pleasing rough trill. To some ears the bird seems to admonish: *"Drink your tea-e-e-e-e-e-e."* (Family *Fringillidae*)

Sacramento Towhee

Pipilo maculatus falcinellus [588g]

Similar to the San Diego Towhee, but with larger white markings in the plumage; the rump, olivaceous or grayish; and with short, weak hind claws.

DISTRIBUTION—From southwestern Oregon south into the interior (Tulare County) of California. (Family *Fringillidae*)

Sacramento Brown Towhee

Pipilo fuscus carolae [591c]

Similar to the California Towhee, but with the upper parts appreciably grayer and more uniform in tone. The throat patch is much paler, and the tail slightly longer.

DISTRIBUTION—Inhabits the interior valleys and foothills of the region west of the Sierra Nevada in California, from about Kern County northward as far as Shasta County. (Family *Fringillidae*)

San Clemente Towhee

Pipilo maculatus clementae [588c]

ADULT MALE—Similar to the Spurred Towhee, but with the upper parts sooty-brown tinged with olive-gray; the rump, lighter; and the upper tail coverts finely barred with dusky. The whole coloration is grayer. Bill and feet, larger.

ADULT FEMALE—Head and neck, dark brown; wings and tail, still darker. Rump, grayish; the feathers bearing darker centers and lighter edgings.

LENGTH—7.77 inches.

DISTRIBUTION—Found on San Clemente Island, off the coast of southern California. (Family *Fringillidae*)

San Diego Towhee

Pipilo maculatus megalonyx [588d]

ADULT MALE — Glossy jet-black, with wings and scapulars prominently and heavily marked with white. Outer tail feathers with white markings on their ends. Black and white strongly contrasting. Otherwise like the San Clemente Towhee.

ADULT FEMALE—Somewhat similar to the male, but with the upper parts, dull brown or sooty-brownish-black.

LENGTH—7.80 inches.

DISTRIBUTION — From the coastal zone of southern California, southward into Lower California. (Family *Fringillidae*)

San Francisco Towhee

Pipilo maculatus falcifer [588h]

Similar to the San Diego Towhee, but with the terminal white spot of the outer tail feather considerably shorter. Also similar to the Oregon Towhee, but with the claws much longer and heavier.

DISTRIBUTION—In central and northern California, along the coastal region. (Family *Fringillidae*)

San Francisco Brown Towhee

Pipilo fuscus petulans [591d]

Similar to the Sacramento Brown Towhee, but with the brown washed with a ruddier tone.

DISTRIBUTION — From Humboldt Bay in the northwestern coastal region of California, to the vicinity of Santa Cruz. (Family *Fringillidae*)

San Lucas Towhee

Pipilo fuscus albigula [591a]

Similar to the Canyon Towhee, but smaller. The abdomen, white, and lacking any brownish coloration.

DISTRIBUTION—Restricted to the southern part of Lower California. (Family *Fringillidae*)

San Pablo Towhee

Pipilo fuscus aripolius [591e]

Resembles the San Lucas Towhee, but with the upper parts much grayer and darker; the breast and sides of the body, somewhat darker and more purely grayish; and the throat, darker.

DISTRIBUTION—The central region of Lower California. (Family *Fringillidae*)

Spurred Towhee

Pipilo maculatus montanus [588a]

Similar to the Arctic Towhee, but with less numerous white markings on the feathers of the upper parts, and no brownish edgings on the feathers of the fore-back. The general tone of the back is blacker than that of the Arctic form. The white tips of the outer tail feathers are shorter.

DISTRIBUTION—From British Columbia southward to Lower California and northern Mexico, and from the Rocky Mountains westward to California.

A close relative of the Arctic Towhee. As its name implies, the Spurred Towhee possesses a longer hind claw. (Family *Fringillidae*)

White-eyed Towhee

Pipilo erythrophthalmus alleni [587a]

Similar to the Red-eyed Towhee (Chewink), but having only two outer tail feathers with *prominent* white tips; and with the iris of the eye, white or whitish.

DISTRIBUTION—Along the Atlantic Coast zone, from the region about Charleston, South Carolina, southward into Florida.

This bird, the southern form of our common Chewink, gives voice to a song which is shorter than that of its northern relative, and to a call note of *chewink,* which is sharper, higher in pitch, and more nasal. The *wink* syllable is snapped up like a little musical whip-lash. The White-eyed Towhee keeps itself more hidden than the Chewink of the north, and when forced to fly out into the open, dashes for the nearest cover, where it at once works itself down through the thick tangle and out of sight. (Family *Fringillidae*)

TREE-DUCK

Black-bellied Tree-duck

Dendrocygna autumnalis autumnalis [177]

ADULT MALE AND FEMALE—Back, neck, crown, and breast, bright cinnamon-brown. Sides of the head, ashy-gray. End of wing, black. Base of wing and quills with large white patches. Rump and tail, black. Abdomen, black; under tail coverts, white spotted with black.

LENGTH—21.85 inches.

DISTRIBUTION — From the Rio Grande Valley and Nueces River, Texas, southward through Central America.

Like our common Wood Duck, the Black-bellied Tree-duck nests in hol-

low trees, often at a considerable distance from any water. (Family *Anatidae*)

Fulvous Tree-duck

Dendrocygna bicolor helva [178]

ADULT MALE AND FEMALE—Back and wings, blackish brown; the feathers of the middle of the back, broadly

tipped with tawny. Crown, dark brown. Back of neck bears a black stripe. Under parts, head, and shoulders, plain tawny or buffy brown. Upper and under tail coverts, and stripes along the side of the body, creamy white.

LENGTH—20.50 inches.

DISTRIBUTION—Louisiana, Nevada, and central California south into Mexico and South America.

The Fulvous Tree-duck, an Old World species as well as an American, is found most commonly in the tule marshes and irrigated lands of southern California. It nests both on the ground, amid rushes and grasses, and also in trees. Its note is said to be a "squealing whistle." (Chapman). (Family *Anatidae*)

White-faced Tree-duck

Dendrocygna viduata [178.1]

ADULT MALE AND FEMALE—(The sexes closely alike.) Upper parts, dull reddish brown, but with the fore part of the head and face, white; the rest of the head and the upper part of the neck, black. The fore part of the neck bears a white patch. Lower neck and breast, rich chestnut brown. Abdomen and the under tail coverts, black.

LENGTH—20.00 inches.

DISTRIBUTION—Reported as casual in Costa Rica, and as an accidental straggler in New Jersey.

The Tree-ducks (*Dendrocygna*), have rather long legs and necks, short tail, and short rounded wings. They are chiefly arboreal, as their name implies, and are said to perch sometimes in shrubs, and even on stalks of corn. This present tropical South American and West Indian species (the White-faced Tree-duck) has straggled into the United States only accidentally. (Family *Anatidae*)

TROGON FAMILY
Trogonidae

The Trogons are beautifully brilliant birds, ranging through the tropics of America, and also found in Africa and Asia. They are small birds (usually less than twelve inches in length), with short, strong bills, hooked at the tip, and often with serrated tooth-like edges. ("Hen's teeth," therefore, are no joke among the Trogons.) The wings are pointed, and in some species possess many elongated covert feathers. The tail is long, beautifully colored, and in some cases is overlain by upper tail covert feathers much longer than the tail itself. The feet are very peculiar. The tarsus is short, and the toes are arranged two before and two behind, like the Woodpecker (Family *Picidae*), but with the Trogons it is the first and second toes that are reversed. Trogons are birds of the densest tropical forests, keeping well up among the higher branches, and seldom or never descending to the ground. The flight is weak, and some-

what undulatory, like that of wood-peckers. About two-thirds of the sixty trogons known are found in tropical America. The most famous form is the surpassingly gorgeous Quezal (*Pharomacrus mocinno*), the sacred bird of

the Aztecs. Our only North American species is the Coppery-tailed Trogon (*Trogon ambiguus ambiguus*).

NESTING. Trogons nest not too far from the ground in hollow trees, either availing themselves of a natural cavity, or excavating one in sufficiently soft decayed wood. The eggs number three or four, and are unmarked white or pale bluish-white.

TROGON
Coppery-tailed Trogon
Trogon ambiguus ambiguus [389]

ADULT MALE—Upper parts, metallic bronze-green; wings, gray. Middle tail feathers, bronze-green, merging into a rich coppery-reddish-brown and broadly tipped with black. Outer tail feathers, white marked with fine zig-zags of black. Face and throat, black; breast, with a white crescent; rest of under parts, rosy-pink. The wings, short and rounded; the tail, long; and the feet, small and weak. Bill, short and thick, with serrated edges.

ADULT FEMALE—Similar to the male, but with the black feathers replaced by grayish ones; the metallic sheeny feathers of the male, grayish-brown. Middle tail feathers, reddish-brown.

LENGTH—11.50 inches.

DISTRIBUTION—Restricted to the region between southern Texas and Arizona, and south to Mexico.

The brilliant and picturesque Trogon is an inhabitant of the mountain

country in its range, and is found particularly among pines. (Family *Trogonidae*)

TROPIC-BIRD FAMILY
Phaëthontidae

The name of this family, *Phaëthontidae,* is derived from Phaethon, off-spring of the Sun God Apollo, who, begging his father for permission to

drive the chariot of the sun for a single day, lost control of the horses, and driving too near the earth, so scorched it, that at last Jupiter in desperation slew the hapless youth with a thunderbolt. Tropic-birds, like Phaëthon, soar high in the air, often for many hours at a time, and are sometimes encountered far out over the ocean, hundreds of miles from land. Tropic-birds possess long powerful wings; long, sharply pointed bills; webbed feet similar to those of gulls and terns; and tails whose central feathers are long and narrow, and project backward far beyond the others, giving to the bird in flight a long graceful appearance. The plumage is usually white or whitish. Although no tropic-bird reaches the shores of the United States, yet three occur in the North American ocean fauna contained in the single genus *Phaëthon.*

NESTING. No nest is made by the tropic-bird, the egg being deposited in a hole or crevice among the rocks, or sometimes in a similar situation in a tree. Breeding is carried on on isolated oceanic islands. The birds nest in colonies or rookeries, and both sexes share in the labors and responsibilities of incubation. A single egg is laid at a breeding. Its color may be chalky-white, whitish, reddish-brown, or buffy, and speckled or spotted with purplish, gray, or brown.

TROPIC-BIRD
Red-billed Tropic-bird
Phaëthon aethereus [113]

Similar to the Yellow-billed Tropic-bird, but with its upper parts finely barred with black, and the bill red.

DISTRIBUTION—Ranges farther south in the Atlantic Ocean than the Yellow-billed species. It has been recorded in American waters off the Newfoundland Banks, and in Bermuda. (Family *Phaëthontidae*)

Red-tailed Tropic-bird
Phaëthon rubricaudus rothschildi [113.1]

Similar to the Yellow-billed Tropic-bird, but with the middle tail feathers bright carmine with black shafts.

DISTRIBUTION—An accidental visitant off Guadalupe Island, coast of Lower California. (Family *Phaëthontidae*)

Yellow-billed Tropic-bird
Phaëthon lepturus catesbyi [112]

ADULT MALE AND FEMALE—Plumage, white; but with a black band through the eye; and with the outer edge of and a broad mark in the wing, black. Flanks, streaked. Bill, long and

sharp. Middle tail feathers, much elongated and tinged with salmon; their shafts, black. The tail is more than half the length of the whole bird.
LENGTH—30.00 inches.
DISTRIBUTION—Abundant in the Bermuda Islands. Rare on our coast. For general account, see Family *Phaëthontidae*.

TURKEY FAMILY
Meleagrididae

The characteristics of the domestic turkey, too well-known to need description here, apply also to the members of the Family *Meleagrididae*. The family is confined to North and Central America. Four turkeys, resident within the borders of North America, are all contained in the genus *Meleagris*.

NESTING. The nests of Turkeys are placed on the ground, either in a

thicket, or among tall dense weeds and grasses, and are usually very effectively concealed. They are composed of grasses and leaves, and are somewhat sunken in a depression. From nine to eighteen eggs (normally from nine to twelve) are laid. They are either creamy-white or yellowish, and spotted uniformly over the surface with reddish-brown. When hatched the young run about like domestic chicks.

TURKEY
Eastern Turkey
Meleagris gallopavo silvestris [310a]

Similar to the common domestic Turkey of our farmyards, but with the feathers of the upper tail coverts and of the tail, tipped with chestnut-brown instead of with white.
LENGTH—About 49.00 inches.
DISTRIBUTION—From central Pennsylvania southward to the Gulf States, and westward from Nebraska, Kansas, Oklahoma, and the eastern part of Texas.

This splendid bird, sometimes attaining a weight of sixteen to forty pounds, formerly occurred over the greater part of eastern North America, extending its present restricted range as far north as Ontario and through the New England States. It is now virtually extirpated in Canada, and in most of the Northern States, and is decreasing rapidly in numbers elsewhere. In earlier days it was very common in New England, particularly in Massachusetts. It is now believed that the last authentic record of a Turkey's having been shot in Massachusetts is that of a specimen taken on Mt. Tom in the winter of 1850–51. Escaped

domestic Turkeys are sometimes shot in New England by hunters, but we are referring to the Wild Turkey (*Meleagris gallopavo silvestris*). During the breeding season, Turkeys are not gregarious, but at other times they are found in small flocks of a dozen individuals more or less. They are birds of the woodlands, not of the open, and roost in trees at night. Their notes and habits are like those of the domestic Turkey. (Family *Meleagrididae*)

Florida Turkey
Meleagris gallopavo osceola [310b]

Similar to the Eastern Turkey, but smaller, and with less white in the wings. The male weighs from about twelve to twenty-two pounds.

DISTRIBUTION—Restricted to southern Florida. (Family *Meleagrididae*)

Merriam's Turkey
Meleagris gallopavo merriami [310]

Similar to the Eastern Turkey, but with the feathers of the upper tail coverts and of the tail tipped with whitish.

DISTRIBUTION—"Mountains of southern Colorado, New Mexico, Arizona, and western Texas; and northern Chihuahua and Sonora, Mexico." (Bailey.) (Family *Melagrididae*)

Rio Grande Turkey
Meleagris gallopavo intermedia [310c]

Similar to the Eastern Turkey, but with the tips of the feathers of the upper tail coverts and of the tail, a light brownish instead of with rich chestnut-brown.

DISTRIBUTION—"Lowlands of southern Texas and northeastern Mexico." (A.O.U. Check List.) (Family *Meleagrididae*)

TURNSTONE
Black Turnstone
Arenaria melanocephala [284]

ADULT MALE AND FEMALE—Upper back, black with bronzy-greenish

sheen. Crown, same. Rest of the head, neck, throat, and upper breast, black; the sides and forehead, spotted with white. A white spot before the eyes. Abdomen and sides, white.

LENGTH—9.00 inches.

DISTRIBUTION—From Point Barrow, Alaska, to Santa Margarita Island, Lower California, on the Pacific Coast.

This Turnstone is similar in its habits to the Ruddy Turnstone, but lacks the striking rufous-brown of the latter. It is slightly smaller. (Family *Charadriidae*)

European Turnstone

Arenaria interpres interpres [283]

Similar to the Ruddy Turnstone, but somewhat larger, and with black the prevailing color of the upper parts. LENGTH—6.00 inches.

DISTRIBUTION—This European Turnstone is found on the west coast of Greenland, and has been reported as accidental in Massachusetts. (Family *Charadriidae*)

Ruddy Turnstone

Arenaria interpres morinella [283a]

ADULT MALE AND FEMALE—Upper parts and wings, variegated with reddish-brown, black, and white. Tail, with a white base, a black band near the end, and a white tip. Throat and breast, black and white. Abdomen, pure white. Head, white; its sides marked strikingly with black. Bill, black. Legs and feet, orange. LENGTH—9.50 inches.

DISTRIBUTION—This nearly cosmopolitan species breeds in the Arctic regions, and from northern and western Alaska westward to western Baffin Land. In winter it is found from North Carolina to southern Brazil and central Chile, and from central California to Texas; Louisiana, and Mississippi. During its migrations, it is likely to be found almost anywhere in North America.

This strikingly-colored Plover may be seen on the outer beaches in small flocks, running about here and there, industriously turning over shells, bits of drift-wood, and stones in search of crustaceans and insects. It is somewhat larger than the common Spotted Sandpiper, and is short-bodied and robust.

Its arresting pattern and colors have given to it the name Calico Bird. When it flies, its surprising stripings of black and white, and its areas of reddish-brown are most attractive. Its notes are a series of rapidly repeated trills. Turnstones do not confine their

dietary attention entirely to marine creatures, but also feed to a considerable extent upon grasshoppers (i.e., locusts), and in this respect render a very valuable service to agriculture. Slugs, worms, and in fact any small invertebrates that the bird discovers in its turning and flipping over of anything moveable, are greedily devoured. (Family *Charradriidae*)

VEERY

Veery

Hylocichla fuscescens fuscescens [756]

ADULT MALE AND FEMALE—Upper parts, tawny-brown. Under parts, white; sides of the breast and throat, faintly washed with flesh color, and faintly spotted with light brown. These markings not visible at a distance. Rest of under parts, clear white. LENGTH—7.52 inches.

DISTRIBUTION — From Newfoundland and Manitoba south to northern New Jersey, northern Illinois, and along the Allegheny Mountains into Pennsylvania. It winters in Central America.

The Veery, or Wilson's Thrush, is a more secretive bird than the common

Wood Thrush; it inhabits denser, more bushy woodlands, usually near water, swampy areas, or the dark defiles among hills, and keeps, at all times, nearer the ground. Infrequently a pair of birds may be found nesting on a high dry hillside, particularly if this acclivity rises abruptly from some deep stream valley. The song of the Veery, which is quite unique, has given the bird its name. It consists of a rolling, half-whispered, half-sung, weird-sounding strain, which can be passably imitated (after some practice) by whistling and singing at the same time the syllables *a-rrh'eeu, rrh'eeu, rrh'ayu, rrh'ayu;* or, as some have phrased it, *veery veery, vaary, vaary.* The rolling *spiral* character of the song strikes every observer as being

unlike any other note uttered by our eastern birds. Coming through the darkling depths of some damp wooded valley just before dusk, when the bird often sings its best, the song takes on a pleasingly eerie, almost spectral quality. (Family *Turdidae*)

VERDIN
Arizona Verdin
Auriparus flaviceps flaviceps [746]

ADULT MALE AND FEMALE—Upper parts, gray; shoulder patch, reddish-brown; forehead, sometimes marked with orange; crown, olive. Head, neck, and upper breast, bright yellow. Under parts, white or whitish.

LENGTH—4.30 inches.
DISTRIBUTION—From southwestern Utah and southern Nevada to southern Texas and southern California, and across into northern Mexico.

A bright, active, agitated little sprite is the Verdin, as it fidgets and scolds

about in the thorn bushes, like a Warbler and a Kinglet combined. (Family *Paridae*)

Cape Verdin
Auriparus flaviceps lamprocephalus [746a]

Similar to the Arizona Verdin, but with a yellower head.
DISTRIBUTION—Restricted to Lower California. (Family *Paridae*)

VIREO FAMILY
Vireonidae

Vireos, formerly known as greenlets, are small, greenish, grayish-yellowish, or olive-green birds, with lighter, usually white or whitish, under parts, not marked with spots, stripes, nor streaks. They inhabit the leafy portions of trees, moderately high up, or near the tops. They are not remarkable for their songs (except in a very few instances), and are insectivorous in their diet. The wings are slightly longer than the tail, and are not pointed nor slender.

Vireos are residents only of the Americas, and number some one hundred and fifty species and subspecies. Most of them are confined to the tropics, but twenty-five reach North America, all contained in the single genus *Vireo*.

NESTING. Vireos' nests are little, perfectly-formed, rather deep cup-like structures, suspended between the

small fork of a branch, often out some distance from the main trunk of a sapling or larger tree, from four or five to twenty, thirty, or more feet from the ground. (A Blue-headed Vireo's nest, which I once watched for several summers on the side of a mountain in New Hampshire, was at least fifty feet from the ground, and about twenty feet out from the main trunk.) The nests are composed of strips of bark (often fragments and strips of white and golden birch bark), grasses, strips of weed bark, other soft vegetable fibers, with the addition sometimes of mosses and lichens. The whole may be bound together with spider web silk, and the like. The three to five eggs are pure white, pinkish-white, or creamy, spotted with browns and purples.

VIREO
Arizona Vireo
Vireo belli arizonae [633c]

Similar to the Least Vireo, but with the upper parts more decidedly tinged with olive; and the sides of the body and the flanks, more markedly washed with a yellowish-olive. It seems to be intermediate between the Least Vireo and the Texas Vireo.

DISTRIBUTION—From southeastern California along the Colorado River, southern Arizona, southwestern New Mexico, and the central portion of western Texas, extending southward into Mexico to Chihuahua and Sinaloa. (Family *Vireonidae*)

Bell's Vireo
Vireo belli belli [633]

ADULT MALE AND FEMALE—Upper parts, olive-brown, washed with greenish on the upper tail coverts. Wings and tail, brownish; the former with two narrow, faint, grayish bars. Throat, white; the rest of the under parts, dull sulphur-yellowish-white; under tail coverts, yellow.
LENGTH—5.00 inches.

DISTRIBUTION—The Mississippi Valley and Great Plains region, from Indiana west to the Dakotas, and south to Texas and into Mexico, sometimes straggling eastward and northward as far as New Hampshire. (Family *Vireonidae*)

Bermuda Vireo
Vireo griseus bermudianus [631b]

Similar to the White-eyed Vireo, but with no yellow on the sides.
DISTRIBUTION—Found only in the Bermuda Islands. (Family *Vireonidae*)

Black-capped Vireo
Vireo atricappilus [630]

ADULT MALE—Back, olive-green, brighter in strong light. A yellowish white wing bar. Top and sides of the head, black. Ring around the eye, and line to base of the bill, white. Under parts, white; the sides washed with faint grayish.
ADULT FEMALE—Similar to the male, but grayer; the top and sides of the head, slate-gray.
LENGTH—4.55 inches.

DISTRIBUTION—From southwestern Kansas south and west to western and central Texas, passing south into southern Mexico in the fall.

This sprightly little Vireo, with its striking head markings, frequents low growths in canyons and on ridges, where it fidgets about in a nervous vigorous way, stopping now and then

to jerk out its loud, clear, bright song, phrased in true Vireo fashion, and sounding like the syllables *quee-you, quich-you-you,* repeated again and again, with several variations. (Family *Vireonidae*)

Black-whiskered Vireo
Vireo calidris barbatulus [623]

Similar to the Red-eyed Vireo, but browner on the back, and with a dark streak on the sides of the throat.

DISTRIBUTION—In southern Florida, Cuba and the Bahama Islands, passing in winter into Central America. (Family *Vireonidae*)

Blue-headed Vireo
Vireo solitarius solitarius [629]

ADULT MALE AND FEMALE—Top and sides of the head, bluish-slaty-gray, with a decided bluish cast in strong light. Ring around the eye, and line to the base of the upper mandible, white. Back, grayish-olive, with a slightly greenish hue when strongly lighted. Two white wing bars. Throat and breast, white; abdomen, grayish-white; its sides faintly washed with a yellowish-green.

LENGTH—5.61 inches.

DISTRIBUTION—From New Brunswick and Manitoba southward into southern New England and New York, and along the higher Allegheny Mountains. In winter it passes into Florida and southward in Central America.

The dignified Blue-headed Vireo (often called the Solitary Vireo) passes through the Eastern States in its migrations as a relatively silent species, though in the fall its voice may sometimes be heard on clear, quiet mornings and evenings. In song, this species is similar to its Red-eyed cousin, but gives forth notes which are purer in tone, more delicate, more deliberate, and with now and then a pleasing double-note, quite different

from any of the Red-eye's notes. On its nesting grounds the bird prefers a mixture of deciduous and coniferous trees, such as are to be found in the mountains of New England at moderate altitudes where the red spruces begin. (Family *Vireonidae*)

Cassin's Vireo
Vireo solitarius cassini [629a]

Similar to the Blue-headed Vireo, but with darker back; under parts, grayer.

DISTRIBUTION—From British Columbia and Idaho along the Pacific Coast zone, and spreading through Nevada and Lower California. In winter it is found in New Mexico, Arizona, and northern Mexico. (Family *Vireonidae*)

Eastern Warbling Vireo
Vireo gilvus gilvus [627]

ADULT MALE AND FEMALE—Upper parts, brownish-gray; the crown, the same color as the back. A broad whitish streak extends over the eye. Under parts, grayish-white, slightly tinged on the abdomen and on the sides with faint yellowish.

LENGTH—5.80 inches.

DISTRIBUTION—From the region of Hudson Bay south to the Gulf of Mexico, and westward to the Great Plains. In winter it is found in Mexico.

This useful Vireo is one of the most persistent singers of its family. From early morning until after sundown, its voice may be heard pursuing its rich

and tranquil way, not even pausing during the heat of the day when most bird notes are hushed. Fortunately the song is relatively rather low-pitched, rich, languid, deliberate, and alto-

gether pleasing—even soothing—in quality; otherwise the singer might not be a particularly welcome performer. The Warbling Vireo haunts the tops of tall leafy trees in forests, and often those along the shady streets of towns and villages, and in public parks. (Family *Vireonidae*)

Frazar's Vireo
Vireo huttoni cognatus [632d]

Similar to the Stephen's Vireo, but with the rump and upper tail coverts not so decidedly olive-green; and with the under parts showing almost no or no yellowish cast. The upper breast is not washed with an olive-buff tone.

DISTRIBUTION—Restricted to the Cape District of Lower California. (Family *Vireonidae*)

Gray Vireo
Vireo vicinior [634]

Somewhat similar to the Blue-headed Vireo, but with the upper parts and

sides of the head, a dull gray; and wing bars, faint or absent. Under parts, dull grayish-white.

DISTRIBUTION—Southern California to western Texas, and southern Nevada to northwestern Mexico. (Family *Vireonidae*)

Hutton's Vireo
Vireo huttoni huttoni [632]

ADULT MALE AND FEMALE—Upper parts, dull olive-brownish-gray; with a wash of greenish on the wings, upper tail coverts, and tail. Two narrow white wing bars. Ring around the eye, and lores, whitish. Under parts, dull

whitish, washed on the sides with yellowish.

LENGTH—4.50 inches.

DISTRIBUTION—In California, west of the Sierra Nevada Mountains. (Family *Vireonidae*)

Key West Vireo

Vireo griseus maynardi [631a]

Similar to the White-eyed Vireo, but with a heavier bill and lighter sides.

DISTRIBUTION—Confined to Florida and its keys. (Family *Vireonidae*)

Least Vireo

Vireo belli pusillus [633a]

Similar to the Bell's Vireo, but with upper parts grayer; and with wings, tail, and upper tail coverts washed with olive. Under parts, white; the sides flushed with olive-greenish.

DISTRIBUTION—From Arizona and central California south into the northern part of Lower California and into northwestern Mexico. (Family *Vireonidae*)

Mountain Solitary Vireo

Vireo solitarius alticola [629c]

Similar to the Blue-headed (or Solitary) Vireo, but larger, and with the

darker head color extending down over the upper and middle back region.

DISTRIBUTION — Southeastern portion of the United States, in the Allegheny Mountains from North Carolina southward into Georgia, passing south into Florida for the winter. (Family *Vireonidae*)

Philadelphia Vireo

Vireo philadelphicus [626]

ADULT MALE AND FEMALE—Upper parts, gray, tinged with greenish when seen in strong light. Crown, gray without a greenish hue. Sides of the head, light gray, with a whitish line over the eye. Under parts, very light lemon-yellowish-white.

LENGTH—4.75 inches.

DISTRIBUTION — From the central Canadian zone south into Maine, New Hampshire, and westward, wintering from Guatemala southward in the tropics.

This curious little Vireo, or Greenlet, sings like the Red-eyed Vireo, and closely resembles the Tennessee Warbler. Fortunately for those who wish

to make its acquaintance, it is a particularly fearless bird, and not much given to burying itself in the tops of leafy trees, as are most of its congeners, but comes out into the edges of low-growing bushes and small shrubs. Although its song is so similar to the Red-eye's as usually to pass for it, yet close attention will sometimes detect a consistently higher pitch to the notes, and a feebleness and tremulousness of utterance, absent from the Red-eye's assured and confident strain. From the Tennessee Warbler, the Philadelphia Vireo may be distinguished by its typical Vireo bill (heavier than the Warbler's), and by its somewhat heavier body. (Family *Vireonidae*)

Plumbeous Vireo

Vireo solitarius plumbeus [629b]

Similar to the Blue-headed Vireo, but with entire upper parts, a dark slaty-gray; and with the sides of the body washed with a leaden-gray.

DISTRIBUTION—From the southwestern part of the Dakotas, southward and westward through Wyoming and the Rocky Mountain region into northern Mexico. In winter it is found as far south as southern Mexico. During the breeding season these birds rise to elevations of about 10,000 feet in the higher Rockies. (Family *Vireonidae*)

Red-eyed Vireo

Vireo olivaceus [624]

ADULT MALE AND FEMALE—Upper parts, light grayish-olive; greenish in strong light. Crown, darker gray, bordered on each side by a blackish line. Line over the eye, white. Iris of eye, bright garnet. Wing bars, absent. Under parts, white.

LENGTH—6.23 inches.

DISTRIBUTION—From British Columbia and the Rocky Mountain region, east to Labrador, and south to the Gulf of Mexico. It winters in Central and South America.

The Red-eyed Vireo, or Greenlet as it is sometimes called, is a very common songster of tall trees, whether in city streets, parks, or the countryside. Nor

is the bird absent in the dense forests of the North. From the leafy tops of such trees, it pours forth its never-ending, tri-syllabic song; perhaps the commonest of bird notes in the summer months. Right through the heat of summer, this tireless little species sings almost without a break, using (it seems) the words of Wilson Flagg's representation: *you see it; you hear it; you know it; you believe it.* The bird's habit of feeding and singing

high up among the leafy tips of branches where it is concealed by its verdant screen, and its unobtrusive colors make it more often heard than seen. Its nest is one of the commonest encountered in the winter woods—a small cup-shaped structure about the size of one's fist, slung between a small tree fork, and situated about eight or ten feet from the ground. It is usually a light silver-gray—a sort of "weathered silver" like the clapboards of an old country house. The bright red color of the iris, from which the bird derives its name, is not visible, except at a very short distance and in very strong light. (Family *Vireonidae*)

Rio Grande Vireo

Vireo griseus micrus [631c]

Similar to the White-eyed Vireo, but slightly smaller, and much duller or grayer in general color.

DISTRIBUTION — From southeastern Texas south into northeastern Mexico. (Family *Vireonidae*)

San Lucas Vireo
Vireo solitarius lucasanus [629d]

Similar to the Blue-headed Vireo, but with a longer, heavier bill; and sides of the body washed with yellow.

DISTRIBUTION—Restricted to the Cape Region of Lower California. (Family *Vireonidae*)

Stephen's Vireo
Vireo huttoni stephensi [632a]

Similar to Hutton's Vireo, but with the upper parts, olive-gray; the wing bars, wider; and the whole effect of the plumage, paler.

LENGTH—About 5.00 inches.

DISTRIBUTION—In the mountains of Arizona, western Texas, Mexico, and Lower California. (Family *Vireonidae*)

Texas Vireo
Vireo belli medius [633b]

Similar to the Bell's Vireo, but paler; with the upper parts more grayish, and the under parts less extensively yellow. Somewhat similar to the Arizona and Least Vireos.

DISTRIBUTION—Not found extensively in the United States, but ranging from the southwestern part of Texas, southward into Mexico to Coahuila and Guanajuato; into central Mexico, and on to Guatamela. (Family *Vireonidae*)

Western Warbling Vireo
Vireo gilvus swainsoni [627a]

Similar to the Eastern Warbling Vireo, but slightly smaller, and with the upper parts grayer.

DISTRIBUTION—In the western portion of the country from British Columbia to Mexico, and from the Pacific Coast east to the Rocky Mountains. In winter it is confined to Mexico. (Family *Vireonidae*)

White-eyed Vireo
Vireo griseus griseus [631]

ADULT MALE AND FEMALE—Upper parts, olive-greenish-gray, appearing yellowish-green in strong light. Ring around the eye, and a line to the base of the upper mandible, yellow. Two yellowish-white wing bars. Iris of eye, white, giving it a stary aspect. Throat, grayish-white; middle of abdomen, pure white. Sides of breast and abdomen, yellowish.

LENGTH—5.27 inches.

DISTRIBUTION—From Minnesota and New Hampshire southwestward to Texas and Florida. In winter it is found in Florida, Mexico, and Central America.

This little Vireo might be called the "Thicket Vireo," for the bird is most often found in scrubby thickets, usually in low wet situations. It is an

inquisitive, excitable bird, and when disturbed commences a scolding, mewing, buzzing note, or breaks out into a sharp startling song, which may be interpreted into the words *what's the matter; what is it; chicka-dee-day; can't-see-you-sir-today;* each phrase strongly accented on the first word. The White-eye is the coloratura and general mimic in its family. (Family *Vireonidae*)

Yellow-green Vireo
Vireo flavoviridis flavoviridis [625]

Similar to the common Red-eyed Vireo, but with greener upper parts, and with the sides of the body, greenish-yellow.

DISTRIBUTION—From the lower portions of the Rio Grande southward through Central America into northern South America. (Family *Vireonidae*)

Yellow-throated Vireo
Vireo flavifrons [628]

ADULT MALE AND FEMALE—Upper parts, olive-grayish, with a greenish-yellow cast in strong light. Upper tail coverts and lower portion of back, gray. Wings with two whitish bars. Ring around the eye, and line to base of upper mandible, yellow. Throat and breast, bright yellow; abdomen, whitish.

LENGTH—9.95 inches.

DISTRIBUTION — From Newfoundland and Manitoba southward over the entire eastern United States to Florida and Texas, wintering in the tropical Americas.

The Yellow-throat is essentially a bird of the tree tops, where it feeds, sings, and builds its nest. Though it wears a brilliant throat and breast, quite

conspicuous when the bird is seen out of its natural setting, yet amid the sunlit leaves of its airy haunts, it is almost perfectly concealed. The song of the Yellow-throated Vireo is rich and deep—as might almost be ex-

pected out of such a throat—and consists of phrases of two or three notes each, with a pause between each phrase. It is recognizable as a typical Vireo song, and identifiable as the Yellow-throat's performance by reason of its rich, throaty, deliberate, studied character. Its nest is of the usual Vireo design, but studded all over its exterior with bits of lichen. (Family *Vireonidae*)

VULTURE FAMILY
Cathartidae

The name *Cathartidae* comes from the Greek *kathartes* meaning cleanser, and refers to the habits of Vultures in devouring carrion, and thus cleansing the fields of offensive matter. The

Cathartidae or New World Vultures range from the tropical Americas into northern North America. Their bills are feebly hooked, the feet bear weak talons, and the wings are broad and long. The great California Vulture and the Condor of the Andes are exceeded in wing-spread only by the Wandering Albatross, and hence are among the greatest of flying birds. The heads and necks of Vultures are usually bare of feathers. Although the openings of the nostrils are very large, they possess a very weak sense of smell. They detect their food by sight from great distances.

NESTING. Among our American Vultures, the common eastern Turkey

Vulture makes no nest, but lays its eggs rather carelessly on the ground in a variety of situations, such as in caves, among rocks, on cliffs (where it is remarkable that they do not roll off), or among sticks and leaves, and the general vegetable litter of the forest floor. Sometimes one may find the eggs in a prostrate, rotted, hollow log, or alongside of and in the shelter of it. In most cases the eggs are placed near water. Nests or rather eggs, have also been found in deserted cabins, or even in old abandoned hog pens. The eggs, occasionally one, usually two, and rarely three, are a dull or creamy white, sometimes unmarked, or very faintly so, but more often irregularly blotched with various shades of brown and sometimes lavender. The Black Vulture of the South nests generally in similar situations. Its eggs are somewhat more elongated than those of the Turkey Vulture, and are whitish, bluish-white, creamy, or pale grayish-green, marked with large blotches of chocolate-brown or dark reddish-brown, sometimes with additional smaller spots and specks of lilac and purplish. The very rare California Vulture, or Condor, nests among the rocks and cliffs of the most inaccessible mountain fastnesses, or sometimes in the hollow of a dead tree or stump. It makes no nest. Its eggs, one or two in number, are an unmarked greenish-white.

VULTURE

Black Vulture

Coragyps atratus atratus [326]

Somewhat similar to the Turkey Vulture, but with the bare skin about the bill, and the head and neck, black. Plumage, black. A light silvery area shows on the under surface of the wings when the bird is in flight.

LENGTH—24.00 inches.

DISTRIBUTION — From the latitude of North Carolina west to the Great Plains, and south into northern South

America. Accidental in northern United States. (Family *Cathartidae*)

Turkey Vulture

Cathartes aura septentrionalis [325]

ADULT MALE AND FEMALE—Head and neck, naked; the skin and area about the base of the bill, bright red. Rest of the body covered with plumage which is black or blackish; the feathers edged with grayish-brown.

LENGTH—30.00 inches.

DISTRIBUTION—The whole of the Western Hemisphere, except from the latitude of southern Connecticut northward. A frequent straggler into the central portion of New England.

The Turkey Vulture is a paradox among birds. The embodiment of grace and majesty in the air, it becomes on the ground an uncouth and loutish object, unseemly alike in appearance and in habits. Its wing-spread of about six feet is exceeded by few of our native birds. No bird soars with more ease and assurance than the Vulture, as with motionless pinions its great veering spirals carry it often above the storm-clouds. It is a gregarious bird—from eight to twenty-five individuals wheeling together far up in the blue, or descending to share a common meal. Its notes are only soft hissings and gruntings, rarely heard. The Vulture, or

Buzzard as it is often called, is of value because of its consumption of carrion which would otherwise befoul the fields. It very rarely attacks living creatures. (Family *Cathartidae*)

WAGTAIL FAMILY
Wagtails and Pipits
Motacillidae

These are terrestrial birds, which never hop, but run rapidly along the ground. Wagtails are marked with gray, black, white, sometimes yellow, and are unstreaked. Pipits are brownish-streaked and resemble Larks. Both possess slender bills, and long, pointed, graceful wings. Nine species and subspecies are found in North America.

NESTING. Wagtails make a compact nest of moss, grasses, fine roots, strips of weed bark, and the like, and line it with feathers, wool, fine grasses, and hair. This structure is tucked snugly

into a hole in a bank, between two rocks, or in a crevice in an old stone wall or stone heap. The eggs are four

or five in number, and are a bluish-white with grayish-brown spots. Our American Pipit, a bird of the open, rather wet, boggy country, makes its nest on the ground. This is a thick-walled, bulky structure of dried coarse and fine grasses, together with some shreds of weed bark. It is lined with finer grasses, and soft plant fiber, but gives the appearance of being composed entirely of moss and dry grass. Sometimes this nest may be tucked into a crevice on the side of a rock, or sunk in a hollow mossy bed. The eggs are a ground color of bluish-white, grayish-white, creamy, or faint brown; lined and streaked with black and dark gray; and heavily spotted with rich brown. From four to six is the normal number in a nest.

WAGTAIL
Alaska Yellow Wagtail
Motacilla flava alascensis [696]

ADULT MALE—Upper parts, olive-greenish in strong light; crown, bluish-slaty-gray, with a prominent white line

over the eye. Wings with yellowish bars. Outer tail feathers, mostly white. Under parts, yellow, fading on the under tail coverts.

ADULT FEMALE—Similar to the male, but uniformly duller; the head and wing bars, brownish.

LENGTH—6.50 inches.

DISTRIBUTION—In Asia, and in eastern Alaska along the coast of the Bering Sea. (Family *Motacillidae*)

Black-backed Wagtail

Motacilla alba lugens [695.1]

In general similar to the White Wagtail, but with darker, almost black upper parts.

DISTRIBUTION — "Kamchatka, Kurile, and Commander islands. Casual on Attu Island, Aleutian Chain." (A.O.U. Check List.) (Family *Motacillidae*)

Swinhoe's Wagtail

Motacilla alba ocularis [695]

Similar to the *Motacilla luzonensis*, but with a relatively smaller head, a gray back, and a black line extending through the eye and ear coverts.

LENGTH—7.80 inches.

DISTRIBUTION—This Asiatic form of Wagtail occurs casually on Attu Island, of the Aleutian Chain, and also at the mouth of the Yukon River in Alaska. It is an accidental straggler in Lower California. (Family *Motacillidae*)

White Wagtail

Motacilla alba alba [694]

ADULT MALE—Upper parts, pale gray; the feathers of the wing coverts

and secondaries with whitish tips. Crown, nape, throat, and upper breast, black. Forehead, face, sides of neck, lower breast, and abdomen, white.

ADULT FEMALE—Similar to the male but with back browner; chin and throat, less black, and mixed with white. Crown, black mixed with grayish.

LENGTH—7.50 inches.

DISTRIBUTION—A European Wagtail, accidental in northern Quebec and Greenland. (Family *Motacillidae*)

WARBLER

Alaska Yellow Warbler

Dendroica aestiva rubiginosa [652b]

Similar to the Eastern Yellow Warbler. The male possesses slightly darker

upper parts, and the female is duller throughout.

DISTRIBUTION—The Alaska Yellow Warbler ranges along the Pacific Coast from Alaska to Vancouver Island, and winters in Mexico and Central America. (Family *Compsothlypidae*)

Audubon's Warbler

Dendroica auduboni auduboni [656]

In general, similar to the Myrtle Warbler, except that the Audubon's possesses a bright yellow throat, and wider, more prominent white wing bars. The female is duller above, with less white in the wings; the yellow is duller, and the breast is grayish.

LENGTH—5.60 inches.

DISTRIBUTION — Western North America, from British Columbia southward along the higher mountains to southern California and New Mexico. It winters in Mexico.

Both in habits and in coloration, the Audubon's Warbler is similar to its

eastern relative, the Myrtle Warbler. (Family *Compsothlypidae*)

Bachman's Warbler
Vermivora bachmani [640]

ADULT MALE—Back of head and neck, bluish-gray; back and rump, bright-olive green. Shoulder (wrist), yellow. Tail, bluish-gray; the outer feathers, white near the tips. Crown, and large patch on the upper breast, black. Throat, lower breast, and abdomen, yellow.

ADULT FEMALE—Upper parts as in the male, but crown patch gray instead of black, and upper breast patch lacking. Under parts, whitish, tinged faintly with yellowish on the throat and breast; abdomen, white.

LENGTH—4.25 inches.

DISTRIBUTION—Southeastern United States, from Virginia and southern Indiana west as far as Louisiana. Winters in Cuba.

Like the Pine Warbler, the Bachman's Warbler is a bird of leisurely motions, frequenting damp woodlands, and brushy situations generally, but also found to some extent along the edges of forests where the trees are not too numerous and high. Wherever it oc-

curs in woodlands, however, it seems to prefer the tops of trees and bushes, especially when giving forth its song. During migration, also, it travels more through the tree tops than near the ground. In song, the bird resembles the Parula Warbler, as it utters a series of wheezy or buzzy notes which run up the scale to an abrupt ending. There is little that is musical about its performance, which resembles the stridulations of some small insect. Bachman's Warbler is a strikingly beautiful bird, with its bright olive-green rump and lower back, its clear

lemon-yellow under parts, and its sharply defined black crown and breast patch. The bird was discovered and described in 1833, but no nest was found until sixty-four years later. (Family *Compsothlypidae*)

Bay-breasted Warbler
Dendroica castanea [660]

ADULT MALE—Whole top of head, chestnut-brown; the rest, black. Back, gray streaked with black; a buffy patch on the side of the neck; two white wing bars. Throat, breast, and sides of the body, chestnut-brown; abdomen, white.

ADULT FEMALE—Upper parts, olive-gray faintly streaked with blackish;

top of head, lighter and more buffy.
Under parts, buffy; with throat, breast,
and sides very faintly tinged with
brownish.

LENGTH—5.63 inches.

DISTRIBUTION — Eastern North
America, from the Hudson Bay country and Labrador south to the latitude
of northern New England and north-

ern Michigan; passing south in the
fall through the more southerly states
into Central and northern South
America for the winter.

This self-contained and aristocratic-
mannered Warbler is a member of the
upper circles of the bird world, and
pursues its dignified way clad in gar-
ments of good taste, and giving voice
to a song which does not compel attention. As it moves in unhurried and
decorous fashion among the foliage
of the upper branches, these characteristics of manner, dress, and voice,
all tend toward the bird's concealment, and give it a reputation for
greater rarity than is actually the case.
The Bay-breast's song is a thin, fine,
high, musically sibilous performance,
with a slight crescendo and diminuendo, and sounds like the syllables
*swiss, swiss, swiss, swiss, swiss, swiss,
swiss.* This strain is confusingly similar
to the song of the Black-poll Warbler,
and somewhat similar to that of the
Blackburnian Warbler, with which the
Bay-breast is often associated in its
nesting regions among the northern

mountains. This is our only Warbler
displaying chestnut-brown color on
the throat, breast, and sides. (Family
Compsothlypidae)

Black and White Warbler
Mniotilta varia [636]

ADULT MALE—Upper parts, strikingly streaked with jet black and pure
white; sides, more finely streaked; rest
of under parts, pure white; but throat
only sometimes white, often black.

ADULT FEMALE—Not so black above;
sides less streaked; throat, pure white.

LENGTH—5.30 inches.

DISTRIBUTION — Whole of eastern
North America as far west as the
Rocky Mountains; winters in the West
Indies and the northern parts of
South America.

This little black-and-white-striped,
mouse-like, active Warbler is often
known as the Black and White
Creeper, from its habit of crawling
about over the bark of tree trunks
and larger branches, in its incessant
search after insects, their eggs and

larvae, which are hidden in the crevices of the bark. Were it not for its
constant motion, it would be a difficult
bird to locate, so well do its stripes
simulate the light and dark shadow
streaks on the trees. Sometimes, but

not often, it may be seen swinging from the tips of twigs, as do many of the other Warblers. However, its habits as a creeping bird confine it usually to flatter surfaces.

Its song, delivered without apparent effort, and given forth as it creeps about, is a very thin, fine, wiry, high *See teé, see teé, see tée,* accented on the second part, and repeated four times. It can be duplicated almost exactly by loudly whispering the syllables through closely set teeth. (Family *Compsothlypidae*)

Black-fronted Warbler

Dendroica auduboni nigrifrons [656a]

Similar to the Audubon's Warbler, but larger and darker.

LENGTH—5.25 inches.

DISTRIBUTION—From southern Arizona southward into the mountains of northern Mexico. (Family *Compsothlypidae*)

Black-poll Warbler

Dendroica striata [661]

ADULT MALE—Whole crown, solid black; sides of head, white. Back, gray streaked with black; two white wing bars. Under parts, white; the sides streaked with black.

ADULT FEMALE — Upper parts, greenish-gray faintly streaked with black; a buffy line over the eye; two white wing bars. Under parts, white; the sides lightly streaked with blackish.

LENGTH—5.56 inches.

DISTRIBUTION — Eastern North America, from Labrador and Alaska southward to northern New England, northern New York, northern Michigan, and westward as far as the Rocky Mountains (Colorado). It winters in the West Indies and the northern portion of South America.

One of the commonest of bird voices in the spring woodlands of the north-

east is the incessant insectoid strain of the Black-poll Warbler. It is composed of about eight thin, high, piercing notes, like the syllables (hissed through the closed teeth) *tsit, tsit, tsit, tsit, tsit, tsit, tsit, tsit,* and given with

a marked crescendo and diminuendo. This song, while not loud nor otherwise arresting to the attention, is noteworthy and pleasing in character in its delicacy and penetration, and is perhaps one of the easiest of Warbler songs to commit to memory. In the spring the male birds are conspicuously black-streaked (and in this respect resemble somewhat the Black and White Creeping Warbler); and sing incessantly; but in the fall they become inconspicuous indeed, in a dress of greenish-gray and yellowish, and slip through the woodlands and coppices with no utterance except an almost imperceptible lisping *tsirp.* The hordes of these little Warblers that pass southward in the fall often seem to inundate the countryside, and fill every tree and bush to overflowing. (Family *Compsothlypidae*)

Black-throated Blue Warbler

Dendroica caerulescens caerulescens [654]

ADULT MALE—Upper parts, slaty-bluish-gray, with a decided blue tone in strong light; a large white patch in the wing, and white markings in the outer tail feathers. Sides of the head, throat, upper breast, and sides of the abdomen, solid black; lower breast and abdomen, white.

ADULT FEMALE—Upper parts, grayish-brown with a slight greenish cast; line over the eye, straw color; a small but prominent white patch in the wing. Under parts, whitish-straw color.

LENGTH—5.28 inches.

DISTRIBUTION — Eastern North America from Labrador and the Hudson Bay country to the Allegheny Mountains, Michigan, and Minnesota; passing the winters in Central and South America.

On spruce-covered mountain slopes of northern United States, the Black-throated Blue Warbler's languid, hoarse, drawled song is a characteristic sound of these dank, cool, boreal forests. In quality of tone the song resembles that of the Black-throated Green Warbler, and may be written *zheea, zheea, zheea, zh'ee weet,* the first syllables slurred downward, and the final syllable rising slightly in pitch and then stopping abruptly. The first three syllables sound like someone hoarsely and musically whispering *dear, dear, dear,* in a melancholy and despondent tone. Black-throated Blues do not seem to be much disturbed

when the nest is approached, but fly about from branch to branch uttering a rich, heavy *chuckk.* The nest itself

is not difficult to locate, being placed usually in a small hemlock or spruce tree, often in a forest clearing or along a mountain trail, and is never very high—from one to ten feet from the ground being the usual altitude. It is a compact, cup-shaped structure, firmly woven about the twigs and needles of its living support, and so well-constructed as to withstand the storms of several winters, though, of course, used only once by the birds. (Family *Compsothlypidae*)

Black-throated Gray Warbler
Dendroica nigrescens [665]

ADULT MALE — Whole head and throat, black; with a small spot of yellow before the eye, and a white stripe

extending from just above it, backwards to the side of the nape; another broad stripe from the base of the bill backwards along the sides of the throat. Upper parts, gray streaked with black. Two white wing bars. Outer tail feathers marked with white. Breast and abdomen, white; the sides streaked with black.

ADULT FEMALE—Similar to the male, but with the head markings often gray instead of black. Throat, usually white, or white with blackish markings.

LENGTH—5.00 inches.

DISTRIBUTION—Among the mountains of the west, from Colorado and Vancouver Island southward to Arizona and Lower California. It winters in Mexico.

The Black-throated Gray Warbler is similar in habits and notes to the Black-throated Green Warbler of the East; but unlike it, prefers bushy and scrubby lands instead of cool, deep, coniferous woods. (Family *Compsothlypidae*)

Black-throated Green Warbler

Dendroica virens virens [667]

ADULT MALE—Upper parts, greenish-olive; cheeks, sides of throat, and forehead, bright yellow; wings, grayish with two broad white bars. Middle of throat, upper breast, and sides of breast, solid black; abdomen, white, its sides streaked narrowly, but prominently, with black.

ADULT FEMALE—Yellow of the plumage much duller than in the male; throat, yellowish white; breast and sides, streaked with blackish; two broad white bars in the wing—generally the same pattern as the male, but paler throughout.

LENGTH—5.00 inches.

DISTRIBUTION—The whole of eastern North America from the Hudson Bay region and Nova Scotia, south along the Allegheny Mountains into South Carolina. Winters in Central America.

The Black-throated Green Warbler is a bird of dark, cool, evergreen forests, where its very characteristic song is one of the familiar summer sounds. Though there are many renditions, the following syllables, harshly whispered through the set teeth, give a close approximation: *zher zhe'e, zher zher zhe'et*. The *zher* syllables are lower in pitch, and the *zhee* and *zheet* syllables higher and accented. The whole song is rather leisurely and drawly, and suggests the peace and tranquillity of the northern hemlock and spruce forests. The Black-throated Green Warbler is very fond of the leaf-rolling caterpillars of the genus *Tortricidae,* as well as others of a similar nature, and hence the bird does

good service to orchardists in destroying these pests. During migration one may often see Black-throated Greens traveling in considerable companies, together with other Warbler species. Being tree Warblers, they are most often seen above one's head, when the white abdomen, and black breast markings are very arresting to the attention. (Family *Compsothlypidae*)

Blackburnian Warbler

Dendroica fusca [662]

ADULT MALE—Head, cheeks, and sides of throat, strikingly marked with black and red-orange; back, black streaked with grayish; a large white patch in the wing; outer tail feathers, marked with white. Throat and breast, flaming red-orange; abdomen, whitish; sides of breast and abdomen, marked with short black streaks.

ADULT FEMALE—Respectively dark gray and yellow wherever the male is black and orange.

LENGTH—5.25 inches.

DISTRIBUTION—The whole of Eastern North America from northern Labrador and the Hudson Bay country, south through the Berkshires, and on along the high Alleghenies into South Carolina. Winters in tropical America.

The glorious Blackburnian Warbler is one of the most flamingly brilliant of our American birds. No one who has seen the male bird in full sunlight in the tip of a dark spruce branch—its

throat and breast blazing out in contrast with its somber surroundings—can ever forget the sight. In our northern coniferous forests the birds are fortunately common. The song of the Blackburnian is peculiar. Like a thin, fine golden thread spinning upward to an almost inaudible conclusion, it rises in the scale higher and higher, and finer and finer, thus: *Si we'et, si we'et, si we'et, s'it.* Many persons are unable to hear any but the first few notes. The final abrupt note may be likened to the musical snapping of a lady's fingernail. This seems to be the song most frequently uttered. Another song runs *See, see, see, see, si, si, s'it.* This Warbler is a forest dweller, and one that keeps well up among the dense branches of trees, mostly conifers. Sometimes the bird dashes out of its bosky covert after a passing insect, snapping it up adroitly on the wing after the fashion of a Flycatcher. (Family *Compsothlypidae*)

Blue-winged Warbler
Vermivora pinus [641]

ADULT MALE—Crown and entire under parts, bright rich lemon-yellow. A narrow black line through the eye; back, bright olive-green; tail, bluish-gray, with white outer feathers; wings, bluish-gray, with two whitish or faintly yellowish bars.

ADULT FEMALE—Similar to the male, but with the head duller; the bright yellow being restricted to the forehead. Under parts, full yellow.

LENGTH—4.80 inches.

DISTRIBUTION—Eastern United States from southern Minnesota and Connecticut southward, passing south of the United States in winter.

The Blue-winged Warbler is a shy, retiring bird, less active and agitated in its motions than most of its family. It possesses the distinction of giving rise to one of the shortest and most insignificant of Warbler songs, which may be adequately represented by the simple syllables *beee, bzzzzz*—drawly, insect-like, and not loud. It is most

often delivered from the topmost twig of a tree or bush, while the singer perches erect and motionless against the sky. The lack of active movement, small size, and trifling, insectoid song, make the Blue-winged Warbler inconspicuous in the field. Hence the bird is often accounted a rare species in regions where it is quite common. A somewhat longer song is infrequently uttered; in some respects similar to that of the Black-throated Green Warbler (q.v.), though less loud: *See, zi-zi-zi-see su'rr.* Since the bird does not warble, its present name seems inappropriate. It might better be called the Blue and Yellow Buzzer. Dry bushy fields, scrubby overgrown pastures, the ragged edges of sparse woodlands, thinly wooded hillsides, and scraggy pine woods with an abundance of underbrush are the usual haunts of the Blue-winged Warbler. (Family *Compsothlypidae*)

Cairn's Warbler

Dendroica caerulescens cairnsi [654a]

Similar to the Black-throated Blue Warbler, but with the back blackish, and the whole bird uniformly darker.

DISTRIBUTION—In the high Allegheny Mountains from Maryland to Georgia; wintering south of the United States in the West Indies.

This subspecies of the Black-throated Blue Warbler closely resembles its lighter relative in habits and in its fondness for the forested slopes of mountains. (Family *Compsothlypidae*)

Calaveras Warbler

Vermivora ruficapilla ridgwayi [645a]

Similar to the Nashville Warbler, but with a brighter yellow rump and under

parts; the female being duller throughout.

DISTRIBUTION—Western North America, from British Columbia and eastern Oregon to the Sierra Nevada Mountains; wintering from Lower California to Texas, and southward into Mexico.

The Calaveras Warbler, a lively, active little midget, is found in California most commonly in the chaparral, where its striking yellow under parts, contrasting strongly with its duller back, make it a most attractive species. (Family *Compsothlypidae*)

California Yellow Warbler

Dendroica aestiva brewsteri [652c]

Four Yellow Warblers occur in North America: the Eastern Yellow Warbler, the Sonora Yellow Warbler, the Alaska Yellow Warbler, and the California Yellow Warbler. All are quite similar in coloration and habits. The California Yellow Warbler (also called the Brewster's Yellow Warbler) is found west of the Sierra Nevada Mountains, in a zone extending from Washington to Southern California. Its wintering region is not known. (Family *Compsothlypidae*)

Canada Warbler

Wilsonia canadensis [686]

ADULT MALE—Upper parts, light slate-gray with a greenish cast; wings and tail, flushed with brownish-olive; crown and region below the eye, blackish; line from the base of the bill, to and around the eye, yellow. Under parts, yellow, bearing a broad band of "necklace-like" streaks across the breast; under tail coverts, white.

ADULT FEMALE — Similar to the male, but duller. The blackish crown is absent, and is sometimes replaced by yellowish-green. The "necklace" of breast streaks is faint, sometimes invisible even from a short distance.

LENGTH—5.61 inches.

DISTRIBUTION — Eastern North America, from Labrador and Manitoba southward to Massachusetts, central New York, and northern Michigan; and southward along the high ridges of the Allegheny Mountains as far as North Carolina. In the fall it passes into Central and South America to spend the winter.

The bright, energetic, optimistic, cheerful Canada Warbler fidgets its restless way among the leaves and tips

of twigs, after the manner of many of the members of its family, in its search for food, and frequently sallies out after flying insects which it dexterously snaps up awing in mid-air, after the fashion of a Flycatcher. So often does it secure its prey in this manner, that it has been dubbed the Canada Flycatcher. Its song is loud, rapid, full, clear, and energetic, and may be rendered *tsee wee tsee we'et, tsee tso'ot,* the two accents falling clearly and markedly as indicated. There are several variations of this performance. On its migrations, the Canada Warbler may often be found in mixed flocks of other Warblers, from which it can be distinguished by its necklace of short black streaks, like an old-fashioned jet chain with "danglers." (Family *Compsothlypidae*)

Cape May Warbler

Dendroica tigrina [650]

ADULT MALE—Top of head, blackish, with a large chestnut-brown (or bay) patch about the eye and on the cheek. Back, grayish streaked with black; a large white patch in the wing. Sides of head, rump, and under parts, yellow; the latter heavily streaked with black.

ADULT FEMALE — Upper parts, greenish-gray; rump, faintly yellow. Under parts, white tinged with yellowish, and faintly streaked with grayish-brown. A light line over the eye, sometimes showing prominently.

LENGTH—5.00 inches.

DISTRIBUTION — Eastern North America, from the region about Hudson Bay southward into the mountains of northern New England and New York State, and westward into Manitoba. It spends its winters in the West Indies and the Bahamas, and occurs sparingly in Central America.

This relatively rare Warbler was named from the accidental circumstance of being first collected, during migration, at Cape May, New Jersey, in 1809. It might more fittingly be called the

"Bay-cheeked Warbler." It neither winters nor nests at Cape May, but some individuals pass through the region in the spring and fall on their journey to and from their nesting grounds in the north. During their migrations the birds may be found

in bushy swamps, open woodlands, thickets, occasionally in orchards, and sometimes even in the shrubbery and trees of the suburbs of towns and villages. It moves about, much of the time, in true Warbler fashion, but not so hurriedly and agitatedly as most of the members of its family. Frequently, for periods of several minutes at a time, it will sit motionless on some conspicuous outer twig, and now and then utter its simple song, which is nothing more than a series of four or five weak, drawly, insect-like notes, resembling the syllables *zee, zee, zee, zee.* It seldom sings during migration. (Family *Compsothlypidae*)

Cerulean Warbler
Dendroica cerulea [658]

ADULT MALE—Upper parts, light blue with grayish tinge, and streaked with blackish. Crown, bordered on each side by a blackish line. Wings with two white bars. Tail feathers spotted with white. Under parts, white; throat divided from upper breast by a band of bluish-gray; sides streaked with light bluish. Legs and feet, dark blue.

ADULT FEMALE—Upper parts, grayish-blue; duller than the male, often

shading into grayish-olive-green, and without black streakings. Sides of head and under parts, whitish, sometimes with a yellowish flush.

LENGTH—4.50 inches.

DISTRIBUTION—Eastern central United States and Canada from southern Ontario to western New York, Tennessee, Missouri, and Michigan; occasionally westward to the Rocky Mountains. It winters in Central and South America.

The Cerulean is the bluest of all our Warblers, and the most delicate, pale sky-blue, ethereal bird of our woodlands. In feeding they range from the tops of trees to the ground, and also fly out after passing insects in the manner of Flycatchers. (Family *Compsothlypidae*)

Chestnut-sided Warbler
Dendroica pennsylvanica [659]

ADULT MALE—Upper parts, greenish-olive streaked with black; crown, bright yellow; cheeks, white; wings with two straw-white bars. A broad black band tapers backward from the base of the bill along each side of the throat. Under parts, white; each side of the breast and abdomen bearing an irregular stripe of bright chestnut-brown.

ADULT FEMALE—Uniformly duller than the male; the black and chestnut markings, broken and inconspicuous.

LENGTH—5.14 inches.

DISTRIBUTION—The whole of eastern North America, and as far south, along the crests of the Allegheny Mountains, as South Carolina. Passes the winter in Central America.

If more dwellers in the country were familiar with the curious song of the Chestnut-sided Warbler, they would be astonished at its numbers. *Chi weé, chi weé, chi weéchu!* the bird says in a strongly accented utterance, which has been happily rendered into the words "I wi'sh to sée Miss Beécher!" Chestnut-sides are denizens of thickets, bushy pastures, and the ragged edges of forests. They are particularly fond of forest clearings which are growing up again. While feeding, it is a bird of moderate heights, but when in song it is to be found in the tops of tall trees and bushes. Well may it choose a prominent stage, for its utterances are

many, and show a multitude of variations from the commonest song described above. While its voice is not loud, nor its songs particularly musical, they are all filled with a vigorous emphatic cheer—it is truly an optimist among our native birds. Besides taking minute insects from the twigs and opening buds, among which it flits, the Chestnut-side often sails out into the air, Flycatcher fashion, and snaps up passing insects on the wing. (Family *Compsothlypidae*)

Colima Warbler
Vermivora crissalis [647.1]

Somewhat similar to the Virginia's Warbler, but with the upper parts a browner tone of gray; the rump and upper tail coverts, chestnut-brown. Crown patch, chestnut-brown. Ring about the eye, buffy-white. Under parts, white or buffy-white; the pectoral region without yellowish.

LENGTH—4.37 inches.

DISTRIBUTION—From the Chisos Mountains of Texas, southward into Mexico. It winters in Mexico south as far as Colima. (Family *Compsothlypidae*)

Connecticut Warbler
Oporornis agilis [678]

ADULT MALE—Head, neck, and upper breast, ashy-gray; the eye encircled by a white ring. Upper parts, olive-greenish-brown; abdomen, bright yellow.

ADULT FEMALE—Upper parts, much as in the male; the eye ring, a buffy-white. Throat and upper breast, faint grayish-brown; abdomen, yellow.

LENGTH—5.40 inches.

DISTRIBUTION — Chiefly in northeastern North America, from Alberta and Manitoba to central Minnesota, northern Michigan, and northern Maine. It winters in northern South America.

The demure Connecticut Warbler, during its migration, is usually found in low damp lands and swampy thickets, or along stream and pond borders among heavy alder growths. Its motions are deliberate and Vireolike, and it keeps well concealed. Although not an accomplished singer, it is a vigorous and pleasing one. Its

songs, loud and emphatic, may be written as *whéecha, whéecha, whéecha, whéecha, whéecha,* with pronounced accentuation. Another lay runs thus: *chu whée you whiddle you chip.* The *whee* and the final *chip* syllables are accented. (Family *Compsothlypidae*)

Dusky Warbler
Vermivora celata sordida [646b]

Similar to both the Orange-crowned Warbler and to the Lutescent Warbler, but uniformly darker, with shorter wings, longer tail, and larger bill and feet.

DISTRIBUTION—Off the coast of California, the Dusky Warblers are to be found breeding on several of the Channel Islands, and sparingly on the mainland. A few winter over here also, from Santa Barbara southward. (Family *Compsothlypidae*)

Eastern Yellow Warbler
Dendroica aestiva aestiva [652]

ADULT MALE—Upper parts, greenish-yellow; wings and tail with a slightly duller cast; crown, bright yellow. Under parts, bright yellow; the breast and sides of the abdomen, faintly streaked with pale reddish-brown.

ADULT FEMALE—Similar to the male, but lacking the bright yellow crown, and the streakings of brown on the under parts.

LENGTH—5.10 inches.

DISTRIBUTION—All over North America in general, except Alaska, and the extreme northern Pacific Coast; and from western Texas to Arizona. It winters in Central and South America.

This bird is the most completely yellow of our yellow-marked birds. In the shade it often has a very dull cast, but in the bright sunlight it appears entirely yellow, like an animated lump of gold among the branches. It haunts damp bushy spots, the edges of roadsides that run through low wet land, orchards, and rural gardens. In subdued light, the greenish tone of the plumage blends almost exactly with the color of the tiny expanding leaves among which the bird spends its hyper-active existence in that tireless search after minute insects which constitute its food. As it flits about in its eager search, it utters now and then its cheerful, vigorous, and loud song, sometimes almost penetrating in its insistence—*wee-wee-wee-wee, see, see, wéet*—the last syllable strongly accented. To most persons the song

suggests a large reserve of cheerful energy and optimism which cannot be suppressed. The nest, often found because of its silvery-gray color, is woven compactly together from plant down, glistening weed bark, and other soft vegetable fibers, and is firmly wedged and fastened in a fork of a bush, from two to five feet from the ground. (Family *Compsothlypidae*)

Florida Pine Warbler
Dendroica pinus florida [671a]

Similar to the Northern Pine Warbler, but with much less greenish in the plumage; with the head and back a more decided tone of yellow, and with the bill a trifle longer.

DISTRIBUTION—The southern portion of Florida. (Family *Compsothlypidae*)

Florida Prairie Warbler
Dendroica discolor collinsi [673a]

Similar to the Northern Prairie Warbler, but differing chiefly in its lack of black markings on the sides, and pronounced brownish-red streakings on the back. The female is similar, with a much lighter breast and whitish throat.

DISTRIBUTION—Florida, in the myrtle swamps of the interior, and in the mangrove swamps of the southern part of the coast. (Family *Compsothlypidae*)

Golden-cheeked Warbler
Dendroica chrysoparia [666]

ADULT MALE—Upper parts, throat, and upper breast, black with an olive-greenish cast in strong light. Sides of head and neck, and forehead patch, bright yellow; a narrow black line through the eye and downward towards side of neck. Wings with two white bars. Lower breast and abdomen, white; the sides sparingly streaked with black. White in the outer tail feathers.

ADULT FEMALE—Similar to the male but duller; with the upper parts, greenish-olive and faintly streaked. Throat and upper breast, a soiled yellowish.

LENGTH—5.00 inches.

DISTRIBUTION—From western and southern Texas southward through eastern Mexico into the mountain country of southern Guatemala.

A common bird in central Texas, where it inhabits the growths of juniper, or "cedar brakes." (Family *Compsothlypidae*)

Golden Pileolated Warbler
Wilsonia pusilla chryseola [685b]

Similar to the Northern Pileolated Warbler, but much brighter greenish on the back, and much brighter deeper-yellow on the under parts. The forehead is a rich orange-yellow.

DISTRIBUTION—The Pacific Coast of North America from British Columbia to southern California and Oregon, and southward into Lower California and to Mexico. (Family *Compsothlypidae*)

Golden-winged Warbler
Vermivora chrysoptera [642]

ADULT MALE—Upper parts, ashy-bluish-gray; crown of head, bright yellow. The wing bears near its shoulder (wrist) a large patch of bright yellow. White patches on the sides of the tail. Sides of the head, whitish, bearing a black stripe, which, beginning narrowly at the base of the bill, widens as it passes through the eye and backwards to the nape. The throat bears a large black patch. Under parts, white or ashy-white.

ADULT FEMALE—Similar in pattern to the male, but with the black everywhere replaced by gray. Yellow of crown and wing, not so brilliant.

LENGTH—5.10 inches.

DISTRIBUTION—Eastern United States from the latitude of northern Vermont to South Carolina, passing to Central America in winter.

The yellow patch in the wing, the black throat, and the black eyeband are the field marks of this strikingly colored bird. The yellow crown, seen

against the sky, is not always conspicuous. Dry, partially wooded, and bushy hillsides; and broken, pine-covered country are the usual haunts of the Golden-winged Warbler. Although it often frequents low bushes and damp situations, and even makes its nest close to or upon the ground, yet it seems to be observed most commonly among the upper branches of trees.

When it sings it mounts to the top of a low tree or bush and there utters its simple, four-syllabled, wheezy little song, which can be well represented by the syllables *wee, zree, zree, zhreet.* The buzzy notes ascend the scale rapidly to an abrupt, sharp ending. The bird is one of our tireless singers, and its musical wheeze may be heard without cessation throughout the entire course of a hot summer morning when other bird notes are hushed. The Golden-winged Warbler is an active searcher among the newly opening leaf and flower buds, where it destroys many noxious insects. (Family *Compsothlypidae*)

Grace's Warbler
Dendroica graciae graciae [664]

Similar to the Yellow-throated Warbler, but lacking the black markings on the side of the head. The female is similar but duller.

LENGTH—5.00 inches.

DISTRIBUTION—Southwestern North America from southwestern Colorado, Arizona, and New Mexico, southward into Mexico.

This bird is found in the mountains of our southwest, where it inhabits co-

niferous forests at high altitudes. (Family *Compsothlypidae*)

Hermit Warbler
Dendroica occidentalis [669]

ADULT MALE—Head, bright yellow; crown, flecked with black; throat,

black. Upper parts, olive-gray streaked with black; two white wing bars. Outer tail feathers, white. Under parts, white; the sides sometimes faintly streaked with black.

ADULT FEMALE—Crown, dull yellow; throat, grayish-yellow, sometimes with a grayish patch. Upper parts, unstreaked gray. Breast and abdomen, much as in the male.

LENGTH—5.00 inches.

DISTRIBUTION—In the higher mountains of western North America, from

British Columbia to California, and from the Pacific Coast to the Rocky Mountains. It winters from Lower California through Mexico into Guatemala.

The Hermit Warbler, deriving its name from its eremetical habits of keeping itself well within the recesses of the great forests of the northern mountains, is a shy species. Frequently, during its search of the tips of twigs for lurking insects, it jerks out its insignificant insect-like song, *tsweely, tsweely, tsweely, tseet!*—a strain somewhat reminiscent of that of our eastern Blackburnian Warbler. (Family *Compsothlypidae*)

Hooded Warbler
Wilsonia citrina [684]

ADULT MALE—Forehead and sides of head, bright yellow, enclosed by a black hood extending from the crown in a narrowing line to the throat and upper breast, where it widens to form an ample bib. Back, olive-greenish-brown. Lower breast and abdomen, yellow; outer tail feathers, white.

ADULT FEMALE—Similar in pattern to the male, but with the black markings, faint gray or absent—very variable.

LENGTH—5.67 inches.

DISTRIBUTION—Eastern portion of the United States, from southern Connecticut, central New York, and southern Michigan to the Gulf. It winters in Central America.

The sight of a male Hooded Warbler in the leafy tip of a twig in full sunlight is one of the delights of even the experienced watcher of birds. It is extremely active in its search of tiny insect food among the tips of twigs, and often dashes out after a passing insect, which it snaps up awing, Fly-

catcher-wise. Its song is unusually loud and compelling for so small a bird. (Family *Compsothlypidae*)

Kennicott's Willow Warbler

Acanthopneuste borealis kennicotti [747]

ADULT MALE AND FEMALE—Upper parts, dull olive-green, with a whitish line over the eye from the base of the bill, and a narrow whitish wing-bar. Tail, similar to the back, without any white markings. Under parts, white tinged with faint yellowish; sides of the body, washed with greenish.

LENGTH—5.00 inches.

DISTRIBUTION—This Asiatic species wanders eastward as far as into western Alaska, and the Commander Islands.

This little Warbler (in reality a Thrush) is the only one of the Willow Warblers that has extended its range

into the New World. Its call note is a short *dzit*, and its song resembles that of the Common Redpoll. (Family *Turdidae*)

Kentucky Warbler

Oporornis formosus [677]

ADULT MALE—Crown, and irregular strip from the base of the bill below eye and along the side of the throat, black. Line over and partially about the eye, yellow. Upper parts, olive-greenish-brown; under parts, bright yellow.

ADULT FEMALE—Similar in pattern, but gray where the male is black.

LENGTH—5.40 inches.

DISTRIBUTION—Eastern United States from southern New York and New England, southern Michigan, and eastern Nebraska to the Gulf States.

The Kentucky Warbler is a typical ground Warbler, found usually in damp woodlands, especially along their edges where bushes abound, or in swampy thickets, or along the bushy margins of ponds and streams. It seldom mounts high in a tree, and at all times is shy and difficult to observe. It does not hop, but walks mincingly about, as if afraid of wetting its feet; frequently wagging its tail up and down after the manner of the Water-thrushes. Its song resembles that of the

Carolina Wren—a sweet, clear whistled strain, *twee, twee, twee, tweetle, tweetle, tweetle.* Sometimes the introductory *twee* notes are absent, and the *tweetle* notes increased to four or five in number. (Family *Compsothlypidae*)

Kirtland's Warbler
Dendroica kirtlandi [670]

ADULT MALE—Upper parts, bluish-gray streaked with black. Under parts,

pale yellow; the sides sparingly streaked with black.
ADULT FEMALE—Similar to the male, but duller, and with a distinctly brownish cast.

LENGTH—5.75 inches.
DISTRIBUTION—Eastern United States, distributed sporadically and locally from Ontario, westward as far as Illinois, and southward into Florida. It winters in the Bahama Islands.

The Kirtland's Warbler bears the distinction of being the rarest of all North American Warblers. It flirts, or wags its tail more flexibly and vigorously than any other Warbler on our continent. (Family *Compsothlypidae*)

Lucy's Warbler
Vermivora luciae [643]

ADULT MALE—Upper parts, mouse-gray; with rump and crown patch, chestnut. Prominent white ring about

the eye. Under parts, white, washed with pale brownish on the upper breast and sides.
ADULT FEMALE—Similar to the male, sometimes identical in coloration, but usually with a smaller (or no) crown patch, or with this patch and the rump lighter in color.
LENGTH—4.20 inches.
DISTRIBUTION—From Arizona and southwestern Utah to northwestern Mexico.

Lucy's Warbler is one of the demurely-colored, active little birds of the bush-covered stream bottoms of the West, and is one of the characteristic inhabitants of the mesquite country. Its song is a clear, sweet, but subdued little trill, with an abrupt ending. It frequently nests in a hole in a giant cactus. (Family *Compsothlypidae*)

Lutescent Warbler
Vermivora celata lutescens [646a]

Similar to the Orange-crowned Warbler, but with greener upper parts, and yellower under parts.

DISTRIBUTION—From the Kenai Peninsula, Alaska, southward along the Pacific Coast to southern California, and eastward to Colorado. It winters from California southward into Mexico.

The faint, sweet trilled song of this bird, rising in pitch and intensity toward the middle of the strain, and

then falling in both towards its end, is heard from bushy hillsides and is, to dwellers in southern California, one of the first signs of spring. It is a bird of small trees and bushes seldom being seen, except in migration, anywhere else. (Family *Compsothlypidae*)

Macgillivray's Warbler
Oporornis tolmiei [680]

Similar to the Mourning Warbler, but with one quarter of a distinct white eye-ring above the eye, and another quarter below the eye—giving the appearance of two white spots.

DISTRIBUTION—Western North America from the Pacific Coast to the Rocky Mountains; and from British Columbia to western Texas and the mountains of Lower California. It winters from Lower California through Mexico to Central America and Colombia.

The Macgillivray's Warbler is extremely common in the West, especially near water in the bushy and chaparral regions. (Family *Compsothlypidae*)

Magnolia Warbler
Dendroica magnolia [657]

ADULT MALE — Head, ashy-gray, with a white line over the eye and a black cheek patch. Rump patch, bright yellow; a large white patch in the wing and a white patch midway in each of the tail feathers. Under parts, bright yellow, heavily streaked on the breast and sides with black.

ADULT FEMALE—Similar in pattern to the male, but duller.

LENGTH—5.12 inches.

DISTRIBUTION—Eastern North America from Quebec and the Hudson Bay region south to central New England (among the mountains), northern Michigan, and along the Allegheny Mountains into Pennsylvania. It spends its winters in Central America. During its migrations it is found as far west as the Rocky Mountains.

This strikingly-patterned and brilliantly-colored Warbler is a denizen of moderate woodlands, generally of coniferous trees, though in migration it is often found among deciduous growths, in company with troops of other Warblers, where it may often be seen in orchards or among the trees of village streets. An extremely active, agile, and vivacious bird, it fidgets about among the leaves and twigs, seemingly without a moment's pause or rest, during the daylight hours. Though it usually keeps itself concealed near the center of the tree, it sometimes comes out into the full sunlight, where its brilliant yellow under parts gleam arrestingly against the dark background of spruce or hemlock. There are several variations to the bird's song, the commonest being three or four sweetly sibilant, and quickly-uttered double notes, the second half of each accented, and with an upward inflection at the close of the song, thus: *zee rée, zee rée, zee rée, zee rée-it.* The bird's food consists largely

of small insects such as aphids, beetles, and caterpillars. It is particularly fond of canker worms, and other small geometrids. (Family *Compsothlypidae*)

Mangrove Warbler

Dendroica erithachorides castaneiceps [653]

ADULT MALE—Upper parts, greenish-olive; wings, darker. Entire head, above and below, reddish-chestnut-brown. Under parts, yellow, faintly streaked on the breast and sides with reddish-brown. Inner vanes of tail feathers, light yellow.

ADULT FEMALE—Upper parts, greenish-olive; under parts, plain unstreaked yellow.

LENGTH—5.00 inches.

DISTRIBUTION—From the Cape Region of Lower California southward into Mexico and along the Pacific Coast of Central America.

The Mangrove Warbler is our only Warbler species with an entire chest-

nut-brown head. (Family *Compsothlypidae*)

Middendorff's Grasshopper Warbler

Locustella ochotensis [747.1]

The Grasshopper "Warblers" are small reddish-brown, soft-plumaged little birds, about five and a half inches long, with pale yellowish-white, pale brownish, or whitish under parts; plain, but sometimes spotted or streaked. The tail is rather short and rounded, and the under tail coverts are long, reaching out over the tips of the outer tail feathers.

DISTRIBUTION—The Middendorff's Grasshopper Warbler, an Asiatic species, found also at Kamchatka, and on the Kuriles and Bering islands, and on the Moluccas, occurs as an accidental straggler on Nunivak Island, Alaska.

Grasshopper Warblers are so-called because of their notes, which are like those of a grasshopper—shrill, strident, and monotonous. The birds do not warble. They are found in bushy situations, preferring those which are low and wet. (Family *Sylviidae*)

Mourning Warbler

Oporornis philadelphia [679]

ADULT MALE—Head and neck, bluish-gray; back, greenish-brown. Throat, grayish-black shading to transverse, ripply, black, crepe-like markings on the upper breast, where it is sharply marked off from the bright yellow abdomen.

ADULT FEMALE—Similar to the male, but with the head, neck, and breast, grayish-brown.

LENGTH—5.63 inches.

DISTRIBUTION—Eastern North America from Nova Scotia and Manitoba south to northern New England,

northern New York, and eastern Nebraska, and along the Allegheny Mountains into West Virginia. It winters in Central America and northern South America.

This dainty little Warbler, about the size of a Chipping Sparrow, is a shy, silent species, especially on migration, and closely resembles the Connecticut Warbler, but lacks the white eye ring. (Family *Compsothlypidae*)

Myrtle Warbler

Dendroica coronata [655]

ADULT MALE—Upper parts, bluish-gray streaked with darker; crown patch, rump patch, and patches on the sides of the breast under the wing, bright yellow; two white wing bars; cheeks, black; throat, white. Sides of upper breast, heavily splotched with black, becoming streaked on the sides

of the abdomen. The three outer tail feathers bear prominent white spots.

ADULT FEMALE—Upper parts, browner than in the male; under parts, not so heavily marked nor streaked; yellow, not so brilliant.

LENGTH—5.65 inches.

DISTRIBUTION—Eastern North America from Labrador and Alaska south to northern New England and Minnesota. It spends the winter sparingly in central New England and Kansas; increasing in numbers from this latitude to the West Indies and Central America. It is the only Warbler to be found in the New England States in winter, where it is confined chiefly to the coastal regions where Bayberry (*Myrica carolinensis*) affords it an abundance of the waxy berries which constitute its chief food during the cold months. The "wax" of the Bayberry is chemically a true fat, and hence digestible, and heat-productive. Berries of the red cedar are also eaten extensively.

Myrtle Warblers travel together in small flocks, and are often seen to advantage among the bare branches, where they flit constantly about with

scarcely a moment's pause. During all this flitting here and there, the yellow rump patch—an excellent field mark —is prominently displayed. Insects are captured awing, after the deft manner of Flycatchers. The song is a sweet, slightly husky trill, preceded by several musically sibilous notes, thus: *wee, see, see, see, se-e-e-e-e-e-e-e.* The final trill is reminiscent of the song of the Junco. The two species are often heard singing together in the mountains of northern New England. (Family *Compsothlypidae*)

Nashville Warbler

Vermivora ruficapilla ruficapilla [645]

ADULT MALE AND FEMALE—Head, ashy-gray, bearing a small and somewhat indistinct chestnut patch on the crown. Upper parts, greenish-brown; under parts, bright yellow. (Female sometimes lacks crown patch.)

LENGTH—4.77 inches.

DISTRIBUTION—Eastern North America, from Labrador and the Hudson Bay country southward to central Connecticut, southern New York; and westward to northern Illinois. It winters south of the United States, mainly in Central America; and in its migrations is most commonly found in the Mississippi Valley.

The Nashville is among the smallest, and surely among the most active of all our Warblers. It is never still for a moment but ' flits nervously and agitatedly from twig to twig, dropping now and then upon the ground; its forays carrying it from the ground level to the tops of low trees and bushes. It seldom rises much higher than fifteen or twenty feet. It is not a bird of great forests and tall timber, but occurs rather where there are bushes and small trees. It prefers open sunny situations, and may therefore be found in old, abandoned, scrubby fields, or in the bushy margins of woodlands, or in alders along the banks of streams, or where young birches are growing up in forest clearings, or along the bushy sides of coun-

try roads. The Nashville's commonest song consists of about six hurried, musically hissing notes, falling in pitch, and resembling the whispered syllables *weét tsee, weét tsee, weét, tsee, tittle, tittle, tittle.* The last three

tittle notes, sweetly twittering in character, are sometimes omitted. The nest is tucked into a depression in the ground, often concealed by overarching growths of grasses, ferns, mosses, lycopodiums, etc. (Family *Compsothlypidae*)

Northern Parula Warbler

Compsothlypis americana usneae [648a]

ADULT MALE—Upper parts, including sides of the head and neck, bluish-gray; a square yellowish-green patch (like a saddle) in the middle of the back; wings with two white bars. Throat and breast, yellow, separated by a wide bar of rich brown. Abdomen, white, washed on the sides with brownish.

ADULT FEMALE—Duller than the male; the breast and sides of the abdomen lacking the brownish cast.

LENGTH—4.73 inches.

DISTRIBUTION—New England, New York, the Northern States, and Canada, passing into the Gulf States and southward in the fall.

The Parula is a most surprisingly colored little midget in its jacket of green, yellow, brown, and white. Particularly interesting is its greenish saddle, which comes into view as the bird swings from the tip of a twig. This species is our smallest Warbler and takes its place, together with the Ruby-crowned and Golden-crowned Kinglets, the

Winter Wren, and the Hummingbirds, among our very smallest birds. It is extremely active and restless, and often travels in large companies together with other Warbler species. They frequent the tops of trees and the tips of branches, moving ceaselessly about in their search for insects, and pausing now and again to utter their peculiar and characteristic song—an insignificant series of sweetly buzzing notes, rising regularly up the scale and ending in a sharp little *zip*, "as if one were winding up a little watch" (Hoffman). *Zee, zee, zee, zee, zip!* the song may be written, and usually consists of five notes. It is decidedly insectoid. The bird uniquely fashions its nest from the Old-Man's Beard Lichen (*Usnea*), commonly nesting in swamps in the southern portion of its range. (Family *Compsothlypidae*)

Northern Pileolated Warbler
Wilsonia pusilla pileolata [685a]

Similar to the Wilson's Warbler, but with the upper parts a brighter olive-

green, and the under parts a deeper yellow.

DISTRIBUTION—On the Alaskan coast, and in the interior, the Northern Pileolated Warbler is one of the common birds. From this region it ranges south through Oregon and along the Rocky Mountain zone into western Texas, and in its migrations spreads over all of western North America, and east as far as Minnesota. It winters in Central America. (Family *Compsothlypidae*)

Olive Warbler
Peucedramus olivaceus [651]

ADULT MALE—Head, neck, and upper breast, rich chestnut or orange-brown; rest of upper parts, olive-gray. Two white wing bars. A broad black bar through the eye. Under parts, grayish-white.

ADULT FEMALE—The head is yellower than in the male, and the eye-bar is dark gray. Breast, yellow; abdomen, white.

LENGTH—5.20 inches.

DISTRIBUTION—From the mountains of Arizona and New Mexico south into the highlands of Mexico and Guatemala.

A bird of rather leisurely movements, with a clear liquid song consisting of

several notes, like the syllables *quirt quirt quirt*, in a descending scale. (Family *Compsothlypidae*)

Orange-crowned Warbler
Vermivora celata celata [646]

ADULT MALE—Upper parts, gray-ish-olive-green; the head bearing on its crown a partly concealed, dull orange patch. Under parts, dull yel-

lowish-green; the throat and upper breast faintly streaked with grayish-brown.

ADULT FEMALE—Similar to the male but grayer; the crown patch being duller, or absent.

LENGTH—5.00 inches.

DISTRIBUTION—Central North America from Manitoba and the mountains of New Mexico to Alaska. Winters from California to Mexico.

The Orange-crowned Warbler, found in the interior of the western part of our country, is less well known than its two close relatives, the Lutescent Warbler and the Dusky Warbler, which it somewhat resembles. (Family *Compsothlypidae*)

Pine Warbler
Dendroica pinus pinus [671]

ADULT MALE—Upper parts, olive-greenish-gray; wings with two fairly conspicuous white bars. Under parts, clear bright yellow; brightest on the throat and upper breast, and paling on the lower abdomen to ashy-white. Sides, faintly streaked with blackish. The tail, when spread, shows two white patches near its outer tips.

ADULT FEMALE—Upper parts, greenish-gray with a brownish tinge; wing bars, narrower and duller than the male's, and only faintly visible. Throat, yellow, paling abruptly on the breast to a faintly yellowish-white. Abdomen, whitish.

LENGTH—5.52 inches.

DISTRIBUTION—Eastern North America from Manitoba, New Brunswick, and Minnesota, south to the Gulf of Mexico. Winters in the Gulf States, and in this season is found as far north as Virginia and southern Illinois.

The Pine Warbler, the earliest Warbler to arrive in the spring in our northeastern states, is largely confined, except in migration, to pine woods, where it may be found searching the branches, needle bundles, and cones for minute insects. It is more leisurely in its movements than most of our Warblers, and is apt to feed at lower levels, sometimes dropping on the ground, and then flying up quickly. Occasionally it sallies out and snaps up some luckless insect, after the manner of the Flycatchers. As the bird feeds, it pauses now and then to utter

its sweet, vibrant trill, which somewhat resembles the songs of the Chipping Sparrow and the Junco: *tsi, tsi, tsi, si-si-si-si-si-si-si-si-si.* The trill seems to be "shaken out" says one observer, referring to the visible vibration of the bird's body as it sings. "Why, all of it sings," remarked a young bird lover, watching a Pine Warbler for the first time! (Family *Compsothlypidae*)

Prairie Warbler

Dendroica discolor discolor [673]

ADULT MALE—Upper parts, olive-green, with light reddish-brown streakings in the middle of the back. Sides of head and throat, and under parts, bright yellow. Line through the eye, one below the eye, and a large spot on the side of the throat, black. Sides of breast and abdomen, prominently streaked with black. The tips of the outer tail feathers bear white patches which show plainly when the tail is spread.

ADULT FEMALE—Similar to the male, except that the reddish-brown markings of the back are faint or absent altogether.

LENGTH—4.75 inches.

DISTRIBUTION—Eastern United States between southern Ontario, southern Michigan, Florida, and Massachusetts. Winters in southern Florida and the West Indies.

Bushy fields and pastures, forest clearings growing up into thickets, hot dry scrubby pine-tracts, and hillsides covered with small cedars are the favorite haunts of the greenish-yellow Prairie Warbler. The birds are especially numerous in pine-barren regions, where they may be seen flitting about in the agitated manner common to Warblers, tilting their tails up and down, and frequently spreading them, thus displaying momentarily the white patches near the tips. While actively searching for all sorts of minute insects, the Prairie Warbler seems to have a preference for aphids, or plant lice, and these creatures form a considerable proportion of its dietary. The song is one of those peculiar wiry, insectoid, insignificant songs, so common among the family of birds misnamed "warblers." It can be closely imitated by hissing through set teeth the syllables

zee, zee, zee, zee, zee, zeé, zee; the next to the last note being accented. The performance has several varia-

tions. It resembles very nearly the song of the Northern Parula Warbler. (Family *Compsothlypidae*)

Prothonotary Warbler

Protonotaria citrea [637]

ADULT MALE—Entire head, and most of the under parts, rich, flaming yellow verging to orange. Wings and tail, bluish-gray; the latter showing large white patches when spread. Bill, rather prominent, being long, straight, sharp, and dark.

ADULT FEMALE—Similar, but uniformly duller; the head being an olive-yellow rather than clear and flaming.

LENGTH—5.50 inches.

DISTRIBUTION—Eastern North America from southern Minnesota, Virginia, and Ohio, southward into the Gulf States. Winters in the tropics.

The Prothonotary Warbler in full sunlight is one of the loveliest sights in a field-lover's experience. No other Warbler offers so large an expanse of flaming orange-yellow to the eye. This is especially true during the mating season, when the males, in the course of their amorous advances to the females, spread their wings and tails, and erect the feathers of the head and breast, turning this way and that, seemingly the better to display their aureate charms. Prothonotary Warblers are birds of swamps, inundated forests, or occasionally of the low marshy banks of streams, particularly of those bordered by a dense growth of willows. However, they do not nest in tangles of vegetation, as many swamp-inhabiting birds do, but fashion a soft container for the eggs at the bottom of a hole in a tree, much after the manner of the Bluebird or Chickadee. In this respect the bird is unique, being the only North American Warbler to nest in such a situation. During the mating season especially, the males give voice to a loud, emphatic song, the clear notes being all on the same pitch, and sounding

like the syllables *twheet, twheet, twheet, twheet, twheet.* (Family *Compsothlypidae*)

Red-faced Warbler

Cardellina rubrifrons [690]

ADULT MALE AND FEMALE—Throat, forehead, and a zone extending back to nape, bright red. Crown, and sides of same, black. Nape patch and rump, white. Upper parts, gray. Under parts, white or grayish-white.

LENGTH—5.00 inches.

DISTRIBUTION—Southwestern North America from southern Arizona and the western half of New Mexico southward into Guatemala.

The Red-faced Warbler is a mountain-loving bird, found among the spruces

and other coniferous trees. (Family *Compsothlypidae*)

Sennett's Warbler

Compsothlypis pitiayumi nigrilora [649]

Similar to the Northern Parula Warbler, but lacking the black breast band, and possessing on the breast only a faint tinge of brownish. The yellow extends farther down on the breast and sides, and the lores are blackish.

DISTRIBUTION—From the southern portion of the Rio Grande Valley in Texas, southward into eastern Mexico. (Family *Compsothlypidae*)

Socorro Warbler

Compsothlypis graysoni [649.1]

Similar in general to the Northern Parula Warbler.

ADULT MALE—Upper parts, dull slate-gray; back, dull olive-green; lores, grayish. Two narrow white or whitish wing bars. Under parts, dingy yellow and white. Inner webs of outer tail feathers, marked with small white patches.

ADULT FEMALE—Upper parts, dull olive-gray; wing bars, very narrow and sometimes absent.

LENGTH—About 4.75 inches.

DISTRIBUTION—In Mexico, on Socorro Island; straggling occasionally to southern Lower California. (Family *Compsothlypidae*)

Sonora Yellow Warbler

Dendroica aestiva sonorana [652a]

Similar to the Eastern Yellow Warbler. The male is a much brighter yellow above and below; and the female, duller above and paler yellow below.

DISTRIBUTION—From western Texas and southern Arizona south into northern Mexico, and, in winter, as far south as Guatemala and Nicaragua. (Family *Compsothlypidae*)

Southern Parula Warbler

Compsothlypis americana americana [648]

Similar to the Northern Parula Warbler but with the bill larger and the wing shorter. The breast-band of this species is narrower and the chestnut color lighter.

DISTRIBUTION—South Atlantic and Gulf States east of Texas, along the Atlantic Coast as far north as the District of Columbia, and westward to Illinois. It winters from the Gulf States southward.

The Southern Parula Warbler is merely a slightly smaller and slightly paler edition of the northern species. In habit and song it is virtually the same. (Family *Compsothlypidae*)

Sutton's Warbler

Dendroica potomac

(Note: This bird described in "The Cardinal" of January, 1940, has not yet been accepted as a new species.)

The male is somewhat similar to the Yellow-throated Warbler, but "with a triangular yellowish patch on the back, a smaller bill, shorter wings and tail, the black patch on the sides of the face and throat is rectangular rather than triangular, and the post-auricular region [region behind the ear] is only very faintly white (light grayish); the sides and flanks are without any black streaking, and the white patches on the outer retrices [tail feathers] are not so extensive." (Haller.) The female is similar to the male, but slightly duller, and with the markings not so sharply defined.

This proposed new species, named in honor of Dr. George M. Sutton, is represented by two specimens, a male and a female, collected by Karl W. Haller in the eastern panhandle of West Virginia, between the Potomac and the Shenandoah rivers, in May and June of 1939. The song of the bird is similar to that of the Southern Parula Warbler, and its coloration is between this and the Yellow-throated Warbler (as noted above). If this bird proves to be a new species, it will be interesting indeed. Haller (The Cardinal, Jan. 1940) says of it, "It is strange that this new Warbler has escaped notice for so many years, especially in a region which has been so thoroughly worked. Perhaps it has escaped detection because of certain similarities already mentioned. There is no doubt in my mind that additional specimens will be found, if every bird that sings a Parula-like song is carefully observed." (Family *Compsothlypidae*)

Swainson's Warbler

Limnothlypis swainsoni [638]

ADULT MALE AND FEMALE—Upper parts, olive-brown; stripe over the eye, yellowish or brownish-white. Under parts, pale yellow, tinged on the sides with olive.

LENGTH—6.00 inches.

DISTRIBUTION—Southeastern United States, from southern Virginia, southern Indiana, and southern Missouri, south to the Gulf of Mexico.

This rare Warbler, is found only in coastal swamps and lowlands throughout its range. Its dull and unobtrusive colors render it an inconspicuous member of its family. It somewhat resem-

bles the Worm-eating Warbler (except for its lack of head-stripes), and reminds one, in the field, of a Vireo, both by reason of its sober plumage and its leisurely movements. Its song is like that of the Northern Waterthrush in general character—loud, clear, vigorous, and rich. (Family *Compsothlypidae*)

Sycamore Warbler

Dendroica dominica albilora [663a]

Similar to the Yellow-throated Warbler, and in the south-central states known also as the Sycamore Yellowthroat.

DISTRIBUTION—Throughout the Mississippi Valley, from Kansas, southern Indiana, southern Illinois, and West Virginia, southwestward into Texas. It migrates only a comparatively short distance in the fall, spending its winters in Mexico and Central America. (Family *Compsothlypidae*)

Tennessee Warbler

Vermivora peregrina [647]

ADULT MALE—Head, light gray with a narrow white line over the eye;

rest of upper parts, olive-green in strong light, olive-grayish in shadow.

ADULT FEMALE—Similar to the male, but with the head washed with greenish (most apparent in strong light), and with the under parts showing a faint yellowish tinge.

LENGTH—5.00 inches.

DISTRIBUTION—Eastern and northern North America, from Alaska and Quebec south to northern New England, northern New York, and Minnesota; and (during the migration seasons) west to the Rocky Mountains. It spends its winters in Central America, and the northern portions of South America.

This bird, one of the most plainly marked of our Warblers, may be identified by its grayish head and white line over the eye. It closely resembles the Red-eyed Vireo and the Philadelphia Vireo, but from them may be distinguished by its slender, sharp bill, and more active movements. The

Tennessee Warbler nests far to the north, generally in wet, swampy woodlands, where larches and spruces abound; but during the seasons of migration in the spring and fall it may be seen in any region where there are trees, keeping itself usually near the middle or among the higher branches, and seldom descending near the ground. The unobtrusive colors of the bird render it inconspicuous, and it would be overlooked by most observers were it not for its active movements and frequently uttered song. This consists of a rapid repetition of about ten thin, high, sibilant, staccato notes, which rise slightly in pitch toward the middle of the song, and fall toward the end. It may be closely imitated by whispering through set teeth the syllables *sit, sit, sit, sit, sit, sit, sit, sit.* This Warbler has the curious habit of puncturing wild grapes and drinking the juice, but its chief food is insects. (Family *Compsothlypidae*)

Townsend's Warbler
Dendroica townsendi [668]

Similar to the Black-throated Green Warbler, but with a heavy, elongated black patch about the eye, and with

yellow on the under parts where the Black-throated Green Warbler is white.

LENGTH—5.10 inches.

DISTRIBUTION—Western North America, from Alaska eastward to western Colorado, and western Texas, and southward into the mountains of southern California. It winters in Mexico.

A drawly, buzzy, somewhat languid song coming from among coniferous trees is quite likely, in western United States, to proclaim the presence of the Townsend's Warbler. In appearance, habits, and song, the bird is quite similar to our eastern Black-throated Green Warbler. (Family *Compsothlypidae*)

Virginia's Warbler
Vermivora virginiae [644]

ADULT MALE—Upper parts, gray, with a bright yellowish-green rump, and a chestnut crown patch. Ring around the eye, prominently white. Under parts, white with a large yellow patch between the upper breast and the throat.

ADULT FEMALE—Similar to the male, but duller throughout.

LENGTH—4.50 inches.

DISTRIBUTION—In the Rocky Mountain region, from Nevada, Colorado, and Wyoming, southward into Mexico.

This extremely restless little Warbler is found most commonly in tangles, low bushes, and in fringes of cottonwoods and willows that border the banks of streams. During the nesting season it becomes increasingly agitated, and slips, darts, and flutters here and there, uttering almost continually its sweet Yellow-Warbler-like song. (Family *Compsothlypidae*)

Wayne's Warbler
Dendroica virens waynei [667a]

Similar to the Black-throated Green Warbler, but with the areas of black on the throat and sides of the breast slightly reduced, and with the yellow on the sides of the head somewhat paler in tone. The female is duller and paler throughout.

DISTRIBUTION—Occurs only along the coast of South Carolina. (Family *Compsothlypidae*)

Western Fan-tailed Warbler
Euthlypis lachrymosa tephra [688.1]

ADULT MALE—Upper parts, slaty-gray; the back with an olive cast. Tail, slaty-black tipped with white. Head, blackish and bearing a yellow median crown stripe. Chin, white; rest of under parts, lemon-yellow. Sides of the body, washed with olive; under tail coverts, yellowish-white.

ADULT FEMALE — Similar to the male, but with the upper parts somewhat lighter, and the back appreciably washed with olive.

LENGTH—About 5.60 inches.

DISTRIBUTION — Found in western Mexico, and in the region about Santo Domingo in northern Lower California. (Family *Compsothlypidae*)

Western Palm Warbler
Dendroica palmarum palmarum [672]

Similar to the Yellow Palm Warbler, but with the line over the eye and the under parts, whitish or a pale straw color—not a definite yellow as in the eastern bird. In all its markings, the western bird is duller in color, and slightly smaller.

LENGTH—5.25 inches.

DISTRIBUTION—North America, from British America to the west of Hudson Bay, passing south in winter through the Mississippi Valley, and sometimes through the North Atlantic States, to its wintering grounds in Florida and the West Indies. (Family *Compsothlypidae*)

Wilson's Warbler
Wilsonia pusilla pusilla [685]

ADULT MALE—Crown-patch, black. Upper parts, olive-green; forehead, sides of head, and under parts, bright yellow.

ADULT FEMALE—Similar, but with the crown-patch either lacking entirely, or only faintly visible.

LENGTH—5.00 inches.

DISTRIBUTION — Eastern North America, from Labrador and Hudson Bay southward through Nova Scotia, northeastern Maine, and Ontario; sometimes in Colorado and other portions of the Rocky Mountains. It winters in Mexico and Central America.

This energetic little midget in green, yellow, and black, might very well be termed the "green and yellow Flycatcher," for it is constantly dashing out of its covert after some luckless

insect, which it adroitly snaps up after the manner of the true Flycatchers. As it feeds among the opening leaves and blossoms, it fidgets about, flipping its wings and twitching its tail, and appears to be in a continuous state of high agitation. Its song is sibilantly sweet, and consists of a series of rapid bubbling or twittering notes, in two parts, thus: *tlee, tlee, tlee, tlee; tsee, tsee, tsee*. The second or *tsee* part of the song is more rapid than the first part, and sometimes prolonged into a pleasing little trill. These parts may be reversed; or one part may be given without the other. (Family *Compsothlypidae*)

Worm-eating Warbler
Helmitheros vermivorus [639]

ADULT MALE AND FEMALE—Upper parts, olive-greenish with a brownish cast; head, lighter, with two heavy black lines on the crown, and two thinner black lines through the eyes.

Throat and upper breast, buffy-white; breast and abdomen, white.

LENGTH—5.51 inches.

DISTRIBUTION—Eastern United States from southern Connecticut, through New York to southern Illinois and southern Wisconsin southward.

Winters south of the United States in the Bahamas, Cuba, Panama, and adjoining regions. Occasionally it is found wintering in southern Florida.

The Worm-eating Warbler is a bird of dry bushy hillsides, or conversely, of dense thickets in low swampy lands. It is one of the "ground warblers," feeding largely on or near the ground, creeping mouselike among the tangled twigs and piles of leaves; but occasionally flying up into the tips of low branches, or into small trees—not often climbing very high. Its fare, like that of the Warblers in general, consists of leaf and bud insects, and any small forms which it may find in its search on the ground. Its clear-cut head stripes, and sleek olive and white body colors make it a very trim and dapper, almost tailored bird, but not one which would attract the observer, even with its song. This, like its plumage is unobtrusive—a series of buzzy chipping notes, mostly on the same pitch, and not clearly enunciated, but all run together. The whole performance has been likened to that of the Chipping Sparrow, but is buzzier and less musical. The nest is placed on the ground, and is composed of bits of bark, leaves, rootlets, and grasses, and is invariably lined with the tops of the pigeon wheat moss (*Polytrichum*). The Worm-eating Warbler is unique among the North American species in being the only representative of its genus (*Helmitheros*) on our continent. (Family *Compsothlypidae*)

Yellow Palm Warbler

Dendroica palmarum hypochrysea [672a]

ADULT MALE AND FEMALE—Top of head, chestnut-brown; with a prominent yellow line over the eye, and a dark line through it. Back, grayish-brown. Under parts, bright yellow; the sides of the breast and abdomen streaked with brown.

LENGTH—5.43 inches.

DISTRIBUTION — Eastern North America, from the region east of Hudson Bay and Nova Scotia southward into New England, passing down through the Atlantic States and along the Allegheny Mountains in the fall, to its wintering territory which extends from Florida into Louisiana.

The Yellow Palm Warbler is a ground Warbler, and is to be looked for in thickets along country roads, in

scrubby fields and old pastures overgrown with low bushes, or among willows and alders in swampy areas and along woodland stream courses. After alighting, it pumps the tail vigorously several times after the manner

of the Phoebe, and then continues the
pumping with less vigor—an almost
constant motion which will identify
the bird as far as one can see it
clearly. The song, somewhat resembling that of the Chipping Sparrow,
is a faint, sweet, sibilant, rapid *swit,
swit, swit, swit, swit, swit*. (Family
Compsothlypidae)

Yellow-throated Warbler
Dendroica dominica dominica [663]

ADULT MALE—Upper parts, gray;
forehead and anterior half of the
crown, blackish. The wings show two
white bars, and the outer tail feathers
bear two white patches near their tips.
The eye carries a yellow line before
it, and a white line over it. An irregular black patch on the cheek extends as a tapering line downward
on the sides of the throat. Throat and
breast, yellow; abdomen, white; its
sides streaked with black.
ADULT FEMALE—Similar, but the
black head and throat markings not
so extensive.
LENGTH—5.25 inches.
DISTRIBUTION—Southeastern United
States from Virginia to Florida. It
spends its winter in Florida and into
the West Indies.

The Yellow-throated Warbler is a
bright, cheerful singer, with a decided preference for the tops and
higher branches of sycamore trees;
hence its other name of Sycamore
Yellow-throat. Living in the tops of
trees is advantageous for the young
birds, since they can there be edu-
cated "in the higher branches." (Family *Compsothlypidae*)

WATER-THRUSH
Grinnell's Water-thrush
Seiurus noveboracensis notabilis [675a]

A slightly larger edition of the Northern Water-thrush, with darker upper
parts and whitish under parts.

LENGTH—5.50 inches.
DISTRIBUTION—Western North
America, and the Pacific Coast from
Alaska southward to Minnesota, west-
ern Nebraska, and Illinois. It winters

from the extreme southern United
States south to Lower California, Mexico, and northern South America. In
habits and song it is similar to the two
other Water-thrushes of its genus.
(Family *Compsothlypidae*)

Louisiana Water-thrush
Seiurus motacilla [676]

Similar to the Northern Water-thrush
in pattern, but with the under parts
and the line over the eye whitish instead of yellowish. The line over the
eye is always white. The under parts
are sometimes tinged with a faint straw
color.
LENGTH—6.28 inches.
DISTRIBUTION—Eastern United
States, from southern New England to
the Gulf States, and west as far as
Minnesota. It winters from northern
Mexico southward, and in the Bahamas.

This large ground-warbler, miscalled a
thrush, and sometimes known as the
Southern Water-thrush, is slightly
larger and paler than its northern relative. Its song, confusingly similar to
that of the Northern Water-thrush, is
longer, and more erratic and varied.
In general habits the two species are
quite similar. (Family *Compsothlypidae*)

Northern Water-thrush

Seiurus noveboracensis noveboracensis
[675]

ADULT MALE AND FEMALE—Upper parts, dark brown, with a prominent straw-colored or yellow line over the eye. Under parts, yellowish or straw-colored, heavily streaked with black.
LENGTH—6.04 inches.

DISTRIBUTION—Eastern North America, from Newfoundland and the Hudson Bay country southward through New England and Illinois,

and along the Allegheny Mountains into West Virginia. It winters in Florida, and from there southward into northern South America.

The Northern Water-thrush is a Ground-warbler, not a Thrush. It walks with a rather jerky motion, teetering up and down, or raising and depressing its tail as it makes its way daintily over the leaves of the forest floor, or steps mincingly from stone to stone in a woodland brook. Wherever there are small bosky brooks cascading over stones in sheltered ravines, there one may see and hear these exquisitely-groomed and fastidious birds at their best. The song of the bird may be described as a clear, ringing, energetic, joyous, staccato *tweet, tweet, tweet, t'eu, t'eu, t'eu-wee, t'eu.* The bird sings from a perch elevated about twenty or more feet from the ground—usually a limb; not the tip of a twig or the top of a tree—directly over, or near a running stream. (Family *Compsothlypidae*)

WATER-TURKEY

Water-turkey

Anhinga anhinga [118]

ADULT MALE—Plumage, greenish-black with glossy reflections; head and neck, flecked with grayish. Upper back, with silvery spots; wings, spotted and streaked with silvery-gray, and bearing a wide silvery-grayish-white band. Tail, white-tipped.

ADULT FEMALE — Similar to the male, but with the upper parts darker, and with the entire head, neck, and breast, brownish-gray.
LENGTH—34.00 inches.

DISTRIBUTION—From South Carolina and southern Illinois southward into subtropical and tropical America. In winter its northern limits are the Gulf States.

The curious Water-turkey, which has no relationship at all with Turkeys, should be called the American Darter

or the Anhinga. An account of its habits will be found under DARTERS (Family *Anhingidae*).

WAXWING FAMILY
Bombycillidae

Waxwings are sleek-plumaged, fawn-colored, trim, "tailored" birds. Two of the species possess hard, shiny, sealing-wax-like, bright red droplets of pigment on the tips of the secondary wing feathers. The heads of Waxwings are crested with longish soft feathers, and their wings are relatively long and pointed. The base of the bill is bare, no bristles being present. When perched, the birds assume an erect, aristocratic attitude. Of the three species of Waxwings inhabiting the Northern Hemisphere, two are reported from North America: the Cedar Waxwing (*Bombycilla cedrorum*) and the Bohemian Waxwing (*Bombycilla garrula pallidiceps*).

NESTING. Waxwings construct somewhat bulky nests of small twigs, root-

lets, some weed stems, and the like; often including bits of bark, paper, or a piece of string. This structure is lined with weed bark, soft dry grasses, some leaves, and a few feathers. The nests are placed about twenty feet or so from the ground. Our native Waxwing often builds in orchards. The eggs number from three to five, and in color are a pale bluish, bluish-gray, or olive-gray, spotted and blotched with browns or dark purples.

WAXWING
Bohemian Waxwing
Bombycilla garrula pallidiceps [618]

Similar to the Cedar Waxwing, but larger, and differing chiefly in the white in the wing, and in the reddish-brown forehead, cheeks, and under tail coverts.

DISTRIBUTION—Far northern North America, from Hudson Bay south-

ward, irregularly to California, Colorado, Illinois, and Pennsylvania. (Family *Bombycillidae*)

Cedar Waxwing
Bombycilla cedrorum [619]

ADULT MALE AND FEMALE—Upper parts, olive-brownish-gray, slightly darker on the wings and tail. Tail with a prominent terminal yellow band, and the tips of the secondary wing-feathers with small, drop-like, bright red, sealing-wax-like tips. Crested head, neck, and under parts, soft fawn-brown, becoming olive-yellow on the flanks, yellowish on the abdomen, and white on the under tail coverts. The crest of the head is not always raised.

LENGTH—7.19 inches.

DISTRIBUTION—From Labrador westward to Saskatchewan and southward to Oregon, Kansas, and along the Allegheny Mountains as far south as South Carolina. In winter it spreads southward into the West Indies and Costa Rica.

Cedar Waxwings are among our trimmest, neatest, most tailored, most aristocratic birds. Traveling in flocks, they attract much attention by their habits of sailing out over the shores of a wooded pond, and capturing insects on the wing, somewhat after the manner of the Flycatchers. Small fruits, i.e., wild cherries, cedar berries, bird cherries, and the like, are among their favorite fare. The crest of the head is raised to its fullest extent only when the bird is alarmed, or especially alert; hence it is not always apparent. When stretching the

neck upward, the crest is laid along the back of the neck, and disappears altogether. The only note of the Waxwing is an extremely thin, fine, high *zeeee, zeeee*, not perceptible to all ears. (Family *Bombycillidae*)

WEAVER-BIRD FAMILY
Ploceidae

The Weaver-birds are an Old World family. They build closely woven nests, globular or pear-like, with an opening on the side. The familiar cage-birds such as the waxbills, Java sparrows, and others, belong to this large family, which contains about two hundred and fifty members. In general, they resemble the finches (Family *Fringillidae*). The bill is heavy and conical, and the plumage of the species shows such general colors and patterns as are found among our true sparrows, finches, buntings, etc. Two spe-

cies of Weaver-birds have been introduced into this country, the English (or House) Sparrow, and the European Tree Sparrow. The former is

widely distributed, and extremely common.

NESTING. Many of the members of this family construct pensile nests, but our common English or House Sparrow throws together a mass of grasses and straws, often with the admixture of string, bits of paper or cloth, etc., lining the whole with any soft materials it can secure, and placing it in a hollow tree, a bird house (unfortunately), sometimes behind window blinds, or in the cornice of a building; in fact, in any nook or crevice well above the ground, which affords lodgment and protection. The eggs, from four to nine in number, are a dull white or light grayish, speckled and spotted lightly or heavily with dark gray, and shades of brown, and are quite variable. The European Tree Sparrow (naturalized in the United States) constructs a similar nest, and lays similar eggs.

WHEATEAR
European Wheatear
Oenanthe oenanthe oenanthe [765]

Similar to the Greenland Wheatear, but somewhat smaller.

DISTRIBUTION—This is an Asiatic species, and reaches the continent of North America by migrating in summer into Alaska, where it is found chiefly in the warmer coastal zone.

Its habits are similar to those of its European congener. (Family *Turdidae*)

Greenland Wheatear

Oenanthe oenanthe leucorhoa [765a]

ADULT MALE—Upper parts, light gray; the cheeks and wings black or blackish. Forehead and upper tail coverts, white. The basal portion of the tail, white; its end, black. Under parts, white, flushed with light brownish or grayish-brown.

ADULT FEMALE—Similar to the male in pattern, but with the colors duller.

LENGTH—6.25 inches.

DISTRIBUTION—This bird, a western European species, is found breeding in Greenland, and on the adjoining mainland of North America, spreading rarely as far south as the St. Lawrence River, and very rarely beyond.

This rare and attractive European species very seldom reaches the United States. As it flits about in the open

barren country of the North, or ascends the slopes of the higher mountains, it sings a varied, sweet song, in whose notes may be recognized imitations of those of many other birds. A characteristic habit of the bird, is the frequent flirting of its flexible tail. (Family *Turdidae*)

WHIMBREL

Whimbrel

Phaeopus phaeopus phaeopus [267]

ADULT MALE AND FEMALE—General plumage, dark reddish-brown-ashy, mottled with dusky spots; similar to the European Curlew, but darker. Crown, dark brown with a broad, pale median streak.

LENGTH—About 18.00 inches.

DISTRIBUTION — This Old World bird is an occasional visitant in Greenland, and an accidental visitant in Nova Scotia and on Long Island (New York), where there is but one record.

The Whimbrel may be described as a smaller edition of the European Curlew. Two of its common names in England are Half-Curlew and Jack Curlew. Here the bird occurs only as a spring and fall migrant, breeding in the Orkney and Shetland islands. (Family *Scolopacidae*)

WHIP-POOR-WILL

Eastern Whip-poor-will

Antrostomus vociferus vociferus [417]

ADULT MALE—Upper parts, a mixture of black, gray, buffy-brown, and yellowish-brown. Throat, black; upper breast, black crossed by a narrow white band. Abdomen, buffy speckled with black. Middle pair of tail feathers, similar to the back; the outer pair, white for the terminal half of their length.

ADULT FEMALE—Similar, but with the breast band buffy instead of white, and with the outer tail feathers only narrowly tipped with buffy-white.

LENGTH—9.75 inches.

DISTRIBUTION—From New Brunswick and Manitoba southward to the Gulf States, and westward to the Great Plains.

The Whip-poor-will speaks its name plainly! When near a singing bird, the observer will often hear a slight *cluck* note, as though a tiny spring-catch had been tripped in the bird's throat, to set in motion the mechanism which produces the unusual song. No nest is made by the Whip-poor-will, the two whitish eggs marked with lilac and brown being deposited on the bare ground in any depression sufficiently deep to keep them from rolling away. Nocturnal and crepuscular insects, cap-

tured on the wing in the bird's capacious mouth, constitute the food of this retiring and eremitical species. (Famiiy *Caprimulgidae*)

Stephen's Whip-poor-will

Antrostomus vociferus arizonae [417a]

Similar to the Eastern Whip-poor-will, but larger, with the bristles about the mouth longer, and with a brownish throat-patch.

DISTRIBUTION—"Arizona, New Mexico, and southwestern Texas, south over mountains bordering the tablelands of Mexico, to Guatemala." (Bailey.) (Family *Caprimulgidae*)

WIDGEON
European Widgeon

Mareca penelope [136]

ADULT MALE—Back and sides of the body finely marked with wavy black and white lines. Crown, light creamy-brown. Head and neck, reddish-brown; throat, blackish. Upper breast, vinaceous; lower breast and abdomen, white.

ADULT FEMALE — Back, grayish-brown with small lighter bars. Tertials, reddish-brown bordered by pinkish-brown. Greater wing coverts, brownish-gray tipped with black. Head and throat, deep pinkish-brown finely streaked and barred with black;

crown, darker. Upper breast and sides, the same, but without black markings. Lower breast and abdomen, white.

LENGTH—18.00 inches.

DISTRIBUTION—In North America this Duck occurs rarely but regularly in British Columbia, California, in the upper Mississippi Valley, and along the Atlantic Coast from the Gulf of St. Lawrence to Florida.

The Widgeon (or Wigeon) is, next to the Mallard, the most familiar fresh-water Duck in the British Isles. It is a very loquacious species. Its loud, piercing, wild, whistled cry sounds

somewhat like the syllable *whe-e-e-u-u-w*. It is often known as the Whew Duck or Whewer. It is one of the wariest and shyest of water fowl. (Family *Anatidae*)

WILLET
Eastern Willet

Catoptrophorus semipalmatus semipalmatus [258]

ADULT MALE AND FEMALE—Upper parts, brownish gray. Fore neck and upper breast, white streaked with dusky; sides barred with buff. Wings, blackish; when spread, show a prominent white patch. Abdomen, white. Basal half of the tail, white.

LENGTH—15.00 inches.

DISTRIBUTION—From southern New Jersey to Florida; wintering from the Gulf States into South America. After the breeding season is over, some individuals straggle as far north as Maine.

Willets are denizens of beaches, and of both fresh and salt marshes. As the birds fly about, they utter a continu-

ous *pilly-willy-willet, pilly-willy-willet,* in tiresome iteration. They somewhat resemble the Yellow-legs, but are larger, and show a conspicuous long white patch in the spread wing. (Family *Scolopacidae*)

Western Willet
Catoptrophorus semipalmatus [258a]

Similar to the Eastern Willet, but somewhat larger, with the upper parts slightly paler, and not so heavily marked with black either above or below.

DISTRIBUTION—In the western portions of the United States, from Manitoba to Texas. In winter it is found in southern California, and eastward into the Gulf States, and southward into Mexico. On the Atlantic Coast the bird occurs as a rare migrant, from South Carolina to Florida. (Family *Scolopacidae*)

WOODCOCK
American Woodcock
Philohela minor [228]

ADULT MALE AND FEMALE—Upper parts, grayish-brown mixed with black and reddish-brown. Front of crown, slaty-gray; back of head, barred with brownish-yellow. A dark line from the eye to the base of the bill. Under parts, buffy tinged lightly with cinnamon-brown, and washed on the flanks with a more decided tone of the same. Tail, black tipped with whitish. Eye, large and set far back in the head. Bill, nearly three inches long.

LENGTH—11.00 inches.

DISTRIBUTION—From north of Labrador and Manitoba southward to Florida, breeding chiefly in the northernmost parts of its range. In winter it is found from southern New Jersey across to southern Illinois, and southward to the Gulf States.

Woodcocks feed in the lowlands, where they bore into the soft mud or soil for worms and other small invertebrates. On their migrations, however, they often take shelter in rather dry

bushy hillsides. In spring the mating song of the male is one of the most astonishing of bird performances. It is given at dusk, and consists of a series of liquid, bubbling notes, and whistles, as the bird scales downward from a considerable height. This song is introduced, and concluded, by a series of nasal *peeent* notes, much like the flying calls of the Nighthawk. This exhibition, so unexpected from such a heavy, prosaic-looking bird, is given in both the morning and the evening twilights, sometimes protracted until after dark. I have heard it on the side of a New Hampshire mountain, long after ten o'clock, when some very faint traces of the sunset color still lingered along the horizon. When flushed, the Woodcock darts away in a curious zig-zag flight, its erratic progress being accompanied by a whistling sound, as the air swishes through its stiff primary feathers. (Family *Scolopacidae*)

European Woodcock
Scolopax rusticola rusticola [227]

Similar in general to the American Woodcock, but much larger; the wings barred with reddish-brown, and the under parts barred with black.

DISTRIBUTION—Occurs as an accidental straggler in eastern North America. (Family *Scolopacidae*)

WOODPECKER FAMILY
Picidae

Woodpeckers are characterized by straight, sharp, chisel-shaped bills; tails with stiffened and pointed feathers, which are used as props in climb-

ing; and in almost all cases, feet stout and strong, with two toes directed forward and two backward. In typical forms, the tongue is long, extensible, and armed with a hard, spear-like tip, which is thrust out far beyond the tips of the mandibles, and the prey impaled thereon. Many Woodpeckers have loud, far-reaching voices, like sharp cries, but possess no powers of song. Their mating call is a drumming with the bill upon some resonant bit of wood, or any sonorous substance. The birds nest generally in a deep vertical cavity in a tree-trunk or limb, which tunnel they excavate for themselves. Woodpeckers are found in all parts of the world where forests occur, except in the Australian region and in Madagascar. Of the approximately seven hundred species which are now known, sixty-four species and subspecies are found in North America, representing ten genera. The largest of these is the genus *Dryobates*, containing twenty-eight species and subspecies.

NESTING. The nests of our Woodpeckers are made in holes, i.e., vertical tunnels in trees; the cavities usually being excavated by the birds which lay the eggs, though sometimes a deserted hole will be used, or some natural cavity taken advantage of. Some species hew out holes in the giant cactuses of the Far West, and the great Ivory-billed Woodpecker customarily nests in a cypress. In general, however, any tree trunk or large limb, soft enough to be tunneled, will be used, for the birds do not hew their dwellings out of living hard wood. (In countries where trees are rare or absent altogether, some species of Woodpeckers burrow in banks, after the manner of our Kingfishers or Bank Swallows, or lay their eggs in any natural cavities in the soil which will afford protection; in extreme cases resorting to the brain cavity of an old bleached mammal skull.) Where Woodpeckers nest in trees, there is usually a soft bed of rotted chips at the bottom of the cavity for the reception of the eggs. The eggs of Woodpeckers are white, with a shiny, porcelain-like surface.

WOODPECKER
Alaskan Three-toed Woodpecker
Picoïdes tridactylus fasciatus [401a]

Similar to the American Three-toed Woodpecker, but with a broad white patch on the back, instead of ladder-like markings.

DISTRIBUTION — The northwestern portion of North America through British Columbia into Washington, and eastward into the region of the Great Bear Lake, and the Mackenzie River Valley. (Family *Picidae*)

Alpine Three-toed Woodpecker
Picoïdes tridactylus dorsalis [401b]

Similar to the American Three-toed Woodpecker, but larger, with the white markings of the back running together into more or less of a continuous white medial band.

DISTRIBUTION — From British Columbia and Idaho south along the Rocky Mountains into New Mexico. (Family *Picidae*)

American Three-toed Woodpecker
Picoïdes tridactylus bacatus [401]

ADULT MALE—Back, barred with black and white; wing feathers, spotted with the same. The middle of the crown bears a bright orange-yellow patch. A white line from the eye passes backward. Middle tail feathers, black; the outer ones, black and white. Sides of body, barred with black and white. Under parts, white.

ADULT FEMALE—Similar, but with the crown patch spotted with black and white, instead of orange-yellow.

LENGTH—8.75 inches.

DISTRIBUTION—From the far northern portions of North America westward to the Rocky Mountains, and southward into Maine, the White Mountains, northern New York, and across to northern Minnesota. In winter it spreads south as far as central New England, central New York, and northern Illinois.

This Woodpecker, often called the Ladder-back because of the markings between the wings, like its relative, the Arctic Three-toed Woodpecker, renders a service to the cause of forest conservation which cannot easily be

overestimated. It destroys countless thousands of insects injurious to standing and fallen timber, and consumes less vegetable matter than its Arctic cousin. In all essentials of flight, notes, nesting, food, and general habits, it is similar to this congener, also. Very little detailed study of this interesting species has been made, but enough is known to induce us to spare no efforts to protect this valuable bird, and to encourage its occupation of our northern forests. From the Arctic Three-toed Woodpecker, this species may be distinguished by the ladder-like black and white markings of the back. (Family *Picidae*)

Ant-eating Woodpecker
Balanosphyra formicivora formicivora [407]

ADULT MALE—Upper parts, sides of the head, and the breast band, glossy greenish. Region about the base of the bill, and the chin, black, surrounded by a band of white or yellow. Crown, red. Breast, bluish-black streaked with white. Rump, patch in the wing, and the abdomen, white.

ADULT FEMALE—Similar to the male, but with a black band between the white or yellow forehead and the red crown.

LENGTH—9.25 inches.

DISTRIBUTION—From Texas to Arizona, and southward to the Isthmus of Tehuantepec, in Mexico.

The Ant-eating Woodpeckers are familiar and well-loved denizens of live-oak groves, where they work industriously filling up tree trunks and nearby telegraph poles with acorns. They indulge in an unusual habit for Woodpeckers, that of sailing out into the air after passing insects, in the manner of Flycatchers. Their voices are constant and conversational; *jacob, jacob, jacob,* they seem to say, as they go about their work. (Family *Picidae*)

Arctic Three-toed Woodpecker

Picoïdes arcticus [400]

ADULT MALE—Upper parts, glossy black, with a bright orange-yellow patch in the middle of the crown. Wing feathers, spotted with white, giving to the wings a white-barred appearance when closed. A broad white line from the nostril passes below the eye, and a fine white line through it. Middle tail feathers, black; the outer ones, white, except at their bases. Sides of the body, barred with black and white. Under parts, white.

ADULT FEMALE—Similar, but without the crown patch.

LENGTH—9.50 inches.

DISTRIBUTION — The whole of the northern portion of North America from the Arctic region south to New England, New York, Michigan, Minnesota, and Idaho, and along the Sierra Nevada Mountains as far south as Lake Tahoe.

One of the quietest and most industrious of our Woodpeckers, the Arctic Three-toe pursues his almost ascetic life virtually within the confines of coniferous forests, chiefly those of spruce and balsam. The bird is never

common anywhere, but occurs most frequently where forest fires have left standing the dead boles of coniferous trees. It is not a wary species, and will not fly far, even upon the near approach of an observer. Its habits are restless, and it hitches from spot to spot, or flies from tree to tree with great rapidity. The shrill call note, *cherk, cherk,* is not frequently uttered. (Family *Picidae*)

Arizona Woodpecker

Dryobates arizonae arizonae [398]

ADULT MALE — Upper parts, unmarked brown. Nape, red, bordered by prominent white patches. Wings, spotted with white; and outer tail feathers, barred with white. Under parts, white, heavily spotted with brown.

ADULT FEMALE — Similar to the male, but lacking the red on the head.

LENGTH—8.00 inches.

DISTRIBUTION—From the mountains

of the southwestern part of New Mexico and southern Arizona, southward into the northwestern portion of Mexico.

This rather rare Woodpecker inhabits oak forests on the sides of mountains, roughly between the altitudes of four thousand to seven thousand feet. They

often travel in small flocks—rather unlike Woodpeckers in general (except the Red-cockaded Woodpecker)— alighting near the bottoms of tree trunks and then working their way over the entire tree, even out along the smaller branches. They are rather shy birds, and take flight upon the approach of an observer, or hide behind limbs and trunks, peering out first on one side and then on the other, to take note of the movements of their scrutinizer. Apparently they are not much given to chiselling into the tree itself in their search for insect food, but look about among the interstices of the bark, and the angles of the twigs, even inspecting the folds of buds, flowers, and foliage. Their notes are sharp and penetrating, but not especially loud. (Family *Picidae*)

Batchelder's Woodpecker

Dryobates pubescens leucurus [394b]

Similar to the Northern Downy Woodpecker, but with the wing coverts showing few or no white markings. No streakings on the under tail coverts.

DISTRIBUTION—Confined to the Rocky Mountains of the United States. (Family *Picidae*)

Brewster's Woodpecker

Centurus uropygialis brewsteri [411b]

Similar to the Gila Woodpecker, but smaller, and often bearing a larger bill. The black bars of the rump and upper tail coverts are narrower, and more numerous, and the white and black bars of the tail itself are also narrower and less prominent.

DISTRIBUTION — "Cape district of Lower California, north to San Ignacio, and on Santa Margarita Island." (A.O.U. Check List.) (Family *Picidae*)

Cabanis's Woodpecker

Dryobates villosus hyloscopus [393d]

Similar to Harris's Woodpecker, but somewhat smaller, and with white instead of smoky under parts.

DISTRIBUTION—In the arid zone of the southwestern United States, and thence southward into the mountains of Zacatecas, Mexico. (Family *Picidae*)

Cactus Woodpecker

Dryobates scalaris cactophilus [396b]

Similar to the Texas Woodpecker, of which subspecies the Cactus Woodpecker is the representative in the southwestern United States.

DISTRIBUTION — Southwestern United States. (Family *Picidae*)

California Woodpecker

Balanosphyra formicivora bairdi [407a]

Similar to the Ant-eating Woodpecker; but with the breast band solid jet black; and with a heavier bill.

LENGTH—9.25 inches.

DISTRIBUTION—In the Pacific Coast region, from Oregon southward into the northern portion of Lower California.

The habits of this bird are similar to those of the Ant-eating Woodpecker. Its food consists largely of acorns dur-

ing most of the year, but it also devours large numbers of caterpillars, grasshoppers, large beetles, flies, ants; as well as berries, small fruits, and some green corn. Like its smaller cousin, it bores large holes in the trunks of trees—often in dead redwoods, which it fills with acorns. Sometimes also it stores these nuts in holes in fence posts, telegraph poles, the cornerposts of buildings, and even the wooden spires of churches. (Family *Picidae*)

Cardón Woodpecker
Centurus uropygialis cardonensis [411a]

Similar to the Gila Woodpecker, but with coloration uniformly much darker.

DISTRIBUTION—"Latitude 28 degrees and 30 degrees across the peninsula of Lower California and north along the western rim of the Colorado Desert to about latitude 32 degrees." (A.O.U. Check List.) (Family *Picidae*)

Chihuahua Woodpecker
Dryobates villosus icastus [393h]

Resembles the Cabanis's Woodpecker, but possesses slightly longer wings and an appreciably smaller bill.

DISTRIBUTION—"Southwestern New Mexico and southern Arizona south over northwestern Mexico to Zucatecas, Coahuila, and Jalisco." (A.O.U. Check List.) (Family *Picidae*)

Eastern Hairy Woodpecker
Dryobates villosus villosus [393]

ADULT MALE AND FEMALE—This species is almost an exact counterpart in coloration and pattern of the Northern Downy Woodpecker, except that in the Hairy, the outer tail feathers are pure white and unmarked. The female of this species, like the Downy, lacks the bright scarlet on the nape.

LENGTH—9.40 inches.

DISTRIBUTION—The whole of the eastern portion of the North American continent, from northern Canada south into North Carolina.

This fine Woodpecker, a larger "edition" of the familiar Downy, is similar

in its habits, notes, and nesting to its smaller congener. Its long, loud call of *peek, peek, peek, pe-e-e-e-e-e-k,* a staccato shout of much vigor, may often be heard for a mile or more on a quiet spring day. In the spring, also, the male drums off its marital invitations in the form of impetuous hammerings upon a resonant dead limb or loose piece of bark, producing a rolling tattoo which throbs through the silent woods sometimes for a distance of several miles. The Hairy Woodpecker, unlike the Downy, is not a bird of dooryards and village streets, but prefers wilder country, sparsely populated regions, and wild hill and mountain regions. It is wary of human approach, as a rule, but occasionally may be induced to come to feeding stations, and after a time loses its fear of man, and finally may be a frequent visitor at the suet. It nests in large holes in trees, sometimes in orchards not far from the farmhouse. (Family *Picidae*)

Florida Pileated Woodpecker

Ceophloeus pileatus floridanus [405b]

Similar to the Southern Pileated Woodpecker, but with the black in the plumage even blacker (less slaty or sooty); somewhat smaller; and with the bill relatively shorter and broader.

DISTRIBUTION—From Orange County, Florida, south into the central and southern parts. (Family *Picidae*)

Gairdner's Woodpecker

Dryobates pubescens gairdneri [394a]

ADULT MALE—Upper parts, jet black; forehead, dingy whitish. Nape, bright scarlet. Stripe down the middle of the back, white. Middle and greater wing coverts, black, or slightly spotted with white. Outer tail feathers, white barred with black. Under parts, dusky-gray or light brownish.

ADULT FEMALE—Similar to the male, but without the scarlet marking on the nape.

LENGTH—6.63 inches.

DISTRIBUTION—From British Columbia southward into southern California, and eastward slightly beyond the eastern sides of the Cascade Ranges and the Sierra Nevada.

This Woodpecker is the Pacific slope representative of our common Eastern Downy Woodpecker, but is slightly smaller. In its appearance and habits it conforms to the Hairy Woodpecker, but is less wild, and more often found in the vicinity of man's dwellings, especially in orchards, where its work of destroying wood-boring beetle larvae is much appreciated. (Family *Picidae*)

Gila Woodpecker

Centurus uropygialis uropygialis [411]

ADULT MALE—Crown, red. Head, grayish-brown. Back and rump, finely barred with black and white. Middle and outer tail feathers, marked with

white. Under parts, grayish-brown; the middle portion of the abdomen, yellowish.

ADULT FEMALE—Similar to the male, but without the red crown.

LENGTH—9.00 inches.

DISTRIBUTION—In southeastern California along the Colorado River; in southern Arizona and southwestern New Mexico; and southward through

Lower California and into the western part of Mexico and Jalisco.

The habits of this Woodpecker are similar to those of the California Woodpecker. Its flight notes of *huit, huit* are said to be similar to the notes of the Phainopepla. Its commonest call note is a heavy, harsh *tcheurr, tscheurr*. From the Golden-fronted Woodpecker, which it resembles, the Gila Woodpecker may be distinguished by its general brownish cast; the white markings of the central tail feathers; the black-and-white-barred rump; and the absence of any yellow on the head. It makes its nest most commonly in the giant cactus. (Family *Picidae*)

Golden-fronted Woodpecker
Centurus aurifrons [410]

ADULT MALE—Back, finely barred with black and white; rump, white. Tail, black; its outer feathers barred

with white. Forehead, yellow; crown, red; nuchal patch, yellow, orange, or red. Under parts, light gray; the abdomen, washed with yellowish.

ADULT FEMALE—Similar to the male, but lacking the red crown, and with the yellow of the plumage paler.

LENGTH—10.50 inches.

DISTRIBUTION—From the central and southern portions of Texas, south-ward into Mexico as far as Mexico City.

In Texas this Woodpecker is a common bird, nesting in the mesquites, oaks, and pecans, and in the vicinity of houses, in telegraph poles and bird boxes. Bailey says of it, *"Aurifrons* makes enough noise for a dozen, his loud penetrating voice ringing across the road as you drive through the mesquites. One of his common calls is a rattle like that of the California Woodpecker. When he flies he shows his white rump and wing spots, and on the rare occasions when you catch a glimpse of him you can see the yellow of his neck above the black and white barrings of his back." (Family *Picidae*)

Harris's Woodpecker
Dryobates villosus harrisi [393c]

Similar to the Eastern Hairy Woodpecker, but with the wing coverts usually lacking the white markings, and with the under parts washed with a dusky-brownish.

DISTRIBUTION—From British Columbia southward along the Pacific Coast zone into northern California. (Family *Picidae*)

Ivory-billed Woodpecker
Campephilus principalis [392]

ADULT MALE—Upper parts, glossy black. A white stripe begins just below the eye, and passes down the side of the neck to join the one from the other side in the middle of the back. Head, with a prominent, large, scarlet crest. Wings, marked with white. The central tail feathers, much elongated and very stiff; the outer ones, very short. Over the nostrils project stiff white bristles. Under parts, glossy-black. Bill, large and ivory-white in color.

ADULT FEMALE—Similar to the male, but with a black instead of a scarlet crest.

LENGTH—20.00 inches.

DISTRIBUTION — Formerly ranged over a large part of southeastern United States, but now restricted to the lower Mississippi Valley, and the Gulf States, especially in Alabama and Florida. In danger of extinction.

The Ivory-bill is one of our most splendid Woodpeckers, or indeed of any of our native birds. It retreats before the inroads of civilization, and is even now threatened with extermination. Its favorite haunts are the cypress forests in our southern states, where it is restricted to small localities. Recent extensive studies of this bird, the most exhaustive ever made, have just been completed by Dr. A. A. Allen. The Ivory-bill is even larger

than the huge Pileated Woodpecker. It is longer than the Fish Crow of the coast. Its voice is loud and penetrating. (Family *Picidae*)

Lewis's Woodpecker
Asyndesmus lewisi [408]

ADULT MALE AND FEMALE—Upper parts, iridescent greenish-black. Collar, gray. Face, dull crimson. Throat and breast, gray; grading to a soft rose color on the abdomen. The plumage of the under parts is harsh and hairy.

LENGTH—11.00 inches.

DISTRIBUTION — From the Black Hills and the eastern slopes of the

Rocky Mountains westward to the Pacific slope; and from the southern portion of British Columbia and Alberta southward to Arizona. In winter it is found in the southern part of California and western Texas, and casually in western Kansas. This is one of the commonest Woodpeckers in its range, flying with a crow-like figure and flight, and showing its diagnostic broad wings and short tail. (Family *Picidae*)

Lower California Hairy Woodpecker
Dryobates villosus scrippsae [393k]

Similar to the Cabanis's Woodpecker, but more decidedly smaller and with the dusky-white of the breast more extended.

DISTRIBUTION—In the peninsula of Lower California, in the Sierra Juarez and the Sierra San Pedro Martir. (Family *Picidae*)

Mearns's Woodpecker
Balanosphyra formicivora aculeata [407c]

In general size and coloration, midway between the Ant-eating Woodpecker and the California Woodpecker, but with the throat less yellow than in either of these, and the bill shorter and slenderer. The white stripings of the upper breast, more pronounced than in the California Woodpecker, and less so than in the Ant-eating sub-species.

DISTRIBUTION—Found in Arizona, New Mexico, and western Texas; extending south through northwestern Mexico as far as Durango. (Family *Picidae*)

Modoc Woodpecker
Dryobates villosus orius [393j]

Similar to the White-breasted Woodpecker, but larger, and with the under parts whitish tinged with brownish. (Family *Picidae*)

Narrow-fronted Woodpecker
Balanosphyra formicivora angustifrons [407b]

Similar to the Ant-eating Woodpecker, but smaller, and with the throat a brighter yellow.

DISTRIBUTION—In the Cape Region of Lower California. (Family *Picidae*)

Nelson's Downy Woodpecker
Dryobates pubescens nelsoni [394d]

Similar to the Northern Downy Woodpecker, but larger and whiter, being the largest of the *pubescens* group.

DISTRIBUTION—Occurs in Alaska. (Family *Picidae*)

Newfoundland Woodpecker
Dryobates villosus terraenovae [393g]

Similar to the Eastern Hairy Woodpecker, but somewhat larger; with more black on the upper parts, and with the white areas reduced both in size and in numbers, especially in the wings.

LENGTH—10.50 inches.

DISTRIBUTION—Restricted to Newfoundland. (Family *Picidae*)

Northern Downy Woodpecker
Dryobates pubescens medianus [394c]

ADULT MALE—Back, black with a broad white median stripe; nape, bright scarlet. A white stripe extends above and below the eye, and the wings and their coverts are spotted with black and white. Middle tail feathers, black; the outer ones, white bearing several black bars. Under parts, white.

ADULT FEMALE—Similar, but lacking the scarlet nape patch.

LENGTH—6.83 inches.

DISTRIBUTION—Over the whole of eastern North America south as far as South Carolina.

The Downy Woodpecker is a bird of roadside trees, village streets, orchards, parks, and small woods—rather than

of deep forests, though it may be encountered wherever there are trees. Its social instincts lead it to associate with Chickadees, Titmice, Nuthatches, and Creepers, and during the winter months it is often found in such a miscellaneous company. Its sharp, yet not unmusical *peek, peek,* announces its presence as it hitches its way up the trunk of a tree, and out along a branch, tapping here and there in its interminable search for insects hidden in or beneath the bark. On warm days in spring it often gives voice to a vigorous *peek, peek, peek, pe-e-e-e-e-e-e-e-k*, the last syllable running off into a rolling, staccato trill. At mating time the male drums an exuberant rolling tattoo upon some resonant dry limb, producing one of the most characteristic and pleasing sounds of the spring countryside. No Woodpecker deserves better at our hands than the friendly little Downy, for it is the natural guardian of trees, consuming enormous numbers of injurious insects, such as the codling moth, apple borer, various leaf miners, bronze birch borer, maple borer, pine weevil, and various scale insects, gall insects, and aphids. (Family *Picidae*)

Northern Hairy Woodpecker

Dryobates villosus septentrionalis [393a]

Similar to the Eastern Hairy Woodpecker, but about an inch longer.

DISTRIBUTION—From Alaska down into British America. (Family *Picidae*)

Northern Pileated Woodpecker

Coephloeus pileatus abieticola [405a]

ADULT MALE—Upper parts, black or fuscous black. The entire top of the head, bright scarlet; the feathers, much elongated and forming a backwardly projecting crest, which can be raised. Line through the eye, black or fuscous, bordered above and below by a broad band of white. The white band, broadening as it goes, passes down the sides of the neck to the shoulders. Before the eye, the band is tinged with sulphur-yellow. The bill is large, long, and yellowish. A scarlet stripe from its base runs along the side of the throat. Basal half of the

wing feathers, white; the remainder, black, forming large white patches which are prominently displayed when the bird is in flight. Under parts, fuscous; the feathers often narrowly margined with ashy-white.

ADULT FEMALE—Similar, but without the red head-markings.

LENGTH—17.60 inches.

DISTRIBUTION—From the far northern portions of Canada (about latitude 63°) south, locally, in the heavily wooded regions, throughout all the continent, except the Southern States.

The great Pileated Woodpecker, or Logcock, is, next to the Ivory-billed Woodpecker, our largest North American Woodpecker. In flight the bird

looks somewhat like a crow, but shows large white wing patches as it proceeds through the air in a typically Woodpeckerish undulating flight. The notes of this great bird are many. Its common call is similar to that of the Flicker, but louder, harsher, and wilder. The noise of its hammering— the mating call of the male bird— resounds through the woods like the sound of a woodsman's hammer, and is plainly audible several miles away. Its large squarish excavations may often be seen, sometimes many in one tree trunk, where the bird has been feeding on the larvae of wood-boring beetles. (Family *Picidae*)

Northern White-headed Woodpecker
Dryobates albolarvatus albolarvatus [399]

ADULT MALE—Entire bird, black, except for a white patch on the wings, a white head and neck, and a red patch on the back of the head.

ADULT FEMALE—Similar to the male, but lacking the red on the head.

LENGTH—9.15 inches.

DISTRIBUTION—From the mountains of southern British Columbia to the southern portion of California, and eastward to the Blue Mountains of Oregon, eastern Idaho, and along the eastern slopes of the Sierra Nevada.

The White-headed Woodpecker is the acrobat among the members of its family, hanging upside down, or dropping backwards down the trunk of a

tree with equal ease. Unlike most Woodpeckers, it often pries off the bark rather than chisels into it, in search of its insect food. Its call note, similar to that of the Hairy Wood-peckers, is a sharp *peeek*, though the note is deeper, and seems to have a burring quality. The White-head is a bird of the heavy pine woods of moun-

tains. It is especially fond of the seeds of pine cones. This item forms about one half its dietary. It also takes many insects, the majority of them being ants. (Family *Picidae*)

Nuttall's Woodpecker
Dryobates nuttalli [397]

ADULT MALE—Upper parts, barred with black and white. Crown, black, sometimes streaked with white. Back

of head shows a red patch, and then a white one. Shoulders bear a black band. Middle tail feathers, black; outer ones, white, with two small black bars. Under parts, white; the sides spotted with black.

ADULT FEMALE—Similar to the male, but lacking the red on the head.

LENGTH—7.00 inches.

DISTRIBUTION—From southern Ore-gon, west of the Cascade Mountains and the Sierra Nevada, southward into the northern portion of Lower Cali-fornia. (Family *Picidae*)

Queen Charlotte Woodpecker
Dryobates villosus picoideus [393f]

Similar to the Eastern Hairy Wood-pecker, but with the white patch be-tween the wings marked with black; the flanks streaked with black, and the under parts, a dusky-whitish.

DISTRIBUTION—Restricted to the Queen Charlotte Islands of British Columbia. (Family *Picidae*)

Red-bellied Woodpecker

Centurus carolinus [409]

ADULT MALE—Entire crown and back of neck, scarlet. Back, barred with black and white. Upper tail coverts, white marked with streaks of black. Outer tail feathers, and the inner vanes of the middle ones, barred with black and white. Cheeks, sides of throat, and under parts, ashy-white. The region about the base of the bill, and the middle of the breast and abdomen, sometimes suffused with reddish.

ADULT FEMALE—Similar, but with the crown ashy-gray instead of scarlet; this latter color being restricted to the nape.

LENGTH—9.50 inches.

DISTRIBUTION—Over the eastern United States east of the Great Plains, from Maryland, Ontario, and South Dakota (sometimes straggling as far north as Massachusetts), southward to Florida and Texas. In winter it is found from Virginia and southern Ohio southward.

The Red-bellied Woodpecker is a bird of woods, forests, cleared lands with sparse tree-stands, country plantations,

and shady village streets. Its familiar harsh, brassy call of *chad, chad, chad,* reiterated with tiresome frequency, is one of the characteristic sounds of many a southern plantation. In the spring it gives voice to a true Woodpeckerish "trill"—a metallic burring *keerrrrrrrrink*—and when mating activities are in full swing, to a guttural *wicker, wicker, wicker,* unpleasant to human senses, but no doubt seductive and sweet to a feathery ear. Although the bird is quite capable of excavating its own nesting hole in a dead tree, it does not scruple to appropriate a cavity delved out by another. This, occurring as it does among Woodpeckers, may be regarded as an act of peculation. After the breeding season is over, many individuals straggle northward—a vacation trip, no doubt, before the coming of winter. Throughout its range the bird is erratically migratory. (Family *Picidae*)

Red-cockaded Woodpecker

Dryobates borealis [395]

ADULT MALE—Crown, black; a small tuft of scarlet feathers on each side of the head behind the eye. Back, barred with black and white; and wings spotted similarly. Middle tail feathers, black; the outer ones white with black bars. Side of head and neck, white. A black stripe extends from the base of the bill downwards and backwards toward the shoulder. Sides of the body, and under tail coverts, white spotted and streaked with black; the rest of the under parts, pure white.

ADULT FEMALE—Similar, but lacking the scarlet feathers of the head.

LENGTH—8.40 inches.

DISTRIBUTION—Southern United States, from Virginia and Arkansas west to eastern Texas.

Wherever there are patches of open pine woods, one may expect to encounter Red-cockaded Woodpeckers, which go trooping in small companies through the tree tops, diligently inspecting every twig, limb, and cone— for like a group of biological students on a field excursion, nothing escapes their scrutiny. They seldom descend from the topmost parts of trees. Sometimes one may see Red-cockaded Woodpeckers in a deciduous woodland, but they are primarily birds of

coniferous growths, and seldom are to be found outside of pine woods, or in heavily forested country of any sort. Not fond of man's society, as is the Downy Woodpecker, they shun orchards and villages, and make their nests and live their lives far afield. Some of their habits are curiously similar to those of the Nuthatches, for they often hang, or crawl head downward, and often, too, give voice to a loud, hoarse, nasal *wank, wank*. The birds perform good service to our forests by devouring enormous numbers of ants, and the larvae of wood-boring beetles. (Family *Picidae*)

Red-headed Woodpecker
Melanerpes erythrocephalus [406]

ADULT MALE AND FEMALE—Entire head, neck, throat, and upper breast, blood-red. Back, bluish-black; bill, bluish-white. Upper tail coverts, white. Distal half of the secondaries, white, forming a prominent white patch in each wing. Tail, black; its outer feathers tipped and margined with

white. Lower breast and abdomen, white; the middle of the latter often suffused with faint pinkish.

LENGTH—9.75 inches.

DISTRIBUTION—From Manitoba and New York west to the Rocky Mountains, and south to Florida and Texas; erratic in its distribution. It spends its winters from about the middle of the United States southward.

This flamboyant bird is the polyglot of the Woodpecker family. Scarcely any other member of the group possesses such a varied repertory of sounds as proceeds from its never-long-silent throat. Some of these are: a long, loud call note, like the syllables *kwee-oh, kwee-oh;* a harsher *kerrruck, kerrruck,* reminiscent of the note of the tree toad (*Hyla versicolor*); a gobbling sort of sound, *yarruh, yarruh, yarruh,* somewhat like the *wicker, wicker, wicker* of the Flicker, and uttered when a pair of birds are together in the spring; and many others consisting of sundry cacklings, chatterings, chirpings, and squawkings, all more or less of a raucous nature. Like its relative, the

Flicker, the Red-head is most often seen in fairly open country, in pastures, cleared lands, along wooded streams, and not infrequently near towns and villages. At times it may be very abundant locally, and at others, comparatively rare or absent altogether. It is

a bird of erratic occupational habits and migratory movements. Unlike other Woodpeckers, it frequently sails out in mid-air to capture some flying insect. (Family *Picidae*)

Rocky Mountain Hairy Woodpecker

Dryobates villosus monticola [393e]

Similar to the Cabanis's Woodpecker, but larger, and with the under parts much more purely white; and the lores entirely or nearly black.

DISTRIBUTION—In the Rocky Mountain region from the central portion of British Columbia, eastern Washington, and Montana, southward into eastern Utah, and northern New Mexico. Eastward to western Nebraska, and western South Dakota. It occurs as a casual visitant in southeastern Alaska. (Family *Picidae*)

San Fernando Woodpecker

Dryobates scalaris eremicus [396c]

Similar to the San Lucas Woodpecker, but larger. The upper parts and under parts are darker; the black bars of the posterior part of the latter region are somewhat wider. The neck bars are wider, and the white bars on the back are on the average narrower, and less regular.

DISTRIBUTION—In Lower California, north of Ukai and Plaia Maria Bay, except in the extreme northeastern part. (Family *Picidae*)

San Lucas Woodpecker

Dryobates scalaris lucasanus [396a]

Similar to the Texas Woodpecker, but with the primary wing coverts bearing at least one row of small white spots; and with the outer tail feathers barred with black only on the terminal half or so, except occasionally on the inner web.

LENGTH—7.50 inches.

DISTRIBUTION—From the Colorado Desert (about latitude 34°), California, southward through Lower California.

A Woodpecker of the valleys, lowlands, and deserts, being found among mesquites and yuccas of hot situations. (Family *Picidae*)

San Pedro Woodpecker

Balanosphyra formicivora martirensis [407d]

Similar to the California Woodpecker, but differing from it chiefly in possessing shorter wings and a slightly shorter, but notably weaker and slenderer bill.

DISTRIBUTION—From about latitude 30° in northwestern Lower California, northward nearly to the United States boundary. (Family *Picidae*)

Sitka Hairy Woodpecker

Dryobates villosus sitkensis [393i]

Similar to the Harris's Woodpecker, but with the under parts paler, less smoky, and with the nasal tufts more buffy.

DISTRIBUTION—Found along the coastal region of southeastern Alaska and northern British Columbia. (Family *Picidae*)

Southern Downy Woodpecker

Dryobates pubescens pubescens [394]

Similar to the Northern Downy Woodpecker, but slightly smaller, and with the under parts, grayish-white.

DISTRIBUTION—From South Carolina, through Georgia and the Gulf States, into Texas. (Family *Picidae*)

Southern Hairy Woodpecker

Dryobates villosus auduboni [393b]

Similar to the Eastern Hairy Woodpecker, but about an inch shorter.

DISTRIBUTION—From South Carolina southward along the coast, and westward through the Gulf States. (Family *Picidae*)

Southern Pileated Woodpecker
Ceophloeus pileatus pileatus [405]

Similar to the Northern Pileated Woodpecker, but somewhat smaller.
DISTRIBUTION—From South Carolina southward through the Southern States. (Family *Picidae*)

Southern White-headed Woodpecker
Dryobates albolarvatus gravirostris [399a]

Resembles the Northern White-headed Woodpecker, but is slightly larger, and with a much heavier bill.
DISTRIBUTION—Found in the mountains of southern California. (Family *Picidae*)

Texas Woodpecker
Dryobates scalaris symplectus [396]

ADULT MALE—Upper parts, barred black and white. Forehead, dusky; crown, red; the feathers of the forepart, specked with white. Middle tail feathers, black; outer ones, barred black and white. Under parts, smoky, lightly spotted with black.
ADULT FEMALE—Similar to the male, but with the crown black.
LENGTH—7.37 inches.
DISTRIBUTION—From California to Texas, and from southern Colorado to Utah, Nevada, and southward into northern Mexico.

The little Speckle-check, as this bird is often called, is an inhabitant of junipers, oaks, piñon pines, cottonwoods, and mesquites, and is seldom found above an elevation of five thousand feet. It prefers the hot valleys to the cool mountain heights. The nests are often made in holes in yuccas,

telegraph poles, and even fence posts. The voice of the bird is thin and fine, but sharp, and distinctly the voice of a Woodpecker. (Family *Picidae*)

Western Pileated Woodpecker
Ceophloeus pileatus picinus [405c]

Similar to the Northern Pileated Woodpecker, but sooty-black, and with the throat usually much marked with sooty. Sides of the body and the flanks, only faintly marked with grayish.
DISTRIBUTION—Along the Pacific coastal district from southern British Columbia to Marin County, California; thence along the Sierra Nevada as far as Fresno County, and eastward to Idaho and western Montana. (Family *Picidae*)

White-breasted Woodpecker
Dryobates villosus leucothorectis [393l]

Quite similar to the Rocky Mountain Hairy Woodpecker, but decidedly smaller, and the wing coverts without white spots.
DISTRIBUTION—From central western Texas and southern Utah to Arizona and New Mexico. (Family *Picidae*)

Willow Woodpecker
Dryobates pubescens turati [394e]

Similar to the Gairdner's Woodpecker, but smaller; the patch over the eye, whiter; the tertial feathers, more or less spotted with white; and the under parts, whiter.

DISTRIBUTION—In California, except in the desert mountain ranges, and on the eastern slopes of the Sierra Nevada; also absent from the coast region north of Marin County, and from the region north of the upper reaches of the Sacramento Valley. (Family *Picidae*)

WOOD WARBLER FAMILY
Warblers, Chats, Yellow-throats, Water-thrushes, Redstarts
Compsothlypidae

The Wood Warblers are small birds, mostly less than six inches in length, with small, sharp, slender bills, and brightly colored plumage, in which, in most species, yellows and greens

predominate. They are active, nervous, flitting sprites for the most part (the Chats and Water-thrushes being exceptions), and are found in woodlands, where they assiduously search among the tips of branches, in the opening leaf and blossom buds, for their minute insect prey. They do not warble, and the name is a misnomer. Mostly their songs are short, sibilant, and insect-like, though the Chats and Water-thrushes give voice to louder, fuller songs. Since they feed upon insects, the whole group is highly migratory, and travels thousands of miles each year between the summer (breeding) and the winter territory. About one hundred and sixty species and subspecies of these birds are now known, confined entirely to the Americas. Of these, eighty-two (contained in sixteen genera) are recorded from North America. The largest genus is *Dendroica* with thirty-three species and subspecies.

NESTING. Most of our Warblers are tree-dwelling birds, feeding and nesting in trees or bushes, although some are terrestrial. Their nests are placed in a variety of situations; in thickets, bushes, rushes, among the branches of trees, sometimes on the ground, and are for the most part small, neat, compact structures of the cup-type, some of them resembling the nests of Vireos in form and size. They are composed of a wide variety of materials, such as fine grasses, plant down, soft weed bark, soft mosses or lichens, hair, pine needles, and the like. Noteworthy among this large family is the Oven-bird, which makes a dome-shaped (or old fashioned oven-shaped) nest of grasses and leaves with a side opening on the ground in the woods; and the Black and White Warbler, whose nest of grasses, mosses, small leaves, rootlets, fern down, etc., is located in the roots of an upturned tree, in a hole in a stump, or on the ground in a depression at the base of a tree or bush. Warblers which nest high in trees, often evergreens from twenty-five to a hundred feet or so, varying with the species, are our Myrtle Warbler, Cerulean Warbler, Bay-breasted Warbler, Yellow-throated Warbler, Blackburnian Warbler, Sycamore Warbler, Black-throated Gray Warbler, Golden-cheeked Warbler, and Pine Warbler. Their eggs number from about three to seven, and are small, thin-shelled, and fragile; in color, a white, delicate bluish-white, greenish-white, grayish, or creamy, speckled with various tints of gray, brown, purple, lilac, etc., the delicate markings often forming an irregular wreath about the larger end.

WREN FAMILY
Troglodytidae

Wrens are small brownish birds, with finely barred tail and wings; never very large (four to six inches); and with rounded wings, short rounded tails, and slender, often decurved bills. They are active, nervous little birds, often cocking their tails up over their backs, and bobbing up and down on their tiny legs (as though on springs), scolding in a harsh, buzzy voice, or

chattering like a tiny wooden mill. Their songs are bright, energetic, bubbling, musical, repeated over and over again, and usually not very long. Wrens occur in both hemispheres. Over three hundred and fifty forms are known, of which about three hundred and twenty are found in the Western Hemisphere, mainly in the tropics. Forty-six species and subspecies have been reported from North America, contained in nine genera.

NESTING. Our Wrens (with the exception of the Marsh Wrens) nest in the natural cavities of rocks and trees, sometimes amid the roots or in the hard clay among the roots of a large upturned tree (as the Winter Wren), though the House Wren prefers the crevice of some old building, or a comfortable nesting box put up for the purpose. House Wrens also may select the most unusual and amusing nooks for their nests as, for example, the inside of an old boot, a tin can, an unused lamp on a high lamp post, the pocket of an old coat hung up in a favorable spot. These Wrens are especially fond of old apple orchards, where old trees and stumps afford a multitude of holes and crevices of all sorts. Deserted Woodpecker holes are very often used. Nests of all Wrens are rather bulky structures. The House Wren constructs its nest of a large number of small twigs, weed stems, straws, grasses, strips of bark, feathers, and the like. The Cactus Wren fashions a flask-shaped nest, the flask lying on its side, the narrow opening serving as a doorway. The Marsh Wrens make globular nests of grasses, with a side opening, and line these structures with finer grasses, cattail and other plant down, and a few feathers. These birds indulge in the curious habit of making several nests in a restricted locality, ultimately depositing their eggs in only one (though it may be that they maintain, in some cases, two families). The House Wren is known to be polygamous, and one male may often take charge of two families in the same garden. The eggs of Wrens in general are white, grayish-white, or pinkish-white; sometimes unmarked, but usually finely speckled with tones of reddish-brown. Sometimes the eggs are a plain brown, or a pale greenish-blue.

WREN

Alaska Wren
Nannus hiemalis alascensis [723]

Similar to the Eastern Winter Wren, but larger, and slightly more heavily barred.

DISTRIBUTION—On Kodiak Island, off the Aleutian Peninsula of Alaska. (Family *Troglodytidae*)

Alberta Marsh Wren
Telmatodytes palustris laingi [725f]

Similar to the Western Marsh Wren, but less brown; the color livelier, and not so dull.

DISTRIBUTION—Found in Alberta and western Saskatchewan, Canada. (Family *Troglodytidae*)

Aleutian Wren

Nannus hiemalis meligerus [723.1]

Similar to its neighbor, the Alaska Wren, but with the upper tail coverts and abdomen more heavily barred, and the plumage in general a darker gray, with less of a brownish tinge.

DISTRIBUTION—On the western Aleutian Islands. (Family *Troglodytidae*)

Baird's Wren

Thryomanes bewicki eremophilus [719b]

Similar to the Bewick's Wren, but larger and grayer.

DISTRIBUTION — Southern Nevada, Utah, Colorado, and California south into Mexico. (Family *Troglodytidae*)

Bewick's Wren

Thryomanes bewicki bewicki [719]

ADULT MALE AND FEMALE—Upper parts, deep, unmarked cinnamon-brown; edges of wings, sometimes slightly barred with black. Middle tail

feathers, grayish-brown, slightly barred on the sides with blackish; outer tail feathers, black tipped with grayish-white. Prominent grayish-white line over the eye. Under parts, grayish-white; the flanks showing a brownish wash.

LENGTH—5.00 inches.

DISTRIBUTION—The Mississippi Valley from about the latitude of central Illinois, westward to the Great Plains; eastward to the Allegheny Mountains; and locally from southern New Jersey to Georgia through the Atlantic States.

What the House Wren, or Jenny Wren, is to the East, the Bewick's Wren is to the Middle West. It is a bright, bustling, cheery sprite, common about the home grounds, and filling the air with its loud, clear, varied song. Its general behavior is more deliberate, perhaps less agitated, than that of the eastern House Wren. (Family *Troglodytidae*)

Bryant's Cactus Wren

Heleodytes brunneicapillus bryanti [713a]

Similar to the Northern Cactus Wren, but with buffy, more thickly spotted under parts. Three outer tail feathers, barred with white.

DISTRIBUTION—Southern California, and Lower California. (Family *Troglodytidae*)

Canyon Wren

Catherpes mexicanus conspersus [717a]

ADULT MALE AND FEMALE—Upper parts, light brown, graying on the head, and speckled blackish and white. Tail, light reddish-brown, with narrow barrings of black. Throat and breast, unmarked white, shading gradually to a dark brown on the lower abdomen. Line over the eye, faint.

LENGTH—5.62 inches.

DISTRIBUTION—From Colorado westward to the Sierra Nevada and Cascade ranges, and from Idaho southward into Mexico.

A denizen of the rocks, this attractively colored little Wren slips in and out among the most forbidding boulders and small crags of deep canyons, pausing on some elevated place now and then to pour out its sweet, liquid, song. Hoffman has superlatively described the performance as "the spray of a waterfall in the sunshine." Bailey says the song is given "out of pure exuberance of happiness," and that it possesses a "rhapsody and rich vibrant quality which has suggested the name

of bugler for him—and glorious little bugler he surely is." (Family *Troglodytidae*)

Carolina Wren

Thryothorus ludovicianus ludovicianus [718]

ADULT MALE AND FEMALE—Upper parts, rich brown, with a prominent broad white line over the eye. Throat, white; rest of under parts, white tinged with buffy.

LENGTH—5.50 inches.

DISTRIBUTION—From Massachusetts (though uncommonly), and the lower part of the Hudson Valley, across to southern Iowa and northern Illinois, and south to the Gulf States.

The Carolina Wren is one of our finest singers. From the top of some vine tangle or bush—sometimes from the recesses—he pours out his loud, vigorous, cheerful, markedly accented strain, which Hoffman has put into syllables that cannot be improved: *twip pity, twip pity; whiddy yóu, whiddy yóu, whiddy yóu; thrï' ou, thrï' ou, thrï' ou.* To some ears the bird says

tea kettle, tea kettle, tea kettle; boil it, boil it, boil it; tip it, tip it, tip it, and

so on, often with many variations. Its common alarm note is a velvety *meeuuw,* somewhat like the note of the Catbird, though less nasal. (Family *Troglodytidae*)

Catalina Wren

Thryomanes bewicki catalinae [719i]

Similar to the Sooty Wren, but with the upper parts a still darker and slightly duller brown, and with a heavier bill and larger feet.

DISTRIBUTION — Restricted to the Santa Catalina Island, California. (Family *Troglodytidae*)

Cedros Island Wren

Thryomanes bewicki cerroensis [719j]

Similar to the San Clemente Wren, but with the upper parts darker, the flanks lighter, and the bill much shorter.

DISTRIBUTION—On Cedros Island, and in the central part of the peninsula of Lower California. (Family *Troglodytidae*)

Common Rock Wren

Salpinctes obsoletus obsoletus [715]

ADULT MALE AND FEMALE—Upper parts, grayish-brown, with fine fleckings of black and white, paling to a light brown on the rump. Tail, tipped with buffy-brown, and with an inner band of black. Middle tail feathers,

brown barred with blackish. Under parts, whitish; chest, marked with rows of fine blackish dots and streaks. Flanks, brownish.

LENGTH—5.75 inches.

DISTRIBUTION — From British Columbia southward into Lower California, and across into northern Mexico; and from the western portion of Nebraska westward to the Pacific Coast.

The Rock Wren is an inhabitant of rocky, sterile hill and mountain sides, where cliffs, and long talus slopes abound. Unlike its relative, the Canyon Wren, it is found in the driest of rocky country, often far from streams. Its obliterative colors fit it perfectly for its life among granites and lichens. Its song, somewhat wrenlike, is of a tinkling, bubbling, varied quality; but harsh, metallic, and hard, as though the sharp rocks and flinty boulders among which the bird sings, were themselves trying to break into song. (Family *Troglodytidae*)

Dotted Wren

Catherpes mexicanus punctulatus [717b]

Similar to the Canyon Wren but smaller, and more thickly spotted. (Family *Troglodytidae*)

Eastern House Wren

Troglodytes aëdon aëdon [721]

ADULT MALE AND FEMALE—Upper parts, brown; the wings and tail, finely and faintly barred with black. Under parts, whitish-gray; the flanks faintly barred with black. Bill, relatively long and slender.

LENGTH—5.0c inches.

DISTRIBUTION—Over the whole of eastern North America as far north as southern Maine, Montreal, and Manitoba. In winter it is found from about the latitude of South Carolina westward into the Mississippi Valley, and southward into Mexico.

The House Wren, or Jenny Wren, is a familiar little sprite of our open woodlands, orchards, gardens, and close home grounds. It takes most kindly to the bird boxes erected for it—too kindly, perhaps, for if in one box it elects to make its breeding nest, it often fills up other boxes with small sticks to keep out what might be too-near neighbors! Everyone loves the

Wren. Its active, almost agitated ways, its funny perky little body, its loud optimistic song—often sung throughout the day—keep a pleasing stir of cheerful life about any garden or farm. Wrens are seen continually in gardens, searching about on the ground among the plants for whatever insects they

may find. The birds in this way perform a very valuable service. A pair of Wrens in a small garden render insecticides entirely unnecessary. The song of the Wren is a rather short, rolling, bubbling, cheerful, vigorous effusion of *ter, weedle-weedle-weedle; raddle raddle raddle,* sometimes prolonged. The *bubbling* character of the song is its most prominent feature. (Family *Troglodytidae*)

Eastern Winter Wren
Nannus hiemalis hiemalis [722]

ADULT MALE AND FEMALE—Upper parts, dark brown; the wings and tail, finely and narrowly barred with blackish. Line over the eye, buffy. Under parts, light brownish, barred finely and narrowly with blackish and whitish. Tail, very short.

LENGTH—4.06 inches.

DISTRIBUTION—From Newfoundland, Quebec, and southern Manitoba, southward to northern New England, New York, central Michigan, and Wisconsin, and south along the higher Allegheny Mountains to North Carolina. In winter it is found from Massachusetts westward to Illinois, and thence south into Florida.

A comical, brown, jumpy, perky, agitated, buzzing, tail-over-back midget is the Winter Wren, found in winter haunting old brush piles and tangles, and in summer inhabiting cool dank evergreen woods, rocky ravines among the mountains, or high up on mountain sides where spruces abound. Here it pours forth a song which is one of the wonders of the bird world—a protracted, silvery, broken, bubbling tinkle; thin, fine, and high, and often repeated. It is unlike the music of any other bird, and once heard never can be forgotten. It is a long song, and Thoreau remarked of it ". . . . the note was so incessant that at length you only noticed it when it ceased."

The Winter Wren is a true sprite of the mountains in the northern parts of its range, especially in the mountains of New England, where it is a denizen of the wilds, retreating silently before man's encroachment upon its airy solitudes. It is one of our smallest birds; only about four inches long, and its

habit of cocking its ridiculous little tail up over its back makes it appear even smaller. "The Winter Wren has no tail to speak of," said the teacher. In reporting this afterwards, a little child said, "Teacher said the Wren had a tail, but *you mustn't talk about it.*" (Family *Troglodytidae*)

Florida Wren
Thryothorus ludovincianus miamensis [718a]

Similar to the Carolina Wren, but larger and darker.

DISTRIBUTION—The southern half of the Florida peninsula. (Family *Troglodytidae*)

Guadalupe Wren
Thryomanes brevicauda [720]

Similar to the Bewick's Wren, but smaller. Tail, dull grayish-brown, finely and faintly barred with dark gray; the outer feathers, tipped with brownish-gray.

DISTRIBUTION — Restricted to Guadalupe Island, off the coast of

Lower California. (Family *Troglodytidae*)

Guadalupe Rock Wren

Salpinctes obsoletus guadeloupensis [716]

Similar to the Common Rock Wren, but with shorter wings and tail, and slightly longer bill and legs. It is darker; with a more brownish tinge than its congener; and the breast, more heavily speckled.

DISTRIBUTION — Restricted to Guadalupe Island, off the coast of Lower California. (Family *Troglodytidae*)

Kiska Wren

Nannus hiemalis kiskensis [722c]

Similar to the Aleutian Wren, but the wings, tail, and tarsus, shorter; the upper parts, lighter and more grayish-brown; the posterior part of the body, less decidedly barred. Under parts, darker.

DISTRIBUTION — Found on Kiska and Little Kiska islands, in the Aleutian archipelago. (Family *Troglodytidae*)

Kodiak Wren

Nannus hiemalis helleri [722b]

Similar to the Western Winter Wren, but slightly larger and paler.

DISTRIBUTION—Found on Kodiak Island, Alaska. (Family *Troglodytidae*)

Lomita Wren

Thryothorus ludovicianus lomitensis [718b]

Similar to the Carolina Wren, but with the upper parts, browner; rump with whitish flecks. Under parts, whitish, faintly washed with buff. Flanks, usually finely barred with darker.

DISTRIBUTION — Restricted to the southeastern part of Texas. (Family *Troglodytidae*)

Long-billed Marsh Wren

Telmatodytes palustris palustris [725]

ADULT MALE AND FEMALE—Back, wings, and tail, brown; middle of back, blackish-brown streaked with white; tail, barred with black. Top of head, blackish-brown, with a prominent white line over the eye. Sides of head, buffy. Under parts, white; sides washed with light buff.

LENGTH—5.20 inches.

DISTRIBUTION—From Massachusetts and Manitoba west to the Rocky Mountains, and south to the Gulf States. In winter it is found from southern New England southward into Mexico.

The Long-billed Marsh Wren is a fairly common inhabitant of tidal marshes, and of cattail marshes along the valleys of rivers, nesting in the

bushes that border such areas. They are amusing little birds, as they slip in and out of the sedges, clinging to the upright stalks, with tails cocked over their backs, and scolding in a harsh, buzzy, typical wren-like manner, or pouring out their bubbling, wren-like song. The nest is globular, with a side opening. Many nests are made by the male in the vicinity of the *one* nest that contains the eggs. (Family *Troglodytidae*)

Louisiana Marsh Wren

Telmatodytes palustris thryophilus [725h]

Similar to the Marian's Marsh Wren but with the upper parts a paler, grayer brown, and the whole top of the head lighter. The upper tail coverts are either plain or barred, and the upper breast is unmarked.

DISTRIBUTION—Louisiana and Texas, along the coastal zone. (Family *Troglodytidae*)

Marian's Marsh Wren

Telmatodytes palustris marianae [725e]

Similar to the Long-billed Marsh Wren, but with the upper parts darker, the sides of the body brownish, and

the under tail coverts (and sometimes the breast) barred or spotted with blackish.

DISTRIBUTION — Restricted to the Gulf of Mexico coast of Florida. (Family *Troglodytidae*)

Nicasio Wren

Thryomanes bewicki marinensis [719f]

Similar to the Vigor's Wren, but with its upper parts a brighter brown, and the flanks and under tail coverts washed with a deeper brown.

DISTRIBUTION—From southwestern Oregon into northwestern California south to San Francisco. (Family *Troglodytidae*)

Northern Cactus Wren

Heleodytes brunneicapillus couesi [713]

ADULT MALE AND FEMALE—Upper parts, brown; the feathers of the back with white streaks. Prominent white line over the eye. Middle tail feathers, brownish barred with black; the remainder, black, with white band near their tips. Throat and breast, white, heavily blotched and spotted with black and blackish; rest of under parts, buffy, sparsely streaked with blackish. LENGTH—7.50 inches.

DISTRIBUTION — From southern Texas to southern California, and from southwestern Utah south into central Mexico.

The Cactus Wren is the largest of our Wrens, sometimes measuring eight inches in length. It is a resident of the arid cactus, mesquite, and yucca deserts, where its large size, as it sits atop some prickly perch, renders it very conspicuous. Its voice is harsh, "prickly," and arid, perfectly congruous with its surroundings. It gives utterance to no such sweet, bubbling songs as do many of its relatives; but calls, in a monotonous, harsh tone, *choot-choot-choot-choot* or *chut-chut-*

chut-chut. When alarmed its notes are a harsher and more nasal *chaaa, chaaa, chaaa*. The nest of this strange bird is packed in among the most formidable thorns of the cholla cactus. It is a long purse-like mass of grass stalks, softly lined with feathers—a perfect protection for the nestlings. (Family *Troglodytidae*)

Prairie Marsh Wren

Telmatodytes palustris dissaëptus [725d]

Similar to the Long-billed Marsh Wren, but somewhat longer; with the upper parts, more russet-brown; and the flanks, rich cinnamon-brown.

DISTRIBUTION—From the Canadian Border southward to Indiana and the central portion of the Mississippi Valley. In winter it is found along the Gulf Coast of the United States, extending down into southern Florida, and southward into central Mexico, and across to Vera Cruz. (Family *Troglodytidae*)

San Clemente Wren

Thryomanes bewicki leucophrys [719.1]

Similar to the Bewick's Wren, but with the upper parts grayer and paler, and the bill longer.

DISTRIBUTION—Restricted to the San Clemente Island off the coast of southern California. (Family *Troglodytidae*)

San Diego Wren

Thryomanes bewicki correctus [719k]

Similar to the San Joaquin Wren, but with the upper parts a lighter and browner tone; the tail, longer, bearing paler light colored bars.

DISTRIBUTION—Along the coastal zone in California, from the western side of the San Joaquin Valley (San Benito and Monterey counties), southward through the region about San Diego, and on nearly to the Mexican border. (Family *Troglodytidae*)

San Joaquin Wren

Thryomanes bewicki drymoecus [719g]

Similar to the Sooty Wren, but with the upper parts much more rufous-brown.

DISTRIBUTION — On the western slopes of the Sierra Nevada, and in the Sacramento and lower half of the San Joaquin river valleys of California; extending north to south central Oregon and east to the Warner Mountains. (Family *Troglodytidae*)

San Lucas Cactus Wren

Heleodytes brunneicapillus affinis [713b]

Similar to the Northern Cactus Wren, but with the white flanks bearing large, rounded, or tear-shaped spots; the tail feathers (except the middle pair), barred with white. The upper parts are paler than in the northern species, and the chin is pure unmarked white.

DISTRIBUTION — Restricted to the southern portion of Lower California. (Family *Troglodytidae*)

Santa Cruz Wren

Thryomanes bewicki nesophilus [719h]

Similar to the Sooty Wren, but with the sides of the body a darker and more rufous-brown.

DISTRIBUTION — Restricted to the Santa Cruz and Santa Rosa islands, off the coast of California. (Family *Troglodytidae*)

Seattle Wren

Thryomanes bewicki calophonus [719e]

Similar to the Bewick's Wren, but with a slightly larger bill, and the flanks browner.

DISTRIBUTION—From southern Vancouver Island and the valley of the Fraser River, into northern Washington, on the Pacific slope. Often called the Northwest Bewick's Wren. (Family *Troglodytidae*)

Semidi Wren

Nannus hiemalis semidiensis [722f]

Similar to the Alaska Wren, but less brown and more gray, especially on the upper parts; and with a longer bill.

DISTRIBUTION—On the Semidi Islands, off the southern coast of the Alaskan Peninsula. (Family *Troglodytidae*)

Short-billed Marsh Wren

Cistothorus stellaris [724]

ADULT MALE AND FEMALE—Upper parts, brown streaked with black and white; no distinct line over the eye (as there is in the Long-billed species). Under parts, buffy; sides washed with a darker shade. Bill, short.

LENGTH—4.00 inches.

DISTRIBUTION—From Massachusetts (occasionally New Hampshire), and Manitoba, westward to Utah, and southward to the Gulf States. In winter it is found from the Gulf States southward.

The Short-billed Marsh Wren is found in sedgy meadows, along stream courses, or in the borders of marshy ponds. Sometimes there are hundreds of pairs of birds nesting in a sort of colony in one area. It is thoroughly wren-like in its actions, clinging to the upright weed and sedge-stalks, with its tail often cocked over its back, bobbing up and down and scolding in a buzzy harsh voice, or energetically giving forth its simple song. This lacks the bubbling, rolling quality of the House Wren's performance, but instead sounds like the song of one of the Sparrows, or better, like the noise made by a small sewing machine, running more and more rapidly,

thus: *tsip, tsip, tsip, sip-sip-sipper sipper sipper*. The nest is globular, with

a side opening, and is attached to the upright stalks of large grasses. (Family *Troglodytidae*)

Sooty Wren

Thryomanes bewicki charienturus [719d]

ADULT MALE AND FEMALE—Upper parts, grayish-brown, brightening to a slightly reddish-brown on the rump. Middle tail feathers, dull brown barred with black; outermost feathers, black tipped with grayish-white; their outer webs, barred with whitish; remainder of tail feathers, tipped with light brown. Under parts, white or whitish; the under tail coverts, heavily barred with black.

LENGTH—5.50 inches.

DISTRIBUTION—From about the latitude of Pasadena, California, south along the coast to the region of Vizcaino Bay, Lower California, and Santa Catalina Island. Often called the Southwest Bewick's Wren. (Family *Troglodytidae*)

Suisun Marsh Wren

Telmatodytes palustris aestuarinus [725g]

Similar to the Tule Wren, but darker and larger.

DISTRIBUTION—West central California, in the region of the confluence of the San Joaquin and Sacramento rivers, and southward to the region of Tulare County. In winter it spreads into Oregon, and into southern California. (Family *Troglodytidae*)

Tanaga Wren
Nannus hiemalis tanagensis [722d]

Similar to its neighbor, the Kiska Wren, but with the upper parts browner, and somewhat lighter; especially on the lower back, rump, and upper tail coverts. Under parts, lighter; and wings, somewhat longer.

DISTRIBUTION—On Tanaga, Adak, and Atka islands, and probably on other neighboring islands in the Aleutian Archipelago. (Family *Troglodytidae*)

Texas Wren
Thryomanes bewicki cryptus [719c]

Similar to the Bewick's Wren, but a trifle larger and with grayer upper parts.

DISTRIBUTION — Texas (except in the extreme western corner), and northeastern Mexico. Probably also occurs in Kansas and Oklahoma. (Family *Troglodytidae*)

Tule Wren
Telmatodytes palustris paludicola [725a]

Similar to the Long-billed Marsh Wren, but with browner under parts, and the upper tail coverts barred with black, and the middle tail feathers more heavily barred with black.

DISTRIBUTION—British Columbia to southern California, along the coastal zone. It spends its winters from Washington to Guatemala. (Family *Troglodytidae*)

Unalaska Wren
Nannus hiemalis petrophilus [722e]

Similar to the Alaska Wren, but with lighter, browner upper parts, and

much paler under parts, a shorter wing, and a longer bill.

DISTRIBUTION — On Unalaska, Amaknak, and Akutan islands of the Aleutian Archipelago. (Family *Troglodytidae*)

Vigor's Wren
Thryomanes bewicki spilurus [719a]

Similar to the Bewick's Wren, but smaller, and with the upper parts of a grayer cast.

DISTRIBUTION—Restricted to California, between the Sierra Nevada Mountains and the latitude of Santa Cruz Island. (Family *Troglodytidae*)

Western House Wren
Troglodytes aëdon parkmani [721a]

Similar to the Eastern House Wren, but with grayer upper parts.

DISTRIBUTION — From British Columbia southward along the Pacific Coast to southern California. In winter it is found from southern California southward. (Family *Troglodytidae*)

Western Marsh Wren
Telmatodytes palustris plesius [725c]

Similar to the Long-billed Marsh Wren, but with upper tail coverts faintly barred with gray, middle tail feathers similarly barred, and under parts faint buffy.

DISTRIBUTION — From British Columbia and Alberta eastward to the Rocky Mountains, and southward into Texas and Mexico; absent on the Pacific Coast. (Family *Troglodytidae*)

Western Winter Wren
Nannus hiemalis pacificus [722a]

Similar to the Eastern Winter Wren, but darker throughout, with darker barrings.

DISTRIBUTION—From Alaska southward along the Pacific Coast to southern California, as far east as Idaho. In winter it spreads southward into Mexico. (Family *Troglodytidae*)

White-throated Wren
Catherpes mexicanus albifrons [717]

Similar to the Canyon Wren, but larger and darker throughout; the wings showing rusty bars.
LENGTH—6.25 inches.
DISTRIBUTION—From the extreme southeastern portion of Texas, along the lower Rio Grande Valley, and into northeastern Mexico. (Family *Troglodytidae*)

Worthington's Marsh Wren
Telmatodytes palustris griseus [725b]

Similar to the Long-billed Marsh Wren, but lighter throughout.
DISTRIBUTION — Restricted to the coast of South Carolina and Georgia. (Family *Troglodytidae*)

WREN-TIT FAMILY
Chamaeidae

The Wren-tits are a kind of intermediate race between the Wrens (Family *Troglodytidae*), and the Titmice (Family *Paridae*), yet possessing

characteristics that place them in a separate family. They are small birds, about six and a half inches long, with grayish-brown plumage and long tails. The bill is relatively short, with the upper mandible curved downward. The feathers of the neck and chin are terminated by fine bristles; the wings are short and rounded; the tail is long and rounded. The family is

composed of only one genus (*Chamaea*), and one species represented by five subspecies, all occurring in California. This is the only family of perching birds whose members are restricted to the continent of North America.

NESTING. Wren-tits make a thick-walled, compact, cup-like nest of grasses, rootlets, fine weed stems, and narrow strips of bark; lined with cattle- or horse-hair. It is placed in low bushes about three or four feet from the ground, rarely higher. The eggs, from three to five, are a pale bluish-green.

WREN-TIT
Coast Wren-tit
Chamaea fasciata phaea [742b]

Similar to the Pallid Wren-tit, but with much browner upper parts, shading to a sooty color on the head. Under parts, dark ruddy-brown faintly streaked with dark gray.
DISTRIBUTION — Southern Oregon, south along the coast to Monterey County, California. (Family *Chamaeidae*)

Gambel's Wren-tit
Chamaea fasciata fasciata [742]

ADULT MALE AND FEMALE—Upper parts, grayish or olive-brown; the head, somewhat darker. Under parts, cinnamon-brown; throat and breast, streaked. Tail, long; the central feathers longer than the outer ones.
LENGTH—6.50 inches.
DISTRIBUTION—From San Francisco Bay southward into the northern portion of Lower California.

On the chaparral covered slopes of the hillsides of California, the loud, penetrating, rolling song of the Wren-tit is one of the characteristic songs of spring. *Heep, heep, heep, heep— heepit, heepit, heepit* is the common form of the strain, which, however, has many variations. To some ears, it is reminiscent of the song of the Eastern Field Sparrow, but louder, more staccato, more ringing, and given with more vigor than the demure little lay of the eastern bird. Wren-tits keep themselves well concealed among the bushes close to the ground. In flight, the long flexible tail (more than half the length of the bird's body) is flipped up and down in a nervous fashion. (Family *Chamaeidae*)

Pallid Wren-tit
Chamaea fasciata henshawi [742a]

Similar to the Gambel's Wren-tit, but with the colors of the plumage very much paler, and with a much grayer, more ashy cast.

DISTRIBUTION—In southern California, from Shasta County in the

foothills and valleys of the interior, and along the coastal region from Santa Barbara County to the Mexican border. (Family *Chamaeidae*)

Ruddy Wren-tit
Chamaea fasciata rufula [742c]

Similar to the Coast Wren-tit, but paler, and with the upper parts a clearer, sepia brown. The under parts are a lighter, vinaceous brown.

DISTRIBUTION—The "humid transitional coastal strip of California from

Del Norte County south to Santa Cruz County." (A.O.U. Check List.) (Family *Chamaeidae*)

San Pedro Wren-tit
Chamaea fasciata canicauda [742d]

Similar to the Gambel's Wren-tit, but paler; in fact, the palest of all the *fasciata* group.

DISTRIBUTION—In the northwestern third of Lower California. (Family *Chamaeidae*)

YELLOW-LEGS
Greater Yellow-legs
Totanus melanoleucus [254]

ADULT MALE AND FEMALE—Upper parts, pale gray and blackish, speckled with white. Basal half of the tail, pure white. Under parts, white; the throat streaked with dark gray; and the breast and sides spotted and barred with gray. Legs, yellow.

LENGTH—14.00 inches.

DISTRIBUTION—In North America the bird breeds from the latitude of Minnesota and northern Illinois northward. In winter it is found from California and the Gulf States southward as far as southern South America.

The loud, cheerful whistled *kew kew kew kew kew* announces the presence of this striking bird of the shores and marshes. In New England and adjacent regions it makes the longest stay of any of our transient birds, being found from the middle of April through the month of May, and again, on its northward trek, from about the middle of July through October. Its long legs, yellow in the fall, are conspicuous, and when it rises in flight it displays a prominent white area at the base of the tail. In flight the bird is slender and graceful, and flies high overhead. The Greater Yellowlegs is a denizen of grassy marshes, shores, and sometimes mud flats. They are rather wary birds, and at the first alarm, rise and make off, with shrill cries. The flesh of these unfortunate birds is not especially fine, nor is there a great deal of it. As a game bird it is

much inferior to other members of its family, such as the Woodcock and the Upland Plover. From the Lesser Yellow-legs, this species may be distinguished by its greater size, and from the way in which its bill is slightly upturned; the bill of the Lesser being perfectly straight. (Family *Scolopacidae*)

Lesser Yellow-legs
Totanus flavipes [255]

Similar to the Greater Yellow-legs, but nearly four inches shorter.

DISTRIBUTION—From northern Canada and Alaska to British Columbia and Manitoba, migrating chiefly east of the Rocky Mountains, and wintering sparingly in Florida, Louisiana, and Mexico, but chiefly in Argentina, Chile, and Patagonia. It is also found in Bermuda, Greenland, Lower California, California, and the Pribilof Islands. (Family *Scolopacidae*)

YELLOW-THROAT
The Yellow-throats
Geothlypis and *Chamaethlypis*

Nine Yellow-throats are found in North America, all very similar to the Northern Yellow-throat (*Geothlypis trichas brachidactyla*), which see. The other Yellow-throats are:

BELDING'S YELLOW-THROAT (*Geothlypis beldingi beldingi*), 682, found in the southern section of California.

FLORIDA YELLOW-THROAT (*Geothlypis trichas ignota*), 681b.

GOLDMAN'S YELLOW-THROAT (*Geothlypis beldingi goldmani*), 682a, similar to the Belding's Yellow-throat.

MARYLAND YELLOW-THROAT (*Geothlypis trichas trichas*), 681, slightly larger and slightly less yellow; and with a more southerly range than its northern relative.

RIO GRANDE YELLOW-THROAT (*Chamaethlypis poliocephala poliocephala*), 682.1, occurring in the lower Rio Grande River Valley, and extending southward into Mexico.

SALT MARSH YELLOW-THROAT (*Geothlypis trichas sinuosa*), 681e, inhabiting the salt marshes of San Francisco Bay.

TULE YELLOW-THROAT (*Geothlypis trichas scirpicola*), 681f, so-called from the tules among which it lives.

WESTERN YELLOW-THROAT (*Geothlypis trichas occidentalis*), 681a, confined to the Rocky Mountains.

Yellow-throats are birds of bushes, vine tangles, marshes, and, in general, thick, inaccessible places, where they slip mouse-like through the dark aisles of such impenetrable situations. Their notes are characteristic; the songs being rather short, vigorously-jerked-out phrases, strongly accented, and recognizable by those who know the song of any one species well. The call notes are heavy *tchucks* or *tchits,* and the scolding notes are harsh, buzzy, and reminiscent of the scolding notes of the Wrens. Like most other members of the Warbler family (*Compsothlypidae*), the motions of Yellow-throats are rapid and more rapid than many, for the birds are continually slipping and sliding through their tangled coverts, peering here and there under leaves and scrutinizing first the twigs, grasses, and sedges above, and then the ground beneath, or agitatedly flitting from one spot to another. (Family *Compsothlypidae*)

Northern Yellow-throat

Geothlypis trichas brachidactyla [681d]

ADULT MALE—Upper parts, dark olive-green; entire forehead and broad domino mask, with a point extending downward toward the side of the throat, jet black. Throat and breast, rich lemon-yellow; abdomen, dull yellow, graying on the sides.

ADULT FEMALE—Paler than the male throughout, and lacking the black domino mask; abdomen, white or whitish.

LENGTH—5.33 inches.

DISTRIBUTION—Northeastern North America from Newfoundland to New Jersey; westward to northern Ontario and the eastern part of the Dakotas, southward through the Mississippi Valley to the northern portions of the Gulf States, and westward to eastern Texas. Winters in Mexico, Central America, and the Bahamas.

Bushes and tangles in damp situations are the haunts of this comical little Warbler, which, crawling and slipping among masses of interlaced twigs and vines, seems to be playing hide-and-seek with the anxious and eager observer, who may circle the spot several times without catching more than a

glimpse of the little yellow tormentor. Left undisturbed, the bird mounts into the top of its leafy bailiwick, or peers out from one side, and there jerks out its loud, clear, defiant song, *chee wi'tchity, wi'tchity, wi'tchity;* a strongly accented phrase, and one perfectly familiar to all country dwellers. Another very common version of the song sounds like the syllables *ch'ew it, you witches; ch'ew it, you witches; ch'ew it, you witches,* with the strong beat on the *chew* syllable. There are several other, not so common variations of the song, differing with the locality, but all songs are very strongly and characteristically accented. The Yellow-throat is one of the most strikingly colored and attractive of our Warblers. (Family *Compsothlypidae*)

Systematic or Classified List of North American Birds

THE FOLLOWING SYSTEMATIC OR CLASSIFIED LIST, giving the names of all birds ever reported for North America, is reproduced from the American Ornithologists' Union "Check List of North American Birds." Each species and subspecies of bird has been assigned by the A.O.U. a distinguishing number which is not changed. As new species and subspecies have been described since this list was begun, their numbers do not follow in sequence; however, the families' numbers do.

The *scientific* names consist of two (sometimes three) parts. The first name is the name of the genus, or the generic name; the second name is the name of the species, or the specific name; the third name (not always present) is the name of the subspecies, or the subspecific name.

After the scientific name of a bird there follows (without separation by punctuation) the name of the person who first put the species or subspecies on record. This person is known as the describer. If the name of the describer is enclosed in parentheses, it indicates that the bird has been taken out of the genus where he originally placed it, and located in its present genus. This is often made necessary by the results of the subsequent study of the specimens.

To find the account of any of the birds in the following list, consult the body of the book, under the proper alphabetical order for the desired bird, e.g. for the Black-tailed Shearwater, see under Shearwater, Black-tailed. Families will be found under their *common* names, e.g. Loons.

SYSTEMATIC OR CLASSIFIED LIST OF NORTH AMERICAN BIRDS

ORDER GAVIIFORMES—Loons

1. Family Gaviidae—Loons

7 Common Loon, *Gavia immer immer* (Brünnich)
7a Lesser Loon, *Gavia immer elasson* Bishop
8 Yellow-billed Loon, *Gavia adamsi* (Gray)
10 Pacific Loon, *Gavia arctica pacifica* (Lawrence)

10a Green-throated Loon, *Gavia arctica viridigularis* Dwight
11 Red-throated Loon, *Gavia stellata* (Pontoppidan)

ORDER COLYMBIFORMES—Grebes

2. *Family Colymbidae*—Grebes
   2 Holboell's Grebe, *Colymbus grisegena holboelli* (Reinhardt)
   3 Horned Grebe, *Colymbus auritus* Linnaeus
   4 Eared Grebe, *Colymbus nigricollis californicus* (Heermann)
   5 Mexican Grebe, *Colymbus dominicus brachypterus* Chapman
   1 Western Grebe, *Aechmophorus occidentalis* (Lawrence)
   6 Pied-billed Grebe, *Podilymbus podiceps podiceps* (Linnaeus)

ORDER PROCELLARIIFORMES—Tube-nosed Swimmers

3. *Family Diomedeidae*—Albatrosses
   81 Black-footed Albatross, *Diomedea nigripes* Audubon
   82 Short-tailed Albatross, *Diomedea albatrus* Pallas
   82.1 Laysan Albatross, *Diomedea immutabilis* Rothschild
   83 Yellow-nosed Albatross, *Thalassogeron chlororhynchos* (Gmelin)

4. *Family Procellariidae*—Shearwaters, Fulmars, and Petrels
   96 Slender-billed Shearwater, *Puffinus tenuirostris* (Temminck)
   95 Sooty Shearwater, *Puffinus griseus* (Gmelin)
   90 Manx Shearwater, *Puffinus puffinus puffinus* (Brünnich)
   93 Black-vented Shearwater, *Puffinus opisthomelas* Coues
   93.1 Townsend's Shearwater, *Puffinus auricularis* Townsend
   92 Audubon's Shearwater, *Puffinus lherminieri lherminieri* Lesson
   92.1 Allied Shearwater, *Puffinus assimilis baroli* Bonaparte
   95.1 Pale-footed Shearwater, *Puffinus carneipes* Gould
   91 Pink-footed Shearwater, *Puffinus creatopus* Coues
   89 Greater Shearwater, *Puffinus gravis* (O'Reilly)
   88a Mediterranean Shearwater, *Puffinus diomedea diomedea* (Scopoli)
   88 Cory's Shearwater, *Puffinus diomedea borealis* Cory
   96.1 Wedge-tailed Shearwater, *Thyellodroma cuneata* (Salvin)
   96.2 New Zealand Shearwater, *Thyellodroma bulleri* (Salvin)
   97 Black-tailed Shearwater, *Adamastor cinereus* (Gmelin)
   98 Black-capped Petrel, *Pterodromo hasitata* (Kuhl)
   98.1 Bermuda Petrel, *Pterodroma cahow* (Nichols and Mowbray)
   99 Scaled Petrel, *Pterodroma inexpectata* (Forster)
   101 Bulwer's Petrel, *Bulweria bulweri* (Jardine and Selby)
   86 Atlantic Fulmar, *Fulmarus glacialis glacialis* (Linnaeus)
   86.1 Pacific Fulmar, *Fulmarus glacialis rodgersi* Cassin
   102 Pintado Petrel, *Daption capense* (Linnaeus)

5. *Family Hydrobatidae*—Storm Petrels
   105 Forked-tailed Petrel, *Oceanodroma furcata* (Gmelin)
   106 Leach's Petrel, *Oceanodroma leucorhoa leucorhoa* (Vieillot)
   105.2 Kaeding's Petrel, *Oceanodroma leucorhoa kaedingi* Anthony
   106a Beal's Petrel, *Oceanodroma leucorhoa beali* Emerson

106.1 Guadalupe Petrel, *Oceanodroma macrodactyla* Bryant
106.2 Madeira Petrel, *Oceanodroma castro castro* (Harcourt)
107 Black Petrel, *Oceanodroma melania* (Bonaparte)
108 Ashy Petrel, *Oceanodroma homochroa* (Coues)
108.1 Socorro Petrel, *Oceanodroma socorroensis* Townsend
104 Storm Petrel, *Hydrobates pelagicus* (Linnaeus)
103 Least Petrel, *Halocyptena microsoma* Coues
109 Wilson's Petrel, *Oceanites oceanicus* (Kuhl)
110 White-bellied Petrel, *Fregetta tropica tropica* (Gould)
111 White-faced Petrel, *Pelagodroma marina hypoleuca* (Webb, Berthelot, and Moquin-Tandon)

ORDER PELECANIFORMES—Totipalmate Swimmers

6. *Family Phaëthontidae*—Tropic-birds
 113 Red-billed Tropic-bird, *Phaëthon aethereus* Linnaeus
 112 Yellow-billed Tropic-bird, *Phaëthon lepturus catesbyi* Brandt
 113.1 Red-tailed Tropic-bird, *Phaëthon rubricaudus rothschildi* (Mathews)

7. *Family Pelecanidae*—Pelicans
 125 White Pelican, *Pelecanus erythrorhynchos* Gmelin
 126 Eastern Brown Pelican, *Pelecanus occidentalis occidentalis* Linnaeus
 127 California Brown Pelican, *Pelecanus occidentalis californicus* Ridgway

8. *Family Sulidae*—Boobies and Gannets
 114 Atlantic Blue-faced Booby, *Sula dactylatra dactylatra* Lesson
 114a Pacific Blue-faced Booby, *Sula dactylatra californica* Rothschild
 114.1 Blue-footed Booby, *Sula nebouxi* Milne-Edwards
 115 White-bellied Booby, *Sula leucogaster leucogaster* (Boddaert)
 115.1 Brewster's Booby, *Sula brewsteri* Goss
 116 Red-footed Booby, *Sula piscator* (Linnaeus)
 117 Gannet, *Moris bassana* (Linnaeus)

9. *Family Phalacrocoracidae*—Cormorants
 119 European Cormorant, *Phalacrocorax carbo carbo* (Linnaeus)
 120 Double-crested Cormorant, *Phalacrocorax auritus auritus* (Lesson)
 120a Florida Cormorant, *Phalacrocorax auritus floridanus* (Audubon)
 120b White-crested Cormorant, *Phalacrocorax auritus cincinatus* (Brandt)
 120c Farallon Cormorant, *Phalacrocorax auritus albociliatus* Ridgway
 121 Mexican Cormorant, *Phalacrocorax olivaceus mexicanus* (Brandt)
 122 Brandt's Cormorant, *Phalacrocorax penicillatus* (Brandt)
 123 Pelagic Cormorant, *Phalacrocorax pelagicus pelagicus* Pallas
 123b Baird's Cormorant, *Phalacrocorax pelagicus resplendens* Audubon
 124 Red-faced Cormorant, *Phalacrocorax urile* (Gmelin)

10. *Family Anhingidae*—Darters
 118 Water-turkey, *Anhinga anhinga* (Linnaeus)

11. *Family Fregatidae*—Man-o'-war-birds
 128 Man-o'-war-bird, *Fregata magnificens* Mathews

ORDER CICONIIFORMES—Herons, Storks, Ibises, Flamingos, and allies

12. Family Ardeidae—Herons and Bitterns

192 Great White Heron, *Ardea occidentalis* Audubon
194 Great Blue Heron, *Ardea herodias herodias* Linnaeus
194b Ward's Heron, *Ardea herodias wardi* Ridgway
194c Treganza's Heron, *Ardea herodias treganzai* Court
194a Northwestern Coast Heron, *Ardea herodias fannini* Chapman
194d California Heron, *Ardea herodias hyperonca* Oberholser
194e Espíritu Santo Heron, *Ardea herodias sancti-lucae* Thayer and Bangs
195 European Heron, *Ardea cinerea cinerea* Linnaeus
196 American Egret, *Casmerodius albus egretta* (Gmelin)
197 Snowy Egret, *Egretta thula thula* (Molina)
197a Brewster's Egret, *Egretta thula brewsteri* Thayer and Bangs
198 Reddish Egret, *Dichromanassa rufescens rufescens* (Gmelin)
198a Dickey's Egret, *Dichromanassa rufescens dickeyi* van Rossem
199 Louisiana Heron, *Hydranassa tricolor ruficollis* (Gosse)
200 Little Blue Heron, *Florida caerulea caerulea* (Linnaeus)
201 Eastern Green Heron, *Butorides virescens virescens* (Linnaeus)
201a Frazar's Green Heron, *Butorides virescens frazari* (Brewster)
201c Anthony's Green Heron, *Butorides virescens anthonyi* (Mearns)
202 Black-crowned Night Heron, *Nycticorax nycticorax hoactli* (Gmelin)
203 Yellow-crowned Night Heron, *Nyctanassa violacea violacea* (Linnaeus)
203a Bancroft's Night Heron, *Nyctanassa violacea bancrofti* Huey
190 American Bittern, *Botaurus lentiginosus* (Montagu)
191 Eastern Least Bittern, *Ixobrychus exilis exilis* (Gmelin)
191a Western Least Bittern, *Ixobrychus exilis hesperis* Dickey and van Rossem

13. Family Ciconiidae—Storks and Wood Ibises

188 Wood Ibis, *Mycteria americana* Linnaeus

14. Family Threskiornithidae—Ibises and Spoonbills

186 Eastern Glossy Ibis, *Plegadis falcinellus falcinellus* (Linnaeus)
187 White-faced Glossy Ibis, *Plegadis guarauna* (Linnaeus)
184 White Ibis, *Guara alba* (Linnaeus)
185 Scarlet Ibis, *Guara rubra* (Linnaeus)
183 Roseate Spoonbill, *Ajaia ajaja* (Linnaeus)

15. Family Phoenicopteridae—Flamingos

182 Flamingo, *Phoenicopterus ruber* Linnaeus

ORDER ANSERIFORMES—Screamers, Swans, Geese, and Ducks

16. Family Anatidae—Swans, Geese, and Ducks

178.2 Mute Swan, *Sthenelides olor* (Gmelin)
179 Whooper Swan, *Cygnus cygnus* (Linnaeus)
180 Whistling Swan, *Cygnus columbianus* (Ord)
181 Trumpeter Swan, *Cygnus buccinator* Richardson

172 Common Canada Goose, *Branta canadensis canadensis* (Linnaeus)
172b White-cheeked Goose, *Branta canadensis occidentalis* (Baird)
172d Lesser Canada Goose, *Branta canadensis leucopareia* (Brandt)
172a Hutchins's Goose, *Branta canadensis hutchinsi* (Richardson)
172c Cackling Goose, *Branta canadensis minima* Ridgway
173a American Brant, *Branta bernicla hrota* (Müller)
174 Black Brant, *Branta nigricans* (Lawrence)
175 Barnacle Goose, *Branta leucopsis* (Bechstein)
176 Emperor Goose, *Philacte canagica* (Sevastianoff)
171 White-fronted Goose, *Anser albifrons albifrons* (Scopoli)
171a Tule Goose, *Anser albifrons gambelli* (Hartlaub)
171.1 Bean Goose, *Anser fabalis* (Latham)
171.2 Pink-footed Goose, *Anser brachyrhynchus* Baillon
169 Lesser Snow Goose, *Chen hyperborea hyperborea* (Pallas)
169a Greater Snow Goose, *Chen hyperborea atlantica* Kennard
169.1 Blue Goose, *Chen caerulescens* (Linnaeus)
170 Ross's Goose, *Chen rossi* (Cassin)
177 Black-bellied Tree-duck, *Dendrocygna autumnalis autumnalis* (Linnaeus)
178 Fulvous Tree-duck, *Dendrocygna bicolor helva* Wetmore and Peters
178.1 White-faced Tree-duck, *Dendrocygna viduata* (Linnaeus)
141.2 Sheld-duck, *Tadorna tadorna* (Linnaeus)
141.1 Ruddy Sheldrake, *Casarca ferruginea* (Pallas)
132 Common Mallard, *Anas platyrhynchos platyrhynchos* Linnaeus
132a Greenland Mallard, *Anas platyrhynchos conboschas* Brehm
133.1 New Mexican Duck, *Anas diazi novimexicana* Huber
133a Red-legged Black Duck, *Anas rubripes rubripes* Brewster
133 Common Black Duck, *Anas rubripes tristis* Brewster
134 Florida Duck, *Anas fulvigula fulvigula* Ridgway
134a Mottled Duck, *Anas fulvigula maculosa* Sennett
135 Gadwall, *Chaulelasmus streperus* (Linnaeus)
136 European Widgeon, *Mareca penelope* (Linnaeus)
137 Baldpate, *Mareca americana* (Gmelin)
143 American Pintail, *Dafila acuta tzitzihoa* (Vieillot)
143.1 Bahama Pintail, *Dafila bahamensis bahamensis* (Linnaeus)
137.1 Falcated Teal, *Eunetta falcata* (Georgi)
138 European Teal, *Nettion crecca* (Linnaeus)
139 Green-winged Teal, *Nettion carolinense* (Gmelin)
139.1 Baïkal Teal, *Nettion formosum* (Georgi)
140 Blue-winged Teal, *Querquedula discors* (Linnaeus)
141 Cinnamon Teal, *Querquedula cyanoptera* (Vieillot)
142 Shoveller, *Spatula clypeata* (Linnaeus)
144 Wood Duck, *Aix sponsa* (Linnaeus)
146 Redhead, *Nyroca americana* (Eyton)
146.1 Pochard, *Nyroca ferina* (Linnaeus)
150 Ring-necked Duck, *Nyroca collaris* (Donovan)
147 Canvas-back, *Nyroca valisineria* (Wilson)
148 Greater Scaup Duck, *Nyroca marila* (Linnaeus)
149 Lesser Scaup Duck, *Nyroca affinis* (Eyton)
149.1 Tufted Duck, *Nyroca fuligula* (Linnaeus)

145 Rufous-crested Duck, *Netta rufina* (Pallas)
151a European Golden-eye, *Glaucionetta clangula clangula* (Linnaeus)
151 American Golden-eye, *Glaucionetta clangula americana* (Bonaparte)
152 Barrow's Golden-eye, *Glaucionetta islandica* (Gmelin)
153 Buffle-head, *Charitonetta albeola* (Linnaeus)
154 Old-squaw, *Clangula hyemalis* (Linnaeus)
155 Eastern Harlequin Duck, *Histrionicus histrionicus histrionicus* (Linnaeus)
155a Western Harlequin Duck, *Histrionicus histrionicus pacificus* Brooks
156 Labrador Duck, *Camptorhynchus labradorius* (Gmelin)
157 Steller's Eider, *Polysticta stelleri* (Pallas)
159 Northern Eider, *Somateria mollissima borealis* (Brehm)
160 American Eider, *Somateria mollissima dresseri* Sharpe
161 Pacific Eider, *Somateria v-nigra* Gray
162 King Eider, *Somateria spectabilis* (Linnaeus)
158 Spectacled Eider, *Arctonetta fischeri* (Brandt)
164 Velvet Scoter, *Melanitta fusca* (Linnaeus)
165 White-winged Scoter, *Melanitta deglandi* (Bonaparte)
166 Surf Scoter, *Melanitta perspicillata* (Linnaeus)
163 American Scoter, *Oidemia americana* Swainson
167 Ruddy Duck, *Erismatura jamaicensis rubida* (Wilson)
168 Masked Duck, *Nomonyx dominicus* (Linnaeus)
131 Hooded Merganser, *Lophodytes cucullatus* (Linnaeus)
129 American Merganser, *Mergus merganser americanus* Cassin
130 Red-breasted Merganser, *Mergus serrator* Linnaeus

ORDER FALCONIFORMES—Birds of Prey

17. Family Cathartidae—American Vultures

325 Turkey Vulture, *Cathartes aura septentrionalis* Wied
326 Black Vulture, *Coragyps atratus atratus* (Meyer)
324 California Condor, *Gymnogyps californianus* (Shaw)

18. Family Accipitridae—Kites, Hawks, and allies

328 White-tailed Kite, *Elanus leucurus majusculus* Bangs and Penard
327 Swallow-tailed Kite, *Elanoïdes forficatus forficatus* (Linnaeus)
329 Mississippi Kite, *Ictinia misisippiensis* (Wilson)
330 Everglade Kite, *Rostrhamus sociabilis plumbeus* Ridgway
334 Eastern Goshawk, *Astur atricapillus atricapillus* (Wilson)
334a Western Goshawk, *Astur atricapillus striatulus* Ridgway
332 Sharp-shinned Hawk, *Accipiter velox velox* (Wilson)
333 Cooper's Hawk, *Accipiter cooperi* (Bonaparte)
337 Eastern Red-tailed Hawk, *Buteo borealis borealis* (Gmelin)
337f Florida Red-tailed Hawk, *Buteo borealis umbrinus* Bangs
337a Krider's Hawk, *Buteo borealis krideri* Hoopes
337b Western Red-tailed Hawk, *Buteo borealis calurus* Cassin
337d Harlan's Hawk, *Buteo borealis harlani* (Audubon)
339 Northern Red-shouldered Hawk, *Buteo lineatus lineatus* (Gmelin)
339a Florida Red-shouldered Hawk, *Buteo lineatus alleni* Ridgway
339c Insular Red-shouldered Hawk, *Buteo lineatus extimus* Bangs
339d Texas Red-shouldered Hawk, *Buteo lineatus texanus* Bishop

339b Red-bellied Hawk, *Buteo lineatus elegans* Cassin
343 Broad-winged Hawk, *Buteo platypterus platypterus* (Vieillot)
342 Swainson's Hawk, *Buteo swainsoni* Bonaparte
340 Zone-tailed Hawk, *Buteo albonotatus* Kaup
341 Sennett's White-tailed Hawk, *Buteo albicaudatus hypospodius* Gurney
344 Short-tailed Hawk, *Buteo brachyurus* Vieillot
347a American Rough-legged Hawk, *Buteo lagopus s. johannis* (Gmelin)
348 Ferruginous Rough-legged Hawk, *Buteo regalis* (Gray)
335 Harris's Hawk, *Parabuteo unicinctus harrisi* (Audubon)
346 Mexican Goshawk, *Asturina plagiata plagiata* Schlegel
345 Mexican Black Hawk, *Urubitinga anthracina anthracina* (Lichtenstein)
349 Golden Eagle, *Aquila chrysaëtos canadensis* (Linnaeus)
351 Gray Sea Eagle, *Haliaeetus albicilla* (Linnaeus)
352a Northern Bald Eagle, *Haliaeetus leucocephalus alascanus* Townsend
352 Southern Bald Eagle, *Haliaeetus leucocephalus leucocephalus* (Linnaeus)
352.1 Steller's Sea Eagle, *Thallasoaëtus pelagicus* (Pallas)
331 Marsh Hawk, *Circus hudsonius* (Linnaeus)
364 Osprey, *Pandion haliaëtus carolinensis* (Gmelin)

19. Family Falconidae—Caracaras and Falcons

362 Audubon's Caracara, *Polyborus cheriway auduboni* Cassin
363 Guadalupe Caracara, *Polyborus lutosus* Ridgway
353 White Gyrfalcon, *Falco rusticolus candicans* Gmelin
354c Asiatic Gyrfalcon, *Falco rusticolus uralensis* Sewertzov and Menzbier
354b Black Gyrfalcon, *Falco rusticolus obsoletus* Gmelin
355 Prairie Falcon, *Falco mexicanus* Schlegel
356 Peregrine Falcon, *Falco peregrinus peregrinus* Tunstall
356a Duck Hawk, *Falco peregrinus anatum* Bonaparte
356b Peale's Falcon, *Falco peregrinus pealei* Ridgway
359 Aplomado Falcon, *Falco fusco-coerulescens septentrionalis* Todd
357 Eastern Pigeon Hawk, *Falco columbarius columbarius* Linnaeus
357a Black Pigeon Hawk, *Falco columbarius suckleyi* Ridgway
357b Richardson's Pigeon Hawk, *Falco columbarius richardsoni* Ridgway
357c Western Pigeon Hawk, *Falco columbarius bendirei* Swann
358.1 Merlin, *Falco aesalon aesalon* Tunstall
359.1 Kestrel, *Falco tinnunculus tinnunculus* Linnaeus
360 Eastern Sparrow Hawk, *Falco sparverius sparverius* Linnaeus
360a Desert Sparrow Hawk, *Falco sparverius phalaena* (Lesson)
360b San Lucas Sparrow Hawk, *Falco sparverius peninsularis* Mearns
360c Little Sparrow Hawk, *Falco sparverius paulus* (Howe and King)

ORDER GALLIFORMES—Gallinaceous Birds and Hoatzins

20. Family Cracidae—Curassows and Guans
311 Chachalaca, *Ortalis vetula vetula* (Wagler)

21. Family Tetraonidae—Grouse and Ptarmigans
297 Dusky Grouse, *Dendragapus obscurus obscurus* (Say)
297b Richardson's Grouse, *Dendragapus obscurus richardsoni* (Douglas)

297d Fleming's Grouse, *Dendragapus obscurus flemingi* Taverner
297a Sooty Grouse, *Dendragapus fuliginosus fuliginosus* (Ridgway)
297e Sitka Grouse, *Dendragapus fuliginosus sitkensis* Swarth
297c Sierra Grouse, *Dendragapus fuliginosus sierrae* Chapman
297f Mount Pinos Grouse, *Dendragapus fuliginosus howardi* Dickey and van Rossem
298 Hudsonian Spruce Grouse, *Canachites canadensis canadensis* (Linnaeus)
298c Canada Spruce Grouse, *Canachites canadensis canace* (Linnaeus)
298b Alaska Spruce Grouse, *Canachites canadensis osgoodi* Bishop
298d Valdez Spruce Grouse, *Canachites canadensis atratus* Grinnell
299 Franklin's Grouse, *Canachites franklini* (Douglas)
300 Eastern Ruffed Grouse, *Bonasa umbellus umbellus* (Linnaeus)
300a Canada Ruffed Grouse, *Bonasa umbellus togata* (Linnaeus)
300d Nova Scotia Ruffed Grouse, *Bonasa umbellus thayeri* Bangs
300b Gray Ruffed Grouse, *Bonasa umbellus umbelloides* (Douglas)
300e Yukon Ruffed Grouse, *Bonasa umbellus yukonensis* Grinnell
300c Oregon Ruffed Grouse, *Bonasa umbellus sabini* (Douglas)
301 Willow Ptarmigan, *Lagopus lagopus albus* (Gmelin)
301c Ungava Ptarmigan, *Lagopus lagopus ungavus* Riley
301a Allen's Ptarmigan, *Lagopus lagopus alleni* Stejneger
301d Alaska Ptarmigan, *Lagopus lagopus alascensis* Swarth
301b Alexander's Ptarmigan, *Lagopus lagopus alexandrae* Grinnell
302 Rock Ptarmigan, *Lagopus rupestris rupestris* (Gmelin)
302a Reinhardt's Ptarmigan, *Lagopus rupestris reinhardi* (Brehm)
303 Welch's Ptarmigan, *Lagopus rupestris welchi* Brewster
302b Nelson's Ptarmigan, *Lagopus rupestris nelsoni* Stejneger
302c Turner's Ptarmigan, *Lagopus rupestris atkhensis* Turner
302e Chamberlain's Ptarmigan, *Lagopus rupestris chamberlaini* Clark
302g Sanford's Ptarmigan, *Lagopus rupestris sanfordi* Bent
302d Townsend's Ptarmigan, *Lagopus rupestris townsendi* Elliot
302.1 Evermann's Ptarmigan, *Lagopus rupestris evermanni* Elliot
302h Kellogg's Ptarmigan, *Lagopus rupestris kelloggae* Grinnell
302f Dixon's Ptarmigan, *Lagopus rupestris dixoni* Grinnell
304a Kenai White-tailed Ptarmigan, *Lagopus leucurus peninsularis* Chapman
304 Northern White-tailed Ptarmigan, *Lagopus leucurus leucurus* (Richardson)
304b Rainier White-tailed Ptarmigan, *Lagopus leucurus rainierensis* Taylor
304c Southern White-tailed Ptarmigan, *Lagopus leucurus altipetens* Osgood
306 Heath Hen, *Tympanuchus cupido cupido* (Linnaeus)
305 Greater Prairie Chicken, *Tympanuchus cupido americanus* (Reichenbach)
305a Attwater's Prairie Chicken, *Tympanuchus cupido attwateri* Bendire
307 Lesser Prairie Chicken, *Tympanuchus pallidicinctus* (Ridgway)
308 Northern Sharp-tailed Grouse, *Pedioecetes phasianellus phasianellus* (Linnaeus)
308a Columbian Sharp-tailed Grouse, *Pedioecetes phasianellus columbianus* (Ord)
308b Prairie Sharp-tailed Grouse, *Pedioecetes phasianellus campestris* Ridgway
309 Sage Hen, *Centrocercus urophasianus* (Bonaparte)

22. *Family Perdicidae*—Partridges and Quails

    288.1 European Partridge, *Perdix perdix perdix* (Linnaeus)
    289 Eastern Bob-white, *Colinus virginianus virginianus* (Linnaeus)
    289a Florida Bob-white, *Colinus virginianus floridanus* (Coues)
    289c Key West Bob-white, *Colinus virginianus insulanus* Howe
    289b Texas Bob-white, *Colinus virginianus texanus* (Lawrence)
    291 Masked Bob-white, *Colinus ridgwayi* Brewster
    293 Arizona Scaled Quail, *Callipepla squamata pallida* Brewster
    293a Chestnut-bellied Scaled Quail, *Callipepla squamata castanogastris* Brewster
    294 California Quail, *Lophortyx californica californica* (Shaw)
    294a Valley Quail, *Lophortyx californica vallicola* (Ridgway)
    294b Catalina Quail, *Lophortyx californica catalinensis* Grinnell
    294c San Quintín Quail, *Lophortyx californica plumbea* Grinnell
    294d San Lucas Quail, *Lophortyx californica achrustera* Peters
    295 Gambel's Quail, *Lophortyx gambeli gambeli* Gambel
    295a Olathe Quail, *Lophortyx gambeli sanus* Mearns
    292 Mountain Quail, *Oreortyx picta palmeri* Oberholser
    292a Plumed Quail, *Oreortyx picta picta* (Douglas)
    292b San Pedro Quail, *Oreortyx picta confinis* Anthony
    296 Mearns's Quail, *Cyrtonyx montezumae mearnsi* Nelson

23. *Family Phasianidae*—Pheasants

    309.1 Ring-necked Pheasant, *Phasianus colchicus torquatus* Gmelin

24. *Family Meleagrididae*—Turkeys

    310a Eastern Turkey, *Meleagris gallopavo silvestris* Vieillot
    310b Florida Turkey, *Meleagris gallopavo osceola* Scott
    310c Rio Grande Turkey, *Meleagris gallopavo intermedia* Sennett
    310 Merriam's Turkey, *Meleagris gallopavo merriami* Nelson

ORDER GRUIFORMES—Cranes, Rails, and allies

25. *Family Gruidae*—Cranes

    204 Whooping Crane, *Grus americana* (Linnaeus)
    205 Little Brown Crane, *Grus canadensis canadensis* (Linnaeus)
    206 Sandhill Crane, *Grus canadensis tabida* (Peters)
    206a Florida Crane, *Grus canadensis pratensis* Meyer

26. *Family Aramidae*—Limpkins

    207 Limpkin, *Aramus pictus pictus* (Meyer)

27. *Family Rallidae*—Rails, Gallinules, and Coots

    208 King Rail, *Rallus elegans elegans* Audubon
    210 California Clapper Rail, *Rallus obsoletus obsoletus* Ridgway
    210.1 Light-footed Rail, *Rallus obsoletus levipes* Bangs
    209 Belding's Rail, *Rallus obsoletus beldingi* Ridgway
    210a Yuma Clapper Rail, *Rallus obsoletus yumanensis* Dickey
    211 Northern Clapper Rail, *Rallus longirostris crepitans* Gmelin
    211c Wayne's Clapper Rail, *Rallus longirostris waynei* Brewster

211b Florida Clapper Rail, *Rallus longirostris scotti* Sennett
211d Mangrove Clapper Rail, *Rallus longirostris insularum* Brooks
211a Louisiana Clapper Rail, *Rallus longirostris saturatus* Ridgway
212 Virginia Rail, *Rallus limicola limicola* Vieillot
212.1 Water Rail, *Rallus aquaticus aquaticus* Linnaeus
213 Spotted Crake, *Porzana porzana* (Linnaeus)
214 Sora, *Porzana carolina* (Linnaeus)
215 Yellow Rail, *Coturnicops noveboracensis* (Gmelin)
216 Black Rail, *Creciscus jamaicensis stoddardi* Coale
216.1 Farallon Rail, *Creciscus jamaicensis coturniculus* (Ridgway)
217 Corn Crake, *Crex crex* (Linnaeus)
218 Purple Gallinule, *Ionornis martinica* (Linnaeus)
219 Florida Gallinule, *Gallinula chloropus cachinnans* Bangs
220 European Coot, *Fulica atra atra* Linnaeus
221 American Coot, *Fulica americana americana* Gmelin

ORDER CHARADRIIFORMES—Shore Birds, Gulls, Auks, and allies

28. Family Jacanidae—Jaçanas
288 Mexican Jaçana, *Jaçana spinosa gymnostoma* (Wagler)

29. Family Haematopodidae—Oyster-catchers
285 European Oyster-catcher, *Haematopus ostralegus ostralegus* Linnaeus
286 American Oyster-catcher, *Haematopus palliatus palliatus* Temminck
286.1 Frazar's Oyster-catcher, *Haematopus palliatus frazari* Brewster
287 Black Oyster-catcher, *Haematopus bachmani* Audubon

30. Family Charadriidae—Plovers, Turnstones, and Surf-birds
269 Lapwing, *Vanellus vanellus* (Linnaeus)
275 Ringed Plover, *Charadrius hiaticula hiaticula* Linnaeus
276 Little Ringed Plover, *Charadrius dubius curonicus* Gmelin
277 Piping Plover, *Charadrius melodus* Ord
279 Mongolian Plover, *Charadrius mongolus mongolus* Pallas
278 Western Snowy Plover, *Charadrius nivosus nivosus* (Cassin)
278a Cuban Snowy Plover, *Charadrius nivosus tenuirostris* (Lawrence)
274 Semipalmated Plover, *Charadrius semipalmatus* Bonaparte
280 Wilson's Plover, *Pagolla wilsonia wilsonia* (Ord)
280a Belding's Plover, *Pagolla wilsonia beldingi* Ridgway
281 Mountain Plover, *Eupoda montana* (Townsend)
273 Killdeer, *Oxyechus vociferus vociferus* (Linnaeus)
269.1 Dotterel, *Eudromias morinellus* (Linnaeus)
271 European Golden Plover, *Pluvialis apricaria apricaria* (Linnaeus)
272 American Golden Plover, *Pluvialis dominica dominica* (Müller)
272a Pacific Golden Plover, *Pluvialis dominica fulva* (Gmelin)
270 Black-bellied Plover, *Squatarola squatarola* (Linnaeus)
282 Surf-bird, *Aphriza virgata* (Gmelin)
283 European Turnstone, *Arenaria interpres interpres* (Linnaeus)
283a Ruddy Turnstone, *Arenaria interpres morinella* (Linnaeus)
284 Black Turnstone, *Arenaria melanocephala* (Vigors)

31. Family Scolopacidae—Woodcock, Snipe, and Sandpipers

228 American Woodcock, *Philohela minor* (Gmelin)
227 European Woodcock, *Scolopax rusticola rusticola* Linnaeus
229 European Snipe, *Capella gallinago gallinago* (Linnaeus)
230 Wilson's Snipe, *Capella delicata* (Ord)
230.2 European Jack Snipe, *Lymnocryptes minimus* (Brünnich)
264 Long-billed Curlew, *Numenius americanus americanus* Bechstein
264a Northern Curlew, *Numenius americanus occidentalis* Woodhouse
264.1 European Curlew, *Numenius arquatus arquatus* (Linnaeus)
267 Whimbrel, *Phaeopus phaeopus phaeopus* (Linnaeus)
268 Bristle-thighed Curlew, *Phaeopus tahitiensis* (Gmelin)
265 Hudsonian Curlew, *Phaeopus hudsonicus* (Latham)
266 Eskimo Curlew, *Phaeopus borealis* (Forster)
261 Upland Plover, *Bartramia longicauda* (Bechstein)
263 Spotted Sandpiper, *Actitis macularia* (Linnaeus)
256 Eastern Solitary Sandpiper, *Tringa solitaria solitaria* Wilson
256a Western Solitary Sandpiper, *Tringa solitaria cinnamomea* (Brewster)
257.1 Wood Sandpiper, *Rhyacophilus glareola* (Linnaeus)
259 Wandering Tattler, *Heteroscelus incanus* (Gmelin)
259.1 Polynesian Tattler, *Heteroscelus brevipes* (Vieillot)
258 Eastern Willet, *Catoptrophorus semipalmatus semipalmatus* (Gmelin)
258a Western Willet, *Catoptrophorus semipalmatus inornatus* (Brewster)
254 Greater Yellow-legs, *Totanus melanoleucus* (Gmelin)
255 Lesser Yellow-legs, *Totanus flavipes* (Gmelin)
253.1 Iceland Redshank, *Totanus totanus robustus* Schioler
234 American Knot, *Calidris canutus rufus* (Wilson)
234.1 Eastern Asiatic Knot, *Calidris tenuirostris* (Horsfield)
235 Purple Sandpiper, *Arquatella maritima* (Brünnich)
235b Pribilof Sandpiper, *Arquatella ptilocnemis ptilocnemis* (Coues)
235a Aleutian Sandpiper, *Arquatella ptilocnemis couesi* Ridgway
235c Commander Sandpiper, *Arquatella ptilocnemis quarta* (Hartert)
238 Sharp-tailed Sandpiper, *Pisobia acuminata* (Horsfield)
239 Pectoral Sandpiper, *Pisobia melanotos* (Vieillot)
240 White-rumped Sandpiper, *Pisobia fuscicollis* (Vieillot)
241 Baird's Sandpiper, *Pisobia bairdi* (Coues)
242 Least Sandpiper, *Pisobia minutilla* (Vieillot)
242.1 Long-toed Stint, *Pisobia subminuta* (Middendorff)
242.2 Rufous-necked Sandpiper, *Pisobia ruficollis* (Pallas)
244 Curlew Sandpiper, *Erolia testacea* (Pallas)
243 Dunlin, *Pelidna alpina alpina* (Linnaeus)
243a Red-backed Sandpiper, *Pelidna alpina sakhalina* (Vieillot)
231 Eastern Dowitcher, *Limnodromus griseus griseus* (Gmelin)
232 Long-billed Dowitcher, *Limnodromus griseus scolopaceus* (Say)
233 Stilt Sandpiper, *Micropalama himantopus* (Bonaparte)
246 Semipalmated Sandpiper, *Ereunetes pusillus* (Linnaeus)
247 Western Sandpiper, *Ereunetes mauri* Cabanis
262 Buff-breasted Sandpiper, *Tryngites subruficollis* (Vieillot)
249 Marbled Godwit, *Limosa fedoa* (Linnaeus)
250a Bar-tailed Godwit, *Limosa lapponica lapponica* (Linnaeus)
250 Pacific Godwit, *Limosa lapponica baueri* Naumann

251 Hudsonian Godwit, *Limosa haemastica* (Linnaeus)
252 Black-tailed Godwit, *Limosa limosa limosa* (Linnaeus)
260 Ruff, *Philomachus pugnax* (Linnaeus)
248 Sanderling, *Crocethia alba* (Pallas)
245 Spoon-bill, Sandpiper, *Eurynorhynchus pygmeus* (Linnaeus)

32. Family *Recurvirostridae*—Avocets and Stilts
225 Avocet, *Recurvirostra americana* Gmelin
226 Black-necked Stilt, *Himantopus mexicanus* (Müller)

33. Family *Phalaropodidae*—Phalaropes
222 Red Phalarope, *Phalaropus fulicarius* (Linnaeus)
224 Wilson's Phalarope, *Steganopus tricolor* (Vieillot)
223 Northern Phalarope, *Lobipes lobatus* (Linnaeus)

34. Family *Stercorariidae*—Jaegers and Skuas
36 Pomarine Jaeger, *Stercorarius pomarinus* (Temminck)
37 Parasitic Jaeger, *Stercorarius parasiticus* (Linnaeus)
38 Long-tailed Jaeger, *Stercorarius longicaudus* (Vieillot)
35 Northern Skua, *Catharacta skua* Brünnich
35.1 Chilean Skua, *Catharacta chilensis* (Bonaparte)

35. Family *Laridae*—Gulls and Terns
42 Glaucous Gull, *Larus hyperboreus* Gunnerus
43 Iceland Gull, *Larus leucopterus* Vieillot
44 Glaucous-winged Gull, *Larus glaucescens* Naumann
47 Great Black-backed Gull, *Larus marinus* Linnaeus
48 Slaty-backed Gull, *Larus schistisagus* Stejneger
49 Western Gull, *Larus occidentalis occidentalis* Audubon
49b Wyman's Gull, *Larus occidentalis wymani* Dickey and Van Rossem
49a Yellow-footed Gull, *Larus occidentalis livens* Dwight
50 Lesser Black-backed Gull, *Larus fuscus graellsi* Brehm
51a Herring Gull, *Larus argentatus smithsonianus* Coues
51b Thayer's Gull, *Larus argentatus thayeri* Brooks
52 Vega Gull, *Larus argentatus vegae* Palmen
53 California Gull, *Larus californicus* Lawrence
54 Ring-billed Gull, *Larus delawarensis* Ord
55 Short-billed Gull, *Larus canus brachyrhynchus* Richardson
55.1 Black-headed Gull, *Larus ridibundus ridibundus* Linnaeus
58 Laughing Gull, *Larus atricilla* Linnaeus
59 Franklin's Gull, *Larus pipixcan* Wagler
60 Bonaparte's Gull, *Larus philadelphia* (Ord)
60.1 Little Gull, *Larus minutus* Pallas
57 Heermann's Gull, *Larus heermanni* Cassin
39 Ivory Gull, *Pagophila alba* (Gunnerus)
40 Atlantic Kittiwake, *Rissa tridactyla tridactyla* (Linnaeus)
40a Pacific Kittiwake, *Rissa tridactyla pollicaris* Ridgway
41 Red-legged Kittiwake, *Rissa brevirostris* (Bruch)
61 Ross's Gull, *Rhodostethia rosea* (MacGillivray)

62 Sabine's Gull, *Xema sabini* (Sabine)
63 Gull-billed Tern, *Gelochelidon nilotica aranea* (Wilson)
68 Trudeau's Tern, *Sterna trudeaui* Audubon
69 Forster's Tern, *Sterna forsteri* Nuttall
70 Common Tern, *Sterna hirundo hirundo* Linnaeus
71 Arctic Tern, *Sterna paradisaea* Brünnich
72 Roseate Tern, *Sterna dougalli dougalli* Montagu
73 Aleutian Tern, *Sterna aleutica* (Baird)
75 Eastern Sooty Tern, *Sterna fuscata fuscata* Linnaeus
75a Socorro Sooty Tern, *Sterna fuscata crissalis* (Lawrence)
76 Bridled Tern, *Sterna anaethetus melanoptera* Swainson
74 Least Tern, *Sterna antillarum antillarum* (Lesson)
74a Brown's Tern, *Sterna antillarum browni* Mearns
65 Royal Tern, *Thalasseus maximus maximus* (Boddaert)
66 Elegant Tern, *Thalasseus elegans* (Gambel)
67 Cabot's Tern, *Thalasseus sandvicensis acuflavidus* (Cabot)
64 Caspian Tern, *Hydroprogne caspia imperator* (Coues)
77 Black Tern, *Chlidonias nigra surinamensis* (Gmelin)
78 White-winged Tern, *Chlidonias leucoptera* (Temminck)
79 Noddy Tern, *Anoüs stolidus stolidus* (Linnaeus)

36. *Family Rynchopidae*—Skimmers
    80 Black Skimmer, *Rynchops nigra nigra* Linnaeus

37. *Family Alcidae*—Auks, Murres, and Puffins
    33 Great Auk, *Platus impennis* (Linnaeus)
    32 Razor-billed Auk, *Alca torda* Linnaeus
    30 Atlantic Murre, *Uria aalge aalge* (Pontoppidan)
    30a California Murre, *Uria aalge californica* (Bryant)
    31 Brünnich's Murre, *Uria lomvia lomvia* (Linnaeus)
    31a Pallas's Murre, *Uria lomvia arra* (Pallas)
    34 Dovekie, *Alle alle* (Linnaeus)
    27 Black Guillemot, *Cepphus grylle grylle* (Linnaeus)
    28 Mandt's Guillemot, *Cepphus grylle mandti* (Mandt)
    29 Pigeon Guillemot, *Cepphus columba* Pallas
    23 Marbled Murrelet, *Brachyramphus marmoratus* (Gmelin)
    24 Kittlitz's Murrelet, *Brachyramphus brevirostris* (Vigors)
    25 Xantus's Murrelet, *Endomychura hypoleuca* (Xantus)
    26 Craveri's Murrelet, *Endomychura craveri* (Salvadori)
    21 Ancient Murrelet, *Synthliboramphus antiquus* (Gmelin)
    16 Cassin's Auklet, *Ptychoramphus aleuticus* (Pallas)
    17 Paroquet Auklet, *Cyclorrhynchus psittacula* (Pallas)
    18 Crested Auklet, *Aethia cristatella* (Pallas)
    20 Least Auklet, *Aethia pusilla* (Pallas)
    19 Whiskered Auklet, *Aethia pygmaea* (Gmelin)
    15 Rhinoceros Auklet, *Cerorhinca monocerata* (Pallas)
    13 Atlantic Puffin, *Fratercula arctica arctica* (Linnaeus)
    13a Large-billed Puffin, *Fratercula arctica naumanni* Norton
    14 Horned Puffin, *Fratercula corniculata* (Naumann)
    12 Tufted Puffin, *Lunda cirrhata* (Pallas)

ORDER COLUMBIFORMES—Pigeon-like Birds

38. Family Columbidae—Pigeons and Doves

   314 White-crowned Pigeon, *Columba leucocephala* Linnaeus
   314.1 Scaled Pigeon, *Columba squamosa* Bonnaterre
   312 Band-tailed Pigeon, *Columba fasciata fasciata* Say
   312a Viosca's Pigeon, *Columba fasciata vioscae* Brewster
   313 Red-billed Pigeon, *Columba flavirostris flavirostris* Wagler
   313.1 Rock Dove, *Columba livia livia* Gmelin
   317 Zenaida Dove, *Zenaida zenaida zenaida* (Bonaparte)
   316 Eastern Mourning Dove, *Zenaidura macroura carolinensis* (Linnaeus)
   316a Western Mourning Dove, *Zenaidura macroura marginella* (Woodhouse)
   315 Passenger Pigeon, *Ectopistes migratorius* (Linnaeus)
   315.1 Chinese Spotted Dove, *Spilopelia chinensis chinensis* (Scopoli)
   315.2 Ringed Turtle Dove, *Streptopelia risoria* (Linnaeus)
   319 Eastern White-winged Dove, *Melopelia asiatica asiatica* (Linnaeus)
   319a Western White-winged Dove, *Melopelia asiatica mearnsi* Ridgway
   320 Eastern Ground Dove, *Columbigallina passerina passerina* (Linnaeus)
   320a Mexican Ground Dove, *Columbigallina passerina pallescens* (Baird)
   320b Bahama Ground Dove, *Columbigallina passerina bahamensis* (Maynard)
   321 Inca Dove, *Scardafella inca inca* (Lesson)
   318 White-fronted Dove, *Leptotila fulviventris angelica* Bangs and Penard
   322 Key West Quail-dove, *Oreopeleia chrysia* (Bonaparte)
   322.1 Ruddy Quail-dove, *Oreopeleia montana* (Linnaeus)

ORDER PSITTACIFORMES—Parrots, Paroquets, Macaws, and allies

39. Family Psittacidae—Parrots, Paroquets, and Macaws

   382 Carolina Paroquet, *Conuropsis carolinensis carolinensis* (Linnaeus)
   382a Louisiana Paroquet, *Conuropsis carolinensis ludovicianus* (Gmelin)
   382.1 Thick-billed Parrot, *Rhynchopsitta pachyrhyncha* (Swainson)

ORDER CUCULIFORMES—Cuckoo-like Birds

40. Family Cuculidae—Cuckoos, Road-runners, and Anis

   388.1 Himalaya Cuckoo, *Cuculus optatus* Gould
   388.2 Baker's Cuckoo, *Cuculus canorus bakeri* Hartert
   386a Maynard's Cuckoo, *Coccyzus minor maynardi* Ridgway
   387 Yellow-billed Cuckoo, *Coccyzus americanus americanus* (Linnaeus)
   387a California Cuckoo, *Coccyzus americanus occidentalis* Ridgway
   388 Black-billed Cuckoo, *Coccyzus erythropthalmus* (Wilson)
   385 Road-runner, *Geococcyx californianus* (Lesson)
   383 Smooth-billed Ani, *Crotophaga ani* Linnaeus
   384 Groove-billed Ani, *Crotophaga sulcirostris sulcirostris* Swainson
   384a San Lucas Ani, *Crotophaga sulcirostris pallidula* Bangs and Penard

ORDER STRIGIFORMES—Owls

41. Family Tytonidae—Barn Owls
  365 Barn Owl, *Tyto alba pratincola* (Bonaparte)

42. Family Strigidae—Typical Owls
  373m Eastern Screech Owl, *Otus asio naevius* (Gmelin)
  373 Southern Screech Owl, *Otus asio asio* (Linnaeus)
  373a Florida Screech Owl, *Otus asio floridanus* (Ridgway)
  373b Texas Screech Owl, *Otus asio mccalli* (Cassin)
  373i Hasbrouck's Screech Owl, *Otus asio hasbroucki* Ridgway
  373g Aiken's Screech Owl, *Otus asio aikeni* (Brewster)
  373e Rocky Mountain Screech Owl, *Otus asio maxwelliae* (Ridgway)
  373h MacFarlane's Screech Owl, *Otus asio macfarlanei* (Brewster)
  373d Kennicott's Screech Owl, *Otus asio kennicotti* (Elliot)
  373j Brewster's Screech Owl, *Otus asio brewsteri* Ridgway
  373c California Screech Owl, *Otus asio bendirei* (Brewster)
  373k Pasadena Screech Owl, *Otus asio quercinus* Grinnell
  373f Mexican Screech Owl, *Otus asio cineraceus* (Ridgway)
  373l Sahuaro Screech Owl, *Otus asio gilmani* Swarth
  373.2 Xantus's Screech Owl, *Otus asio xantusi* (Brewster)
  374 Flammulated Screech Owl, *Otus flammeolus* (Kaup)
  373.1 Spotted Screech Owl, *Otus trichopsis* (Wagler)
  375b Arctic Horned Owl, *Bubo virginianus subarcticus* Hoy
  375f Labrador Horned Owl, *Bubo virginianus heterocnemis* (Oberholser)
  375 Great Horned Owl, *Bubo virginianus virginianus* (Gmelin)
  375j Montana Horned Owl, *Bubo virginianus occidentalis* Stone
  375g St. Michael Horned Owl, *Bubo virginianus algistus* (Oberholser)
  375i Northwestern Horned Owl, *Bubo virginianus lagophonus* (Oberholser)
  375c Dusky Horned Owl, *Bubo virginianus saturatus* Ridgway
  375d Pacific Horned Owl, *Bubo virginianus pacificus* Cassin
  375a Western Horned Owl, *Bubo virginianus pallescens* Stone
  375e Dwarf Horned Owl, *Bubo virginianus elachistus* Brewster
  376 Snowy Owl, *Nyctea nyctea* (Linnaeus)
  377 Siberian Hawk Owl, *Surnia ulula pallasi* Buturlin
  377a American Hawk Owl, *Surnia ulula caparoch* (Müller)
  379 Rocky Mountain Pygmy Owl, *Glaucidium gnoma pinicola* Nelson
  379d Vancouver Pygmy Owl, *Glaucidium gnoma swarthi* Grinnell
  379c Coast Pygmy Owl, *Glaucidium gnoma grinnelli* Ridgway
  379a California Pygmy Owl, *Glaucidium gnoma californicum* Sclater
  379.1 Hoskin's Pygmy Owl, *Glaucidium gnoma hoskinsi* Brewster
  380 Ferruginous Pygmy Owl, *Glaucidium brasilianum ridgwayi* Sharpe
  381 Whitney's Elf Owl, *Micropallas whitneyi whitneyi* (Cooper)
  381a Texas Elf Owl, *Micropallas whitneyi idoneus* Ridgway
  381b Sanford's Elf Owl, *Micropallas whitneyi sanfordi* Ridgway
  378 Western Burrowing Owl, *Speotyto cunicularia hypugaea* (Bonaparte)
  378a Florida Burrowing Owl, *Speotyto cunicularia floridana* Ridgway
  368 Northern Barred Owl, *Strix varia varia* Barton
  368a Florida Barred Owl, *Strix varia alleni* Ridgway
  368b Texas Barred Owl, *Strix varai helveola* Bangs

369 California Spotted Owl, *Strix occidentalis occidentalis* (Xantus)
369a Northern Spotted Owl, *Strix occidentalis caurina* (Merriam)
369b Mexican Spotted Owl, *Strix occidentalis lucida* (Nelson)
370 Great Gray Owl, *Scotiaptex nebulosa nebulosa* (Forster)
370a Siberian Gray Owl, *Scotiaptex nebulosa barbata* (Latham)
366 Long-eared Owl, *Asio wilsonianus* (Lesson)
367 Short-eared Owl, *Asio flammeus flammeus* (Pontoppidan)
371 Richardson's Owl, *Cryptoglaux funerea richardsoni* (Bonaparte)
371a Tengmalm's Owl, *Cryptoglaux funerea magna* (Buturlin)
372 Saw-whet Owl, *Cryptoglaux acadica acadica* (Gmelin)
372a Queen Charlotte Owl, *Cryptoglaux acadica brooksi* Fleming

ORDER CAPRIMULGIFORMES—Goatsuckers and allies

43. Family caprimulgidae—Goatsuckers

416. Chuck-will's-widow, *Antrostomus carolinensis* (Gmelin)
417 Eastern Whip-poor-will, *Antrostomus vociferus vociferus* (Wilson)
417a Stephens's Whip-poor-will, *Antrostomus vociferus arizonae* Brewster
418 Nuttall's Poor-will, *Phalaenoptilus nuttalli nuttalli* (Audubon)
418b Dusky Poor-will, *Phalaenoptilus nuttalli californicus* Ridgway
418c Desert Poor-will, *Phalaenoptilus nuttalli hueyi* Dickey
418d San Ignacio Poor-will, *Phalaenoptilus nuttalli dickeyi* Grinnell
419 Merrill's Pauraque, *Nyctidromus albicollis merrilli* Sennett
420 Eastern Nighthawk, *Chordeiles minor minor* (Forster)
420b Florida Nighthawk, *Chordeiles minor chapmani* Coues
420e Howell's Nighthawk, *Chordeiles minor howelli* Oberholser
420f Cherrie's Nighthawk, *Chordeiles minor aserriensis* Cherrie
420c Sennett's Nighthawk, *Chordeiles minor sennetti* Coues
420a Western Nighthawk, *Chordeiles minor henryi* Cassin
420d Pacific Nighthawk, *Chordeiles minor hesperis* Grinnell
421 Texas Nighthawk, *Chordeiles acutipennis texensis* Lawrence
421a San Lucas Nighthawk, *Chordeiles acutipennis inferior* Oberholser

ORDER MICROPODIFORMES—Swifts and Hummingbirds

44. Family Micropodidae—Swifts

422 Black Swift, *Nephœcetes niger borealis* (Kennerly)
423 Chimney Swift, *Chaetura pelagica* (Linnaeus)
424 Vaux's Swift, *Chaetura vauxi* (Townsend)
424.1 White-rumped Swift, *Micropus pacificus pacificus* (Latham)
425 White-throated Swift, *Aëronautes saxatalis saxatalis* (Woodhouse)

45. Family Trochilidae—Hummingbirds

437 Lucifer Hummingbird, *Calothorax lucifer* (Swainson)
428 Ruby-throated Hummingbird, *Archilochus colubris* (Linnaeus)
429 Black-chinned Hummingbird, *Archilochus alexandri* (Bourcier and Mulsant)
430 Costa's Hummingbird, *Calypte costae* (Bourcier)
431 Anna's Hummingbird, *Calypte anna* (Lesson)

432 Broad-tailed Hummingbird, *Selasphorus platycercus platycercus* (Swainson)
433 Rufous Hummingbird, *Selasphorus rufus* (Gmelin)
434 Allen's Hummingbird, *Selasphorus alleni* (Henshaw)
435 Heloise's Hummingbird, *Atthis heloisa heloisa* (De Lattre and Lesson)
436 Calliope Hummingbird, *Stellula calliope* (Gould)
426 Rivoli's Hummingbird, *Eugenes fulgens* (Swainson)
427a Texas Blue-throated Hummingbird, *Lampornis clemenciae clemenciae* (Lesson)
427 Arizona Blue-throated Hummingbird, *Lampornis clemenciae bessophilus* (Oberholser)
438 Rieffer's Hummingbird, *Amazilia tzacatl tzacatl* (De la Llave)
439 Buff-bellied Hummingbird, *Amazilia yucatanensis chalconota* Oberholser
439.1 Salvin's Hummingbird, *Amazilia salvini* (Brewster)
440 Xantus's Hummingbird, *Hylocharis xantusi* (Lawrence)
440.1 White-eared Hummingbird, *Hylocharis leucotis leucotis* (Vieillot)
441 Broad-billed Hummingbird, *Cynanthus latirostris* (Swainson)

ORDER TROGONIFORMES—Trogons

46. Family Trogonidae—Trogons

389 Copper-tailed Trogon, *Trogon ambiguus ambiguus* Gould

ORDER CORACIIFORMES—Kingfishers, Motmots, Rollers, Bee-eaters, and Hornbills

47. Family Alcedinidae—Kingfishers

390 Eastern Belted Kingfisher, *Megaceryle alcyon alcyon* (Linnaeus)
390a Western Belted Kingfisher, *Megaceryle alcyon caurina* (Grinnell)
390.1 Ringed Kingfisher, *Megaceryle torquata torquata* (Linnaeus)
391 Texas Kingfisher, *Chloroceryle americana septentrionalis* (Sharpe)

ORDER PICIFORMES—Woodpeckers, Jacamars, Toucans, and Barbets

48. Family Picidae—Woodpeckers

412a Northern Flicker, *Colaptes auratus luteus* Bangs
412 Southern Flicker, *Colaptes auratus auratus* (Linnaeus)
413a Northwestern Flicker, *Colaptes cafer cafer* (Gmelin)
413 Red-shafted Flicker, *Colaptes cafer collaris* Vigors
413b San Pedro Flicker, *Colaptes cafer martirensis* Grinnell
415 Guadalupe Flicker, *Colaptes cafer rufipileus* Ridgway
414a Mearns's Gilded Flicker, *Colaptes chrysoides mearnsi* Ridgway
414b San Fernando Flicker, *Colaptes chrysoides brunnescens* Anthony
414 Cape Gilded Flicker, *Colaptes chrysoides chrysoides* (Malherbe)
405a Northern Pileated Woodpecker, *Ceophloeus pileatus abieticola* Bangs
405 Southern Pileated Woodpecker, *Ceophloeus pileatus pileatus* (Linnaeus)
405b Florida Pileated Woodpecker, *Ceophloeus pileatus floridanus* (Ridgway)

405c Western Pileated Woodpecker, *Ceophloeus pileatus picinus* (Bangs)

409 Red-bellied Woodpecker, *Centurus carolinus* (Linnaeus)

410 Golden-fronted Woodpecker, *Centurus aurifrons* (Wagler)

411 Gila Woodpecker, *Centurus uropygialis uropygialis* Baird

411a Cardón Woodpecker, *Centurus uropygialis cardonensis*

411b Brewster's Woodpecker, *Centurus uropygialis brewsteri* Ridgway

406 Red-headed Woodpecker, *Melanerpes erythrocephalus* (Linnaeus)

407 Ant-eating Woodpecker, *Balanosphyra formicivora formicivora* (Swainson)

407c Mearns's Woodpecker, *Balanosphyra formicivora aculeata* (Mearns)

407a California Woodpecker, *Balanosphyra formicivora bairdi* (Ridgway)

407d San Pedro Woodpecker, *Balanosphyra formicivora martirensis* Grinnell and Swarth

407b Narrow-fronted Woodpecker, *Balanosphyra formicivora angustifrons* (Baird)

408 Lewis's Woodpecker, *Asyndesmus lewis* Gray

402 Yellow-bellied Sapsucker, *Sphyrapicus varius varius* (Linnaeus)

402a Red-naped Sapsucker, *Sphyrapicus varius nuchalis* Baird

403a Northern Red-breasted Sapsucker, *Sphyrapicus varius ruber* (Gmelin)

403 Southern Red-breasted Sapsucker, *Sphyrapicus varius daggetti* Grinnell

404 Williamson's Sapsucker, *Sphyrapicus thyroideus thyroideus* (Cassin)

404a Natalie's Sapsucker, *Sphyrapicus thyroideus nataliae* (Malherbe)

393a Northern Hairy Woodpecker, *Dryobates villosus septentrionalis* (Nuttall)

393g Newfoundland Woodpecker, *Dryobates villosus terraenovae* Batchelder

393 Eastern Hairy Woodpecker, *Dryobates villosus villosus* (Linnaeus)

393b Southern Hairy Woodpecker, *Dryobates villosus auduboni* (Swainson)

393i Sitka Hairy Woodpecker, *Dryobates villosus sitkensis* Swarth

393f Queen Charlotte Woodpecker, *Dryobates villosus picoideus* Osgood

393c Harris's Woodpecker, *Dryobates villosus harrisi* (Audubon)

393d Cabanis's Woodpecker, *Dryobates villosus hyloscopus* Cabanis and Heine

393k Lower California Hairy Woodpecker, *Dryobates villosus scrippsae* Huey

393j Modoc Woodpecker, *Dryobates villosus orius* Oberholser

393e Rocky Mountain Hairy Woodpecker, *Dryobates villosus monticola* Anthony

393l White-breasted Woodpecker, *Dryobates villosus leucothorectis* Oberholser

393h Chihuahua Woodpecker, *Dryobates villosus icastus* Oberholser

394c Northern Downy Woodpecker, *Dryobates pubescens medianus* (Swainson)

394 Southern Downy Woodpecker, *Dryobates pubescens pubescens* (Linnaeus)

394d Nelson's Downy Woodpecker, *Dryobates pubescens nelsoni* Oberholser

394b Batchelder's Woodpecker, *Dryobates pubescens leucurus* (Hartlaub)

394a Gairdner's Woodpecker, *Dryobates pubescens gairdneri* (Audubon)

394e Willow Woodpecker, *Dryobates pubescens turati* (Malherbe)
396 Texas Woodpecker, *Dryobates scalaris symplectus* Oberholser
396b Cactus Woodpecker, *Dryobates scalaris cactophilus* Oberholser
396c San Fernando Woodpecker, *Dryobates scalaris eremicus* Oberholser
396a San Lucas Woodpecker, *Dryobates scalaris lucasanus* (Xantus)
397 Nuttall's Woodpecker, *Dryobates nuttalli* (Gambel)
398 Arizona Woodpecker, *Dryobates arizonae arizonae* (Hargitt)
395 Red-cockaded Woodpecker, *Dryobates borealis* (Vieillot)
399 Northern White-headed Woodpecker, *Dryobates albolarvatus albolarvatus* (Cassin)
399a Southern White-headed Woodpecker, *Dryobates albolarvatus gravirostris* (Grinnell)
400 Arctic Three-toed Woodpecker, *Picoïdes arcticus* (Swainson)
401 American Three-toed Woodpecker, *Picoïdes tridactylus bacatus* Bangs
401b Alpine Three-toed Woodpecker, *Picoïdes tridactylus dorsalis* Baird
401a Alaska Three-toed Woodpecker, *Picoïdes tridactylus fasciatus* Baird
392 Ivory-billed Woodpecker, *Campephilus principalis* (Linnaeus)

ORDER PASSERIFORMES—Perching Birds

49. *Family Cotingidae*—Cotingas
   441.1 Xantus's Becard, *Platypsaris aglaiae albiventris* (Lawrence)

50. *Family Tyrannidae*—Tyrant Flycatchers
   444 Eastern Kingbird, *Tyrannus tyrannus* (Linnaeus)
   445 Gray Kingbird, *Tyrannus dominicensis dominicensis* (Gmelin)
   446 Couch's Kingbird, *Tyrannus melancholicus couchi* Baird
   446a Lichtenstein's Kingbird, *Tyrannus melancholicus chloronotus* Berlepsch
   446b West Mexican Kingbird, *Tyrannus melancholicus occidentalis* Hartert and Goodson
   447 Arkansas Kingbird, *Tyrannus verticalis* Say
   448 Cassin's Kingbird, *Tyrannus vociferans* Swainson
   442 Fork-tailed Flycatcher, *Muscivora tyrannus* (Linnaeus)
   443 Scissor-tailed Flycatcher, *Muscivora forficata* (Gmelin)
   449 Derby Flycatcher, *Pitangus sulphuratus derbianus* (Kaup)
   451 Sulphur-bellied Flycatcher, *Myiodynastes luteiventris swarthi* van Rossem
   452a Northern Crested Flycatcher, *Myiarchus crinitus boreus* Bangs
   452 Southern Crested Flycatcher, *Myiarchus crinitus crinitus* (Linnaeus)
   453 Arizona Crested Flycatcher, *Myiarchus tyrannulus magister* Ridgway
   453a Mexican Crested Flycatcher, *Myiarchus tyrannulus nelsoni* Ridgway
   454 Ash-throated Flycatcher, *Myiarchus cinerascens cinerascens* (Lawrence)
   454b Lower California Flycatcher, *Myiarchus cinerascens pertinax* Baird
   455a Olivaceous Flycatcher, *Myiarchus tuberculifer olivascens* Ridgway
   456 Eastern Phoebe, *Sayornis phoebe* (Latham)
   458 Black Phoebe, *Sayornis nigricans nigricans* (Swainson)
   458a San Quintín Phoebe, *Sayornis nigricans salictaria* Grinnell
   458b San Lucas Phoebe, *Sayornis nigricans brunnescens* Grinnell

457 Say's Phoebe, *Sayornis saya saya* (Bonaparte)
457a San José Phoebe, *Sayornis saya quiescens* Grinnell
463 Yellow-bellied Flycatcher, *Empidonax flaviventris* (Baird and Baird)
465 Acadian Flycatcher, *Empidonax virescens* (Vieillot)
466 Little Flycatcher, *Empidonax trailli brewsteri* Oberholser
466a Alder Flycatcher, *Empidonax trailli trailli* (Audubon)
467 Least Flycatcher, *Empidonax minimus* (Baird and Baird)
468 Hammond's Flycatcher, *Empidonax hammondi* (Xantus)
469 Wright's Flycatcher, *Empidonax wrighti* Baird
469.1 Gray Flycatcher, *Empidonax griseus* Brewster
464 Western Flycatcher, *Empidonax difficilis difficilis* Baird
464a San Lucas Flycatcher, *Empidonax difficilis cineritius* Brewster
470a Buff-breasted Flycatcher, *Empidonax fulvifrons pygmaeus* Coues
460 Coues's Flycatcher, *Myiochanes pertinax pallidiventris* (Chapman)
461 Eastern Wood Pewee, *Myiochanes virens* (Linnaeus)
462 Western Wood Pewee, *Myiochanes richardsoni richardsoni* (Swainson)
462a Large-billed Wood Pewee, *Myiochanes richardsoni peninsulae* (Brewster)
459 Olive-sided Flycatcher, *Nuttallornis mesoleucus* (Lichtenstein)
471 Vermilion Flycatcher, *Pyrocephalus rubinus mexicanus* Sclater
472 Beardless Flycatcher, *Camptostoma imberbe* Sclater

51. Family Alaudidae—Larks

473 Skylark, *Alauda arvensis arvensis* Linnaeus
474a Pallid Horned Lark, *Otocoris alpestris arcticola* Oberholser
474k Hoyt's Horned Lark, *Otocoris alpestris hoyti* Bishop
474 Northern Horned Lark, *Otocoris alpestris alpestris* (Linnaeus)
474c Desert Horned Lark, *Otocoris alpestris leucolaema* (Coues)
474b Prairie Horned Lark, *Otocoris alpestris praticola* Henshaw
474d Texas Horned Lark, *Otocoris alpestris giraudi* Henshaw
474g Streaked Horned Lark, *Otocoris alpestris strigata* Henshaw
474i Dusky Horned Lark, *Otocoris alpestris merrilli* Dwight
474m Island Horned Lark, *Otocoris alpestris insularis* Townsend
474e California Horned Lark, *Otocoris alpestris actia* Oberholser
474n Magdalena Horned Lark, *Otocoris alpestris enertera* Oberholser
474f Ruddy Horned Lark, *Otocoris alpestris rubea* Henshaw
474l Montezuma Horned Lark, *Otocoris alpestris occidentalis* McCall
474h Scorched Horned Lark, *Otocoris alpestris adusta* Dwight
474o Mohave Horned Lark, *Otocoris alpestris ammophila* Oberholser
474j Sonora Horned Lark, *Otocoris alpestris leucansiptila* Oberholser

52. Family Hirundinidae—Swallows

615.1 Bahama Swallow, *Callichelidon cyaneoviridis* (Bryant)
615 Violet-green Swallow, *Tachycineta thalassina lepida* Mearns
615a San Lucas Swallow, *Tachycineta thalassina brachyptera* Brewster
614 Tree Swallow, *Iridoprocne bicolor* (Vieillot)
616 Bank Swallow, *Riparia riparia riparia* (Linnaeus)
617 Rough-winged Swallow, *Stelgidopteryx ruficollis serripennis* (Audubon)
615.2 European Martin, *Chelidonaria urbica urbica* (Linnaeus)
613 Barn Swallow, *Hirundo erythrogaster* Boddaert
613.1 European Swallow, *Hirundo rustica rustica* Linnaeus

612 Northern Cliff Swallow, *Petrochelidon albifrons albifrons* (Rafinesque)
612a Lesser Cliff Swallow, *Petrochelidon albifrons tachina* Oberholser
612b Mexican Cliff Swallow, *Petrochelidon albifrons melanogaster* (Swainson)
612.1 Cuban Cliff Swallow, *Petrochelidon fulva cavicola* Barbour and Brooks
612.1a Coahuila Cliff Swallow, *Petrochelidon fulva pallida* Nelson
611 Purple Martin, *Progne subis subis* (Linnaeus)
611a Western Martin, *Progne subis hesperia* Brewster
611.1 Cuban Martin, *Progne cryptoleuca* Baird
611.2 Gray-breasted Martin, *Progne chalybea chalybea* (Gmelin)

53. Family Corvidae—Jays, Magpies, and Crows

484 Canada Jay, *Perisoreus canadensis canadensis* (Linnaeus)
484a Rocky Mountain Jay, *Perisoreus canadensis capitalis* Ridgway
484b Alaska Jay, *Perisoreus canadensis fumifrons* Ridgway
485 Oregon Jay, *Perisoreus obscurus obscurus* Ridgway
485a Gray Jay, *Perisoreus obscurus griseus* Ridgway
477 Northern Blue Jay, *Cyanocitta cristata cristata* (Linnaeus)
477a Florida Blue Jay, *Cyanocitta cristata florincola* Coues
477b Semple's Blue Jay, *Cyanocitta cristata semplei* Todd
478 Steller's Jay, *Cyanocitta stelleri stelleri* (Gmelin)
478d Queen Charlotte Jay, *Cyanocitta stelleri carlottae* Osgood
478e Coast Jay, *Cyanocitta stelleri carbonacea* Grinnell
478a Blue-fronted Jay, *Cyanocitta stelleri frontalis* (Ridgway)
478c Black-headed Jay, *Cyanocitta stelleri annectens* (Baird)
478b Long-crested Jay, *Cyanocitta stelleri diademata* (Bonaparte)
479 Florida Jay, *Aphelocoma coerulescens* (Bosc)
481c Long-tailed Jay, *Aphelocoma californica immanis* Grinnell
481d Nicasio Jay, *Aphelocoma californica oocleptica* Swarth
481 California Jay, *Aphelocoma californica californica* (Vigors)
481b Belding's Jay, *Aphelocoma californica obscura* Anthony
481a Xantus's Jay, *Aphelocoma californica hypoleuca* Ridgway
480 Woodhouse's Jay, *Aphelocoma californica woodhousei* (Baird)
480.2 Texas Jay, *Aphelocoma californica texana* Ridgway
481.1 Santa Cruz Jay, *Aphelocoma insularis* Henshaw
482 Arizona Jay, *Aphelocoma sieberi arizonae* (Ridgway)
482a Couch's Jay, *Aphelocoma sieberi couchi* (Baird)
483 Green Jay, *Xanthoura luxuosa glaucescens* Ridgway
475 American Magpie, *Pica pica hudsonia* (Sabine)
476 Yellow-billed Magpie, *Pica nutalli* (Audubon)
486a Northern Raven, *Corvus corax principalis* Ridgway
486 American Raven, *Corvus corax sinuatus* Wagler
487 White-necked Raven, *Corvus cryptoleucus* Couch
488 Eastern Crow, *Corvus brachyrhynchos brachyrhynchos* Brehm
488c Southern Crow, *Corvus brachyrhynchos paulus* Howell
488a Florida Crow, *Corvus brachyrhynchos pascuus* Coues
488b Western Crow, *Corvus brachyrhynchos hesperis* Ridgway
489 Northwestern Crow, *Corvus brachyrhynchos caurinus* Baird
490 Fish Crow, *Corvus ossifragus* Wilson

490.1 Rook, *Corvus frugilegus frugilegus* Linnaeus
490.2 Hooded Crow, *Corvus cornix cornix* Linnaeus
492   Piñon Jay, *Cyanocephalus cyanocephalus* (Wied)
491   Clark's Nutcracker, *Nucifraga columbiana* (Wilson)

54. *Family Paridae*—Titmice, Verdins, and Bush-tits

735   Black-capped Chickadee, *Penthestes atricapillus atricapillus* (Linnaeus)
735a Long-tailed Chickadee, *Penthestes atricapillus septentrionalis* (Harris)
735b Oregon Chickadee, *Penthestes atricapillus occidentalis* (Baird)
735c Yukon Chickadee, *Penthestes atricapillus turneri* (Ridgway)
736   Carolina Chickadee, *Penthestes carolinensisca rolinensis* (Audubon)
736b Florida Chickadee, *Penthestes carolinensis impiger* (Bangs)
736a Plumbeous Chickadee, *Penthestes carolinensis agilis* (Sennett)
737   Mexican Chickadee, *Penthestes sclateri eidos* Peters
738b Grinnell's Chickadee, *Penthestes gambeli grinnelli* van Rossem
738c Short-tailed Chickadee, *Penthestes gambeli abbreviatus* Grinnell
738a Bailey's Chickadee, *Penthestes gambeli baileyae* (Grinnell)
738d San Pedro Chickadee, *Penthestes gambeli atratus* Grinnell and Swarth
738   Mountain Chickadee, *Penthestes gambeli gambeli* (Ridgway)
738e Inyo Chickadee, *Penthestes gambeli inyoensis* Grinnell
739   Alaska Chickadee, *Penthestes cinctus alascensis* (Pražák)
740   Hudsonian Chickadee, *Penthestes hudsonicus hudsonicus* (Forster)
740b Columbian Chickadee, *Penthestes hudsonicus columbianus* (Rhoads)
740a Acadian Chickadee, *Penthestes hudsonicus littoralis* (Bryant)
741   Chestnut-backed Chickadee, *Penthestes rufescens rufescens* (Townsend)
741a Nicasio Chickadee, *Penthestes rufescens neglectus* (Ridgway)
741b Barlow's Chickadee, *Penthestes rufescens barlowi* (Grinnell)
731   Tufted Titmouse, *Baeolophus bicolor* (Linnaeus)
732   Black-crested Titmouse, *Baeolophus atricristatus atricristatus* (Cassin)
732a Sennett's Titmouse, *Baeolophus atricristatus sennetti* Ridgway
733c Oregon Titmouse, *Baeolophus inornatus sequestratus* Grinnell and Swarth
733   Plain Titmouse, *Baecolophus inornatus inornatus* (Gambel)
733d San Diego Titmouse, *Baeolophus inornatus transpositus* Grinnell
733e San Pedro Titmouse, *Baeolophus inornatus murinus* Ridgway
733b Ashy Titmouse, *Baeolophus inornatus cineraceus* (Ridgway)
733a Gray Titmouse, *Baeolophus inornatus griseus* (Ridgway)
734   Bridled Titmouse, *Baeolophus wollweberi annexus* (Cassin)
746   Arizona Verdin, *Auriparus flaviceps flaviceps* (Sundevall)
746a Cape Verdin, *Auriparus flaviceps lamprocephalus* Oberholser
743   Coast Bush-tit, *Psaltriparus minimus minimus* (Townsend)
743a California Bush-tit, *Psaltriparus minimus californicus* Ridgway
743c Black-tailed Bush-tit, *Psaltriparus minimus melanurus* Grinnell and Swarth
743b Grinda's Bush-tit, *Psaltriparus minimus grindae* Ridgway
744   Lead-colored Bush-tit, *Psaltriparus minimus plumbeus* (Baird)
745   Lloyd's Bush-tit, *Psaltriparus minimus lloydi* Sennett

55. *Family Sittidae*—Nuthatches

727   White-breasted Nuthatch, *Sitta carolinensis carolinensis* Latham
727b Florida Nuthatch, *Sitta carolinensis atkinsi* Scott

727c Rocky Mountain Nuthatch, *Sitta carolinensis nelsoni* Mearns
727a Slender-billed Nuthatch, *Sitta carolinensis aculeata* Cassin
727e Inyo Nuthatch, *Sitta carolinensis tenuissima* Grinnell
727f San Pedro Nuthatch, *Sitta carolinensis alexandrae* Grinnell
727d San Lucas Nuthatch, *Sitta carolinensis lagunae* Brewster
728 Red-breasted Nuthatch, *Sitta canadensis* Linnaeus
729 Brown-headed Nuthatch, *Sitta pusilla pusilla* Latham
729a Gray-headed Nuthatch, *Sitta pusilla caniceps* Bangs
730 Pygmy Nuthatch, *Sitta pygmaea pygmaea* Vigors
730b Black-eared Nuthatch, *Sitta pygmaea melanotis* van Rossem
730a White-naped Nuthatch, *Sitta pygmaea leuconucha* Anthony

56. *Family Certhiidae*—Creepers
726 Brown Creeper, *Certhia familiaris americana* Bonaparte
726b Rocky Mountain Creeper, *Certhia familiaris montana* Ridgway
726a Mexican Creeper, *Certhia familiaris albescens* Berlepsch
726d Sierra Creeper, *Certhia familiaris zelotes* Osgood
726c California Creeper, *Certhia familiaris occidentalis* Ridgway

57. *Family Chamaeidae*—Wren-tits
742b Coast Wren-tit, *Chamaea fasciata phaea* Osgood
742c Ruddy Wren-tit, *Chamaea fasciata rufula* Ridgway
742 Gambel's Wren-tit, *Chamaea fasciata fasciata* (Gambel)
742a Pallid Wren-tit, *Chamaea fasciata henshawi* Ridgway
742d San Pedro Wren-tit, *Chamaea fasciata canicauda* Grinnell and Swarth

58. *Family Cinclidae*—Dippers
701 Dipper, *Cinclus mexicanus unicolor* Bonaparte

59. *Family Troglodytidae*—Wrens
721 Eastern House Wren, *Troglodytes aëdon aëdon* Vieillot
721a Western House Wren, *Troglodytes aëdon parkmani* Audubon
722 Eastern Winter Wren, *Nannus hiemalis hiemalis* (Vieillot)
723.1 Aleutian Wren, *Nannus hiemalis meligerus* (Oberholser)
722c Kiska Wren, *Nannus hiemalis kiskensis* Oberholser
723 Alaska Wren, *Nannus hiemalis alascensis* (Baird)
722d Tanaga Wren, *Nannus hiemalis tanagensis* Oberholser
722e Unalaska Wren, *Nannus hiemalis petrophilus* Oberholser
722f Semidi Wren, *Nannus hiemalis semidiensis* Brooks
722b Kodiak Wren, *Nannus hiemalis helleri* (Osgood)
722a Western Winter Wren, *Nannus hiemalis pacificus* (Baird)
719 Bewick's Wren, *Thryomanes bewicki bewicki* (Audubon)
719c Texas Wren, *Thryomanes bewicki cryptus* Oberholser
719b Baird's Wren, *Thryomanes bewicki eremophilus* Oberholser
719e Seattle Wren, *Thryomanes bewicki calophonus* Oberholser
719f Nicasio Wren, *Thryomanes bewicki marinensis* Grinnell
719a Vigors's Wren, *Thryomanes bewicki spilurus* (Vigors)
719g San Joaquin Wren, *Thryomanes bewicki drymoecus* Oberholser
719k San Diego Wren, *Thryomanes bewicki correctus* Grinnell
719h Santa Cruz Wren, *Thryomanes bewicki nesophilus* Oberholser
719i Catalina Wren, *Thryomanes bewicki catalinae* Grinnell
719.1 San Clemente Wren, *Thryomanes bewicki leucophrys* (Anthony)

719d Sooty Wren, *Thryomanes bewicki charienturus* Oberholser
719j Cedros Island Wren, *Thryomanes bewicki cerroensis* (Anthony)
720 Guadalupe Wren, *Thryomanes brevicauda* Ridgway
718 Carolina Wren, *Thryothorus ludovicianus ludovicianus* (Latham)
718a Florida Wren, *Thryothorus ludovicianus miamensis* Ridgway
718b Lomita Wren, *Thryothorus ludovicianus lomitensis* Sennett
713 Northern Cactus Wren, *Heleodytes brunneicapillus coues* (Sharpe)
713a Bryant's Cactus Wren, *Heleodytes brunneicapillus bryanti* Anthony
713b San Lucas Cactus Wren, *Heleodytes brunneicapillus affinis* (Xantus)
725 Long-billed Marsh Wren, *Telmatodytes palustris palustris* (Wilson)
725b Worthington's Marsh Wren, *Telmatodytes palustris griseus* (Brewster)
725e Marian's Marsh Wren, *Telmatodytes palustris marianae* (Scott)
725h Louisiana Marsh Wren, *Telmatodytes palustris thryophilus* Oberholser
725f Alberta Marsh Wren, *Telmatodytes palustris laingi* Harper
725d Prairie Marsh Wren, *Telmatodytes palustris dissaëptus* (Bangs)
725c Western Marsh Wren, *Telmatodytes palustris plesius* (Oberholser)
725a Tule Wren, *Telmatodytes palustris paludicola* (Baird)
725g Suisun Marsh Wren, *Telmatodytes palustris aestuarinus* Swarth
724 Short-billed Marsh Wren, *Cistothorus stellaris* (Naumann)
717 White-throated Wren, *Catherpes mexicanus albifrons* (Giraud)
717a Cañon Wren, *Catherpes mexicanus conspersus* Ridgway
717b Dotted Wren, *Catherpes mexicanus punctulatus* Ridgway
715 Common Rock Wren, *Salpinctes obsoletus obsoletus* (Say)
716 Guadalupe Rock Wren, *Salpinctes obsoletus guadeloupensis* Ridgway

60. Family *Mimidae*—Mockingbirds and Thrashers

703 Eastern Mockingbird, *Mimus polyglottos polyglottos* (Linnaeus)
703a Western Mockingbird, *Mimus polyglottos leucopterus* (Vigors)
704 Catbird, *Dumetella carolinensis* (Linnaeus)
705 Brown Thrasher, *Toxostoma rufum* (Linnaeus)
706 Sennett's Thrasher, *Toxostoma longirostre sennetti* (Ridgway)
709 San Lucas Thrasher, *Toxostoma cinereum cinereum* (Xantus)
709a Mearns's Thrasher, *Toxostoma cinereum mearnsi* (Anthony)
708 Bendire's Thrasher, *Toxostoma bendirei* (Coues)
707a Palmer's Thrasher, *Toxostoma curvirostre palmeri* (Coues)
707 Curve-billed Thrasher, *Toxostoma curvirostre curvirostre* (Swainson)
707b Brownsville Thrasher, *Toxostoma curvirostre oberholseri* Law
710 California Thrasher, *Toxostoma redivivum redivivum* (Gambel)
710b Sonoma Thrasher, *Toxostoma redivivum sonomae* Grinnell
711 Leconte's Thrasher, *Toxostoma lecontei lecontei* Lawrence
711a Desert Thrasher, *Toxostoma lecontei arenicola* (Anthony)
712 Crissal Thrasher, *Toxostoma dorsale dorsale* Henry
712a Trinidad Thrasher, *Toxostoma dorsale trinitatis* Grinnell
702 Sage Thrasher, *Oreoscoptes montanus* (Townsend)

61. Family *Turdidae*—Thrushes, Bluebirds, Stonechats, and Solitaires

760 Red-winged Thrush, *Arceuthornis musicus* (Linnaeus)
761 Eastern Robin, *Turdus migratorius migratorius* Linnaeus
761b Southern Robin, *Turdus migratorius achrusterus* (Batchelder)
761c Northwestern Robin, *Turdus migratorius caurinus* (Grinnell)
761a Western Robin, *Turdus migratorius propinquus* Ridgway

762 San Lucas Robin, *Turdus confinis* Baird
761.1 European Blackbird, *Turdus merula merula* Linnaeus
763 Pacific Varied Thrush, *Ixoreus naevius naevius* (Gmelin)
763a Northern Varied Thrush, *Ixoreus naevius meruloides* (Swainson)
755 Wood Thrush, *Hylocichla mustelina* (Gmelin)
759 Alaska Hermit Thrush, *Hylocichla guttata guttata* (Pallas)
759c Dwarf Hermit Thrush, *Hylocichla guttata nanus* (Audubon)
759d Monterey Hermit Thrush, *Hylocichla guttata slevini* Grinnell
759e Sierra Hermit Thrush, *Hylocichla guttata sequoiensis* (Belding)
759f Mono Hermit Thrush, *Hylocichla guttata polionota* Grinnell
759a Audubon's Hermit Thrush, *Hylocichla guttata auduboni* (Baird)
759b Eastern Hermit Thrush, *Hylocichla guttata faxoni* Bangs and Penard
758 Russet-backed Thrush, *Hylocichla ustulata ustulata* (Nuttall)
758a Olive-backed Thrush, *Hylocichla ustulata swainsoni* (Tschudi)
757 Gray-checked Thrush, *Hylocichla minima aliciae* (Baird)
757a Bicknell's Thrush, *Hylocichla minima minima* (Lafresnaye)
756 Veery, *Hylocichla fuscescens fuscescens* (Stephens)
756a Willow Thrush, *Hylocichla fuscescens salicicola* Ridgway
766 Eastern Bluebird, *Sialia sialis sialis* (Linnaeus)
766a Azure Bluebird, *Sialia sialis fulva* Brewster
767a Chestnut-backed Bluebird, *Sialia mexicana bairdi* Ridgway
767 Western Bluebird, *Sialia mexicana occidentalis* Townsend
767b San Pedro Bluebird, *Sialia mexicana anabelae* Anthony
768 Mountain Bluebird, *Sialia currucoides* (Bechstein)
765 European Wheatear, *Oenanthe oenanthe oenanthe* (Linnaeus)
765a Greenland Wheatear, *Oenanthe oenanthe leucorhoa* (Gmelin)
764 Red-spotted Bluethroat, *Cyanosylvia suecica* (Linnaeus)
764.1 Greater Kamchatka Nightingale, *Calliope calliope camtschatkensis* (Gmelin)
754 Townsend's Solitaire, *Myadestes townsendi* (Audubon)

64. Family Sylviidae—Warblers, Gnatcatchers, and Kinglets

747 Kennicott's Willow Warbler, *Acanthopneuste borealis kennicotti* (Baird)
747.1 Middendorff's Grasshopper Warbler, *Locustella ochotensis* (Middendorff)
751 Blue-gray Gnatcatcher, *Polioptila caerulea caerulea* (Linnaeus)
751b Western Gnatcatcher, *Polioptila caerulea amoenissima* Grinnell
751a San Lucas Gnatcatcher, *Polioptila caerulea obscura* Ridgway
752 Plumbeous Gnatcatcher, *Polioptila melanura melanura* Lawrence
752b Margarita Gnatcatcher, *Polioptila melanura margaritae* Ridgway
752a Xantus's Gnatcatcher, *Polioptila melanura abbreviata* Grinnell
753 Black-tailed Gnatcatcher, *Polioptila melanura californica* Brewster
748 Eastern Golden-crowned Kinglet, *Regulus satrapa satrapa* Lichtenstein
748a Western Golden-crowned Kinglet, *Regulus satrapa olivaceus* Baird
749 Eastern Ruby-crowned Kinglet, *Corthylio calendula calendula* (Linnaeus)
749c Western Ruby-crowned Kinglet, *Corthylio calendula cineraceus*
749a Sitka Kinglet, *Corthylio calendula grinnelli* (Palmer)
749b Dusky Kinglet, *Corthylio calendula obscurus* (Ridgway)

63. Family Prunellidae—Accentors

   749.1 Mountain Accentor, *Prunella montanella* (Pallas)

64. Family Motacillidae—Wagtails and Pipits

   694 White Wagtail, *Motacilla alba alba* Linnaeus
   695 Swinhoe's Wagtail, *Motacilla alba ocularis* Swinhoe
   695.1 Black-backed Wagtail, *Motacilla alba lugens* Kittlitz
   696 Alaska Yellow Wagtail, *Motacilla flava alascensis* (Ridgway)
   697 American Pipit, *Anthus spinoletta rubescens* (Tunstall)
   697.1 Japanese Pipit, *Anthus spinoletta japonicus* Temminck and Schlegel
   698 Meadow Pipit, *Anthus pratensis* (Linnaeus)
   699 Red-throated Pipit, *Anthus cervinus* (Pallas)
   700 Sprague's Pipit, *Anthus spraguei* (Audubon)

65. Family Bombycillidae—Waxwings

   618 Bohemian Waxwing, *Bombycilla garrula pallidiceps* Reichenow
   619 Cedar Waxwing, *Bombycilla cedrorum* Vieillot

66. Family Ptilogonatidae—Silky Flycatchers

   620 Phainopepla, *Phainopepla nitens lepida* van Tyne

67. Family Laniidae—Shrikes

   621 Northern Shrike, *Lanius borealis borealis* Vieillot
   621a Northwestern Shrike, *Lanius borealis invictus* Grinnell
   622 Loggerhead Shrike, *Lanius ludovicianus ludovicianus* Linnaeus
   622e Migrant Shrike, *Lanius ludovicianus migrans* Palmer
   622a White-rumped Shrike, *Lanius ludovicianus excubitorides* Swainson
   622b California Shrike, *Lanius ludovicianus gambeli* Ridgway
   622f Nelson's Shrike, *Lanius ludovicianus nelsoni* Oberholser
   622c Island Shrike, *Lanius ludovicianus anthonyi* Mearns

68. Family Sturnidae—Starlings

   493 Starling, *Sturnus vulgaris vulgaris* Linnaeus
   493.1 Crested Mynah, *Aethiopsar cristatellus cristatellus* (Linnaeus)

69. Family Vireonidae—Vireos

   630 Black-capped Vireo, *Vireo atricapillus* Woodhouse
   631 White-eyed Vireo, *Vireo griseus griseus* (Boddaert)
   631a Key West Vireo, *Vireo griseus maynardi* Brewster
   631b Bermuda Vireo, *Vireo griseus bermudianus* Bangs and Bradlee
   631c Rio Grande Vireo, *Vireo griseus micrus* Nelson
   632 Hutton's Vireo, *Vireo huttoni huttoni* Cassin
   632a Stephens's Vireo, *Vireo huttoni stephensi* Brewster
   632d Frazar's Vireo, *Vireo huttoni cognatus* Ridgway
   633 Bell's Vireo, *Vireo belli belli* Audubon
   633b Texas Vireo, *Vireo belli medius* Oberholser
   633c Arizona Vireo, *Vireo belli arizona* Ridgway
   633a Least Vireo, *Vireo belli pusillus* Coues
   634 Gray Vireo, *Vireo vicinior* Coues
   628 Yellow-throated Vireo, *Vireo flavifrons* Vieillot

629 Blue-headed Vireo, *Vireo solitarius solitarius* (Wilson)
629c Mountain Vireo, *Vireo solitarius alticola* Brewster
629b Plumbeous Vireo, *Vireo solitarius plumbeus* Coues
629a Cassin's Vireo, *Vireo solitarius cassini* Xantus
629d San Lucas Vireo, *Vireo solitarius lucasanus* Brewster
623 Black-whiskered Vireo, *Vireo calidris barbatulus* (Cabanis)
625 Yellow-green Vireo, *Vireo flavoviridis flavoviridis* (Cassin)
624 Red-eyed Vireo, *Vireo olivaceus* (Linnaeus)
626 Philadelphia Vireo, *Vireo philadelphicus* (Cassin)
627 Eastern Warbling Vireo, *Vireo gilvus gilvus* (Vieillot)
627a Western Warbling Vireo, *Vireo gilvus swainsoni* Baird

70. *Family Coerebidae*—Honey Creepers
635 Bahama Honey Creeper, *Coereba bahamensis* (Reichenbach)

71. *Family Compsothlypidae*—Wood Warblers
636 Black and White Warbler, *Mniotilta varia* (Linnaeus)
637 Prothonotary Warbler, *Protonotaria citrea* (Boddaert)
638 Swainson's Warbler, *Limnothlypis swainsoni* (Audubon)
639 Worm-eating Warbler, *Helmitheros vermivorus* (Gmelin)
642 Golden-winged Warbler, *Vermivora chrysoptera* (Linnaeus)
641 Blue-winged Warbler, *Vermivora pinus* (Linnaeus)
640 Bachman's Warbler, *Vermivora bachmani* (Audubon)
647 Tennessee Warbler, *Vermivora peregrina* (Wilson)
646 Orange-crowned Warbler, *Vermivora celata celata* (Say)
646a Lutescent Warbler, *Vermivora celta lutescens* (Ridgway)
646b Dusky Warbler, *Vermivora celata sordida* (Townsend)
645 Nashville Warbler, *Vermivora ruficapilla ruficapilla* (Wilson)
645a Calaveras Warbler, *Vermivora ruficapilla ridgwayi* van Rossem
644 Virginia's Warbler, *Vermivora virginiae* (Baird)
647.1 Colima Warbler, *Vermivora crissalis* (Salvin and Godman)
643 Lucy's Warbler, *Vermivora luciae* (Cooper)
648a Northern Parula Warbler, *Compsothlypis americana pusilla* (Wilson)
648 Southern Parula Warbler, *Compsothlypis americana americana* (Linnaeus)
649 Sennett's Warbler, *Compsothlypis pitiayumi nigrilora* (Coues)
649.1 Socorro Warbler, *Compsothlypis graysoni* Ridgway
651 Olive Warbler, *Peucedramus olivaceus* (Giraud)
652 Eastern Yellow Warbler, *Dendroica aestiva aestiva* (Gmelin)
652b Alaska Yellow Warbler, *Dendroica aestiva rubiginosa* (Pallas)
652c California Yellow Warbler, *Dendroica aestiva brewsteri* Grinnell
652a Sonora Yellow Warbler, *Dendroica aestiva sonorana* Brewster
653 Mangrove Warbler, *Dendroica erithachorides castaneiceps* Ridgway
657 Magnolia Warbler, *Dendroica magnolia* (Wilson)
650 Cape May Warbler, *Dendroica tigrina* (Gmelin)
654 Black-throated Blue Warbler, *Dendroica caerulescens caerulescens* (Gmelin)
654a Cairns's Warbler, *Dendroica caerulescens cairnsi* Coues
655 Myrtle Warbler, *Dendroica coronata* (Linnaeus)
656 Audubon's Warbler, *Dendroica auduboni auduboni* (Townsend)
656a Black-fronted Warbler, *Dendroica auduboni nigrifrons* Brewster

665 Black-throated Gray Warbler, *Dendroica nigrescens* (Townsend)
668 Townsend's Warbler, *Dendroica townsendi* (Townsend)
667 Black-throated Green Warbler, *Dendroica virens virens* (Gmelin)
667a Wayne's Warbler, *Dendroica virens waynei* Bangs
666 Golden-cheeked Warbler, *Dendroica chrysoparia* Sclater and Salvin
669 Hermit Warbler, *Dendroica occidentalis* (Townsend)
658 Cerulean Warbler, *Dendroica cerulea* (Wilson)
662 Blackburnian Warbler, *Dendroica fusca* (Müller)
663 Yellow-throated Warbler, *Dendroica dominica dominica* (Linnaeus)
663a Sycamore Warbler, *Dendroica dominica albilora* Ridgway
664 Grace's Warbler, *Dendroica graciae graciae* Baird
659 Chestnut-sided Warbler, *Dendroica pensylvanica* (Linnaeus)
660 Bay-breasted Warbler, *Dendroica castanea* (Wilson)
661 Black-poll Warbler, *Dendroica striata* (Forster)
671 Northern Pine Warbler, *Dendroica pinus pinus* (Wilson)
671a Florida Pine Warbler, *Dendroica pinus florida* (Maynard)
670 Kirtland's Warbler, *Dendroica kirtlandi* (Baird)
673 Northern Prairie Warbler, *Dendroica discolor discolor* (Vieillot)
673a Florida Prairie Warbler, *Dendroica discolor collinsi* Bailey
672 Western Palm Warbler, *Dendroica palmarum palmarum* (Gmelin)
672a Yellow Palm Warbler, *Dendroica palmarum hypochrysea* Ridgway
674 Oven-bird, *Seiurus aurocapillus* (Linnaeus)
675 Northern Water-thrush, *Seiurus noveboracensis noveboracensis* (Gmelin)
675a Grinnell's Water-thrush, *Seiurus noveboracensis notabilis* Ridgway
676 Louisiana Water-thrush, *Seiurus motacilla* (Vieillot)
677 Kentucky Warbler, *Oporornis formosus* (Wilson)
678 Connecticut Warbler, *Oporornis agilis* (Wilson)
679 Mourning Warbler, *Oporornis philadelphia* (Wilson)
680 Macgillivray's Warbler, *Oporornis tolmiei* (Townsend)
681d Northern Yellow-throat, *Geothlypis trichas brachidactyla* (Swainson)
681 Maryland Yellow-throat, *Geothlypis trichas trichas* (Linnaeus)
681b Florida Yellow-throat, *Geothlypis trichas ignota* Chapman
681a Western Yellow-throat, *Geothlypis trichas occidentalis* Brewster
681e Salt Marsh Yellow-throat, *Geothlypis trichas sinuosa* Grinnell
681f Tule Yellow-throat, *Geothlypis trichas scirpicola* Grinnell
682a Goldman's Yellow-throat, *Geothlypis beldingi goldmani* Oberholser
682 Belding's Yellow-throat, *Geothlypis beldingi beldingi* Ridgway
682.1 Rio Grande Yellow-throat, *Chamaethlypis poliocephala poliocephala*
    (Baird)
683 Yellow-breasted Chat, *Icteria virens virens* (Linnaeus)
683a Long-tailed Chat, *Icteria virens longicauda* Lawrence
688.1 Western Fan-tailed Warbler, *Euthlypis lachrymosa tephra* Ridgway
690 Red-faced Warbler, *Cardellina rubrifrons* (Giraud)
684 Hooded Warbler, *Wilsonia citrina* (Boddaert)
685 Wilson's Warbler, *Wilsonia pusilla pusilla* (Wilson)
685a Northern Pileolated Warbler, *Wilsonia pusilla pileolata* (Pallas)
685b Golden Pileolated Warbler, *Wilsonia pusilla chryseola* Ridgway
686 Canada Warbler, *Wilsonia canadensis* (Linnaeus)
687 American Redstart, *Septophaga ruticilla* (Linnaeus)
688 Painted Redstart, *Setophaga picta picta* Swainson

72. *Family Ploceidae*—Weaver Finches

    688.2 English Sparrow, *Passer domesticus domesticus* (Linnaeus)
    688.3 European Tree Sparrow, *Passer montanus montanus* (Linnaeus)

73. *Family Icteridae*—Meadowlarks, Blackbirds, and Troupials

    494 Bobolink, *Dolichonyx oryzivorus* (Linnaeus)
    501 Eastern Meadowlark, *Sturnella magna magna* (Linnaeus)
    501c Southern Meadowlark, *Sturnella magna argutula* Bangs
    501a Rio Grande Meadowlark, *Sturnella magna hoopesi* Stone
    501.1 Western Meadowlark, *Sturnella neglecta* Audubon
    497 Yellow-headed Blackbird, *Xanthocephalus xanthocephalus* (Bonaparte)
    498 Eastern Red-wing, *Agelaius phoeniceus phoeniceus* (Linnaeus)
    498c Florida Red-wing, *Agelaius phoeniceus mearnsi* Howell and van Rossem
    498b Maynard's Red-wing, *Agelaius phoeniceus floridanus* Maynard
    498h Gulf Coast Red-wing, *Agelaius phoeniceus littoralis* Howell and van Rossem
    498g Rio Grande Red-wing, *Agelaius phoeniceus megapotamus* Oberholser
    498i Giant Red-wing, *Agelaius phoeniceus arctolegus* Oberholser
    498d Thick-billed Red-wing, *Agelaius phoeniceus fortis* Ridgway
    498j Nevada Red-wing, *Agelaius phoeniceus nevadensis* Grinnell
    498f Northwestern Red-wing, *Agelaius phoeniceus caurinus* Ridgway
    498k San Francisco Red-wing, *Agelaius phoeniceus mailliardorum* van Rossem
    499 Bicolored Red-wing, *Agelaius phoeniceus californicus* Nelson
    498l Kern Red-wing, *Agelaius phoeniceus aciculatus* Mailliard
    498e San Diego Red-wing, *Agelaius phoeniceus neutralis* Ridgway
    498a Sonora Red-wing, *Agelaius phoeniceus sonoriensis* Ridgway
    500 Tricolored Red-wing, *Agelaius tricolor* (Audubon)
    506 Orchard Oriole, *Icterus spurius* (Linnaeus)
    503 Audubon's Oriole, *Icterus melanocephalus auduboni* Giraud
    505 Sennett's Oriole, *Icterus cucullatus sennetti* Ridgway
    505a Arizona Hooded Oriole, *Icterus cucullatus nelsoni* Ridgway
    505b San Lucas Hooded Oriole, *Icterus cucullatus trochiloides* Grinnell
    504 Scott's Oriole, *Icterus parisorum* Bonaparte
    507 Baltimore Oriole, *Icterus galbula* (Linnaeus)
    508 Bullock's Oriole, *Icterus bullocki* (Swainson)
    509 Rusty Blackbird, *Euphagus carolinus* (Müller)
    510 Brewer's Blackbird, *Euphagus cyanocephalus* (Wagler)
    513 Boat-tailed Grackle, *Cassidix mexicanus major* (Vieillot)
    513a Great-tailed Grackle, *Cassidix mexicanus mexicanus* (Gmelin)
    511 Purple Grackle, *Quiscalus quiscula quiscula* (Linnaeus)
    511a Florida Grackle, *Quiscalus quiscula aglaeus* Baird
    511b Bronzed Grackle, *Quiscalus quiscula aeneus* Ridgway
    495 Eastern Cowbird, *Molothrus ater ater* (Boddaert)
    495b Nevada Cowbird, *Molothrus ater artemisiae* Grinnell
    495c California Cowbird, *Molothrus ater californicus* Dickey and van Rossem
    495a Dwarf Cowbird, *Molothrus ater obscurus* (Gmelin)

496a Bronzed Cowbird, *Tangavius aeneus aeneus* (Wagler)
496 Red-eyed Cowbird, *Tangavius aeneus involucratus* Lesson

74. *Family Thraupidae*—Tanagers

607 Western Tanager, *Piranga ludoviciana* (Wilson)
608 Scarlet Tanager, *Piranga erythromelas* Vieillot
609 Hepatic Tanager, *Piranga flava hepatica* Swainson
610 Summer Tanager, *Piranga rubra rubra* (Linnaeus)
610a Cooper's Tanager, *Piranga rubra cooperi* Ridgway

75. *Family Fringillidae*—Grosbeaks, Finches, Sparrows, and Buntings

593 Eastern Cardinal, *Richmondena cardinalis cardinalis* (Linnaeus)
593d Florida Cardinal, *Richmondena cardinalis floridana* (Ridgway)
593e Louisiana Cardinal, *Richmondena cardinalis magnirostris* (Bangs)
593c Gray-tailed Cardinal, *Richmondena cardinalis canicauda* (Chapman)
593a Arizona Cardinal, *Richmondena cardinalis superba* (Ridgway)
593b San Lucas Cardinal, *Richmondena cardinalis ignea* (Baird)
594a Texas Pyrrhuloxia, *Pyrrhuloxia sinuata texana* Ridgway
594 Arizona Pyrrhuloxia, *Pyrrhuloxia sinuata sinuata* (Bonaparte)
594b San Lucas Pyrrhuloxia, *Pyrrhuloxia sinuata peninsulae* Ridgway
595 Rose-breasted Grosbeak, *Hedymeles ludovicianus* (Linnaeus)
596 Black-headed Grosbeak, *Hedymeles melanocephalus melanocephalus* (Swainson)
596a Rocky Mountain Grosbeak, *Hedymeles melanocephalus papago* Oberholser
597 Eastern Blue Grosbeak, *Guiraca caerulea caerulea* (Linnaeus)
597a Western Blue Grosbeak, *Guiraca caerulea interfusa* Dwight and Griscom
597b California Blue Grosbeak, *Guiraca caerulea salicaria* Grinnell
598 Indigo Bunting, *Passerina cyanea* (Linnaeus)
599 Lazuli Bunting, *Passerina amoena* (Say)
600 Varied Bunting, *Passerina versicolor versicolor* (Bonaparte)
600a Beautiful Bunting, *Passerina versicolor pulchra* Ridgway
601 Painted Bunting, *Passerina ciris* (Linnaeus)
603 Bahama Grassquit, *Tiaris bicolor bicolor* (Linnaeus)
603.1 Melodious Grassquit, *Tiaris canora* (Gmelin)
604 Dickcissel, *Spiza americana* (Gmelin)
514.1 Brambling, *Fringilla montifringilla* Linnaeus
514.2 Japanese Hawfinch, *Coccothraustes coccothraustes japonicus* Temminck and Schlegel
514 Eastern Evening Grosbeak, *Hesperiphona vespertina vespertina* (Cooper)
514b Western Evening Grosbeck, *Hesperiphona vespertina brooksi* Grinnell
514a Mexican Evening Grosbeak, *Hesperiphona vespertina montana* Ridgway
516 Cassin's Bullfinch, *Pyrrhula pyrrhula cassini* Baird
517 Eastern Purple Finch, *Carpodacus purpureus purpureus* (Gmelin)
517a California Purple Finch, *Carpodacus purpureus californicus* Baird
518 Cassin's Purple Finch, *Carpodacus cassini* Baird
519 Common House Finch, *Carpodacus mexicanus frontalis* (Say)

519b San Lucas House Finch, *Carpodacus mexicanus ruberrimus* Ridgway
519c San Clemente House Finch, *Carpodacus mexicanus clementis* Mearns
520.1 McGregor's House Finch, *Carpodacus megregori* Anthony
520 Guadalupe House Finch, *Carpodacus amplus* Ridgway
602 Sharpe's Seedeater, *Sporophila morelleti sharpei* Lawrence
515 Canadian Pine Grosbeak, *Pinicola enucleator leucura* (Müller)
515f Kamchatka Pine Grosbeak, *Pinicola enucleator kamtschatkensis* (Dybowski)
515c Alaska Pine Grosbeak, *Pinicola enucleator alascensis* Ridgway
515d Kodiak Pine Grosbeak, *Pinicola enucleator flammula* Homeyer
515e Queen Charlotte Pine Grosbeak, *Pinicola enucleator carlottae* Brooks
515a Rocky Mountain Pine Grosbeak, *Pinicola enucleator montana* Ridgway
515b California Pine Grosbeak, *Pinicola enucleator californica* Price
523 Aleutian Rosy Finch, *Leucosticte griseonucha* (Brandt)
524a Hepburn's Rosy Finch, *Leucosticte tephrocotis littoralis* (Baird)
524 Gray-crowned Rosy Finch, *Leucosticte tephrocotis tephrocotis* (Swainson)
524b Sierra Nevada Rosy Finch, *Leucosticte tephrocotis dawsoni* Grinnell
525 Black Rosy Finch, *Leucosticte atrata* Ridgway
526 Brown-capped Rosy Finch, *Leucosticte australis* Ridgway
526.1 British Goldfinch, *Carduelis carduelis britannica* (Hartert)
527 Hornemann's Redpoll, *Acanthis hornemanni hornemanni* (Holboell)
527a Hoary Redpoll, *Acanthis hornemanni exilipes* (Coues)
528 Common Redpoll, *Acanthis linaria linaria* (Linnaeus)
528a Holboell's Redpoll, *Acanthis linaria holboelli* (Brehm)
528b Greater Redpoll, *Acanthis linaria rostrata* (Coues)
533 Northern Pine Siskin, *Spinus pinus pinus* (Wilson)
533a Mexican Pine Siskin, *Spinus pinus macropterus* (Du Bus)
529 Eastern Goldfinch, *Spinus tristis tristis* (Linnaeus)
529a Pale Goldfinch, *Spinus tristis pallidus* Mearns
529b Willow Goldfinch, *Spinus tristis salicamans* Grinnell
530 Arkansas Goldfinch, *Spinus psaltria psaltria* (Say)
530a Green-backed Goldfinch, *Spinus psaltria hesperophilus* (Oberholser)
531 Lawrence's Goldfinch, *Spinus lawrencei* (Cassin)
521 Red Crossbill, *Loxia curvirostra pusilla* Gloger
521b Newfoundland Crossbill, *Loxia curvirostra percna* Bent
521c Sitka Crossbill, *Loxia curvirostra sitkensis* Grinnell
521d Bendire's Crossbill, *Loxia curvirostra bendirei* Ridgway
521a Mexican Crossbill, *Loxia curvirostra stricklandi* Ridgway
522 White-winged Crossbill, *Loxia leucoptera* Gmelin
586 Texas Sparrow, *Arremonops rufivirgatus rufivirgatus* (Lawrence)
592.1 Green-tailed Towhee, *Oberholseria chlorura* (Audubon)
587 Red-eyed Towhee, *Pipilo erythrophthalmus erythrophthalmus* (Linnaeus)
587b Alabama Towhee, *Pipilo erythrophthalmus canaster* Howell
587a White-eyed Towhee, *Pipilo erythrophthalmus alleni* Coues
588 Arctic Towhee, *Pipilo maculatus arcticus* (Swainson)
588a Spurred Towhee, *Pipilo maculatus montanus* Swarth
588f Nevada Towhee, *Pipilo maculatus curtatus* Grinnell

588b Oregon Towhee, *Pipilo maculatus oregonus* Bell
588g Sacramento Towhee, *Pipilo maculatus falcinellus* Swarth
588h San Francisco Towhee, *Pipilo maculatus falcifer* McGregor
588d San Diego Towhee, *Pipilo maculatus megalonyx* Baird
588c San Clemente Towhee, *Pipilo maculatus clementae* Grinnell
588i Cape Colnett Towhee, *Pipilo maculatus umbraticola* Grinnell and Swarth
588e Large-billed Towhee, *Pipilo maculatus magnirostris* Brewster
589 Guadalupe Towhee, *Pipilo consobrinus* Ridgway
591b Oregon Brown Towhee, *Pipilo fuscus bullatus* Grinnell and Swarth
591c Sacramento Brown Towhee, *Pipilo fuscus carolae* McGregor
591d San Francisco Brown Towhee, *Pipilo fuscus petulans* Grinnell and Swarth
591.1 California Towhee, *Pipilo fuscus crissalis* (Vigors)
591.1a Anthony's Towhee, *Pipilo fuscus senicula* Anthony
591e San Pablo Towhee, *Pipilo fuscus aripolius* Oberholser
591a San Lucas Towhee, *Pipilo fuscus albigula* Baird
591 Cañon Towhee, *Pipilo fuscus mesoleucus* Baird
592 Abert's Towhee, *Pipilo aberti* Baird
605 Lark Bunting, *Calamospiza melanocorys* Stejneger
541 Ipswich Sparrow, *Passerculus princeps* Maynard
542a Eastern Savannah Sparrow, *Passerculus sandwichensis savanna* (Wilson)
542d Labrador Savannah Sparrow, *Passerculus sandwichensis labradorius* Howe
542b Western Savannah Sparrow, *Passerculus sandwichensis alaudinus* Bonaparte
542 Aleutian Savannah Sparrow, *Passerculus sandwichensis sandwichensis* (Gmelin)
542e Nevada Savannah Sparrow, *Passerculus sandwichensis nevadensis* Grinnell
542c Bryant's Sparrow, *Passerculus sandwichensis bryanti* Ridgway
543 Belding's Sparrow, *Passerculus beldingi* Ridgway
544 Large-billed Sparrow, *Passerculus rostratus rostratus* (Cassin)
544a San Lucas Sparrow, *Passerculus rostratus guttatus* Lawrence
544b Abreojos Sparrow, *Passerculus rostratus halophilus* (McGregor)
546 Eastern Grasshopper Sparrow, *Ammodramus savannarum australis* Maynard
546a Western Grasshopper Sparrow, *Ammodramus savannarum bimaculatus* Swainson
546b Florida Grasshopper Sparrow, *Ammodramus savannarum floridanus* (Mearns)
545 Baird's Sparrow, *Ammodramus bairdi* (Audubon)
548 Leconte's Sparrow, *Passerherbulus caudacutus* (Latham)
547 Eastern Henslow's Sparrow, *Passerhubulus henslowi susurrans* Brewster
547a Western Henslow's Sparrow, *Passerhubulus henslowi henslowi* (Audubon)
549.1a Acadian Sparrow, *Ammospiza caudacuta subvirgata* (Dwight)
549 Sharp-tailed Sparrow, *Ammospiza caudacuta caudacuta* (Gmelin)
549.1 Nelson's Sparrow, *Ammospiza caudacuta nelsoni* (Allen)

550 Northern Seaside Sparrow, *Ammospiza maritima maritima* (Wilson)
550d Macgillivray's Seaside Sparrow, *Ammospiza maritima macgillivraii* (Audubon)
550a Scott's Seaside Sparrow, *Ammospiza maritima peninsulae* (Allen)
550e Wakulla Seaside Sparrow, *Ammospiza maritima juncicola* (Griscom and Nichols)
550f Howell's Seaside Sparrow, *Ammospiza maritima howelli* (Griscom and Nichols)
550c Louisiana Seaside Sparrow, *Ammospiza maritima fisheri* (Chapman)
550b Texas Seaside Sparrow, *Ammospiza maritima sennetti* (Allen)
551 Dusky Seaside Sparrow, *Ammospiza nigrescens* (Ridgway)
551.1 Cape Sable Seaside Sparrow, *Ammospiza mirabilis* (Howell)
540 Eastern Vesper Sparrow, *Pooecetes gramineus gramineus* (Gmelin)
540b Oregon Vesper Sparrow, *Pooecetes gramineus affinis* (Miller)
540a Western Vesper Sparrow, *Pooecetes gramineus confinis* (Baird)
552 Eastern Lark Sparrow, *Chondestes grammacus grammacus* (Say)
552a Western Lark Sparrow, *Chondestes grammacus strigatus* Swainson
579 Rufous-winged Sparrow, *Aimophila carpalis* (Coues)
580 Rufous-crowned Sparrow, *Aimophila ruficeps ruficeps* (Cassin)
580f Santa Cruz Sparrow, *Aimophila ruficeps obscura* Dickey and van Rossem
580d Ashy Sparrow, *Aimophila ruficeps canescens* Todd
580e Cape Colnett Sparrow, *Aimophila ruficeps lambi* Grinnell
580c Laguna Sparrow, *Aimophila ruficeps sororia* Ridgway
580b Rock Sparrow, *Aimophila ruficeps eremoeca* (Brown)
580a Scott's Sparrow, *Aimophila ruficeps scotti* (Sennett)
575a Bachman's Sparrow, *Aimophila aestivalis bachmani* (Audubon)
575 Pine-woods Sparrow, *Aimophila aestivalis aestivalis* (Lichtenstein)
576 Botteri's Sparrow, *Aimophila botterii botterii* (Sclater)
578 Cassin's Sparrow, *Aimophila cassini* (Woodhouse)
573 Black-throated Sparrow, *Amphispiza bilineata bilineata* (Cassin)
573a Desert Sparrow, *Amphispiza bilineata deserticola* Ridgway
573b Bangs's Sparrow, *Amphispiza bilineata bangsi* Grinnell
574 Bell's Sparrow, *Amphispiza belli belli* (Cassin)
574.1a Gray Sage Sparrow, *Amphispiza belli cinerea* Townsend
574.1 Northern Sage Sparrow, *Amphispiza nevadensis nevadensis* (Ridgway)
574.1b California Sage Sparrow, *Amphispiza nevadensis canescens* Grinnell
566 White-winged Junco, *Junco aikeni* Ridgway
567 Slate-colored Junco, *Junco hyemalis hyemalis* (Linnaeus)
567e Carolina Junco, *Junco hyemalis carolinensis* Brewster
567a Oregon Junco, *Junco oreganus oreganus* (Townsend)
567b Shufeldt's Junco, *Junco oreganus shufeldti* Coale
567f Montana Junco, *Junco oreganus montanus* Ridgway
567c Thurber's Junco, *Junco oreganus thurberi* Anthony
567d Point Pinos Junco, *Junco oreganus pinosus* Loomis
567j Hanson Laguna Junco, *Junco oreganus pontilis* Oberholser
567i Townsend's Junco, *Junco oreganus townsendi* Anthony
572 Guadalupe Junco, *Junco insularis* Ridgway
571 Baird's Junco, *Junco bairdi* Ridgway
567g Pink-sided Junco, *Junco mearnsi* Ridgway

570b Gray-headed Junco, *Junco caniceps* (Woodhouse)
570a Red-backed Junco, *Junco phaeonotus dorsalis* Henry
570 Arizona Junco, *Junco phaeonotus palliatus* Ridgway
559 Eastern Tree Sparrow, *Spizella arborea arborea* (Wilson)
559a Western Tree Sparrow, *Spizella arborea ochracea* Brewster
560 Eastern Chipping Sparrow, *Spizella passerina passerina* (Bechstein)
560a Western Chipping Sparrow, *Spizella passerina arizonae* Coues
561 Clay-colored Sparrow, *Spizella pallida* (Swainson)
562a Timberline Sparrow, *Spizella breweri taverneri* Swarth and Brooks
562 Brewer's Sparrow, *Spizella breweri breweri* Cassin
563 Eastern Field Sparrow, *Spizella pusilla pusilla* (Wilson)
563a Western Field Sparrow, *Spizella pusilla arenacea* Chadbourne
564 Worthen's Sparrow, *Spizella wortheni* Ridgway
565 Mexican Black-chinned Sparrow, *Spizella atrogularis atrogularis* (Cabanis)
565a California Black-chinned Sparrow, *Spizella atrogularis cana* Coues
553 Harris's Sparrow, *Zonotrichia querula* (Nuttall)
554 White-crowned Sparrow, *Zonotrichia leucophrys leucophrys* (Forster)
554a Gambel's Sparrow, *Zonotrichia leucophrys gambeli* (Nuttall)
554c Puget Sound Sparrow, *Zonotrichia leucophrys pugetensis* Grinnell
554b Nuttall's Sparrow, *Zonotrichia leucophrys nuttalli* Ridgway
557 Golden-crowned Sparrow, *Zonotrichia coronata* (Pallas)
558 White-throated Sparrow, *Zonotrichia albicollis* (Gmelin)
585 Eastern Fox Sparrow, *Passerella iliaca iliaca* (Merrem)
585h Alberta Fox Sparrow, *Passerella iliaca altivagans* Riley
585a Shumagin Fox Sparrow, *Passerella iliaca unalaschensis* (Gmelin)
585f Kodiak Fox Sparrow, *Passerella iliaca insularis* Ridgway
585k Valdez Fox Sparrow, *Passerella iliaca sinuosa* Grinnell
585l Yakutat Fox Sparrow, *Passerella iliaca annectens* Ridgway
585g Townsend's Fox Sparrow, *Passerella iliaca townsendi* (Audubon)
585e Sooty Fox Sparrow, *Passerella iliaca fuliginosa* Ridgway
585c Slate-colored Fox Sparrow, *Passerella iliaca schistacea* Baird
585i Warner Mountains Fox Sparrow, *Passerella iliaca fulva* Swarth
585b Thick-billed Fox Sparrow, *Passerella iliaca megarhyncha* Baird
585j Trinity Fox Sparrow, *Passerella iliaca brevicauda* Mailliard
585m Inyo Fox Sparrow, *Passerella iliaca canescens* Swarth
585n Mono Fox Sparrow, *Passerella iliaca monoensis* Grinnell and Storer
585o Yosemite Fox Sparrow, *Passerella iliaca mariposae* Swarth
585d Stephens's Fox Sparrow, *Passerella iliaca stephensi* Anthony
583 Lincoln's Sparrow, *Melospiza lincolni lincolni* (Audubon)
583a Forbush's Sparrow, *Melospiza lincolni gracilis* (Kittlitz)
584 Swamp Sparrow, *Melospiza georgiana* (Latham)
581 Eastern Song Sparrow, *Melospiza melodia melodia* (Wilson)
581t Atlantic Song Sparrow, *Melospiza melodia atlantica* Todd
581u Mississippi Song Sparrow, *Melospiza melodia beata* Bangs
581j Dakota Song Sparrow, *Melospiza melodia juddi* Bishop
581b Mountain Song Sparrow, *Melospiza melodia fallax* (Baird)
581v Modoc Song Sparrow, *Melospiza melodia fisherella* Oberholser
581k Merrill's Song Sparrow, *Melospiza melodia merrilli* Brewster
581r Aleutian Song Sparrow, *Melospiza melodia sanaka* McGregor

581q Bischoff's Song Sparrow, *Melospiza melodia insignis* Baird
581o Kenai Song Sparrow, *Melospiza melodia kenaiensis* Ridgway
581n Yakutat Song Sparrow, *Melospiza melodia caurina* Ridgway
581f Sooty Song Sparrow, *Melospiza melodia rufina* (Bonaparte)
581e Rusty Song Sparrow, *Melospiza melodia morphna* Oberholser
581p Mendocino Song Sparrow, *Melospiza melodia cleonensis* McGregor
581d Samuels's Song Sparrow, *Melospiza melodia samuelis* (Baird)
581s Suisun Song Sparrow, *Melospiza melodia maxillaris* Grinnell
581y Modesto Song Sparrow, *Melospiza melodia mailliardi* Grinnell
581l Alameda Song Sparrow, *Melospiza melodia pusillula* Ridgway
581c Heermann's Song Sparrow, *Melospiza melodia heermanni* Baird
581m San Diego Song Sparrow, *Melospiza melodia cooperi* Ridgway
581h Santa Barbara Song Sparrow, *Melospiza melodia graminea* Townsend
581i San Clemente Song Sparrow, *Melospiza melodia clementae* Townsend
581w San Miguel Song Sparrow, *Melospiza melodia micronyx* Grinnell
581x Coronados Song Sparrow, *Melospiza melodia coronatorum* Grinnell
  and Daggett
581a Desert Song Sparrow, *Melospiza melodia saltonis* Grinnell
581g Brown's Song Sparrow, *Melospiza melodia rivularis* Bryant
539 McCown's Longspur, *Rhynchophanes mccowni* (Lawrence)
536 Lapland Longspur, *Calcarius lapponicus lapponicus* (Linnaeus)
536a Alaska Longspur, *Calcarius lapponicus alascensis* Ridgway
537 Smith's Longspur, *Calcarius pictus* (Swainson)
538 Chestnut-collared Longspur, *Calcarius ornatus* (Townsend)
534 Eastern Snow Bunting, *Plectrophenax nivalis nivalis* (Linnaeus)
534a Pribilof Snow Bunting, *Plectrophenax nivalis townsendi* Ridgway
535 McKay's Snow Bunting, *Plectrophenax hyperboreus* Ridgway
535.1 Rustic Bunting, *Emberiza rustica* Pallas

Index of Other Names of North American Birds

Bird, Meat—see Jay, Canada; see also Nutcracker, Clarke's
Bird, Mock—see Mockingbird
Bird, Mourning—see Plover, Piping
Bird, Myrtle—see Warbler, Myrtle
Bird, Northern Canary—see Siskin, Pine
Bird, Northern Butcher—see Shrike, Northern
Bird of Paradise, Texan—see Flycatcher, Scissor-tailed
Bird, Pasture—see Sparrow, Vesper
Bird, Patriotic—see Woodpecker, Red-headed
Bird, Peabody—see Sparrow, White-throated
Bird, Peto—see Titmouse, Tufted
Bird, Peverly—see Sparrow, White-throated
Bird, Phoebe—see Phoebe
Bird, Potato-bug—see Grosbeak, Rose-breasted
Bird, Prairie—see Lark, Horned
Bird, Preacher—see Vireo, Red-eyed
Bird, Rockweed—see Sandpiper, Purple
Bird, Snake-skin—see Flycatcher, Crested
Bird, Southern Butcher—see Shrike, Loggerhead
Bird, Spring—see Lark, Horned
Bird, Sugar—see Grosbeak, Evening
Bird, Thistle—see Goldfinch, European
Bird, Tick—see Ani, Groove-billed
Bird, Venison—see Jay, Canada
Bird, Wheat—see Lark, Horned
Bird, Winter Butcher—see Shrike, Northern
Bird, Yawker—see Flicker
Bird, Zebra—see Woodpecker, Red-bellied
Bittern, American—see Bittern
Bittern, Dwarf—see Bittern, Least
Bittern, Green—see Heron, Green
Bittern, Little—see Bittern, Least
Blackbird—see Crackle, Purple
Blackbird, Bi-colored—see Red-wing, Bi-colored
Blackbird, Brown-headed—see Cowbird

Blackbird, Cow—see Cowbird
Blackbird, Crow—see Crackle, Purple
Blackbird, Marsh—see Blackbird, Red-winged
Blackbird, Red-shouldered—see Blackbird, Red-winged
Blackbird, Skunk—see Bobolink
Blackbird, Skunk-head—see Bobolink
Blackbird, Swamp—see Blackbird, Red-winged
Blackbird, Thrush—see Blackbird, Rusty
Blackbird, Tri-colored—see Red-wing, Tri-colored
Blackbird, White-winged—see Bobolink; see also Bunting, Lark
Black-breast—see Plover, Black-bellied
Blackbreast, Little—see Sandpiper, Red-backed
Black-cap—see Warbler, Wilson's
Black-cap, Wilson's—see Warbler, Wilson's
Black-foot—see Grouse, Sharp-tailed
Black-head—see Duck, Scaup; see also Grosbeak, Black-headed
Black-head, Big—see Duck, Scaup
Blackhead, Ring-billed—see Duck, Ring-necked
Black-hood—see Sparrow, Harris's
Black-neck—see Duck, Scaup
Black-poll—see Warbler, Black-poll
Black-tail—see Godwit, Hudsonian
Black-throat—see Sparrow, Black-throated; see also Warbler, Black-throated Blue
Black-throat, Bog—see Warbler, Connecticut
Black-throat, Green—see Warbler, Black-throated Green
Blatherskite—see Duck, Ruddy
Blue-bill—see Duck, Ruddy
Blue-bill—see Duck, Scaup
Blue-bill, Greater—see Duck, Scaup
Blue-bill, Marsh—see Duck, Ring-necked
Bluebird, American—see Bluebird
Bluebird, Arctic—see Bluebird, Mountain
Bluebird, California—see Bluebird, Western
Bluebird, Common—see Bluebird

Bluebird, Eastern—see Bluebird
Bluebird, Indigo—see Bunting, Indigo
Bluebird, Wilson's—see Bluebird
Blue-wing—see Teal, Blue-winged
Boatswain—see Jaeger, Parasitic; see also Tropic-bird, Yellow-billed
Boatswain-bird—see Tropic-bird, Yellow-billed
Bob-lincoln—see Bobolink
Bobolink, Prairie—see Bunting, Lark
Bob-white, Arizona—see Bob-white, Masked
Bog-bird—see Woodcock
Bogsucker—see Woodcock
Bog-trotter—see Hawk, Marsh
Bonxie—see Skua
Booby—see Duck, Ruddy
Booby (male)—see Scoter
Booby, Brown—see Booby
Booby, Catesby's—see Booby
Booby, Yellow-footed—see Booby
Bosen-bird—see Tropic-bird, Yellow-billed
Bottle-head—see Plover, Black-bellied
Bottle-nose—see Puffin
Brant—see Goose, Blue
Brant, Bald-headed—see Goose, Blue
Brant, Black—see Brant
Brant, Blue—see Goose, Blue
Brant, Canada—see Goose, Canada
Brant, Common—see Brant
Brant, Eastern—see Brant
Brant, Gray—see Goose, White-fronted
Brant, Harlequin—see Goose, White-fronted
Brant, Light-bellied—see Brant
Brant, Pied—see Goose, White-fronted
Brant, Prairie—see Goose, White-fronted
Brant, Sea—see Scoter, White-winged
Brant, Speckled—see Goose, White-fronted
Brant, Spectacled—see Goose, White-fronted
Brant, White—see Goose, Snow
Brant, White-bellied—see Brant
Brant, White-headed Bald—see Goose, Blue

Brant-bird—see Sandpiper, Red-backed; see also Turnstone, Ruddy; also Godwit, Marbled
Brass-back—see Plover, Golden
Bride, The—see Duck, Wood
Bristle-tail—see Duck, Ruddy
Broad-bill—see Duck, Ruddy; see also Duck, Scaup
Broad-bill, Bastard—see Duck, Ring-necked
Broad-bill, Creek—see Duck, Lesser Scaup
Broad-bill, Hard-headed—see Duck, Ruddy
Broadbill, Red-headed—see Redhead
Broad-bill, River—see Duck, Lesser Scaup
Broady—see Shoveller
Brother, Sleepy—see Duck, Ruddy
Brown-back—see Sandpiper, Pectoral
Brown-back (summer)—see Dowitcher
Brownie—see Sandpiper, Pectoral
Buff-breast—see Knot
Bull, Bog—see Bittern
Bull-bat—see Nighthawk
Bullfinch—see Pyrrhuloxia, Arizona
Bullfinch (in Virginia)—see Towhee
Bullfinch, Pine—see Grosbeak, Pine
Bull-head—see Golden-eye; see also Plover, Black-bellied; also Plover, Golden
Bull-neck—see Canvas-back; see also Duck, Ruddy
Bunting, Bay-winged—see Sparrow, Vesper
Bunting, Black-throated—see Dickcissel
Bunting, Canon—see Towhee, Canon
Bunting, Cow—see Cowbird
Bunting, Field—see Sparrow, Field
Bunting, Green-tailed—see Towhee, Green-tailed
Bunting, Henslow's—see Sparrow, Henslow's
Bunting, Indigo Painted—see Bunting, Indigo
Bunting, Lazuli Painted—see Bunting, Lazuli
Bunting, Savannah—see Sparrow, Savannah

Bunting, Towhee—see Towhee
Bunting, Tree—see Sparrow, Tree
Bunty—see Duck, Ring-necked
Burgomaster—see Gull, Glaucous
Burion—see Finch, House
Bush-bird—see Towhee
Bush-Tit, Yellow-headed—see Verdin
Butter-back—see Buffle-head
Butter-ball—see Buffle-head
Butter-ball—see Duck, Ruddy
Butter-ball, Spoon-billed—see Duck, Ruddy
Butter-bill (male)—see Scoter
Butter-bill, Black (male)—see Scoter
Butter-bird (Jamaica, B.W.I.)—see Bobolink
Butter-box—see Buffle-head
Butterbump—see Bittern
Butter-nose (male)—see Scoter
Buzzard, Black—see Vulture, Black
Buzzard, Broad-winged—see Hawk, Broad-winged
Buzzard, Red-shouldered—see Hawk, Red-shouldered
Buzzard, Red-tailed—see Hawk, Red-tailed
Buzzard, Rough-legged—see Hawk, Rough-legged
Buzzard, Turkey—see Vulture, Turkey

Calico-back—see Turnstone, Ruddy
Calico-bird—see Turnstone, Ruddy
Calico-jacket—see Turnstone, Ruddy
Calloo—see Old-Squaw
Can—see Canvas-back
Canary, Blue—see Bunting, Indigo
Canary, Mexico—see Bunting, Painted
Canary, Tarweed—see Goldfinch, Arkansas
Canary, Wild (incorrect)—see Warbler, Yellow
Canvas-back—see Eider
Carau—see Limpkin
Cardinal, Bullfinch—see Pyrrhuloxia, Arizona
Cardinal, Gray—see Pyrrhuloxia, Arizona
Cardinal, Kentucky—see Cardinal
Casique, Blue-throated—see Hummingbird, Blue-throated
Chad—see Woodpecker, Red-bellied

Chaser, Gull—see Jaeger, Pomarine
Chat—see Chat, Yellow-breasted
Chat, Common—see Chat, Yellow-breasted
Chat, Polyglot—see Chat, Yellow-breasted
Chat, Yellow—see Chat, Yellow-breasted
Chebec—see Flycatcher, Least
Cherrybird (in Adirondacks)—see Sparrow, White-throated
Chewink—see Towhee
Chickadee, Black-capped—see Chickadee
Chickadee, Common—see Chickadee
Chickadee, Eastern—see Chickadee
Chickadee, Tufted—see Titmouse, Tufted
Chicken—see Turnstone, Ruddy
Chicken, Meadow—see Sora
Chicken, Mother Carey's—see Petrel, Storm; see also Petrel, Wilson's
Chicken, Prairie of the Northwest—see Grouse, Sharp-tailed
Chicken, Water—see Coot; see also Gallinule, Florida
Chicken-bill—see Sora
Chicken-bird—see Turnstone, Ruddy
Chip-bird—see Sparrow, Chipping
Chip-bird, Winter—see Sparrow, Tree
Chipper, Arctic—see Sparrow, Tree
Chippy—see Sparrow, Chipping
Chippy, Brown—see Towhee, Canon
Chippy, Field—see Sparrow, Field
Chippy, Meadow—see Sparrow, Seaside
Chippy, Snow—see Sparrow, Tree
Chippy, Winter—see Sparrow, Tree
Choochkie—see Auklet, Least
Chow-Chow—see Cuckoo, Yellow-billed
Chuckatuck—see Turnstone, Ruddy
Chuckle-head—see Plover, Black-bellied
Churca—see Road-Runner
Clape—see Flicker
Clapper, Common—see Rail, Clapper
Clapper, Marsh—see Rail, Clapper
Clucking-hen—see Limpkin
Coat, Blue—see Jay, Blue
Cobb—see Gull, Great Black-backed

Cock, Chaparral—see Road-Runner
Cock, May—see Plover, Black-bellied
Cock of the Desert—see Road-Runner
Cock of the Plains—see Hen, Sage
Cock of the Woods—see Woodpecker, Pileated
Cock, Sage—see Hen, Sage
Cock, Wood—see Woodpecker, Pileated
Cockawee—see Old-Squaw
Coddy-Moddy—see Kittiwake
Coffin-carrier—see Gull, Great Black-backed
Colin, Ridgway's—see Bob-white, Masked
Condor, California—see Vulture, California
Connolly, John—see Old-Squaw
Coot, American—see Coot
Coot, Bay—see Scoter, Surf
Coot, Bell-tongue—see Scoter, White-winged
Coot, Black (male)—see Scoter
Coot, Black and White (male)—see Eider
Coot, Black Sea (male)—see Scoter
Coot, Blossom-billed—see Scoter, Surf
Coot, Booby—see Duck, Ruddy
Coot, Broad-billed (male)—see Scoter
Coot, Box—see Scoter, Surf
Coot, Brant—see Scoter, White-winged
Coot, Brown—see Scoter, Surf
Coot, Brown (female)—see Scoter
Coot, Bull—see Scoter, White-winged
Coot, Bumblebee—see Duck, Ruddy
Coot, Butter-billed (male)—see Scoter
Coot, Butterboat-billed—see Scoter, Surf
Coot, Creek—see Duck, Ruddy
Coot, Gray—see Scoter, Surf
Coot, Gray (female)—see Scoter
Coot, Heavy-tailed—see Duck, Ruddy
Coot, Hollow-billed—see Scoter, Surf
Coot, Hollow-billed (male)—see Scoter
Coot, Horse-head—see Scoter, Surf
Coot, Ivory-billed—see Coot
Coot, Mud—see Coot
Coot, Patch-head—see Scoter, Surf

Coot, Patch-polled—see Scoter, Surf
Coot, Pied-winged—see Scoter, White-winged
Coot, Pumpkin-blossom (male)—see Scoter
Coot, Quill-tailed—see Duck, Ruddy
Coot, Sea—see Scoter, Surf
Coot, Sea (male)—see Scoter
Coot, Skunk-head—see Scoter, Surf
Coot, Sleepy—see Duck, Ruddy
Coot, Smutty (female)—see Scoter
Coot, Speckle-billed—see Scoter, Surf
Coot, Spectacle—see Scoter, Surf
Coot, Surf—see Scoter, Surf
Coot, Uncle Sam—see Scoter, White-winged
Coot, Widgeon—see Duck, Ruddy
Copper-bill (male)—see Scoter
Copperhead—see Blackbird, Yellow-headed
Copper-head—see Golden-eye
Copper-nose (male)—see Scoter
Cormorant, Brown—see Cormorant, Brandt's
Cormorant, Common—see Cormorant
Cormorant, Penciled—see Cormorant, Brandt's
Cormorant, Townsend's—see Cormorant, Brandt's
Cormorant, Tufted—see Cormorant, Brandt's
Corporal, Little Blue—see Hawk, Pigeon
Correcamio—see Road-Runner
Coulterner—see Puffin
Courlan—see Limpkin
Coween or Cowheen—see Old-Squaw
Cow-frog—see Shoveller
Cracker, Long-nosed—see Pintail
Crackle, Rusty—see Blackbird, Rusty
Crake, Black—see Rail, Black
Crake, Carolina—see Sora
Crake, Yellow—see Rail, Yellow
Crane—see Heron, Great Blue
Crane, Blue—see Heron, Great Blue
Crane, Brown—see Crane, Sandhill
Crane, Common Blue—see Heron, Great Blue
Crane, Field—see Crane, Sandhill
Crane, Great White—see Crane, Whooping

Crane, Southern Sandhill—see Crane, Sandhill

Crane, Upland—see Crane, Sandhill

Crane, White—see Crane, Whooping

Creddock—see Turnstone, Ruddy

Creeper, American—see Creeper, Brown

Creeper, American Brown—see Creeper, Brown

Creeper, Black and White—see Warbler, Black and White

Creeper, Blue and White Striped or Pied—see Warbler, Black and White

Creeper, Common—see Creeper, Brown

Creeper, Finch—see Warbler, Parula

Creeper, Little Brown—see Creeper, Brown

Creeper, Pine—see Warbler, Pine

Creeper, Tree—see Creeper, Brown

Creeper, Yellow-throated—see Warbler, Yellow-throated

Crocker—see Brant

Crooked-bill—see Sandpiper, Red-backed

Crossbill, American—see Crossbill

Crossbill, Common—see Crossbill

Crossbill, Red—see Crossbill

Crow, American—see Crow

Crow, Blue—see Jay, Pinon

Crow, Carrion—see Crow; see also Vulture, Turkey; also Vulture, Black

Crow, Clarke's—see Nutcracker, Clarke's

Crow, Common—see Crow

Crow, Pond—see Coot

Crow, Rain—see Cuckoo, Black-billed; see also Cuckoo, Yellow-billed

Crow, Rusty—see Blackbird, Rusty

Crow, Sea—see Coot; see also Oyster-catcher

Crow, Storm—see Cuckoo, Yellow-billed

Crow-bill—see Coot

Crying-bird—see Limpkin

Cub-head—see Golden-eye

Cuckold—see Cowbird

Cuckoo, Ground—see Road-Runner

Cucu—see Yellow-legs, Greater

Cucu, Big—see Yellow-legs, Greater

Cucu, Small—see Yellow-legs

Cur—see Golden-eye

Curlew, Big—see Curlew, Long-billed

Curlew, Black—see Ibis, Glossy

Curlew, Jack—see Curlew, Hudsonian

Curlew, Little—see Curlew, Eskimo

Curlew, Old Hen—see Curlew, Long-billed

Curlew, Pied-wing—see Willet

Curlew, Pink—see Spoonbill, Roseate

Curlew, Red—see Godwit, Marbled

Curlew, Short-billed—see Curlew, Hudsonian

Curlew, Sickle-billed—see Curlew, Long-billed

Curlew, Spanish—see Ibis, White

Curlew, Spike-billed—see Godwit, Marbled

Curlew, Stone—see Willet

Curlew, Stone (young)—see Ibis, White

Curlew, White—see Ibis, White

Cutwater—see Skimmer, Black

Dabchick—see Grebe, Pied-billed

Dabchick, American—see Grebe, Pied-billed

Dabchick, Pied-billed—see Grebe, Pied-billed

Dabchick, Western—see Grebe, Western

Dapper—see Buffle-head; see also Duck, Ruddy

Darling, Everybody's—see Sparrow, Song

Darter—see Water-Turkey

Darter, American—see Water-Turkey

Darter, Big Blue—see Hawk, Cooper's

Darter, Black—see Water-Turkey

Darter, Black-bellied—see Water-Turkey

Darter, Blue—see Goshawk

Darter, Little Blue—see Hawk, Sharp-shinned

Darter, White-bellied (young)—see Water-Turkey

Demoiselle—see Heron, Louisiana

Devil-diver—see Grebe, Horned; see also Grebe, Pied-billed

Dickey—see Duck, Ruddy
Didapper—see Grebe, Pied-billed
Diedapper—see Grebe, Pied-billed
Dinky—see Duck, Ruddy
Dipper—see Duck, Ruddy; see also Grebe, Pied-billed; also Buffle-head; also Grebe, Horned
Dipper, American—see Dipper
Dipper, Broad-billed—see Duck, Ruddy
Dipper, Robin—see Buffle-head
Dip-tail—see Duck, Ruddy
Divedapper—see Grebe, Pied-billed
Diver—see Duck, Ruddy
Diver, Arctic—see Loon, Black-throated
Diver, Black-throated—see Loon, Black-throated
Diver, Dun—see Duck, Ruddy
Diver, Dun (female)—see Merganser
Diver, Eared—see Grebe, Eared
Diver, Great Northern—see Loon
Diver, Holboell's—see Grebe, Holboell's
Diver, Imber—see Loon
Diver, Pink-eyed—see Grebe, Horned
Diver, Red-throated—see Loon, Red-throated
Diver, Ruddy—see Duck, Ruddy
Diver, Saw-bill—see Merganser, Hooded
Doodle, Timber—see Woodcock
Dopper—see Buffle-head; see also Duck, Ruddy
Dotterel, Ringed—see Plover, Ringed
Dotterel, Sea—see Turnstone, Ruddy
Dough- or Doe-bird—see Curlew, Eskimo; see also Godwit, Marbled
Dough- or Doe-bird, Smaller—see Godwit, Hudsonian
Dove—see Dove, Mourning
Dove, Carolina—see Dove, Mourning
Dove, Mourning—see Dove, Ground
Dove, Rain—see Cuckoo, Yellow-billed
Dove, Scaled—see Dove, Inca
Dove, Sea—see Dovekie
Dove, Singing—see Dove, White-winged
Dove, Spotted Greenland—see Guillemot, Black

Dove, Turtle—see Dove, Mourning
Dove, Wild—see Dove, Mourning
Down, John—see Fulmar
Downhead, Devil—see Nuthatch, White-breasted
Downy, Texan—see Woodpecker, Texas
Drake (male)—see Eider
Driller, Black and White—see Woodpecker, Downy
Driver—see Dowitcher
Driver, Stake—see Bittern
Drum, Mire—see Bittern
Duck, Acorn—see Duck, Wood
Duck, American Scaup—see Duck, Scaup
Duck, Blarting—see Gadwall
Duck, Bleating—see Gadwall
Duck, Black Surf—see Scoter, White-winged
Duck, Bridal—see Duck, Wood
Duck, Buffalo-headed—see Buffle-head
Duck, Buffle-headed—see Buffle-head
Duck, Bumblebee—see Buffle-head
Duck, Butter—see Buffle-head; see also Shoveller; also Duck, Ruddy
Duck, Common Wild—see Mallard
Duck, Conjuring—see Buffle-head
Duck, Creek—see Gadwall
Duck, Crow—see Coot; see also Cormorant, Double-crested
Duck, Daub—see Duck, Ruddy
Duck, Deaf—see Duck, Ruddy
Duck, Dipper—see Buffle-head
Duck, Dumpling—see Duck, Ruddy
Duck, Dusky—see Duck, Black
Duck, Eider—see Eider
Duck, English—see Mallard
Duck, Fan-crested—see Merganser, Hooded
Duck, Fish—see Merganser; see also Merganser, Red-breasted
Duck, Fishing—see Merganser; see also Merganser, Redbreasted
Duck, Flock—see Duck, Scaup
Duck, Fool—see Duck, Ruddy
Duck, French—see Mallard
Duck, Golden-eyed—see Golden-eye
Duck, Gray—see Gadwall
Duck, Gray (female)—see Mallard; see also Pintail

Duck, Greater Scaup—see Duck, Scaup

Duck, Guinea—see Loon

Duck, Isle of Shoals—see Eider

Duck, Little Black and White (male) —see Buffle-head

Duck, Little Brown (female)—see Buffle-head

Duck, Little Fishing, or Fish—see Merganser, Hooded

Duck, Little, Saw-bill—see Merganser, Hooded

Duck, Long-tailed—see Old-Squaw

Duck, Mountain—see Duck, Harlequin

Duck, Mussel—see Duck, Scaup

Duck, Painted—see Duck, Harlequin

Duck, Pied—see Duck, Labrador

Duck, Pied Gray (female)—see Pintail

Duck, Raft—see Duck, Scaup; see also Redhead

Duck, Red-headed Raft—see Redhead

Duck, Red-legged—see Duck, Black

Duck, Ring-billed—see Duck, Ringnecked

Duck, Ring-necked Scaup—see Duck, Ring-necked

Duck, Rock—see Duck, Harlequin

Duck, Round-crested—see Merganser, Hooded

Duck, Scaup (with or without qualifying terms)—see Duck, Lesser Scaup

Duck, Sea (female)—see Eider

Duck, Skunk—see Duck, Labrador

Duck, Sleepy—see Duck, Ruddy

Duck, Smoking—see Baldpate

Duck, Spirit—see Buffle-head; see also Golden-eye

Duck, Spoonbill—see Shoveller

Duck, Spring Black—see Duck, Black

Duck, Squam—see Eider

Duck, Squeaking—see Old-Squaw

Duck, Stock—see Mallard

Duck, Summer—see Duck, Wood

Duck, Summer Black—see Duck, Black

Duck, Surf—see Scoter, Surf

Duck, Swallow-tailed—see Old-Squaw

Duck, Tree—see Duck, Wood; see also Merganser, Hooded

Duck, Velvet—see Scoter, Whitewinged

Duck, Wheat—see Baldpate

Duck, White-winged Surf, or Sea Coot, or Scoter—see Scoter, Whitewinged

Duck, Winter—see Old-Squaw; see also Pintail

Duck, Wood—see Merganser, Hooded

Dukelet, Little—see Owl, Screech

Dumb-bird—see Duck, Ruddy

Dun-bird—see Duck, Ruddy

Dunlin, American—see Sandpiper, Red-backed

Dunlin, Red-backed—see Sandpiper, Red-backed

Eagle, American—see Eagle, Bald

Eagle, Black—see Eagle, Bald; see also Eagle, Golden

Eagle, Brown—see Eagle, Golden

Eagle, Fishing—see Osprey

Eagle, Gray—see Eagle, Bald; see also Eagle, Golden

Eagle, Mountain—see Eagle, Golden

Eagle, Ring-tailed—see Eagle, Golden

Eagle, Washington—see Eagle, Bald

Eagle, White-headed—see Eagle, Bald

Eagle, White-headed Sea—see Eagle, Bald

Egg-bird—see Murre, Brünnich's

Egg-bird, California—see Murre, California

Egret, American—see Egret

Egret, Blue—see Heron, Little Blue

Egret, Common—see Egret, Snowy

Egret, Great White—see Egret

Egret, Greater—see Egret

Egret, Lesser—see Egret, Snowy

Egret, Little—see Egret, Snowy

Egret, Little White—see Egret, Snowy

Egret, White—see Egret

Eider, American—see Eider

Eider, Common—see Eider

Eider, Dresser's—see Eider

Eider, Fischer's—see Eider, Spectacled

Ember-Goose—see Loon

Falcon, Peregrine—see Hawk, Duck
Falcon, Pigeon—see Hawk, Pigeon
Falcon, Rusty-crowned—see Hawk, Sparrow
Falcon, Wandering—see Hawk, Duck
Fat-bird—see Sandpiper, Pectoral
Field-bird—see Plover, Golden
Fieldfare—see Robin
Finch, Bay-winged—see Sparrow, Vesper
Finch, Blanding's—see Towhee, Green-tailed
Finch, Blue—see Bunting, Indigo
Finch, Crimson-fronted—see Finch, House
Finch, Ferruginous—see Sparrow, Fox
Finch, Foxy—see Sparrow, Fox
Finch, Grass—see Sparrow, Vesper
Finch, Green—see Sparrow, Texas
Finch, Indigo—see Bunting, Indigo
Finch, Lark—see Sparrow, Lark
Finch, Lincoln's—see Sparrow, Lincoln's
Finch, Painted—see Bunting, Painted
Finch, Pine—see Siskin, Pine
Finch, Seaside—see Sparrow, Seaside
Finch, Swamp—see Sparrow, Song
Finch, Thistle—see Goldfinch, European
Firebird—see Tanager, Scarlet
Fire-bird—see Oriole, Baltimore
Fire-brand—see Warbler, Blackburnian
Fire-tail—see Redstart
Fizzy (male)—see Scoter
Flame-crest—see Kinglet, Golden-crowned
Flamingo, American—see Flamingo
Flamingo, Scarlet—see Flamingo
Flusterer—see Coot
Flycatcher, Black-crested—see Phainopepla
Flycatcher, Black-headed—see Phoebe, Black
Flycatcher, Blue—see Warbler, Black-throated Blue
Flycatcher, Canada—see Warbler, Canada
Flycatcher, Cat—see Catbird
Flycatcher, Dusky—see Phoebe
Flycatcher, Golden-crowned — see

Warbler, Chestnut-sided; see also Warbler, Myrtle
Flycatcher, Golden-winged—see Warbler, Golden-winged
Flycatcher, Great Crested—see Flycatcher, Crested
Flycatcher, Great Crested Yellow-bellied—see Flycatcher, Crested
Flycatcher, Green—see Flycatcher, Acadian
Flycatcher, Green Black-throated—see Warbler, Black-throated Green
Flycatcher, Green-crested—see Flycatcher, Acadian
Flycatcher, Pewit—see Phoebe
Flycatcher, Redstart—see Redstart
Flycatcher, Shining Crested—see Phainopepla
Flycatcher, Small Green-crested—see Flycatcher, Acadian
Flycatcher, Pewee—see Pewee, Wood
Flycatcher, Silky—see Phainopepla
Flycatcher, Small Blue-gray—see Gnatcatcher, Blue-gray
Flycatcher, Swallow-tailed—see Flycatcher, Scissor-tailed
Flycatcher, Sylvan—see Gnatcatcher, Blue-gray
Flycatcher, Tyrant—see Kingbird
Flycatcher, Wilson's—see Warbler, Wilson's
Fly-snapper, Shining—see Phainopepla
Fly-up-the-creek—see Heron, Green
Fou, Grand—see Gannet
Fowl, Floating—see Duck, Scaup
Fox-tail—see Sparrow, Fox
Frost-bird—see Plover, Golden
Frowl—see Murre
Fute—see Curlew, Eskimo

Gallinule, American—see Gallinule, Florida
Gallinule, Common—see Gallinule, Florida
Gamin—see Sparrow, English
Gannet—see Ibis, Wood
Gannet, Booby—see Booby
Gannet, Common—see Gannet
Gannet, White—see Gannet
Garefowl—see Auk, Great

Garoo—see Crane, Whooping

Garrot—see Golden-eye

Garrot, Rocky Mountain—see Golden-eye, Barrow's

Gent, Jan van—see Gannet

Geylle—see Guillemot, Black

Gnatcatcher, Common—see Gnatcatcher, Blue-gray

Goatsucker, Long-winged—see Nighthawk

Goatsucker of Carolina—see Nighthawk

Godwit, American Black-tailed—see Godwit, Hudsonian

Godwit, Black-tailed—see Godwit, Hudsonian

Godwit, Great—see Godwit, Marbled

Godwit, Great Marbled—see Godwit, Marbled

Godwit, Red-breasted—see Godwit, Hudsonian

Godwit, Tell-tale—see Yellow-legs, Greater

Goggle-nose—see Scoter, Surf

Gold-crest—see Kinglet, Golden-crowned

Golden-back—see Plover, Golden

Golden-crown—see Sparrow, Golden-crowned

Golden-eye, American—see Golden-eye

Golden-eye, Rocky Mountain—see Golden-eye, Barrow's

Golden-front — see Woodpecker, Golden-fronted

Gold-Tit—see Verdin

Goony—see Albatross, Black-footed

Goosander, American—Merganser

Goosander, Red-breasted—see Merganser, Red-breasted

Goose, American White-fronted—see Goose, White-fronted

Goose, Bay—see Goose, Canada

Goose, Beach—see Goose, Emperor

Goose, Big Gray—see Goose, Canada

Goose, Black-headed—see Goose, Canada

Goose, Blue Snow—see Goose, Blue

Goose, Blue-winged—see Goose, Blue

Goose, Brant—see Brant

Goose, Brent—see Brant

Goose, Burnt—see Brant

Goose, Clatter—see Brant

Goose, Common Snow—see Goose, Snow

Goose, Common Wild—see Goose, Canada

Goose, Cravat—see Goose, Canada

Goose, Laughing—see Goose, White-fronted

Goose, Lesser Snow—see Goose, Snow

Goose, Long-necked—see Goose, Canada

Goose, Mackerel—see Phalarope, Northern

Goose, Mexican—see Goose, Snow

Goose, Nigger—see Cormorant, Double-crested

Goose, Painted—see Goose, Emperor

Goose, Reef—see Goose, Canada

Goose, Sea—see Phalarope, Northern; see also Phalarope, Red

Goose, Solan—see Gannet

Goose, Soland—see Gannet

Goose, Solon—see Gannet

Goose, White—see Goose, Snow

Goose, White-headed—see Goose, Blue

Goose, Wild—see Goose, Canada

Goose, Yellow-legged—see Goose, White-fronted

Goose-bird—see Godwit, Hudsonian

Goshawk, American—see Goshawk

Grackle, Keel-tailed—see Crackle, Purple

Granny, Old—see Old-Squaw

Grass-bird—see Sandpiper, Baird's; see also Sandpiper, Pectoral

Grass-bird, Hill—see Sandpiper Buff-breasted

Grass-bird, Red—see Sparrow, Song

Gray-back—see Duck, Scaup; see also Knot

Gray-back (winter)—see Dowitcher

Gread-head—see Golden-eye

Grebe, American Eared—see Grebe, Eared

Grebe, American Red-necked—see Grebe, Holboell's

Grebe, Carolina—see Grebe, Pied-billed

Grebe, Red-necked—see Grebe, Holboell's

Grebe, Swan—see Grebe, Western

Grebe, Thick-billed—see Grebe, Piedbilled

Green-back—see Plover, Golden

Green-back, Arkansas—see Goldfinch, Arkansas

Greenhead—see Loon; see also Plover, Golden

Green-head—see Duck, Scaup

Green-head (male)—see Mallard

Greenlet, Bell's—see Vireo, Bell's

Greenlet, Black-capped—see Vireo, Black-capped

Greenlet, Blue-headed—see Vireo, Blue-headed

Greenlet, Philadelphia—see Vireo, Philadelphia

Greenlet, Red-eyed—see Vireo, Red-eyed

Greenlet, Warbling—see Vireo, Warbling

Greenlet, White-eyed—see Vireo, White-eyed

Greenlet, Yellow-throated—see Vireo, Yellow-throated

Green-wing—see Teal, Green-winged

Grosbeak, American Pine—see Grosbeak, Pine

Grosbeak, Canadian—see Grosbeak, Pine

Grosbeak, Canadian Pine—see Grosbeak, Pine

Grosbeak, Cardinal—see Cardinal

Grosbeak, Common—see Grosbeak, Rose-breasted

Grosbeak, Gray—see Pyrrhuloxia, Arizona

Grosbeak, Purple—see Finch, Purple

Grosbeak, Summer—see Grosbeak, Rose-breasted

Grosbeak, Western—see Grosbeak, Black-headed

Ground-bird—see Sparrow, Field; see also Sparrow, Vesper; also Sparrow, Song; also Sparrow, Savannah

Grouse—see Grouse, Ruffed

Grouse, Black—see Partridge, Hudsonian Spruce

Grouse, Canada—see Partridge, Hudsonian Spruce

Grouse, Drumming—see Grouse, Ruffed

Grouse, Eastern Pinnated—see Hen, Heath

Grouse, Franklin's Spruce—see Grouse, Franklin's

Grouse, Mountain—see Grouse, Franklin's

Grouse, Northern Sharp-tailed—see Grouse, Sharp-tailed

Grouse, Pinnated—see Chicken, Prairie

Grouse, Pin-tailed—see Grouse, Sharp-tailed

Grouse, Prairie—see Chicken, Prairie

Grouse, Rocky Mountain Snow—see Ptarmigan, White-tailed

Grouse, Sage—see Hen, Sage

Grouse, Shoulder-knot—see Grouse, Ruffed

Grouse, Snow—see Ptarmigan, White-tailed; see also Ptarmigan, Willow

Grouse, Spotted—see Partridge, Hudsonian Spruce

Grouse, Sprig-tailed—see Grouse, Sharp-tailed

Grouse, Tyee—see Grouse, Franklin's

Grouse, White—see Grouse, Sharp-tailed; see also Ptarmigan, Willow

Grouse, Willow—see Ptarmigan, Willow

Grouse, Wood—see Grouse, Franklin's; see Partridge, Hudsonian Spruce

Guillem, or Gwilym—see Murre

Guillemot, Black-throated—see Murrelet, Ancient

Guillemot, Brünnich's—see Murre, Brünnich's

Guillemot, California—see Murre, California

Guillemot, Foolish—see Murre

Guillemot, Franks'—see Murre, Brünnich's

Guillemot, Polar—see Murre, Brünnich's

Guillemot, Scapular—see Guillemot, Black

Guillemot, Thick-billed—see Murre, Brünnich's

Guillemot, White—see Guillemot, Black

Guillemot, White-winged—see Guillemot, Black

Gulf-bird—see Phalarope, Red

Gull, Arctic Hawk—see Jaeger, Parasitic

Gull, Black-backed—see Gull, Great Black-backed

Gull, Black-headed—see Gull, Bonaparte's; see also Gull, Laughing

Gull, Black-toed—see Jaeger, Parasitic

Gull, Blue—see Gull, Glaucous

Gull, Bonaparte's Rosy—see Gull, Bonaparte's

Gull, Burgomaster—Gull, Glaucous

Gull, Common—see Gull, Herring; see also Gull, Ring-billed

Gull, Fork-tailed—see Gull, Sabine's

Gull, Franklin's Rosy—see Gull, Franklin's

Gull, Harbor—see Gull, Glaucous; see also Gull, Herring

Gull, Hawk-tailed—see Gull, Sabine's

Gull, Ice—see Gull, Glaucous

Gull, Jaeger—see Jaeger, Pomarine

Gull, Kittiwake—see Kittiwake

Gull, Lake—see Gull, Herring; see also Gull, Ring-billed

Gull, Lake Erie—see Tern, Common

Gull, Mackerel—see Tern, Common

Gull, Sea—see Gull, Herring

Gull, Skua—see Skua

Gull, Snow-white—see Gull, Ivory

Gull, Summer—see Tern, Common

Gull, White-headed—see Gull, Heermann's

Gull, Winter—see Gull, Herring

Gull-teaser—see Jaeger, Long-tailed

Gump—see Plover, Black-bellied

Gyrfalcon, Greenland—see Gyrfalcon, White

Gyrfalcon, MacFarlane's—see Gyrfalcon

Hag—see Shearwater, Greater

Hag, Black—see Shearwater, Sooty

Hagdon—see Shearwater, Greater

Hagdon, Black—see Shearwater, Sooty

Haglet—see Shearwater, Greater

Hair-bird—see Sparrow, Chipping

Hairy-crown—see Merganser, Hooded

Hairy-head—see Merganser, Hooded

Halcyon—see Kingfisher, Belted

Hammock-bird—see Oriole, Baltimore

Hang-bird—see Oriole, Baltimore

Hang-nest—see Oriole, Baltimore

Hang-nest, Little—see Vireo, Red-eyed

Hang-nest, Orchard—see Oriole, Orchard

Harfang—see Owl, Snowy

Harlan—see Pintail

Harrier—see Hawk, Marsh

Harrier, Marsh—see Hawk, Marsh

Harry—see Woodpecker, Hairy

Hawfinch, American—see Grosbeak, Evening

Hawk, American Rough-legged—see Hawk, Rough-legged

Hawk, American Sparrow—see Hawk, Sparrow

Hawk, Big Chicken—see Hawk, Red-shouldered

Hawk, Bird—see Hawk, Sharp-shinned

Hawk, Black—see Hawk, Rough-legged; see also Hawk, Swainson's

Hawk, Blue (adult)—see Hawk, Marsh

Hawk, Blue Hen—see Goshawk

Hawk, Brown—see Hawk, Swainson's

Hawk, Bullet—see Hawk, Pigeon; see also Hawk, Sharp-shinned

Hawk, Buzzard—see Hawk, Red-tailed

Hawk, Chicken—see Goshawk; see also Hawk, Cooper's; also Hawk, Red-tailed; also Hawk, Sharp-shinned

Hawk, Dove—see Goshawk

Hawk, Fish—see Osprey

Hawk, Frog—see Hawk, Marsh

Hawk, Grasshopper—see Hawk, Sparrow

Hawk, Great-footed—see Hawk, Duck

Hawk, Hen—see Hawk, Red-shouldered; see also Hawk, Red-tailed; also Hawk, Swainson's

Hawk, Kitty—see Hawk, Sparrow

Hawk, Meat—see Jay, Canada

Hawk, Molly—see Fulmar

Hawk, Mosquito—see Nighthawk

Hawk, Mouse—see Hawk, Rough-legged; see also Hawk, Sparrow; also Hawk, Marsh

Hawk, Partridge—see Goshawk

Hawk, Pigeon—see Hawk, Cooper's; see also Hawk, Sharp-shinned

Hawk, Quail—see Hawk, Cooper's

Hawk, Red—see Hawk, Red-tailed

Hawk, Sea—see Skua

Hawk, Short-winged—see Hawk, Sparrow

Hawk, Snail—see Kite, Everglade

Hawk, Snake—see Kite, Swallow-tailed

Hawk, Sparrow—see Hawk, Sharp-shinned

Hawk, Swallow-tailed—see Kite, Swallow-tailed

Hawk, Swift—see Hawk, Cooper's

Hawk, White-breasted Chicken—see Hawk, Red-tailed

Hawk, White-rumped—see Hawk, Marsh

Hawk, Winter—see Hawk, Red-shouldered

Hawk's eye—see Plover, Golden

Hay-bird—see Sandpiper, Pectoral

Head, Goard, or Gourd—see Ibis, Wood

Head, Iron—see Ibis, Wood

Heigh-ho—see Flicker

Hell-diver—see Buffle-head; see also Loon; also Grebe, Pied-billed; also Grebe, Horned

Hen, Curlew—see Curlew, Long-billed

Hen, Fool—see Grouse, Franklin's; see also Quail, Mearns's

Hen, Fresh-water Marsh—see Rail, King; see also Rail, Virginia

Hen, Indian—see Bittern

Hen, Little American Water—see Sora

Hen, Marsh—see Bittern; see also Coot

Hen, Meadow—see Coot

Hen, Mud—see Coot; see also Rail, King; also Sora

Hen, Pond—see Coot

Hen, Prairie—see Chicken, Prairie

Hen, Red-billed Mud—see Gallinule, Florida

Hen, Sea—see Skua

Hen, Small Mud—see Rail, Virginia

Hen, Water—see Coot; see also Gallinule, Florida

Hen, White-bellied Mud—see Coot

Hen, Wood—see Woodpecker, Pileated

Hen-bill—see Coot

Heron, American Night—see Heron, Black-crowned Night

Heron, Florida—see Heron, Great White

Heron, Gardenia—see Heron, Black-crowned Night

Heron, Great White—see Egret

Heron, Least—see Bittern, Least

Heron, Little Green—see Heron, Green

Heron, Little White—see Egret, Snowy

Heron, Night—see Heron, Black-crowned Night

Heron, Red-shouldered—see Heron, Great Blue

Heron, Snowy—see Egret, Snowy

Heron, White—see Egret

Hickory-head—see Duck, Ruddy

High-holder—see Flicker

High-hole—see Flicker

Hill-bird—see Plover, Upland

Hollow-head—see Plover, Black-bellied

Honker—see Goose, Canada

Hoodlum—see Sparrow, English

Horn, Break—see Merganser

Horse, Sea—see Fulmar

Horse-head—see Scoter, Surf

Hound—see Old-Squaw

Huckleberry-bird—see Sparrow, Field

Huldy, Uncle—see Old-Squaw

Humility—see Willet

Hummer—see Hummingbird, Ruby-throated

Hummer, Anna's—see Hummingbird, Anna's

Hummer, Black-chinned—see Hummingbird, Black-chinned

Hummer, Blue-throated—see Hummingbird, Blue-throated

Hummer, Broad-tailed—see Hummingbird, Broad-tailed

Hummer, Rivoli's—see Hummingbird, Rivoli's

Hummer, Rufous—see Hummingbird, Rufous
Hummingbird—see Hummingbird, Ruby-throated
Hummingbird, Common—see Hummingbird, Ruby-throated
Hummingbird, Refulgent—see Hummingbird, Rivoli's
Hunter, Dung—see Jaeger, Parasitic
Hunter, Gull—see Jaeger, Pomarine

Ibis, Bay—see Ibis, Glossy
Ibis, Green—see Ibis, Glossy
Ibis, Ord's—see Ibis, Glossy
Ice-bird—see Dovekie
Injun, Old—see Old-Squaw
Iron-head—see Golden-eye
Ivory-bill—see Woodpecker, Ivory-billed

Jack—see Curlew, Hudsonian
Jack, Black—see Duck, Lesser Scaup; see also Duck, Ring-necked
Jack, Whisky—see Jay, Canada
Jackdaw, New England—see Crackle, Purple
Jackdaw, Purple—see Grackle, Purple
Jaeger, Arctic—see Jaeger, Long-tailed
Jaeger, Richardson's—see Jaeger, Parasitic
Jay—see Jay, Blue
Jay, Common—see Jay, Blue
Jay, Conifer—see Jay, Steller's
Jay, Mountain—see Jay, Steller's
Jay, Pine—see Jay, Steller's
Jay, Rio Grande Green—see Jay, Green
Jay, Scrub—see Jay, Florida
Jellycoat—see Woodpecker, Red-headed
Jingler—see Golden-eye
Jinny—see Turnstone, Ruddy
John, Whisky—see Jay, Canada
Jo-ree—see Towhee
Junco, Eastern—see Junco, Slate-colored

Kanooska—see Auklet, Crested
Kate, Wood—see Woodpecker, Pileated
Kelinky—see Paroquet, Carolina

Kestrel, American—see Hawk, Sparrow
Kiddaw—see Murre
Killdee—see Killdeer
Killer, Nine—see Shrike, Northern
Killer, Snake—see Road-Runner
Kingfisher—see Kingfisher, Belted
Kingfisher, Texan Green—see Kingfisher, Texas
Kinglet, Golden-crested—see Kinglet, Golden-crowned
Kite, Black-shouldered—see Kite, White-tailed
Kite, Blue—see Kite, Mississippi
Kite, Fork-tailed—see Kite, Swallow-tailed
Kite-tail (male)—see Pintail
Kittiwake, Common—see Kittiwake
Krieker—see Sandpiper, Pectoral
Kow-Kow—see Cuckoo, Black-billed; see also Cuckoo, Yellow-billed

Lady of the Waters—see Heron, Louisiana
Lady-bird—see Pintail
Lanner, American (female)—see Falcon, Prairie
Lanneret, American (male)—see Falcon, Prairie
Lark, Brown—see Pipit
Lark, Common—see Meadowlark
Lark, Field—see Meadowlark
Lark, Field, of the West—see Meadowlark, Western
Lark, Louisiana—see Pipit
Lark, Northern Horned—see Lark, Horned
Lark of the West—see Meadowlark, Western
Lark, Old Field—see Meadowlark
Lark, Red—see Pipit
Lark, Sand—see Sandpiper, Spotted
Lark, Shore—see Lark, Horned
Lark, Snow—see Bunting, Snow
Lark, Winter Horned—see Lark, Horned
Lavy—see Murre
Lawyer—see Cormorant, Double-crested; see also Stilt, Black-necked
Lead-back—see Sandpiper, Red-backed

Leather-back—see Duck, Ruddy
Leucosticte, Gray-crowned—see Finch, Rosy Gray-crowned
Light-wood-knot—see Duck, Ruddy
Linnet—see Finch, House; see also Redfall
Linnet, Gray (immature and female) —see Finch, Purple
Linnet, Pine—see Siskin, Pine
Linnet, Purple—see Finch, Purple
Linnet, Red—see Finch, Purple
Linnet, Red-headed—see Finch, House
Linnet, Redpoll—see Redpoll
Lintie—see Redpoll
Liver—see Ibis, Glossy
Logcock—see Woodpecker, Ivory-billed; see also Woodpecker, Pileated
Longshanks—see Stilt, Black-necked
Longspur, Common—see Longspur, Lapland
Longtail—see Tropic-bird, Yellow-billed
Long-tail—see Old-Squaw
Loon, Arctic—see Loon, Black-throated
Loon, Big—see Loon
Loon, Black-billed—see Loon
Loon, Common—see Loon
Loon, Little—see Loon, Red-throated
Loon, Ring-necked—see Loon
Loon, Sprat—see Loon, Red-throated
Lord-and-Lady—see Duck, Harlequin

Magpie, American—see Magpie
Magpie, Black-billed—see Magpie
Mallard, Black—see Duck, Black
Mallard, Dusky—see Duck, Black
Mallard, Gray (female)—see Mallard
Mallemuck—see Fulmar
Man, Old—see Murrelet, Ancient
Man-o'-war—see Jaeger, Parasitic
Marionette—see Buffle-head
Marlin—see Godwit, Marbled
Marlin, Brown—see Godwit, Marbled
Marlin, Crooked-billed—see Curlew, Hudsonian
Marlin, Field—see Godwit, Hudsonian
Marlin, Red—see Godwit, Marbled
Marlin, Ring-tailed—see Godwit, Hudsonian
Marline-spike—see Jaeger, Parasitic

Marrock—see Murre
Martin—see Martin, Purple
Martin, Bank—see Swallow, Bank
Martin, Bee—see Kingbird; see also Kingbird, Arkansas
Martin, Black—see Martin, Purple
Martin, Field—see Kingbird
Martin, House—see Martin, Purple
Martin, Sand—see Swallow, Bank
Martyr, Bonnet—see Egret, Snowy
Mavis—see Thrasher, Brown
Mavis, Red—see Thrasher, Brown
May-bird—see Bobolink; see also Knot
Meadow-bird—see Bobolink
Meadowlark, Common—see Meadow-lark, Western
Meadowlark, Little—see Dickcissel; see also Sparrow, Lark; also Redpoll
Meadow-wink—see Bobolink
Medlar—see Meadowlark
Medlark—see Meadowlark
Merganser, American—see Merganser
Merganser, Buff-breasted—see Merganser
Merganser, Greater—see Merganser
Merlin, American—see Hawk, Pigeon
Merry-wing—see Golden-eye
Mocker—see Mockingbird
Mocker, Brown—see Thrasher, Brown
Mocker, Sandy—see Thrasher, Brown
Mockingbird, Brown—see Thrasher, Brown
Mockingbird, French—see Shrike, Loggerhead; see also Thrasher, Brown
Mockingbird, Sandy—see Thrasher, Brown
Mockingbird, Slate-colored—see Cat-bird
Mockingbird, Yellow—see Chat, Yellow-breasted
Mollimoke—see Fulmar
Molly, Old—see Old-Squaw
Mongrel—see Sandpiper, Stilt
Moon-bill—see Duck, Ring-necked
Moor-head—see Coot
Moose-bird—see Jay, Canada
Morocco-head (female)—see Merganser
Morocco-jaw—see Scoter, Surf
Moss-head—see Merganser, Hooded

Mouse, Sea—see Duck, Harlequin
Mud-dipper—see Duck, Ruddy
Muddy-belly—see Plover, Golden
Muddy-breast—see Plover, Golden
Mudlark—see Meadowlark
Mud-peep—see Sandpiper, Least
Murrelet, Black-throated—see Murrelet, Ancient
Murrelet, Gray-headed—see Murrelet, Ancient

Necklace, Canada—see Warbler, Canada
Nightingale—see Oven-Bird; see also Veery
Nightingale, American—see Thrush, Hermit
Nightingale (in Manitoba)—see Sparrow, White-throated
Nightjar—see Whip-Poor-Will
Noddy—see Duck, Ruddy; see also Fulmar
Nonpareil—see Bunting, Painted
Norie, Tammy—see Puffin
Nuthatch, Canada—see Nuthatch, Red-breasted
Nuthatch, Carolina—see Nuthatch, White-breasted
Nuthatch, Common—see Nuthatch, White-breasted
Nuthatch, Red-bellied—see Nuthatch, Red-breasted
Nuthatch, White-bellied—see Nuthatch, White-breasted

Orange-crown—see Warbler, Orange-crowned
Oriole, Brown—see Oriole, Orchard
Oriole, Brown-headed—see Cowbird
Oriole, Golden—see Oriole, Baltimore
Oriole, Red-winged—see Blackbird, Red-winged
Oriole, Rusty—see Blackbird, Rusty
Oriole, Sennett's Hooded—see Oriole, Sennett's
Oriole, Tri-colored—see Red-wing, Tri-colored
Ortolan—see Sora
Ortolan, American—see Bobolink
Osprey, American—see Osprey
Ouzel, American Water—see Dipper

Ouzel, Water—see Dipper
Owl, Acadian—see Owl, Saw-whet
Owl, American Barn—see Owl, Barn
Owl, American Long-eared—see Owl, Long-eared
Owl, American Sparrow—see Owl, Richardson's
Owl, Arctic—see Owl, Snowy
Owl, Arctic Saw-whet—see Owl, Richardson's
Owl, Big Hoot—see Owl, Great Horned
Owl, Billy—see Owl, Burrowing
Owl, Canadian—see Owl, American Hawk
Owl, Cat—see Owl, Great Horned; see also Owl, Long-eared
Owl, Day—see Owl, American Hawk
Owl, Ermine—see Owl, Snowy
Owl, Gnome—see Owl, Pygmy
Owl, Golden—see Owl, Barn
Owl, Gray—see Owl, Screech
Owl, Great White—see Owl, Snowy
Owl, Ground—see Owl, Burrowing
Owl, Hoot—see Owl, Barred
Owl, Hudsonian—see Owl, American Hawk
Owl, Kirtland's—see Owl, Saw-whet
Owl, Lesser Horned—see Owl, Long-eared
Owl, Little Horned—see Owl, Screech
Owl, Marsh—see Owl, Short-eared
Owl, Monkey—see Owl, Barn
Owl, Monkey-faced—see Owl, Barn
Owl, Mottled—see Owl, Screech
Owl, Prairie—see Owl, Short-eared
Owl, Rain—see Owl, Barred
Owl, Red—see Owl, Screech
Owl, Round-headed—see Owl, Barred
Owl, Shivering—see Owl, Screech
Owl, Sparrow—see Owl, Richardson's; see also Owl, Saw-whet
Owl, Spectral—see Owl, Great Gray
Owl, Swamp—see Owl, Barred; see also Owl, Short-eared
Owl, Virginia—see Owl, Great Horned
Owl, Virginia Horned—see Owl, Great Horned
Owl, White—see Owl, Barn
Owl, White-fronted—see Owl, Saw-whet

Owl, Whitney's—see Owl, Elf

Owl, Wood—see Owl, Barred

Owl-head—see Plover, Black-bellied

Ox-bird—see Sandpiper, Red-backed

Ox-eye—see Sandpiper, Least; see also Sandpiper, Semipalmated; also Plover, Black-bellied

Ox-eye, Sand—see Sandpiper, Semipalmated

Oyster-catcher, American—see Oyster-catcher

Oyster-catcher, Brown-backed—see Oyster-catcher

Oyster-catcher, Mantled—see Oyster-catcher

Paddy—see Duck, Ruddy

Paddy-whack—see Duck, Ruddy

Paisano—see Road-Runner

Pake, Hookum—see Woodcock

Pale-belly (young)—see Plover, Black-bellied; see also Plover, Golden

Pale-breast—see Plover, Golden

Papabotte—see Plover, Upland

Parrakeet, Carolina—see Paroquet, Carolina

Parrot, Sea—see Puffin; see also Puffin, Tufted

Parrot-bill—see Pyrrhuloxia, Arizona

Partridge—see Bob-white; see also Grouse, Ruffed

Partridge, Birch—see Grouse, Ruffed

Partridge, California—see Quail, California

Partridge, Cedar—see Partridge, Hudsonian Spruce

Partridge, Messena—see Quail, Mearns's

Partridge, Mountain—see Quail, Mountain

Partridge, Night—see Woodcock

Partridge, Plumed—see Quail, Mountain

Partridge, Swamp—see Partridge, Hudsonian Spruce

Partridge, Virginia—see Bob-white

Partridge, Wood—see Partridge, Hudsonian Spruce

Pasture-bird—see Plover, Golden

Patch-head—see Scoter, Surf

Pea-bird—see Oriole, Baltimore

Peak-tail (male)—see Pintail

Peck, Night—see Woodcock

Peep—see Sandpiper, Semipalmated; see also Sandpiper, Spotted; also Sandpiper, Least

Peep, Black-legged—see Sandpiper, Semipalmated

Peep, Bull—see Sanderling; see also Sandpiper, White-rumped

Peep, Little—see Sandpiper, Semipalmated

Peep, Web-footed—see Phalarope, Northern

Peetweet—see Sandpiper, Spotted

Pelican, American White—see Pelican, White

Pelican, Common (of Florida)—see Pelican, Brown

Pelican, Common (of the North)—see Pelican, White

Pelick—see Coot

Penguin—see Auk, Great

Peregrine, American—see Hawk, Duck

Peter, Blue—see Coot

Petrel, Common Fork-tailed—see Petrel, Leach's

Petrel, Common Stormy—see Petrel, Wilson's

Petrel, Fulmar—see Fulmar

Petrel, Leach's Fork-tailed—see Petrel, Leach's

Petrel, Long-legged Storm—see Petrel, Wilson's

Petrel, Wedged-tailed—see Petrel, Least

Petrel, White-rumped—see Petrel, Leach's

Pewee—see Pewee, Wood; see also Phoebe; see also Woodcock

Pewee, Barn—see Phoebe

Pewee, Bridge—see Phoebe

Pewee, Nuttall's—see Flycatcher, Olive-sided

Pewee, Say's—see Phoebe, Say's

Pewee, Small—see Flycatcher, Acadian

Pewee, Water—see Phoebe

Pewee, Western Black—see Phoebe, Black

Pewit—see Pewee, Wood

Phalarope, Flat-billed—see Phalarope, Red

Phalarope, Gray—see Phalarope, Red

Phalarope, Hyperborean—see Phalarope, Northern

Phalarope, Red-necked—see Phalarope, Northern

Phalarope, Summer—see Phalarope, Wilson's

Pheasant—see Grouse, Ruffed

Pheasant, Drumming—see Grouse, Ruffed

Pheasant, Mountain—see Grouse, Ruffed

Pheasant, Water—Merganser, Hooded

Pheasant-dock (male)—see Pintail

Picket-tail (male)—see Pintail

Pick-me-up—see Kittiwake

Pictured-bill—see Scoter, Surf

Pigeon—see Pigeon, Passenger

Pigeon, Blue-headed—see Pigeon, Passenger

Pigeon, Prairie—see Curlew, Eskimo; see also Plover, Golden; also Gull, Franklin's

Pigeon, Red-breasted—see Pigeon, Passenger

Pigeon, Sea—see Dowitcher; see also Gull Bonaparte's; also Guillemot, Pigeon; also Guillemot, Black

Pigeon, White-collared—see Pigeon, Band-tailed

Pigeon, Wild—see Pigeon, Band-tailed; see also Pigeon, Passenger

Pigeon, Wood—see Pigeon, Passenger

Pigeon-tail (male)—see Pintail

Pill-will-willet—see Willet

Pilot—see Plover, Black-bellied

Pinonero—see Jay, Pinon

Pin-tail—see Duck, Ruddy; see also Grouse, Sharp-tailed

Pipit, American—see Pipit

Piramidig—see Nighthawk

Pisk—see Nighthawk

Plaster-bill—see Scoter, Surf

Plover, American Golden—see Plover, Golden

Plover, Bartram's—see Plover, Upland

Plover, Beach—see Plover, Piping; see also Sanderling

Plover, Belted Piping—see Plover, Piping

Plover, Big Yellow-legged—see Yellow-legs, Greater

Plover, Black-breasted—see Plover, Black-bellied

Plover, Black-heart (Ontario)—see Sandpiper, Red-backed

Plover, Bishop—see Turnstone, Ruddy

Plover, Blue—see Knot

Plover, Buff-breasted—see Knot

Plover, Bull-head—see Plover, Black-bellied

Plover, Chattering—see Killdeer

Plover, Chicken—see Turnstone, Ruddy

Plover, Common—see Plover, Golden

Plover, Field—see Plover, Golden; see also Plover, Upland

Plover, Four-toed—see Plover, Black-bellied

Plover, Grass—see Plover, Upland

Plover, Gray (autumn)—see Plover, Black-bellied

Plover, Green—see Plover, Golden

Plover, Highland—see Plover, Upland

Plover, Killdeer—see Killdeer

Plover, Marsh—see Sandpiper, Pectoral

Plover, Mud—see Plover, Black-bellied

Plover, Noisy—see Killdeer

Plover, Pasture—see Plover, Upland

Plover, Prairie—see Plover, Mountain; see also Plover, Upland

Plover, Red-breasted—see Knot

Plover, Red-legged—see Turnstone, Ruddy

Plover, Ring—see Plover, Ringed; see also Plover, Semipalmated

Plover, Ring-necked—see Plover, Semipalmated

Plover, Rock—see Sandpiper, Purple

Plover, Ruddy—see Sanderling

Plover, Sand—see Plover, Piping

Plover, Semipalmated Ring—see Plover, Semipalmated

Plover, Silver—see Knot

Plover, Snowy Ring—see Plover, Snowy

Plover, Spanish—see Willet

Plover, Spotted—see Plover, Golden

Plover, Swiss—see Plover, Black-bellied

Plover, Three-toed—see Plover, Golden

Plover, Western Piping—see Plover, Piping

Plover, Whistling—see Plover, Black-bellied; see also Plover, Golden

Plover, Whistling Field—see Plover, Black-bellied

Plover, Yellow-legged—see Yellow-legs

Poacher—see Baldpate

Pochard or Poachard, American—see Redhead

Pocket-bird—see Tanager, Scarlet

Poke—see Bittern

Politician—see Vireo, White-eyed

Poll, Yellow—see Warbler, Yellow

Pop, Blue—see Grosbeak, Blue

Pope—see Bunting, Painted; see also Puffin

Prairie-bird—see Plover, Golden

Prairiebird, White-winged—see Bunting, Lark

Preacher, The—see Vireo, Red-eyed

Ptarmigan—see Ptarmigan, Willow

Ptarmigan, Common—see Ptarmigan, Willow

Puffin, Cinereous—see Shearwater, Greater

Puffin, Common—see Puffin

Pull-doo—see Coot

Pumper, Thunder—see Bittern

Qua-bird—see Heron, Black-crowned Night

Quail—see Bob-white

Quail, Arizona—see Quail, Gambel's

Quail, Black—see Quail, Mearns's

Quail, Blue—see Quail, Scaled

Quail, Bob-white—see Bob-white

Quail, Fool—see Quail, Mearns's

Quail, Gambel's Valley—see Quail, Gambel's

Quail, Helmet—see Quail, California

Quail, Hooded—see Bob-white, Masked

Quail, Marsh—see Meadowlark

Quail, Montezuma—see Quail, Mearns's

Quail, Mountain—see Ptarmigan, White-tailed

Quail, Ridgway's—see Bob-white, Masked

Quail, Sea—see Auklet, Cassin's; see also Auklet, Crested; also Turnstone, Ruddy

Quail, Top-knot—see Quail, California

Quail, Valley—see Quail, California

Quail, White—see Ptarmigan, White-tailed

Quail-head—see Sparrow, Lark

Quaily—see Plover, Upland

Quandy—see Old-Squaw

Quawk—see Heron, Black-crowned Night

Queleli—see Vulture, California

Quink—see Brant

Rabihorcado—see Man-o'-war-bird

Race, Cape—see Loon, Red-throated

Racer, Cape—see Loon, Red-throated

Rail, Carolina—see Sora

Rail, Chicken-billed—see Sora

Rail, Common—see Sora

Rail, Great Red-breasted—see Rail, King

Rail, Little Black—see Rail, Black

Rail, Little Red-breasted—see Rail, Virginia

Rail, Little Yellow—see Rail, Yellow

Rail, Long-billed—see Rail, Virginia

Rail-bird—see Sora

Ramshack—see Woodpecker, Red-bellied

Raven, Mexican—see Raven

Razor-bill—see Auk, Razor-billed

Recollet—see Waxwing, Cedar

Red-back—see Sandpiper, Red-backed

Redbird—see Cardinal; see also Tanager, Summer

Redbird, Black-winged—see Tanager, Scarlet

Redbird, Crested—see Cardinal

Redbird, Smooth-headed—see Tanager, Summer

Redbird, Summer—see Tanager, Summer

Redbird, Virginia—see Cardinal

Redbreast—see Robin

Red-breast—see Knot
Redbreast, Blue—see Bluebird
Redbreast, Robin—see Robin
Red-eye—see Plover, Semipalmated; see also Vireo, Red-eyed
Redhead—see Woodpecker, Red-headed
Red-head—see Finch, House
Red-legs—see Turnstone, Ruddy
Redpoll, Common—see Redpoll
Redpoll, Lesser—see Redpoll
Redpoll, Little—see Redpoll
Red-poll, Yellow—see Warbler, Palm
Red-shank—see Tern, Common
Redstart, American—see Redstart
Red-tail—see Hawk, Red-tailed
Red-tail, Eastern—see Hawk, Red-tailed
Red-wing—see Blackbird, Red-winged
Red-wing—see Gadwall
Reed-bird—see Bobolink
Rice-bird—see Bobolink
Ring-bill—see Duck, Ring-necked
Ringneck—see Plover, Piping
Ring-neck—see Duck, Ring-necked; see also Plover, Semipalmated
Ringneck, Pale—see Plover, Piping
Ringneck, White—see Plover, Piping
Road-bird—see Sparrow, Lark
Robber, Camp—see Jay, Canada; see also Nutcracker, Clarke's
Robber, Nest—see Jay, Blue
Robber, Sea—see Jaeger, Pomarine
Robert—see Bobolink
Robin, Alaska—see Thrush, Varied
Robin, American—see Robin
Robin, Beach—see Knot
Robin, Blue—see Bluebird
Robin, Canada—see Robin; see also Waxwing, Cedar
Robin, Common—see Robin
Robin, English—see Oriole, Baltimore
Robin, Golden—see Oriole, Baltimore
Robin, Ground—see Towhee
Robin, Marsh—see Towhee
Robin, Northern—see Robin
Robin, Oregon—see Thrush, Varied
Robin, Sea—see Merganser, Red-breasted
Robin, Swamp—**see** Thrush, Hermit;

see also Towhee; also Thrush, Olive-backed; also Thrush, Wood
Robin, Wood—see Thrush, Wood
Robin-breast—see Knot
Rock-bird—see Sandpiper, Purple
Rock-bird, Winter—see Sandpiper, Purple
Roody—see Duck, Ruddy
Rook—see Duck, Ruddy
Rose-breast—see Grosbeak, Rose-breasted
Rotch—see Dovekie
Rough-leg—see Hawk, Rough-legged
Rough-wing—see Swallow, Rough-winged
Ruby-crown—see Kinglet, Ruby-crowned
Ruby-throat—see Hummingbird, Ruby-throated
Russet-back—see Thrush, Russet-backed

Sabre-bill—see Curlew, Long-billed
Saddleback—see Gull, Great Black-backed
Sand-bird—see Sandpiper, White-rumped
Sand-peep—see Sandpiper, Least; see also Sandpiper, Spotted; also Sandpiper, Semipalmated
Sand-peep, Little—see Sandpiper, Least
Sandpiper, American Green—see Sandpiper, Solitary
Sandpiper, American Wood—see Sandpiper, Solitary
Sandpiper, Ash-colored—see Knot
Sandpiper, Bartramian—see Plover, Upland
Sandpiper, Bartram's—see Plover, Upland
Sandpiper, Black-bellied—see Sandpiper, Red-backed
Sandpiper, Bonaparte's—see Sandpiper, White-rumped
Sandpiper, Canute's—see Knot
Sandpiper, Freckled—see Knot
Sandpiper, Green—see Sandpiper, Solitary
Sandpiper, Long-legged—see Sandpiper, Stilt

Sandpiper, Red—see Knot

Sandpiper, Red-breasted—see Knot

Sandpiper, Rock—see Sandpiper, Purple

Sandpiper, Schintz's—see Sandpiper, White-rumped

Sandpiper, Upland—see Plover, Upland

Sandpiper, Wood—see Sandpiper, Solitary

Sand-runner—see Turnstone, Ruddy

Sapsucker or Big Sapsucker (incorrect)—see Woodpecker, Hairy

Sapsucker, The—see Sapsucker, Yellow-bellied

Sapsucker (incorrect)—see Nuthatch, Red-breasted; see also Nuthatch, White-breasted

Sapsucker, Little (incorrect)—see Woodpecker, Downy

Sapsucker, Red-throated—see Sapsucker, Yellow-bellied

Saw-bill—see Merganser; see also Merganser, Red-breasted

Saw-bill, Big—see Merganser

Saw-bill, Common—see Merganser, Red-breasted

Scape-grace—Loon, Red-throated

Scaup, Ring-necked—see Duck, Ring-necked

Scavenger, Black—see Vulture, Black

Scissorbill—see Skimmer, Black

Scoldenore—see Old-Squaw

Scolder—see Old-Squaw

Scop, White—see Scoter, Surf

Scoter, Black (male)—see Scoter

Scoter, Lake Huron—see Scoter, White-winged

Scoter, Velvet—see Scoter, White-winged

Scout—see Murre

Scuttock—see Murre

Sea-pheasant (male)—see Pintail

See-saw—see Sandpiper, Spotted

Sewick—see Flycatcher, Least

Shadbird—see Snipe, Wilson's

Shag—see Cormorant; see also Cormorant, Brandt's; also Cormorant, Double-crested

Shamshack—see Woodpecker, Red-bellied

Shanks, Blue—see Avocet

Sharp-tail—see Grouse, Sharp-tailed

Sharp-tail (male)—see Pintail

Shearwater—see Skimmer, Black

Shearwater, Common Atlantic—see Shearwater, Greater

Shearwater, Dark-bodied—see Shearwater, Sooty

Shearwater, Wandering—see Shearwater, Greater

Sheldrake, American—see Merganser

Sheldrake, Big—see Merganser

Sheldrake, Buff-breasted—see Merganser

Sheldrake, Fresh-water—see Merganser

Sheldrake, Hooded—see Merganser, Hooded

Sheldrake, Little, Wood, Swamp, Pond, Mud, Pickax, or Summer—see Merganser, Hooded

Sheldrake, Long Island—see Merganser, Red-breasted

Sheldrake, Pond—see Merganser

Sheldrake, Red-breasted—see Merganser, Red-breasted

Sheldrake, Salt-water—see Merganser, Red-breasted

Sheldrake, Spring—see Merganser, Red-breasted

Sheldrake, Winter—see Merganser

Shelduck—see Merganser, Red-breasted

Shell-bird—see Merganser, Red-breasted

Shirt-tail—see Woodpecker, Red-headed

Short-neck—see Sandpiper, Pectoral

Shot-pouch—see Duck, Ruddy

Shovel-bill—see Shoveller

Shoveller, Blue-winged—see Shoveller

Shoveller, Red-breasted—see Shoveller

Shrike, Great Northern—see Shrike, Northern

Shrike, Southern Loggerhead—see Shrike, Loggerhead

Shrike, Winter—see Shrike, Northern

Shuffler—see Coot; see also Duck, Scaup

Sickle-bill—see Curlew, Long-billed

Silktail—see Waxwing, Bohemian

Silver-back—see Knot
Simpleton—see Sandpiper, Red-backed
Siskin, American—see Siskin, Pine
Skait-bird—see Jaeger, Parasitic
Skiddaw—see Murre
Skunk-head—see Scoter, Surf
Skunk-top—see Scoter, Surf
Skylark, European—see Skylark
Skylark, Missouri—see Pipit, Sprague's
Skylark, Prairie—see Pipit, Sprague's
Sleepy-head—see Duck, Ruddy
Smee—see Pintail
Smoker—see Curlew, Long-billed
Snake-bird—see Water-Turkey
Snipe, American—see Snipe, Wilson's
Snipe, Big Mud—see Woodcock
Snipe, Big-headed—see Woodcock
Snipe, Blind—see Woodcock
Snipe, Bog—see Snipe, Wilson's
Snipe, Brown (summer)—see Dowitcher
Snipe, Checkered—see Turnstone, Ruddy
Snipe, Common—see Snipe, Wilson's
Snipe, Cow—see Sandpiper, Pectoral
Snipe, Crooked-billed—see Sandpiper, Red-backed
Snipe, Duck—see Willet
Snipe, English—see Snipe, Wilson's
Snipe, Fall—see Sandpiper, Red-backed
Snipe, Frost—see Sandpiper, Stilt
Snipe, Grass—see Sandpiper, Pectoral
Snipe, Gray (winter)—see Dowitcher
Snipe, Gutter—see Snipe, Wilson's
Snipe, Horsefoot—see Knot; see also Turnstone, Ruddy
Snipe, Irish—see Avocet
Snipe, Jack—see Sandpiper, Pectoral; see also Snipe, Wilson's
Snipe, Little Stone—see Yellow-legs
Snipe, Marsh—see Snipe, Wilson's
Snipe, Meadow—see Sandpiper, Pectoral; see also Snipe, Wilson's
Snipe, Prairie—see Plover, Upland
Snipe, Red-breasted (summer)—see Dowitcher
Snipe, River—see Sandpiper, Spotted
Snipe, Robin—see Dowitcher; see also Knot
Snipe, Rock—see Sandpiper, Purple

Snipe, Sand—see Sandpiper, Spotted
Snipe, Sea—see Phalarope, Northern; see also Phalarope, Red
Snipe, Semipalmated—see Willet
Snipe, Squat—see Sandpiper, Pectoral
Snipe, Stone—see Yellow-legs, Greater
Snipe, Surf—see Sanderling
Snipe, Whistling—see Woodcock
Snipe, White—see Sanderling
Snipe, White-bellied—see Knot
Snipe, Winter—see Sandpiper, Purple; see also Sandpiper, Red-backed
Snipe, Wood—see Woodcock
Snowbird—see Bunting, Snow; see also Junco, Slate-colored
Snowbird, Black—see Junco, Slate-colored
Snowbird, Blue—see Junco, Slate-colored
Snowbird, Common—see Junco, Slate-colored
Snowbird, Slate-colored—Junco, Slate-colored
Snowbird, White—see Bunting, Snow
Snowflake—see Bunting, Snow
Snowy, Little—see Egret, Snowy
Snuff-taker—see Scoter, Surf
Soree—see Sora
South-southerly—see Old-Squaw
Sparked-back—see Turnstone, Ruddy
Sparrow, Bush—see Sparrow, Field; see also Sparrow, Song
Sparrow, Canada—see Sparrow, Tree; see also Sparrow, White-throated
Sparrow, Domestic—see Sparrow, English
Sparrow, European House—see Sparrow, English
Sparrow, Field (incorrect)—see Sparrow, Savannah
Sparrow, Fox-colored—see Sparrow, Fox
Sparrow, Grass—see Sparrow, Vesper
Sparrow, Ground—see Sparrow, Field; see also Sparrow, Savannah; also Sparrow, Song
Sparrow, Hair—see Sparrow, Chipping
Sparrow, Hedge—see Sparrow, Song
Sparrow, Hood-crowned—see Sparrow, Harris's

Sparrow, Lincoln's Song—see Sparrow, Lincoln's

Sparrow, Little House—see Sparrow, Chipping

Sparrow, Marsh—see Sparrow, Song

Sparrow, Quail—see Sparrow, Grasshopper

Sparrow, Rush—see Sparrow, Field

Sparrow, Scarlet—see Tanager, Scarlet

Sparrow, Social—see Sparrow, Chipping

Sparrow, Swamp Song—see Sparrow, Swamp

Sparrow, Turkey—see Towhee

Sparrow, White-throated Crown—see Sparrow, White-throated

Sparrow, Winter—see Sparrow, Tree

Sparrow, Wood—see Sparrow, Field

Sparrow, Yellow-winged—see Sparrow, Grasshopper

Speckle-belly—see Gadwall; see also Goose, White-fronted

Speckle-cheek—see Woodpecker, Texas

Spike-bill—see Godwit, Marbled; see also Merganser, Hooded

Spike-tail—see Grouse, Sharp-tailed

Spike-tail (male)—see Pintail

Spindle-tail (male)—see Pintail

Spine-tail—see Duck, Ruddy

Spirit, Shad—see Snipe, Wilson's

Splatter—see Coot

Split-tail (male)—see Pintail

Spoonbill—see Duck, Ruddy; see also Shoveller

Spoonbill, Rosy—see Spoonbill, Roseate

Spot-rump—see Godwit, Hudsonian

Sprig-tail—see Duck, Ruddy

Sprig-tail (male)—see Pintail

Spring-tail (male)—see Pintail

Sprit-tail (male)—see Pintail

Squatter—see Sandpiper, Pectoral

Squawk—see Heron, Black-crowned Night

Squealer—see Duck, Harlequin; see also Plover, Golden

Stare, Crescent—see Meadowlark

Stariki, Crested—see Auklet, Crested

Starling, Orchard—see Oriole, Orchard

Starling, Red-shouldered—see Blackbird, Red-winged

Starling, Red-winged—see Blackbird, Red-winged

Steel-head—see Duck, Ruddy

Stib—see Sandpiper, Red-backed

Stick-tail—see Duck, Ruddy

Stiff-tail—see Duck, Ruddy

Stilt—see Stilt, Black-necked

Stint, Wilson's—see Sandpiper, Least

Stocking, Blue—see Avocet

Stone-bird—see Yellow-legs, Greater

Stone-bird, Little—see Yellow-legs

Stone-pecker—see Turnstone, Ruddy

Stork, American Wood—see Ibis, Wood

Storm Gull—see Skimmer, Black

Strany—see Murre

Streaked-back—see Turnstone, Ruddy

Striker—see Hawk, Cooper's

Striker, Little—see Tern, Least

Striped-head—see Curlew, Hudsonian

Stub-and-twist—see Duck, Ruddy

Sultana (Jamaica)—see Gallinule, Purple

Surfer—see Scoter, Surf

Swaddle-bill—see Shoveller

Swallow, American Barn—see Swallow, Barn

Swallow, Barn—see Swallow, Cliff

Swallow, Barn-loft—see Swallow, Barn

Swallow, Blue-backed—see Swallow, Tree

Swallow, Bridge—see Swallow, Rough-winged

Swallow, Chimney—see Swift, Chimney

Swallow, Crescent—see Swallow, Cliff

Swallow, Eave—see Swallow, Cliff; see also Swallow, Tree

Swallow, Fork-tailed—see Swallow, Barn

Swallow, Jug—see Swallow, Cliff

Swallow, Moon-fronted—see Swallow, Cliff

Swallow, Mud—see Swallow, Cliff

Swallow, Republican—see Swallow, Cliff

Swallow, Rocky Mountain—see Swallow, Cliff

Swallow, Sand—see Swallow, Bank

Swallow, Sea—see Tern, Arctic; see also Tern, Least; also Tern, Forster's; also Tern, Common
Swallow, Stump—see Swallow, Tree
Swallow, Violet-green—see Swallow, Northern Violet-green
Swallow, White-bellied—see Swallow, Tree
Swallow, White-breasted—see Swallow, Tree
Swallow-tail—see Kite, Swallow-tailed
Swan—see Swan, Whistling
Swan, American Whistling—see Swan, Whistling
Swan, Wild—see Swan, Whistling
Swift, American—see Swift, Chimney
Swift, Northern Black—see Swift, Black

Tadpole—see Merganser, Hooded
Tanager, Canada—see Tanager, Scarlet
Tanager, Louisiana—see Tanager, Western
Tarrock—see Kittiwake
Tattler, Lesser Long-legged—see Yellow-legs
Tattler, Long-legged—see Yellow-legs, Greater
Tattler, Solitary—see Sandpiper, Solitary
Teacher—see Oven-Bird
Teal, Brown Diving—see Duck, Ruddy
Teal, Gray—see Duck, Ruddy
Teal, Mud—see Teal, Green-winged
Teal, Red-breasted—see Teal, Cinnamon
Teal, Red-headed—see Teal, Green-winged
Teal, Salt-water—see Duck, Ruddy
Teal, South American—see Teal, Cinnamon
Teal, Spoon-bill—see Shoveller
Teal, Summer—see Teal, Blue-winged
Teal, White-faced—see Teal, Blue-winged
Teal, Winter—see Teal, Green-winged
Teaser—see Jaeger, Parasitic
Teeterer—see Sandpiper, Spotted
Teeter-peep—see Sandpiper, Spotted
Teeter-tail—see Sandpiper, Spotted

Tell-tale, Big—see Yellow-legs, Greater
Tell-tale, Greater—see Yellow-legs, Greater
Tell-tale, Lesser—see Yellow-legs
Tell-tale, Little—see Yellow-legs
Tercel (male)—see Hawk, Duck
Tern, American Black—see Tern, Black
Tern, Anglican—see Tern, Gull-billed
Tern, Boys'—see Tern, Cabot's
Tern, Caspian Sea—see Tern, Caspian
Tern, Cayenne—see Tern, Royal
Tern, Common—see Tern, Arctic
Tern, Crimson-billed—see Tern, Arctic
Tern, Ducal—see Tern, Cabot's
Tern, Egyptian—see Tern, Gull-billed
Tern, Graceful—see Tern, Roseate
Tern, Havell's (immature)—see Tern, Forster's
Tern, Imperial—see Tern, Caspian
Tern, Kentish—see Tern, Cabot's
Tern, Little—see Tern, Least
Tern, Long-tailed—see Tern, Arctic
Tern, McDougall's—see Tern, Roseate
Tern, Marsh—see Tern, Gull-billed
Tern, Minute—see Tern, Least
Tern, Nile—see Tern, Gull-billed
Tern, Nuttall's—see Tern, Gull-billed
Tern, Paradise—see Tern, Arctic
Tern, Pike's—see Tern, Arctic
Tern, Portland—see Tern, Arctic
Tern, Sandwich—see Tern, Cabot's
Tern, Semipalmated—see Tern, Black
Tern, Short-footed—see Tern, Arctic
Tern, Short-tailed—see Tern, Black
Tern, Surinam—see Tern, Black
Tern, Wilson's—see Tern, Common
Ternlet, Silver—see Tern, Least
Thief, Corn—see Jay, Blue
Thief, Maize—see Grackle, Purple
Thrasher—see Thrasher, Brown
Three-toes—see Plover, Golden
Thrush, Alice's—see Thrush, Gray-cheeked
Thrush, Alma's—see Thrush, Olive-backed
Thrush, Aquatic—see Wood-Thrush
Thrush, Black-capped—see Catbird
Thrush, Brown—see Thrasher, Brown

Thrush, Fox-colored—see Thrasher, Brown

Thrush, Golden-crowned—see Oven-Bird

Thrush, Ground—see Thrasher, Brown

Thrush, Migratory—see Robin

Thrush, Mimic—see Mockingbird

Thrush, Mocking—see Mockingbird

Thrush, Red—see Thrasher, Brown

Thrush, Rufous-tailed—see Thrush, Hermit

Thrush, Sage—see Thrasher, Sage

Thrush, Solitary—see Thrush, Hermit

Thrush, Song—see Thrasher, Brown; see also Thrush, Wood

Thrush, Swainson's—see Thrush, Olive-backed

Thrush, Tawny—see Veery

Thrush, Wilson's—see Veery

Tilt-up—see Sandpiper, Spotted

Tinker—see Auk, Razor-billed; see also Murre; also Puffin

Tinkershire—see Murre

Tip-up—see Sandpiper, Spotted

Tip-up, Yellow—see Warbler, Palm

Tit, Black-capped—see Chickadee

Tit, Tufted—see Titmouse, Tufted

Titlark, American—see Pipit

Titlark, Prairie—see Pipit

Titmouse, Black-capped—see Chickadee

Titmouse, Hooded—see Warbler, Hooded

Titmouse, Little Chocolate-breast—see Warbler, Bay-breasted

Titmouse, Wollweber's—see Titmouse, Bridled

Titmouse, Yellow—see Warbler, Yellow

Toad-head—see Plover, Golden

Tomtit, Crested—see Titmouse, Tufted

Tongue, Silver—see Sparrow, Song

Top, Cotton—see Quail, Scaled

Torch-bird—see Warbler, Blackburnian

Tough-head—see Duck, Ruddy

Tow-head—see Merganser, Hooded

Towhee, Chestnut-crowned—see Towhee, Green-tailed

Towhee, Fuscous—see Towhee, Canon

Towhee, Gray—see Towhee, Abert's

Towhee, Red-eyed—see Towhee

Towhee, Spotted—see Towhee, Oregon

Towhee (mistake)—see Bobolink

Towhee-bird—see Towhee

Tramp—see Sparrow, English

Tree-Mouse—see Nuthatch, White-breasted

Tricolor—see Woodpecker, Red-headed

Triddler—see Sandpiper, Pectoral

Tringa, Red Coot-footed—see Phalarope, Red

Troop-fowl—see Duck, Scaup

Trotter, Road—see Lark, Horned

Trout-bird—see Plover, Golden

Turkey, American—see Turkey, Wild

Turkey, American Wild—see Turkey, Wild

Turkey, Colorado—see Ibis, Wood

Turkey, Eastern—see Turkey, Wild

Turkey, Northern—see Turkey, Wild

Turkey, Wood—see Turkey, Wild

Turnstone—see Turnstone, Ruddy

Turnstone, Plover-billed—see Surf-Bird

Twister, Labrador—see Woodcock

Tysty—see Guillemot, Black

Uplander—see Plover, Upland

Vireo, Brotherly-love—see Vireo, Philadelphia

Vireo, Solitary—see Vireo, Blue-headed

Wagell—see Gull, Great Black-backed

Wagtail—see Water-Thrush; see also Water-Thrush, Louisiana

Wagtail, Aquatic Wood—see Wood-Thrush

Wagtail, Golden-crowned—see Oven-Bird

Wagtail, Hudsonian—see Pipit

Wagtail, Kentucky—see Warbler, Kentucky

Wagtail, Water—see Water-Thrush; see also Water-Thrush, Louisiana

Wagtail, Wood—see Oven-Bird

Wake-up—see Flicker

Walk-up—see Flicker

Walloon—see Loon

Wamp—see Eider

Wapacuthu—see Owl, Snowy

Warbler, Autumnal—see Warbler, Black-poll

Warbler, Azure—see Warbler, Cerulean

Warbler, Birch—see Warbler, Nashville

Warbler, Black and White Creeping —see Warbler, Black and White

Warbler, Black and Yellow—see Warbler, Magnolia

Warbler, Black-capped—see Warbler, Wilson's

Warbler, Black-capped Flycatching— see Warbler, Wilson's

Warbler, Black-headed—see Warbler, Hooded

Warbler, Black-masked Ground—see Yellow-throat, Maryland

Warbler, Black-throated Ground— see Warbler, Mourning

Warbler, Bloody-side—see Warbler, Chestnut-sided

Warbler, Blue—see Warbler, Cerulean

Warbler, Blue Golden-winged—see Warbler, Golden-winged

Warbler, Blue Yellow-backed—see Warbler, Parula

Warbler, Blue-eyed Yellow—see Warbler, Yellow

Warbler, Blue-headed Yellow-rumped —see Warbler, Magnolia

Warbler, Blue-winged Swamp—see Warbler, Blue-winged

Warbler, Blue-winged Yellow—see Warbler, Blue-winged

Warbler, Canadian—see Warbler, Canada

Warbler, Canadian Flycatching—see Warbler, Canada

Warbler, Crape—see Warbler, Mourning

Warbler, Creeping—see Warbler, Black and White

Warbler, Evergreen—see Warbler, Black-throated Green

Warbler, Golden—see Warbler, Prothonotary; see also Warbler, Yellow

Warbler, Golden Swamp—see Warbler, Prothonotary

Warbler, Golden-winged Swamp—see Warbler, Golden-winged

Warbler, Green Black-capped—see Warbler, Wilson's

Warbler, Ground—see Yellow-Throat, Maryland

Warbler, Hemlock—see Warbler, Blackburnian

Warbler, Hooded Flycatching—see Warbler, Hooded

Warbler, Jack-pine—see Warbler, Kirtland's

Warbler, Mitered—see Warbler, Hooded

Warbler, Mourning Ground—see Warbler, Mourning

Warbler, Nashville Swamp—see Warbler, Nashville

Warbler, Necklaced—see Warbler, Canada

Warbler, New York—see Water-Thrush

Warbler, Orange-throated—see Warbler, Blackburnian

Warbler, Philadelphia—see Warbler, Mourning

Warbler, Pine-creeping—see Warbler, Pine

Warbler, Quebec—see Warbler, Chestnut-sided

Warbler, Red-crowned—see Warbler, Nashville

Warbler, Redstart—see Redstart

Warbler, Ruby-crowned—see Kinglet, Ruby-crowned

Warbler, Southern Parula—see Warbler, Parula

Warbler, Speckled Canada—see Warbler, Canada

Warbler, Spotted—see Warbler, Magnolia

Warbler, Spotted Canadian—see Warbler, Canada

Warbler, Striped—see Warbler, Black and White

Warbler, Summer—see Warbler, Yellow

Warbler, Swamp—see Warbler, Connecticut; see also Warbler, Tennessee

Warbler, Tamarack—see Warbler, Connecticut

Warbler, Tennessee Swamp—see Warbler, Tennessee

Warbler, Tip-up—see Warbler, Palm

Warbler, Tolmie's—see Warbler, Macgillivray's

Warbler, Varied Creeping—see Warbler, Black and White

Warbler, Wagtail—see Warbler, Palm

Warbler, Western Yellow-rumped—see Warbler, Audubon's

Warbler, Whitepoll—see Warbler, Black and White

Warbler, Willow—see Warbler, Prothonotary

Warbler, Wilson's Black-capped Flycatching—see Warbler, Wilson's

Warbler, Wilson's Flycatching—see Warbler, Wilson's

Warbler, Worm-eating Swamp—see Warbler, Worm-eating

Warbler, Yellow-crowned—see Warbler, Chestnut-sided; see also Warbler, Myrtle

Warbler, Yellow Red-poll—see Warbler, Palm

Warbler, Yellow-rumped—see Warbler, Myrtle

Warbler, Yellow-tailed—see Redstart

Water-partridge—see Duck, Ruddy

Water-Thrush, Large-billed—see Water-Thrush, Louisiana

Water-Thrush, New York—see Water-Thrush

Water-Thrush, Northern—see Water-Thrush

Water-Thrush, Small-billed—see Water-Thrush

Water-Thrush, Southern—see Water-Thrush, Louisiana

Water-Turkey—see Cormorant, Double-crested

Water-witch—see Grebe, Horned; see also Grebe, Pied-billed

Wavey—see Goose, Snow

Wavey, Blue—see Goose, Blue

Wavey, Common—see Goose, Snow

Wavey, Little—see Goose, Snow

Waxwing, Black-throated—see Waxwing, Bohemian

Waxwing, Carolina—see Waxwing, Cedar

Waxwing, Lapland—see Waxwing, Bohemian

Waxwing, Southern—see Waxwing, Cedar

Whale-bird—see Phalarope, Northern; see also Phalarope, Red

Whew—see Widgeon, European

Whewer—see Widgeon, European

Whiffler—see Golden-eye

Whim—see Widgeon, European

Whimbrel, American—see Curlew, Hudsonian

Whistle-Duck—see Golden-eye

Whistler—see Golden-eye; see also Woodcock; also Widgeon, European

Whistler, Brass-eyed—see Golden-eye

Whistle-wing—see Golden-eye

White, Long—see Egret

White-back—see Canvas-back

White-belly—see Baldpate; see also Grouse, Sharp-tailed

White-bill—see Coot

Whitebird—see Bunting, Snow

White-crown—see Sparrow, White-crowned

White-head—see Scoter, Surf

White-rump—see Godwit, Hudsonian

White-shirt—see Woodpecker, Red-headed

White-tail—see Hawk, Sennett's White-tailed

White-throat—see Sparrow, White-throated

White-wing, Black—see Scoter, White-winged

White-wing, Eastern—see Scoter, White-winged

White-wing, May—see Scoter, White-winged

Whitey—see Sanderling

Wicket, Hairy—see Flicker

Wick-up—see Flicker

Wide-awake—see Tern, Sooty

Widgeon—see Widgeon, European

Widgeon, American—Baldpate

Widgeon, Bald—see Baldpate

Widgeon, Blue-billed—see Duck, Scaup

Widgeon, California—see Baldpate

Widgeon, Gray—see Gadwall

Widgeon, Green-headed—see Baldpate

Widgeon, Pied (female)—see Pintail

Widgeon, Southern—see Baldpate

Widgeon, Stiff-tailed—see Duck, Ruddy

Widgeon, Wood—see Duck, Wood

Wife, Old—see Old-Squaw

Willock—see Murre

Will-o'-the-wisp—see Nighthawk

Will-willet—see Willet

Windhover—see Hawk, Sparrow

Witch, Black—see Ani, Groove-billed

Wobble—see Auk, Great

Woodchuck—see Woodpecker, Ivory-billed

Woodcock—see Woodpecker, Ivory-billed

Woodcock, American—see Woodcock

Woodhen—see Woodcock

Woodpecker, American Three-toed—see Woodpecker, Three-toed

Woodpecker, Black—see Woodpecker, Lewis's

Woodpecker, Black-backed Three-toed—Woodpecker, Arctic Three-toed

Woodpecker, Brown-headed (female) —Sapsucker, Williamson's

Woodpecker, Crow—see Woodpecker, Lewis's

Woodpecker, Golden-winged—see Flicker

Woodpecker, Good God—see Woodpecker, Pileated

Woodpecker, Great Black—see Woodpecker, Pileated

Woodpecker, Great God—see Woodpecker, Pileated

Woodpecker, Guinea—see Woodpecker, Hairy

Woodpecker, Ladder-back—see Woodpecker, Three-toed

Woodpecker, Little Guinea—see Woodpecker, Downy

Woodpecker, Lord God—see Woodpecker, Pileated

Woodpecker, Pigeon—see Flicker

Woodpecker, Saguaro—see Woodpecker, Gila

Woodpecker, Tommy—see Woodpecker, Downy

Woodpecker, Tri-colored—see Woodpecker, Red-headed

Woodpecker, White-backed Three-toed—see Woodpecker, Three-toed

Woodpecker, Williamson's—see Sapsucker, Williamson's

Woodpecker, Yellow-bellied—see Sapsucker, Yellow-bellied

Woodpecker, Yellow-shafted—see Flicker

Wood-pigeon—see Flicker

Wool-head—see Buffle-head

Worm-eater—see Warbler, Worm-eating

Wren, Brown—see Wren, House

Wren, Cat-tail—see Wren, Long-billed Marsh

Wren, Common—see Wren, House

Wren, Coues's Cactus—see Wren, Cactus

Wren, Fiery-crowned—see Kinglet, Golden-crowned

Wren, Fresh-water Marsh—see Wren, Short-billed Marsh

Wren, Golden-crowned—see Kinglet, Golden-crowned

Wren, Grass—see Wren, Short-billed Marsh

Wren, Great Carolina—see Wren, Carolina

Wren, Jenny—see Wren, House

Wren, Little Bluish-gray—see Gnatcatcher, Blue-gray

Wren, Long-tailed House—see Wren, Bewick's

Wren, Louisiana—see Wren, Carolina

Wren, Marsh—see Wren, Long-billed Marsh

Wren, Meadow—see Wren, Short-billed Marsh

Wren, Mocking—see Wren, Carolina

Wren, Mouse—see Wren, Winter

Wren, Olive-colored Yellow-throated —see Yellow-throat, Maryland

Wren, Reed—see Wren, Long-billed Marsh

Wren, Ruby-crowned—see Kinglet, Ruby-crowned
Wren, Salt-water Marsh—see Wren, Long-billed Marsh
Wren, Short-tailed—see Wren, Winter
Wren, Short-tailed House—see Wren, House
Wren, Song—see Wren, Bewick's
Wren, Spruce—see Wren, Winter
Wren, Stump—see Wren, House
Wren, Wood—see Wren, House; see also Wren, Winter

Yarrup—see Flicker
Yellowback, Blue—see Warbler, Parula
Yellow-bill (male)—see Scoter
Yellowbird—see Warbler, Yellow
Yellowbird, Summer—see Warbler, Yellow
Yellow-hammer—see Flicker
Yellow-legs, Bastard—see Sandpiper, Stilt
Yellow-legs, Big—see Yellow-legs, Greater
Yellow-legs, Common—see Yellow-legs

Yellow-legs, Lesser—see Yellow-legs
Yellow-legs, Summer—see Yellow-legs
Yellow-legs, Winter—see Yellow-legs, Greater
Yellow-rump—see Warbler, Myrtle
Yellow-shanks, Greater—Yellow-legs, Greater
Yellow-shanks, Lesser—see Yellow-legs
Yellow-shins—see Yellow-legs, Greater
Yellow-throat—see Yellow-throat, Maryland
Yellow-throat, Dominican—see Warbler, Yellow-throated
Yellow-throat, Northern—see Yellow-throat, Maryland
Yellow-throat, Northern Maryland—see Yellow-throat, Maryland
Yellow-throat, Western—see Yellow-throat, Maryland
Yelper—see Yellow-legs, Greater
Yelper, Little—see Yellow-legs

Zebra-back—see Woodpecker, Red-bellied

Index of Scientific Names of Families

Stercorariidae—see Jaeger Family
Strigidae—see Owl Family
Sturnidae—see Starling Family
Sulidae—see Booby Family
Sylviidae—see Kinglet Family

Tetraonidae—see Grouse Family
Thraupidae—see Tanager Family
Threskiornithidae—see Ibis Family

Trochilidae—see Hummingbird Family
Troglodytidae—see Wren Family
Trogonidae—see Trogon Family
Turdidae—see Thrush Family
Tyrannidae—see Flycatcher Family
Tytonidae—see Barn Owl Family

Vireonidae—see Vireo Family

Official State Birds of the United States

ALABAMA	Flicker
ARIZONA	Cactus Wren
ARKANSAS	Mockingbird
CALIFORNIA	California Quail
COLORADO	Lark Bunting
CONNECTICUT	Robin
DISTRICT OF COLUMBIA	Wood Thrush
DELAWARE	Blue Hen Chicken
FLORIDA	Mockingbird
GEORGIA	Brown Thrasher
IDAHO	Mountain Bluebird
ILLINOIS	Cardinal
INDIANA	Cardinal
IOWA	Goldfinch
KANSAS	Western Meadowlark
KENTUCKY	Cardinal
LOUISIANA	Brown Pelican
MAINE	Black Capped Chickadee
MARYLAND	Baltimore Oriole
MASSACHUSETTS	Black Capped Chickadee
MICHIGAN	Robin
MINNESOTA	Goldfinch
MISSISSIPPI	Mockingbird
MISSOURI	Eastern Bluebird
MONTANA	Western Meadowlark
NEBRASKA	Western Meadowlark
NEVADA	Mountain Bluebird
NEW HAMPSHIRE	Purple Finch
NEW JERSEY	Goldfinch
NEW MEXICO	Roadrunner
NEW YORK	Eastern Bluebird
NORTH CAROLINA	Cardinal
NORTH DAKOTA	Western Meadowlark
OHIO	Cardinal
OKLAHOMA	Bobwhite

OREGON	Western Meadowlark
PENNSYLVANIA	Ruffed Grouse
RHODE ISLAND	Bobwhite
SOUTH CAROLINA	Mockingbird
SOUTH DAKOTA	Western Meadowlark
TENNESSEE	Mockingbird
TEXAS	Mockingbird
UTAH	California Gull
VERMONT	Eastern Hermit Thrush
VIRGINIA	Robin
WASHINGTON	Goldfinch
WEST VIRGINIA	Tufted Titmouse
WISCONSIN	Robin
WYOMING	Western Meadowlark

Bibliography

Books Useful to the Layman in the Study of Birds

Alexander, Wilfrid B., BIRDS OF THE OCEAN, G. P. Putnam's Sons, New York, 1928

Allen, Arthur A., THE BOOK OF BIRD LIFE, Van Nostrand Co., New York, 1930

Allen, Arthur A., AMERICAN BIRD BIOGRAPHIES, Comstock Pub. Co., Ithaca, N. Y., 1934

Allen, Arthur A., THE GOLDEN PLOVER AND OTHER BIRDS, Comstock Pub. Co., Ithaca, N. Y., 1939

American Ornithologists' Union, CHECK LIST OF NORTH AMERICAN BIRDS, The Union, 200 Cedar St., Cherrydale, Va., 4th ed. 1931

American Ornithologists' Union, ABRIDGED EDITION (OF THE ABOVE), Washington, D. C., 1935

Bagg, A. C., and Eliot, A. E., BIRDS OF THE CONNECTICUT RIVER VALLEY IN MASSACHUSETTS, Hampshire Bookshop, Northampton, Mass., 1937

Bailey, Mrs. Florence Miriam, HANDBOOK OF BIRDS OF THE WESTERN UNITED STATES, Houghton Mifflin, Boston, Mass., 10th ed. revised, 1927

Ball, Alice E., AMERICAN LAND BIRDS, Tudor Co., New York, 1936

Ball, Alice E., BIRD BIOGRAPHIES, Dodd, Mead, New York, 1923 (same as the above under the different title).

Baker, John H. (editor), AUDUBON GUIDE TO ATTRACTING BIRDS, Doubleday, Doran, New York, 1941

Blanchan, Neltje (Mrs. Nellie Blanchan Doubleday), BIRD NEIGHBORS, Doubleday, Doran, New York, 1922

Blanchan, Neltje (Mrs. Nellie Blanchan Doubleday), BIRDS THAT HUNT AND ARE HUNTED, Doubleday, Doran, New York, 1905

Baynes, Earnest H., WILD BIRD GUESTS (attracting birds), E. P. Dutton Co., New York, 1915

Carr, William H., GLIMPSES OF FAMILIAR BIRDS, Gabriel, New York, 1931

Champion, Paul V., BIRDHOUSES, Bruce, Milwaukee, 1940

Chapman, Frank M., COLOR KEY TO NORTH AMERICAN BIRDS, Appleton, New York, 1912

Chapman, Frank M., HANDBOOK OF THE BIRDS OF EASTERN NORTH AMERICA, Appleton, New York, 1932

Chapman, Frank M., THE TRAVELS OF BIRDS, Appleton, New York, 1916

Chapman, Frank M., WHAT BIRD IS THAT?, Appleton, New York, 1920

Dawson, W. L., THE BIRDS OF CALIFORNIA, 4 vols., South Moulton Co., San Francisco, Calif., 1923.

Dawson, W. L., THE BIRDS OF OHIO, Wheaton Co., Columbus, Ohio, 1903

Dickey, Florence Van Vechten (Mrs. Donald Ryder Dickey), FAMILIAR BIRDS OF THE PACIFIC SOUTHWEST, Stanford University Press, California, 1935

Doubleday, Nellie Blanchan, BIRD BOOK, (combining "Bird Neighbors" and "Birds That Hunt and Are Hunted"), Doubleday, Doran, New York, 1932

Dugmore, A. Radcliffe, BIRD HOMES, THEIR NESTS, EGGS, AND BREEDING HABITS, ETC., Doubleday, McClure, New York, 1900

Eaton, Elon H., BIRDS OF NEW YORK, New York State Museum, Albany, N. Y., 1910–1914

Eckstrom, Mrs. Fannie, THE BIRD BOOK, D. C. Heath, New York, 1901

Eliot, Willard A., BIRDS OF THE PACIFIC COAST, G. P. Putnam, New York, 1923

Forbush, Edward H., BIRDS OF MASSACHUSETTS AND OTHER NEW ENGLAND STATES, Commonwealth of Mass., Boston, Mass., 1925–1929 (3 vols.)

Forbush, Edward H., NATURAL HISTORY OF THE BIRDS OF EASTERN AND CENTRAL NORTH AMERICA, revised and abridged, with the addition of more than 100 species, by John B. May, illustrated in color by Louis Agassiz Fuertes, Alan Brooks, and Roger T. Peterson, Houghton Mifflin, Boston, Mass., 1943

Forbush, Edward H., USEFUL BIRDS AND THEIR PROTECTION, Mass. State Board of Agriculture, Boston, Mass., 1907

Fuertes, L. A., and Brooks, Alan, PORTRAITS OF NEW ENGLAND BIRDS, (the color plates of "Birds of Mass. and Other New England States"), Mass. Sec. of State, Boston, Mass., 1932

Gabrielson, I. N., and Jewett, S. G., BIRDS OF OREGON, Oregon State College, Ore., 1940

Green, Mrs. C. H., BIRDS OF THE SOUTH, University of N. C. Press, Chapel Hill, N. C., 1935

Griscom, Ludlow, BIRDS OF THE NEW YORK CITY REGION, American Museum of Natural History, New York, 1923

Hausman, Leon Augustus, BIRDS OF PREY OF THE NORTH EASTERN UNITED STATES (in press)

Hausman, Leon Augustus, BIRDS OF NEW JERSEY *Series* New Jersey State Experiment Station, Rutgers University, New Brunswick, N. J.

A series of 12 booklets (32 to 64 pp. each), published as Experiment Station Bulletins, numbered as follows:

439—The Hawks of New Jersey
470—The Woodpeckers, Nuthatches, and Creepers of New Jersey
520—The Swallows, Goatsuckers, and Swifts of New Jersey
531—The Sylvids and Flycatchers of New Jersey
544—The Vireos, Cuckoos, and Shrikes of New Jersey
533—Attracting Winter Birds to Garden and Home Grounds
580—The Sparrows of New Jersey
602—The Finches and Buntings of New Jersey
618—The Thrushes and Mimids of New Jersey
646—The Warblers of New Jersey, I. Summer Resident Warblers
678—The Warblers of New Jersey, II. Transient Warblers
690—The Owls of New Jersey

These are sent free to New Jersey residents; ten cents for each booklet to others.

Henderson, Junius, THE PRACTICAL VALUE OF BIRDS, Macmillan, New York, 1927

Herrick, Francis H., WILD BIRDS AT HOME, Appleton, New York, 1935

Hoffman, Ralph, BIRDS OF THE PACIFIC STATES, Houghton Mifflin, Boston, Mass., 1938

Hoffman, Ralph, GUIDE TO THE BIRDS OF NEW ENGLAND AND EASTERN NEW YORK, Houghton Mifflin, Boston, Mass., 1904

Howell, A. N., FLORIDA BIRD LIFE, Coward-McCann, New York, 1932

Knight, Ora W., THE BIRDS OF MAINE, Bangor, Me., 1908

Knowlton, F. H. (edited by Ridgway, Robert), BIRDS OF THE WORLD, Holt, New York, 1909

Ladd, Neil M., HOW TO MAKE FRIENDS WITH THE BIRDS, Doubleday, Doran, New York, 1916

Lincoln, Frederick C., MIGRATION OF AMERICAN BIRDS, Doubleday, Doran, New York, 1939

McKenney, Margaret, BIRDS IN THE GARDEN AND HOW TO ATTRACT THEM, Reynal & Hitchcock, New York, 1939

Mathews, F. Schuyler, FIELD BOOK OF WILD BIRDS AND THEIR MUSIC, G. P. Putnam, New York, 1921

May, John B., THE HAWKS OF NORTH AMERICA, National Audubon Society, New York, 1935

Minot, Henry D. (edited by Brewster, W.), LAND BIRDS AND GAME BIRDS OF NEW ENGLAND, Boston, Mass., 1906

National Geographic Society, THE BOOK OF BIRDS, Nat. Geog. Soc., Washington, D. C., 1939

Nicholson, E. M., THE ART OF BIRD WATCHING, Scribners, New York, 1941

New York State Museum, COLOR PLATES only, from Elon Howard's "Birds of New York," 2nd edition, Albany, N. Y., 1910–1914

Pearson, T. Gilbert (Editor), BIRDS OF AMERICA, 3 vols., University Society, New York, 1917

Pearson, T. Gilbert, BIRDS OF AMERICA (the 3 above volumes in 1), Garden City Pub. Co., New York, 1936

Pellet, Frank C., BIRDS OF THE WILD, De La Mare, New York, 1928

Peterson, Roger Tory, FIELD GUIDE TO THE BIRDS (east of the Rockies), Houghton Mifflin, Boston, Mass., revised edition, 1939

Peterson, Roger Tory, A FIELD GUIDE TO WESTERN BIRDS, Houghton Mifflin, Boston, Mass., 1941

Phillips, John C., and Lincoln, F. C., AMERICAN WATERFOWL, Houghton Mifflin, Boston, Mass., 1930

Reed, Chester A., BIRD GUIDE, Doubleday, Doran, New York, 1925

Reed, Chester A., NORTH AMERICAN BIRDS' EGGS, Doubleday, Page, New York, 1904

Ridgway, Robert, MANUAL OF NORTH AMERICAN BIRDS, Lippincott, Philadelphia, Pa., 4th edition, 1906

Roberts, Thomas S., BIRDS OF MINNESOTA, University of Minnesota Press, Minneapolis, Minn., 1936

Roberts, Thomas S., BIRD PORTRAITS IN COLOR (color plates of the above, separately published), University of Minnesota Press, Minneapolis, Minn., 1936

Saunders, Aretas A., A GUIDE TO BIRD SONGS, Appleton, New York, 1935

Sutton, George M., INTRODUCTION TO THE BIRDS OF PENNSYLVANIA, J. Horace McFarland, Harrisburg, Pa., 1928

Sutton, George M., BIRDS IN THE WILDERNESS, Macmillan, New York, 1936

Taverner, Percy A., CANADIAN LAND BIRDS, David McKay, Philadelphia, Pa., 1939

Taverner, Percy A., CANADIAN WATER BIRDS, GAME BIRDS, AND BIRDS OF PREY, David McKay, Philadelphia, Pa., 1939

Todd, W. E. Clyde, BIRDS OF WESTERN PENNSYLVANIA, Carnegie Museum, Pittsburgh, Pa., 1940

Trafton, Gilbert H., METHODS OF ATTRACTING BIRDS, Houghton Mifflin, Boston, Mass, 1910

Walter, Herbert E., and Alice H., WILD BIRDS IN CITY PARKS, Macmillan, New York, (12th edition, revised), 1926

Weed, Clarence M., and Dearborn, Ned., BIRDS IN THEIR RELATION TO MAN, Lippincott, Philadelphia, Pa., 1935

Wetmore, Alexander, THE MIGRATIONS OF BIRDS, Harvard University Press, Cambridge, Mass., 1930

Wright, Mrs. Mabel Osgood, BIRDCRAFT, Macmillan, New York, (9th edition), 1926

Wyman, Luther E., and Burnell, E. F., FIELDBOOK OF BIRDS OF THE SOUTHWESTERN UNITED STATES, Houghton Mifflin, Boston, Mass., 1925